Autodesk Inventor 2011 for Designers

CADCIM Technologies
525 St. Andrews Drive
Schererville, IN 46375, USA
(www.cadcim.com)

Contributing Author

Sham Tickoo

Professor
Department of Mechanical Engineering Technology
Purdue University Calumet
Hammond, Indiana, USA

CADCIM Technologies

Autodesk Inventor 2011 for Designers
Sham Tickoo

ISBN 978-1-932709-83-4

NOTICE TO THE READER

www.cadcim.com

DEDICATION

*To teachers, who make it possible to disseminate knowledge
to enlighten the young and curious minds
of our future generations*

*To students, who are dedicated to learning new technologies
and making the world a better place to live in*

SPECIAL RECOGNITION

*A special thanks to Mr. Denis Cadu and the ADN team of Autodesk Inc.
for their valuable support and professional guidance to
procure the software for writing this textbook*

THANKS

*To the faculty and students of the MET department of
Purdue University Calumet for their cooperation*

To engineers at CADCIM Technologies for their valuable help

Online Training Program Offered by CADCIM Technologies

CADCIM Technologies provides effective and affordable virtual online training on various software packages including Computer Aided Design and Manufacturing (CAD/CAM), computer programming languages, animation, architecture, and GIS. The training is delivered 'live' via Internet at any time, any place, and at any pace to individuals, students of colleges, universities, and CAD/CAM training centers. The main features of this program are:

Training for Students and Companies in a Class Room Setting

Highly experienced instructors and qualified Engineers at CADCIM Technologies conduct the classes under the guidance of Prof. Sham Tickoo of Purdue University Calumet, USA. This team has authored several textbooks that are rated "one of the best" in their categories and are used in various colleges, universities, and training centers in North America, Europe, and in other parts of the world.

Training for Individuals

The cost effective and time saving initiative of CADCIM Technologies strives to deliver the training in the comfort of your home or work place, thereby relieving you from the hassles of traveling to training centers.

Training Offered on Software Packages

We provide basic and advanced training on the following software packages:

CAD/CAM/CAE: CATIA, Pro/ENGINEER Wildfire, SolidWorks, Autodesk Inventor, Solid Edge, NX, AutoCAD, AutoCAD LT, Customizing AutoCAD, EdgeCAM, and ANSYS

Computer Programming: C++, VB.NET, Oracle, AJAX, and Java

Animation and Styling: Autodesk 3ds Max, 3ds Max Design, Maya, and Alias

Architecture and GIS: Autodesk Revit Architecture, Autodesk Civil 3D, Autodesk Revit Structures, and Autodesk Map 3D

For more information, please visit the following link:

http://www.cadcim.com

Note

The free teaching and learning resources, mentioned in the cover page of this textbook, are available only for the students who buy the textbook from our web site **www.cadcim.com** or the university/college bookstores. We need proof of purchase when you request the technical support from us.

Table of Contents

Chapter 2: Drawing Sketches for Solid Models

Chapter 3: Adding Constraints and Dimensions to Sketches

Chapter 4: Editing, Extruding, and Revolving the Sketches

Chapter 5: Other Sketching and Modeling Options

Chapter 6: Advanced Modeling Tools-I

Chapter 7: Editing Features and Adding Automatic Dimensions to Sketches

Chapter 8: Advanced Modeling Tools-II

Chapter 9: Assembly Modeling-I

Chapter 10: Assembly Modeling-II

Chapter 11: Working with Drawing Views-I

Chapter 12: Working with Drawing Views-II

Chapter 13: Presentation Module

Chapter 14: Working with Special Design Tools

Chapter 15: Working with Sheet Metal Components

Chapter 16: Introduction to Weldments

Chapter 17: Miscellaneous Tools

Preface

Autodesk Inventor 2011

Autodesk Inventor, developed by Autodesk Inc., is one of the world's fastest growing solid modeling software. It is a parametric feature-based solid modeling tool that not only unites the 3D parametric features with 2D tools but also addresses every design-through-manufacturing process. The adaptive technology of this solid modeling tool allows you to handle extremely large assemblies with tremendous ease. Based mainly on the feedback of the users of solid modeling, this tool is known to be remarkably user-friendly and it allows you to be productive from day one.

This solid modeling tool allows you to easily import the AutoCAD, AutoCAD Mechanical, and Mechanical Desktop files with an amazing compatibility. Moreover, the parametric features and assembly parameters are retained when you import the Mechanical Desktop files in Autodesk Inventor.

The drawing views that can be generated using this tool include orthographic view, isometric view, auxiliary view, section view, detailed view, and so on. You can use predefined drawing standard files for generating the drawing views. Moreover, you can retrieve the model dimensions or add reference dimensions to the drawing views whenever you want. The bidirectional associative nature of this software ensures that any modification made in the model is automatically reflected in the drawing views. Similarly, any modifications made in the dimensions in the drawing views are automatically reflected in the model.

Autodesk Inventor 2011 for Designers textbook is written with the intent of helping the people who are into 3D design. This textbook is written with the tutorial point-of-view and the learn-by-doing theme. The mechanical engineering industry examples and tutorials are used in this textbook to ensure that the users can relate the knowledge of this book with the actual mechanical industry designs. The salient features of this textbook are as follows:

- **Tutorial Approach**
    The author has adopted the tutorial point-of-view and the learn-by-doing theme throughout the textbook. This approach guides the users through the process of creating the models in the tutorials.

- **Real-World Projects as Tutorials**

    The author has used about 50 real-world mechanical engineering projects as tutorials in this book. This enables the readers to relate these tutorials to the real-world models in the mechanical engineering industry. In addition, there are about 33 exercises that are also based on the real-world mechanical engineering projects.

- **Coverage of All Autodesk Inventor Modules**

    All modules of Autodesk Inventor are covered in this book including the **Presentation** module for animating the assemblies, the **Sheet Metal** module for creating the sheet metal components, and the **Weldment** module for creating weldments.

- **Tips and Notes**

    Additional information related to various topics is provided to the users in the form of tips and notes.

- **Heavily Illustrated Text**

    The text in this book is heavily illustrated with about 1200 line diagrams and screen capture images.

- **Learning Objectives**

    The first page of every chapter introduces in brief the topics that are covered in that chapter. This helps the users to easily refer to a topic.

- **Command Section**

    In every chapter, the description of a tool begins with the command section that gives a brief information of various methods of invoking that tool.

- **Self-Evaluation Test, Review Questions, and Exercises**

    Every chapter ends with a Self-Evaluation test so that the users can assess their knowledge of the chapter. The answers to the Self-Evaluation test are given at the end of the chapter. Also, the Review Questions and Exercises are given at the end of each chapter and they can be used by the Instructors as test questions and exercises.

Symbols Used in the Text

Note

The author has provided additional information to the users about the topic being discussed in the form of notes.

Tip

Special information and techniques are provided in the form of tips that helps in increasing the efficiency of the users.

New

This symbol indicates the new command or tool introduced in Autodesk Inventor 2011.

Enhanced

This symbol the existing command or tool that has been enhanced in Autodesk Inventor 2011.

Formatting Conventions Used in the Text

Please refer to the following list for the formatting conventions used in this textbook.

- Names of tools, buttons, options, panels, tabs, and Ribbon are written in boldface.

  Example: The **Extrude** tool, the **Finish Sketch** button, the **Modify** panel, the **Sketch** tab, and so on.

- Names of dialog boxes, drop-downs, drop-down lists, list boxes, areas, edit boxes, check boxes, and radio buttons are written in boldface.

  Example: The **Revolve** dialog box, the **Create 2D Sketch** drop-down of **Sketch** panel in the **Model** tab, the **Placement** drop-down of **Hole** dialog box, the **Distance** edit box of **Extrude** dialog box, the **Extended Profile** check box in **Rib** dialog box, the **Drilled** radio button of the **Hole** dialog box, and so on.

- Values entered in edit boxes are written in boldface.

  Example: Enter **5** in the **Radius** edit box.

- Names and paths of the files saved are italicized.

  Example: *C:\Inventor2011\c03*, *c03tut03.prt*, and so on

- The methods of invoking a tool/option from the **Ribbon**, **Quick Access Toolbar**, **Application Menu**, and toolbars are enclosed in a shaded box.

  Ribbon: Get Started > Launch > New
  Quick Access Toolbar: New
  Application Menu: New
  Toolbar: 2D Sketch Standard > New

Naming Conventions Used in the Text

Tool

If you click on an item in a toolbar or a panel of the **Ribbon** and a command is invoked to create/edit an object or perform some action, then that item is termed as **tool**.

For example:
To Create: **Line** tool, **Dimension** tool, **Extrude** tool
To Edit: **Fillet** tool, **Draft** tool, **Trim Surface** tool
Action: **Zoom All** tool, **Pan** tool, **Copy Object** tool

If you click on an item in a toolbar or a panel of the Ribbon and a dialog box is invoked wherein you can set the properties to create/edit an object, then that item is also termed as **tool**, refer to Figure 1.

For example:
To Create: **Create iPart** tool, **Parameters** tool, **Create** tool
To Edit: **Styles Editor** tool, **Document Settings** tool

Figure 1 *Various tools in the Ribbon*

Button

The item in a dialog box that has a 3d shape like a button is also termed as **Button**. For example, **OK** button, **Cancel** button, **Apply** button, and so on. Refer to Figure 2 given below for the terminologies used for the components in a dialog box.

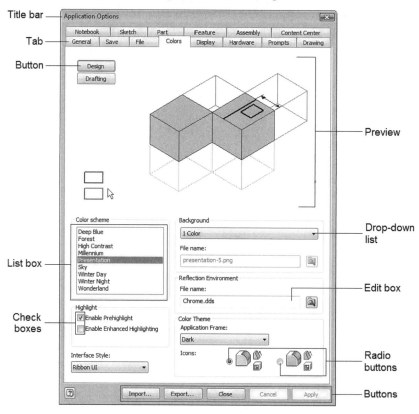

Figure 2 *The components in a dialog box*

Drop-down

A drop-down is one in which a set of common tools are grouped together for creating an object. You can identify a drop-down with a down arrow on it. These drop-downs are given a name based on the tools grouped in them. For example, **Arc** drop-down, **Fillet/Chamfer** drop-down, **Work Axis** drop-down, and so on; refer to Figure 3.

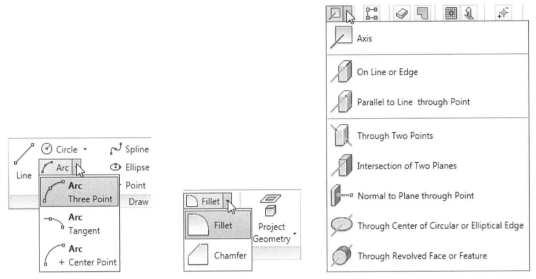

Figure 3 *The **Arc**, **Fillet/Chamfer**, and **Work Axis** drop-downs*

Drop-down List

A drop-down list is one in which a set of options are grouped together. You can set various parameters using these options. You can identify a drop-down list with a down arrow on it. For example, **Extents** drop-down list, **Color Override** drop-down list, and so on; refer to Figure 4.

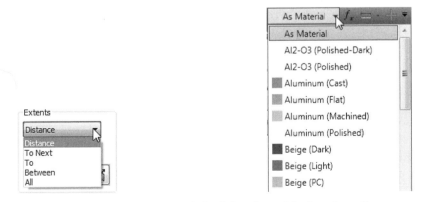

Figure 4 *The **Extents** and the **Color Override** drop-down lists*

Options

Options are the items that are available in shortcut menu, drop-down list, dialog boxes, drop-down lists, and so on. For example, choose the **New Sketch** option from the shortcut menu displayed on right-clicking in the drawing area; choose the **Background Image** option from the **Background** drop-down list; choose the **Front** option from the **Orientation** area; refer to Figure 5.

Figure 5 *Options in the shortcut menu,* ***Background*** *drop-down list, and the* ***Orientation*** *area*

Free Companion Website

It has been our constant endeavor to provide you the best textbooks and services at affordable price. In this endeavor, we have come out with a Free Companion website that will facilitate the process of teaching and learning of Autodesk Inventor 2011. If you purchase this textbook from our website (www.cadcimtech.com), you will get access to the files on the Companion website.

To access the files, you need to register by visiting the **Resources** section at *www.cadcim.com.* The following resources are available for the faculty and students in this website:

Faculty Resources
• **Technical Support**
  You can get online technical support by contacting *techsupport@cadcim.com.*

• **Instructor's Guide**
  Solutions to all review questions and exercises in the textbook are provided in this link to help the faculty members test the skills of the students.

• **PowerPoint Presentations**
  The contents of the book are arranged in PowerPoint slides that can be used by the faculty for their lectures.

- **Part Files**
  The part files used in illustration, tutorials, and exercises are available for free download.

Student Resources

- **Technical Support**
  You can get online technical support by contacting *techsupport@cadcim.com*.

- **Part Files**
  The part files used in illustrations and tutorials are available for free download.

- **Additional Students Projects**
  Various projects are provided for the students to practice.

If you face any problem in accessing these files, please contact the publisher at *sales@cadcim.com* or the author at *stickoo@calumet.purdue.edu* or *tickoo525@gmail.com*.

Chapter 1

Introduction

INTRODUCTION TO Autodesk Inventor 2011

Welcome to the world of Autodesk Inventor. If you are new to the world of three-dimensional (3D) design, then you have joined hands with thousands of people worldwide who are already working with 3D designs. If you are already using any other solid modeling tool, you will find this solid modeling tool more adaptive to your use. You will find a tremendous reduction in the time taken to complete a design using this solid modeling tool.

Autodesk Inventor is a parametric and feature-based solid modeling tool. It allows you to convert the basic two-dimensional (2D) sketch into a solid model using very simple, but highly effective modeling options. This solid modeling tool does not restrict its capabilities to the 3D solid output, but also extends them to the bidirectional associative drafting. This means that you only need to create the solid model. Its documentation, in the form of the drawing views, is easily done by this software package itself. You just need to specify the required view. This solid modeling tool can be specially used at places where the concept of **"collaborative engineering"** is brought into use. Collaborative engineering is a concept that allows more than one user to work on the same design at the same time. This solid modeling package allows more than one user to work simultaneously on the same design.

As a product of Autodesk, this software package allows you to directly open the drawings of the other Autodesk software like AutoCAD, Mechanical Desktop, AutoCAD LT, and so on. This interface is not restricted to the Autodesk software only. You can easily import and export the drawings from this software package to any other software package and vice versa.

To reduce the complicacies of design, this software package provides various design environments. This helps you capture the design intent easily by individually incorporating the intelligence of each of the design environments into the design. The design environments that are available in this solid modeling tool are discussed next.

Part Module

This is a parametric and feature-based solid modeling environment and is used to create solid models. The sketches for the models are also drawn in this environment. All applicable constraints are applied to the sketch automatically while drawing. You do not need to invoke an extra command to apply them. Once the basic sketches are drawn, you can convert them into solid models using simple, but highly effective modeling options. One of the major advantages of using Autodesk Inventor is the availability of the Design Doctor. The Design Doctor is used to calculate and describe errors, if any, in the design. You are also provided with the remedy for removing errors such that the sketches can be converted into features. The complicated features can be captured from this module and can later be used in other parts. This reduces the time taken to create the designer model. These features can be created using the same principles as those for creating solid models.

Assembly Module

This module helps you create the assemblies by assembling multiple components using assembly constraints. This module supports both the bottom-up approach as well as the top-down approach of creating assemblies. This means that you can insert external components into the **Assembly** module or create the components in the **Assembly** module itself. You are allowed to assemble the components using the smart assembly constraints. All the assembly constraints can be added using a single dialog box. You can even preview the components before they are actually assembled. This solid modeling tool supports the concept of making a part or a feature in the part adaptive. An adaptive feature or a part is the one that can change its actual dimensions based upon the need of the environment.

Presentation Module

A major drawback of most solid modeling tools is their limitation in displaying the working of an assembly. The most important question asked by the customers in today's world is how to show the working of any assembly. Most of the solid modeling tools do not have an answer to this question. This is because they do not have proper tools to display an assembly in motion. As a result, the designers cannot show the working of the assemblies to their clients. In cases where it is necessary to show the animation, they have to take the help of some other software packages such as 3D Studio MAX or 3D Studio VIZ. However, keeping this problem in mind, this software package provides a module called the **Presentation** module. In this module, you can animate the assemblies created in the **Assembly** module and view their working. You can also view any interference during the operation of the assembly. The assemblies can be animated using easy steps.

Drawing Module

This module is used for the documentation of the parts or assemblies in the form of drawing views. You can also create the drawing views of the presentation created in the **Presentation** module. All parametric dimensions, added to the components in the **Part** module during the creation of the parts are displayed in the drawing views in this module.

Sheet Metal Module

This module is used to create the sheet metal component. When you invoke a sheet metal file, the sketching environment is active by default. You can draw the sketch of the base sheet in this module and then proceed to the sheet metal module to convert it into the sheet metal component.

GETTING STARTED WITH Autodesk Inventor

Install Autodesk Inventor on your system; the Autodesk Inventor Professional 2011 shortcut icon will automatically be created on the desktop. Double-click on this icon to start the software. You can also start Autodesk Inventor from the taskbar by choosing **Start > Programs** (or **All Programs**)**> Autodesk > Autodesk Inventor 2011 > Autodesk Inventor Professional 2011**, as shown in Figure 1-1.

The system will prepare for starting Autodesk Inventor by loading all required files. After all required files have been loaded, the initial screen of Autodesk Inventor Professional 2011 will be displayed, as shown in Figure 1-2. You can view the recent enhancement and information related to Autodesk Inventor 2011 by choosing the buttons displayed on the **Ribbon**.

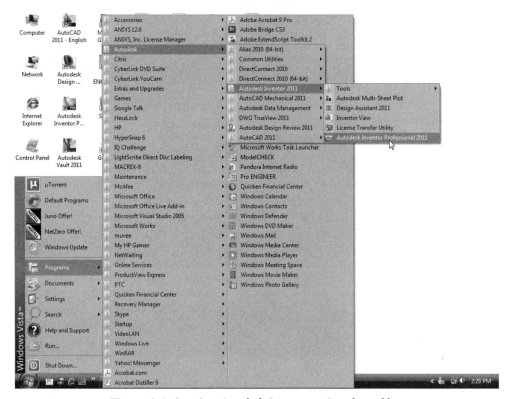

Figure 1-1 *Starting Autodesk Inventor using the taskbar*

To start a new part file, choose the **New** tool from the **Launch** panel of the **Get Started** tab in the **Ribbon**; the **New File** dialog box will be displayed, as shown in Figure 1-3. Alternatively, you can start a new part file by using the **Quick Launch** area of the **Open** dialog box, see Figure 1-4. The **Open** dialog box can be invoked by choosing the **Open** button from the **Get Started** tab of the **Ribbon**. When you start a new session of **Autodesk Inventor Professional 2011**, only the **Start a new file** button will be activated in the **Quick Launch** area of the **Open** dialog box. Choose the **Start a new file** button; the **New File** dialog box will be displayed, refer to Figure 1-3. Choose the **Metric** tab from the **New File** dialog box and then double-click on the **Standard (mm).ipt** template to open a default metric template. As a result, a new part file with the default name Part1.ipt will be opened and you can start working in this file. Also, the sketching environment will be invoked, as shown in Figure 1-5. This figure also displays various components of this screen.

It is evident from Figure 1-5 that the screen of Autodesk Inventor is quite user-friendly. Apart from the components shown in Figure 1-5, you are also provided with various shortcut menus, which are displayed upon right-clicking the mouse in the drawing area. The type of the shortcut menu and its options depend on where or when you are trying to access this menu. For example, when you are inside any command, the options displayed in the shortcut menu will be different from the options displayed when you are not inside any command. The different types of shortcut menus will be discussed when they are used in the textbook.

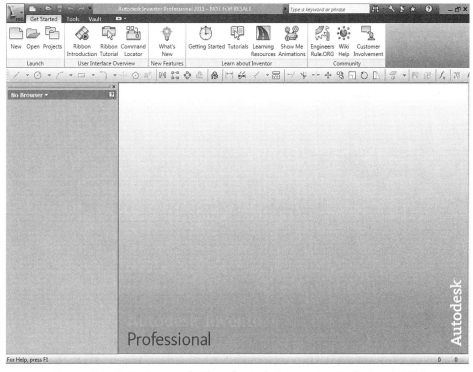

Figure 1-2 Initial screen display of Autodesk Inventor Professional 2011

Figure 1-3 The **New File** dialog box

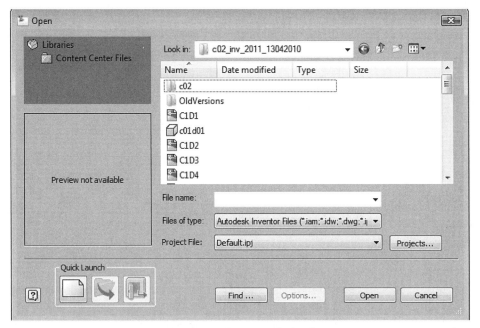

Figure 1-4 The **Open** dialog box

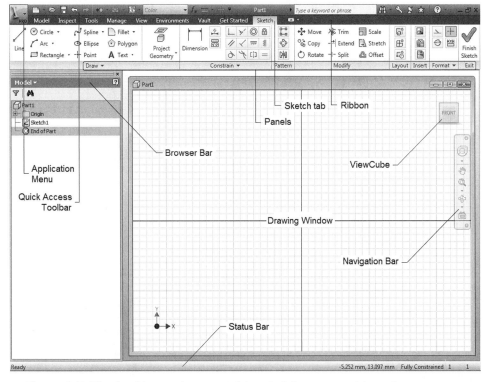

Figure 1-5 The sketching environment of Autodesk Inventor and its main components

Quick Access Toolbar

This toolbar is common to all design environments of Autodesk Inventor. However, some of these options will not be available when you start Autodesk Inventor for the first time. You need to add them using the down arrow given on the right of the **Quick Access Toolbar**, as shown in Figure 1-6. Some of the important options in this toolbar are discussed next.

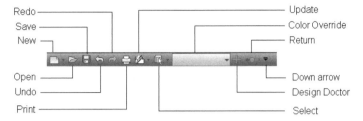

*Figure 1-6 The **Quick Access Toolbar***

Select

This tool is used to set the selection priority. When you choose the down arrow on the right of this tool, six more tools are displayed. These tool are **Select Bodies**, **Select Groups**, **Select Features**, **Select Face and Edges**, **Select Sketch Features**, and **Select Wires**. The **Select Bodies** tool is chosen to set the selection priority to bodies. If this tool is chosen, you can select any individual body in the model. If the choose the **Select Features** tool, you can select any feature in the model. The **Select Faces and Edges** tool is chosen to set the priority to faces and edges. This tool is chosen by default, as a result you can select the faces and edges of the features. The **Select Sketch Features** tool is chosen to set the priority to sketched entities. The remaining two tools, **Select Groups** and **Select Wires** will be activated according to their respective environments when the different groups and wires are available. There are also other tools available in this area, which will be displayed in different modules.

Return

This tool is chosen to exit the sketching environment. Once you have finished drawing the sketch, choose this tool to proceed to the **Part** module where you can convert the sketch into a feature using the required tools.

Update/Local Update

This tool is chosen to update the design after editing.

Color Override

You can use this drop-down list to apply different types of colors or styles to the selected features or component to improve its appearance. It is much easier to identify different components, parts, and assemblies when proper color codes are applied to them.

RIBBON AND TABS

You might have noticed that there is no command prompt in Autodesk Inventor. The complete designing process is carried out by invoking the commands from the tabs in the **Ribbon**.

The **Ribbon** is a long bar available below the **Quick Access Toolbar**. You can change the appearance of the **Ribbon** as per your need. To do so, right-click on it; a shortcut menu will be displayed. Choose **Ribbon Appearance** from this shortcut menu to invoke a cascading menu. Next, choose the required option from the cascading menu.

Autodesk Inventor provides you with different tabs while working with various design environments. This means that the tabs available in the **Ribbon** while working with the **Part**, **Assembly**, **Drawing**, **Sheet Metal**, and **Presentation** environments will be different.

You can also display the toolbars. To do so, choose the **Customize** button from the **Options** panel of the **Tools** tab in the **Ribbon**; the **Customize** dialog box will be displayed. Choose the **Toolbars** tab from this dialog box; the list of all toolbars will be displayed. Select the required toolbar and then choose the **Show** button; the selected toolbar will appear on the screen. Choose the **Close** button to close the **Customize** dialog box.

Tip. *In Autodesk Inventor Professional 2011, the messages and prompts are displayed at the **Status Bar** which is available at the lower left corner of the Autodesk Inventor window.*

Sketch Tab

This is one of the most important tabs in the **Ribbon**. All tools for creating the sketches of the parts are available in this tab. The **Sketch** tab is available only in the sketching environment. The **Sketch** tab is shown in Figure 1-7.

*Figure 1-7 The **Sketch** tab*

Inventor Precise Input Toolbar

You are now aware of the fact that Autodesk Inventor does not provide you with any command prompt. Because of this, you will be restricted from entering the precise values of the sketcher entities. But this problem has been taken care of in Autodesk Inventor by providing you with a very important toolbar called the **Inventor Precise Input** toolbar. This toolbar is used to enter the precise values for the coordinates of the sketcher entities. This toolbar is also available in the **Drawing** and **Assembly** modules for providing precise values. The **Inventor Precise Input** toolbar is shown in Figure 1-8.

*Figure 1-8 The **Inventor Precise Input** toolbar*

Model Tab

This is the second most important tab provided in the **Part** module. Once the sketch is completed, you need to convert it into a feature using the modeling commands. This tab provides all modeling tools that can be used to convert the sketch into a feature. The tools in the **Model** tab are shown in Figure 1-9.

Figure 1-9 The Model tab

The **Create 2D Sketch** button in the **Sketch** panel of the **Model** tab is used to draw a 2D sketch in the sketching environment and is chosen by default when you start a new file in the **Part** module. As the first feature in most designs is a sketched feature, you can directly start working on the sketch of the feature. Once you have completed a sketch, you can choose either the **Return** button from the **Quick Access Toolbar** or the **Finish Sketch** button from the **Exit** panel of the **Sketch** tab in the **Ribbon** to exit the sketching environment. Whenever you need to draw the 2D sketch for another feature, choose this button again. You will be prompted to select the plane for sketching the feature. Once you define the new sketching plane, the sketching environment will be activated.

Sheet Metal Tab

This tab provides the tools that are used to create sheet metal parts. This toolbar will be available only when you are in the sheet metal environment. You can switch from the Modeling environment to the Sheet Metal environment by choosing the **Convert to Sheet Metal** tool from the **Convert** panel of the **Model** tab in the **Ribbon**. The tools in the **Sheet Metal** tab are shown in Figure 1-10.

Figure 1-10 The Sheet Metal tab

Assemble Tab

This tab will be available only when you open any assembly template (with extension *.iam*) from the **New File** dialog box. This tab provides you all tools that are required for assembling components. The tools in the **Assemble** tab are shown in Figure 1-11.

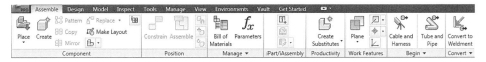

Figure 1-11 The Assemble tab

Place Views Tab

This tab provides the tools that are used to create different views of the components. This tab will be available only when you are in the Drafting environment. The tools in the **Place Views** tab are shown in Figure 1-12.

*Figure 1-12 The **Place Views** tab*

Presentation Tab

This tab provides the tools that are used to create different presentation views of the components. This tab will be available only when you open any presentation template (with extension *.ipn*) in the **New File** dialog box. The tools in the **Presentation** tab are shown in Figure 1-13.

*Figure 1-13 The **Presentation** tab*

Tools Tab

This tab contains tools that are mainly used for setting the preferences and customizing the Autodesk Inventor interface. This tab is available in almost all environments. The tools in the **Tools** tab are shown in Figure 1-14.

*Figure 1-14 The **Tools** tab*

View Tab

The tools in this tab enable you to the control the view, orientation, appearance, and visibility of objects and view windows. This tab is available in almost all environments. The tools in the **View** tab are shown in Figure 1-15.

*Figure 1-15 The **View** tab*

The tools of a particular tab are arranged in different panels in the **Ribbon**. Some of the panels and tools have an arrow on the right, refer to Figure 1-16. These arrows are called down arrows. When you choose these down arrows, some more tools will be displayed as drop-downs, see Figure 1-16.

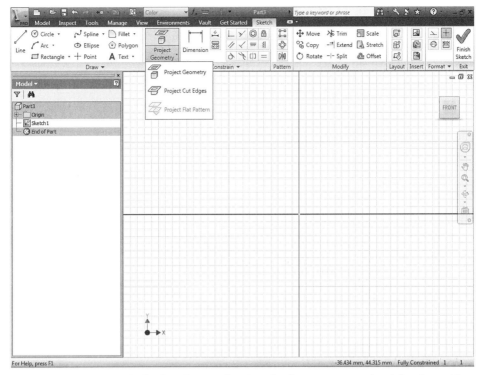

Figure 1-16 *More tools displayed upon choosing the down arrow on the right of a tool in the* ***Ribbon***

Navigation Bar

The **Navigation Bar** is located on the right of the graphics area and contains tools that are used to make the designing process easier and quicker. The navigation tools also help you control the view and orientation of components in the drawing window. The **Navigation Bar** is shown in Figure 1-17

Browser Bar

The **Browser Bar** is available below the **Ribbon** on the left of the drawing window. It displays all the operations performed during the designing process in a sequence. All these operations are displayed in the form of a tree view. You can undock the **Browser Bar** by dragging it from its position to other position. The contents of the **Browser Bar** are different for different environments of Autodesk Inventor. For example, in the **Part** module, it displays various operations that were used in creating the part. Similarly, in the **Assembly** module, it displays all the components along with the constraints that were used to assemble them.

Figure 1-17 *The* ***Navigation Bar***

UNITS FOR DIMENSIONS

In Autodesk Inventor, you can set units at any time by using the **Document Settings** dialog box. You can invoke this dialog box by choosing the **Document Settings** tool from the **Options** panel in the **Tools** tab. After invoking this dialog box, choose the **Units** tab in the dialog box; various areas related to units will be displayed. The options in the **Units** area are used to set the units. To set the unit for linear dimension, select the required unit from the **Length** drop-down. Similarly, to set the unit for angular dimension, select the required unit from the **Angle** drop-down. Next, choose the **OK** button to apply the specified settings and close the dialog box. If you want to apply the specified settings without closing the dialog box, choose the **Apply** button. If you choose the **Apply** button, the **OK** button is replaced by **Close**. Now, you can choose the **Close** button to close the dialog box.

IMPORTANT TERMS AND THEIR DEFINITIONS

Before you proceed further in Autodesk Inventor, it is very important for you to understand the following terms, which are widely used in this book.

Feature-based Modeling

A feature is defined as the smallest building block that can be modified individually. In Autodesk Inventor, the solid models are created by integrating a number of these building blocks. Therefore, the models in Autodesk Inventor are a combination of a number of individual features. These features understand their fit and function properly. As a result, these can be modified, whenever required. Generally, these features automatically adjust their values, if there is any change in their surroundings. For example, a feature created by cutting right through the base feature will automatically adjust its depth, if you increase the depth of the base feature. This provides greater flexibility to the design.

Parametric Modeling

The parametric nature of a software package is defined as its ability to use the standard properties or parameters to define the shape and size of a geometry. The main function of this property is to derive the selected geometry to the new size or shape without considering its original size or shape. For example, you can derive a line of 20 mm that was initially drawn at an angle of 45° to a line of 50 mm and change its orientation to 90°. This property makes the designing process very easy. This is because now you do not need to draw the sketch to the actual dimensions that are required. You just need to draw the sketch to some relative dimensions, and then this solid modeling tool will drive it to the actual values you require.

Bidirectional Associativity

As mentioned earlier, this solid modeling tool does not restrict its capabilities to the 3D solid output. It is also capable of highly effective assembly modeling, drafting, and presentations. There exists a bidirectional associativity between all these environments of Autodesk Inventor. This means that every time, there exists a link between all the environments of Autodesk Inventor. This link ensures that if any modification is made in the model in any one environment, it is automatically reflected in the other environments.

Adaptive

This is a highly effective property that is included in the designing process of this solid modeling tool. In any design, there are a number of components that can be used in various places with a small change in their shape and size. This property makes the part or the feature adapt to its environment. It also ensures that the adaptive part changes its shape and size as soon as it is constrained to other parts. This considerably reduces the time and effort required in creating similar parts in the design.

Design Doctor

The Design Doctor is one of the most important parts of the designing process used in the Autodesk Inventor software. It is a highly effective tool to ensure that the entire design process is error free. The main purpose of the Design Doctor is to make you aware of any problem in the design. The Design Doctor works in the following three steps:

Selecting the Model and Errors in the Model

In this step, the Design Doctor selects the sketch, part, assembly, and so on and determines the errors in it.

Examining Errors

In this step, it examines the errors in the selected design. Each of the errors is individually examined and the required solution is provided.

Providing Solutions for Errors

This is the last step of the working of the Design Doctor. Once it has individually examined each of the errors, it suggests solutions for them. It provides you with a list of methods that can be utilized to remove the errors from the design.

Constraints

These are the logical operations that are performed on the selected design to make it more accurate or define its position with respect to the other design. There are four types of constraints in Autodesk Inventor. All these types are explained next.

Geometric Constraints

These logical operations are performed on the basic sketching entities to relate them to the standard properties like collinearity, concentricity, perpendicularity, and so on. Autodesk Inventor automatically applies these geometric constraints to the sketcher entities at the time of their creation. You do not have to use an extra command to apply these constraints on to the sketcher entities. However, you can also manually apply these geometric constraints on to the sketcher entities. There are twelve types of geometric constraints.

Perpendicular Constraint

This constraint is used to make the selected line segment normal to another line segment.

Parallel Constraint

This constraint is used to make the selected line segments parallel.

Coincident Constraint

This constraint is used to make two points or a point and a curve coincident.

Concentric Constraint

This constraint forces two selected curves to share the same center point. The curves that can be made concentric are arcs, circles, or ellipses.

Collinear Constraint

This constraint forces two selected line segments or ellipse axes to be placed in the same line.

Horizontal Constraint

This constraint forces the selected line segment to become horizontal.

Vertical Constraint

This constraint forces the selected line segment to become vertical.

Tangent

This constraint is used to make the selected line segment or curve tangent to another curve.

Equal

This constraint forces the selected line segments to become equal in length. It can also be used to force two curves to become equal in radius.

Smooth

This constraint adds a smooth constraint between a spline and another entity so that at the point of connection, the line is tangent to the spline.

Fix

This constraint fixes the selected point or curve to a particular location with respect to the coordinate system of the current sketch.

Symmetric

This constraint forces the selected sketched entities to become symmetrical about a sketched line segment, which may or may not be a center line.

Assembly Constraints

The assembly constraints are the logical operations performed on the components in order to bind them together to create an assembly. These constraints are applied to reduce the degrees of freedom of the components. There are four types of assembly constraints which are discussed next.

Mate

The **Mate** constraint is used to make the selected faces of different components coplanar. The model can be placed facing in the same direction or in the opposite direction. You can also specify some offset distance between the selected faces.

Angle

The **Angle** constraint is used to place the selected faces of different components at some angle with respect to each other.

Tangent

The **Tangent** constraint is used to make the selected face of a component tangent to the cylindrical, circular, or conical faces of the other component.

Insert

The **Insert** constraint forces two different circular components to share the same orientation of the central axis. It also makes the selected faces of the circular components coplanar.

Motion Constraints

The motion constraints are the logical operations performed on the components that are assembled using the assembly constraints. There are two types of motion constraints:

Rotation

The **Rotation** constraint is used to rotate one component of the assembly in relation to the other component.

Rotation-Translation Constraint

The **Rotation-Translation** constraint is used to rotate the first component in relation to the translation of the second component.

Transitional Constraints

The transitional constraints are also applied on the assembled components and are used to ensure that the selected face of the cylindrical component maintains contact with the selected faces of the other component when you slide the cylindrical component.

UCS to UCS Constraint

This constraint is used to constrain two components together by their UCS.

 Note

The motion and transitional constraints are applied on the components that have already been assembled using the assembly constraints. Therefore, these constraints work along the degrees of freedom of the components that are not restricted using the assembly constraints.

Consumed Sketch

A consumed sketch is a sketch that is utilized in creating a feature using tools such as **Extrude**, **Revolve**, **Sweep**, **Loft**, and so on.

CYCLING THROUGH ENTITIES

While working on the complicated models, sometimes you may need to select the entities that are not visible in the current view or are hidden behind other entities. To select these types of entities, Autodesk Inventor allows you to cycle through entities using a cycling tool, as shown in Figure 1-18. This tool is displayed automatically when you hold the cursor at a point where more than one entity is available. This cycling tool consists of two arrows at each

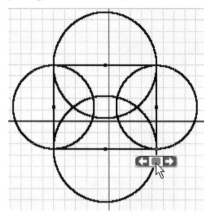

end and a rectangle in between. The left arrow is used to cycle through the previous entities, the right arrow is used to cycle through the next entities, and the rectangle is used to select the highlighted entity. The current entity will be highlighted and displayed in red. Once the required entity is highlighted, move the cursor over the rectangle in the cycling tool and select it using the left mouse button. The highlighted entity will be selected and displayed in blue. Figure 1-18 shows the cycling tool displayed in the sketching environment to cycle through the sketched entities. You can use this tool in all modes and environments of Autodesk Inventor.

Figure 1-18 Cycling through entities

HOTKEYS

As mentioned earlier, there is no command prompt in Autodesk Inventor. However, you can use the keys on the keyboard to invoke some tools. The keys that can be used to invoke the tools are called hotkeys. Remember that the working of the hotkeys will be different for different environments. The use of hotkeys in different environments is given next.

Part Module

The hotkeys that can be used in the **Part** module and their functions are given next.

Hotkey	Function
E	Invokes the **Extrude** tool
R	Invokes the **Revolve** tool
H	Invokes the **Hole** tool
CTRL+SHIFT+L	Invokes the **Loft** tool
CTRL+SHIFT+S	Invokes the **Sweep** tool
F	Invokes the **Fillet** tool
CTRL+SHIFT+K	Invokes the **Chamfer** tool
D	Invokes the **Draft** tool

CTRL+SHIFT+R	Invokes the **Rectangular Pattern** tool
CTRL+SHIFT+O	Invokes the **Circular Pattern** tool
CTRL+SHIFT+M	Invokes the **Mirror** tool
]	Invokes the **Work Plane** tool
/	Invokes the **Work Axis** tool
.	Invokes the **Work Point** tool
CTRL+W	Invokes the **SteewingWheels**
F6	Invokes the **Home view**

The following hotkeys are used in the sketching environment:

Hotkey	Function
L	Invokes the **Line** tool
C	Invokes the **Center Point Circle** tool
D	Invokes the **Dimension** tool
X	Invokes the **Trim** tool
F7	Invokes the **Slice Graphics** tool
F8	Displays all constraints
F9	Hides all constraints

Assembly Module

In addition to the hotkeys of the part modeling tool, the following hot keys can also be used in the **Assembly** module:

Hotkey	Function
P	Invokes the **Place** tool
N	Invokes the **Create** tool
C	Invokes the **Constraint** tool
CTRL+H	Invokes the **Replace** tool
CTRL+SHIFT+H	Invokes the **Replace All** tool
V	Invokes the **Move Component** tool
G	Invokes the **Rotate Component** tool
A	Invokes the **Analyze Interference** tool

Drawing Module

The hotkeys that can be used in the **Drawing** module are given next.

Hotkey	Function
B	Invokes the **Balloon** tool
D	Invokes the **Dimension** tool
O	Invokes the **Ordinate Set** tool
F	Invokes the **Feature Control Frame** tool

In addition to these keys, you can also use some other keys for the ease of designing. Note that you will have to hold some of these keys down and use them in combination with the pointing device. These hotkeys are given next.

Hotkey	Function
F1	Invokes the **Help** command
F2	Invokes the **Pan** tool
F3	Invokes the **Zoom** tool
F4	Invokes the **Free Orbit** tool
F5	Previous view
SHIFT+F5	Next view
ESC	Aborts the current command
SPACEBAR	Invokes the recently used tool
T (In **Presentation** module)	Invokes the **Tweak Components** tool

Customizing Hotkeys

You can customize the settings of hotkeys. To do so, choose the **Customize** tool from the **Options** panel of the **Tools** tab in the **Ribbon**; the **Customize** dialog box will be displayed. Next, choose the **Keyboard** tab; the list of all available commands will be displayed, as shown in Figure 1-19. The options corresponding to the **Keyboard** tab are discussed next.

Categories

Select the required category of command from this drop-down list; the commands related to the selected category will be listed in the list box.

Filter

You can further shortlist the displayed commands from this drop-down list. If you select the **All** option, all commands related to the selected category will be displayed. If you select the **Assigned** option, then the commands to which the hotkeys are assigned will be displayed. Similarly, if you select the **Unassigned** option, then the commands to which the hotkeys are not assigned will be displayed.

Figure 1-19 *The **Customize** dialog box displaying various commands in the **Keyboard** tab*

List Box

The list box has four columns: **Keys**, **Command Name**, **Type**, and **Category**. The **Key** column displays the hotkeys assigned to the commands. The name of the command, its type, and category will be listed in the **Command Name**, **Type**, and **Category** columns, respectively.

To assign hotkeys to a tool, click in the **Keys** column that is associated to the command; an edit box will be displayed. In this edit box, enter the shortcut key that you want to assign. To accept the settings, click on the tick-mark provided at the right side of this edit box. Else, click on the cross-mark provided next to the tick-mark.

Reset All Keys

The **Reset All Keys** button is used to remove all customized hotkeys and restore the default hotkeys.

Copy to Clipboard

Choose this button to copy the contents of the **Keyboard** tab and paste them in other document.

Import

Choose this button to restore the customized settings from the .xml format. Note that before importing the file, all Autodesk Inventor files must be closed.

Export

Choose this button to save the customized settings in the .xml format. Make sure that all Autodesk Inventor files are closed before choosing this button.

Reset All

This button is used to reset all the customized settings of environments, toolbars, and menus. Make sure that all Autodesk Inventor files are closed before choosing this button.

Close

Choose this button to close the **Customize** dialog box.

CREATING THE SKETCH

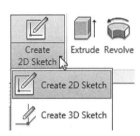

After starting Autodesk Inventor, you can start creating the model in the Part environment. But before creating the model, you need to create its sketch in the Sketching environment. The Sketching environment is invoked automatically when you start a new part file. But if you want to invoke the Sketching environment manually, choose the **Create 2D Sketch** tool from the **Sketch** drop-down in the **Sketch** panel of the **Model** tab, see Figure 1-20. On choosing this tool, the sketching environment is invoked and you can create the 2D sketches. If you choose the **Create 3D sketch** tool from the **Sketch** panel, you can create the 3D sketches.

Figure 1-20 Tools in the *Sketch* drop-down

COLOR SCHEME

Autodesk Inventor allows you to use various color schemes to set the background color of the screen and for displaying the entities on the screen. Note that this book uses the **Presentation** color scheme with a single color background. To change the color scheme, choose the **Application Options** tool from the **Options** panel of the **Tools** tab in the **Ribbon**; the **Application Options** dialog box will be displayed. Choose the **Colors** tab to display the predefined colors. Next, select the **Presentation** option from the **Color scheme** list box in the **Colors** tab. Select **1 Color** from the drop-down list in the **Background** area, refer to Figure 1-21. Choose **Apply** to apply the color scheme to the Autodesk Inventor environment, and then choose **Close**. Note that all the files you open henceforth will use this color scheme.

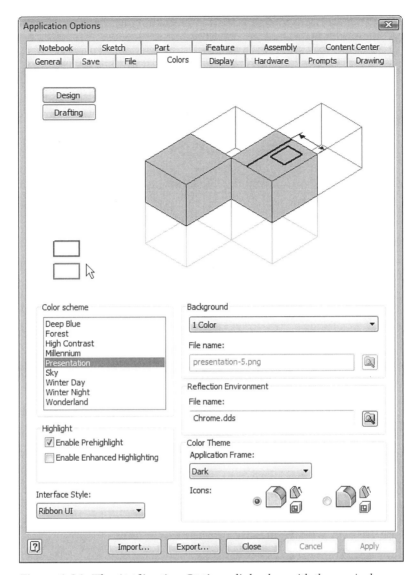

Figure 1-21 The **Application Options** *dialog box with the required options set in the* **Colors** *tab*

Self-Evaluation Test

Answer the following questions and then compare them to those given at the end of this chapter:

1. When you start a new session of Autodesk Inventor Professional 2011, only the **Start a new file** button will be available in the **Quick Launch** area of the **Open** dialog box. (T/F)

2. The **Inventor Precise Input** toolbar is used to specify the precise values for the coordinates of sketcher entities. (T/F)

3. The tools in the **Model** tab enable you to control the view, orientation, appearance, and visibility of objects and view windows. (T/F)

4. You can invoke the **Line** tool by using the _____ hotkey.

5. Press _____ to invoke the recently used tool.

6. Choose the _____ button from the **Customize** dialog box to restore the customized settings in the .xml format.

Review Questions

Answer the following questions:

1. There are twelve types of geometric constraints in Autodesk Inventor. (T/F)

2. Design Doctor works in five steps. (T/F)

3. You can invoke the **Trim** tool by pressing the X key. (T/F)

4. You can use the _____ drop-down list to apply different types of color or style to the selected feature or component to improve its appearance. (T/F)

5. You can invoke the **Analyze Interference** tool in the **Assembly** module by pressing the _____ key.

6. The _____ button is used to draw a 2D sketch in the sketching environment and is chosen by default when you start a new file in the **Part** module.

Answers to Self-Evaluation Test
1. T, **2.** T, **3.** F, **4.** L, **5.** SPACEBAR, **6.** Import

Chapter 2

Drawing Sketches for Solid Models

Learning Objectives

After completing this chapter, you will be able to:
- *Start a new template file to draw sketches.*
- *Set up the sketching environment.*
- *Use various drawing display tools.*
- *Understand the sketcher environment in the Part module.*
- *Get acquainted with sketcher entities.*
- *Specify the position of entities by using dynamic input.*
- *Draw sketches by using various sketcher entities.*
- *Delete sketched entities.*

THE SKETCHING ENVIRONMENT

Most designs created in Autodesk Inventor consist of sketched and placed features. A sketch is the combination of a number of two-dimensional (2D) entities such as lines, arcs, circles, and so on. The features such as extrude, revolve, and sweep that are created by using 2D sketches are known as sketched features. The features such as fillet, chamfer, thread, and shell that are created without using a sketch are known as placed features. In a design, the base feature or the first feature is always a sketched feature. For example, the sketch shown in Figure 2-1 is used to create a solid model, as shown in Figure 2-2. In this figure, the fillets and chamfers are the placed features.

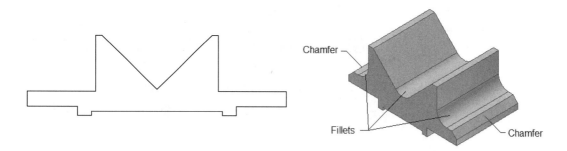

Figure 2-1 *The basic sketch for the solid model*   **Figure 2-2** *A solid model created using the sketched and placed features*

Once you have drawn the basic sketch, refer to Figure 2-1, you need to convert it into a solid model using solid modeling tools.

The sketching environment of Autodesk Inventor can be invoked at any time in the **Part** module or in the **Assembly** module. Unlike other solid modeling programs, here you just need to invoke the **Create 2D Sketch** tool and specify the plane to draw the sketch; the sketching environment will be activated. Also, when you start a new file in the **Part** module, first the sketching environment will be activated. You can draw a sketch in this environment and then proceed to the part modeling environment for converting the sketch into a solid model. The options in the sketching environment will be discussed later in this chapter.

The Open Dialog Box

On starting a new session of Autodesk Inventor, the initial screen will be displayed. Now, choose the **Open** tool from the **Launch** panel of the **Get Started** tab; the **Open** dialog box will be displayed, as shown in Figure 2-3.

The options in the **Open** dialog box are used to create new files and open existing files. You can browse and select the file that you want to open from the list displayed in the dialog box. The preview of the selected file is displayed in the preview window located at the lower left portion of this dialog box, as shown in Figure 2-4. By default, you can open any file created in Autodesk Inventor. This is because by default, the **Files of type** drop-down list displays the **Autodesk Inventor Files (*.iam;*.idw;*.dwg;*.ipt;*.ipn, and *.ide)** option.

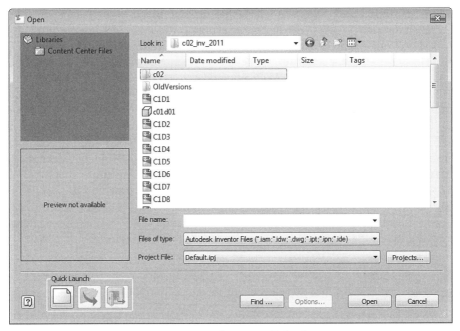

Figure 2-3 The **Open** dialog box

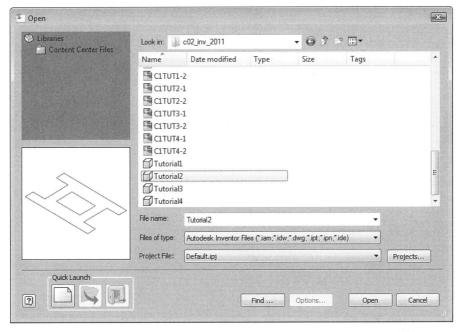

Figure 2-4 The **Open** dialog box showing the preview of the selected file

You can also open the files created in other solid modeling programs such as AutoCAD, Pro/ENGINEER, Alias, SolidWorks, NX, and so on, by selecting the respective options from the **Files of type** drop-down list.

In Autodesk Inventor, a project defines all the files related to a design project you are working on. You can create new projects or retrieve the previously created projects by choosing the **Projects** button available on the right of the **Project File** drop down list in the **Open** dialog box. When you choose the **Projects** button, the **Projects** dialog box will be displayed, as shown in Figure 2-5. All the project folders will be displayed in the upper half of the dialog box and the options regarding the selected project folder will be displayed in the lower half of the dialog box. To add another project folder to this list, choose the **New** button; the **Inventor project wizard** dialog box will be displayed. The **New Vault Project** radio button is selected by default in this dialog box. Choose the **Next** button from the **Inventor project wizard** dialog box. Specify the name of the project in the **Name** text box and the location in the **Project (Workspace) Folder** text box. You can also choose the **Browse for project location** button to specify the location of the project. Next, choose the **Finish** button. Once you have specified the project folder, it will be added in the upper part of the dialog box and its location will be displayed. When you select a project, the options related to it will be shown in the lower part of the dialog box. The **Projects** dialog box with various projects is displayed, refer to Figure 2-5.

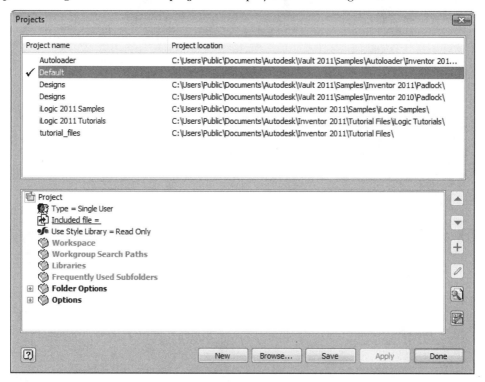

Figure 2-5 *The* **Projects** *dialog box*

On starting a new session in Autodesk Inventor, only the **Start a new file** button will be available in the **Quick Launch** area of the **Open** dialog box. Choose this button; the **New File** dialog box will be displayed, as shown in Figure 2-6. To exit the **Open** dialog box, choose the **Cancel** button.

*Figure 2-6 The **New File** dialog box*

To view help about topics, press F1; the **Autodesk Inventor Help** window will be displayed. In this window, you will find help topics explaining how to use a particular tool or option of Autodesk Inventor. You can select the **Show Help on startup** check box available on the right of the **Autodesk Inventor Help** window to make this window appear whenever you start a new session. You can exit the **Autodesk Inventor Help** window by choosing the **Close** button.

Starting a New File

In Autodesk Inventor, you can start a new file by choosing **New** from the **Get Started** tab or by choosing the **New** option from the **Application Menu**. On doing so, the **New File** dialog box will be displayed, refer to Figure 2-6. Alternatively, you can start a new file by choosing the **New** tool from the **Quick Access Toolbar**.

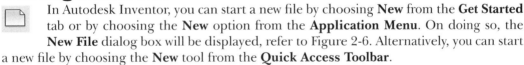

Note
*If you invoke the **New File** dialog box by choosing the **New** tool from the **Quick Access Toolbar** or by choosing **New > New** from the **Application Menu**, only the **Open** button will available in the **Quick Launch** area. You can choose the **Open** tool to invoke the **Open** dialog box and open an existing file in Autodesk Inventor.*

The options in the **New File** dialog box are used to select a template file for starting a design. You can select a template in the **Default**, **English**, **Metric**, or **Mould** tabs. To start a new metric part file, choose the **Metric** tab, as shown in Figure 2-7. The templates that are available on choosing the **Metric** tab are discussed next.

Figure 2-7 *The* **Metric** *tab of the* **New File** *dialog box*

.ipt Templates

Select any *.ipt* template to start a new part file for creating a solid model or a sheet metal component. When you start a new part file, the sketching environment will be automatically active and you can directly start drawing sketches.

.iam Templates

Select any *.iam* template to start a new assembly file for assembling various parts. Similarly, use the *Weldment.iam* template to weld two different components in the **Weldment** module.

.ipn Templates

Select any *.ipn* template to start a new presentation file for animating the assembly. The **Presentation** module marks the basic difference between Autodesk Inventor and other design tools. This module allows you to animate the assemblies created in the **Assembly** module. For example, you can create a presentation in the **Presentation** module that shows a Drill Press Vice assembly in motion.

.idw Templates

Select any *.idw* template to start a new drawing file for generating the drawing views. You can use the drawing templates of various standards that are provided in this tab, such as ANSI, ISO, DIN, GB, JIS, GOST, and BSI.

.dwg Templates

Select any *.dwg* template for creating AutoCAD drawing files. You can use the drawing templates of standards such as JIS, ISO, GB, DIN, BSI, and ANSI.

The **Project File** drop-down list in the **New File** dialog box displays the active project in which the new file has been started. The **Projects** dialog box can be invoked by choosing the **Projects** button from the **New File** dialog box.

INTRODUCTION TO THE SKETCHING ENVIRONMENT

The initial screen appearance in the sketching environment of a *Standard (mm).ipt* file is shown in Figure 2-8. By default, the **Ribbon** is placed at the top of the graphics window, refer to Figure 2-8. You can move this **Ribbon** anywhere in the graphics window. To do so, right-click on the **Ribbon**; a shortcut menu will be displayed. Select the **Undock Ribbon** option from the shortcut menu; the **Ribbon** will be undocked. Now you can drag the **Ribbon** anywhere in the graphics window. It is recommended to place (dock) the **Ribbon** at the top of the graphics window so that you can use the space efficiently. To do so, right-click on the **Ribbon** and choose **Docking Position > Top** from the shortcut menu. Alternatively, double-click on the title bar of the **Ribbon** to dock it.

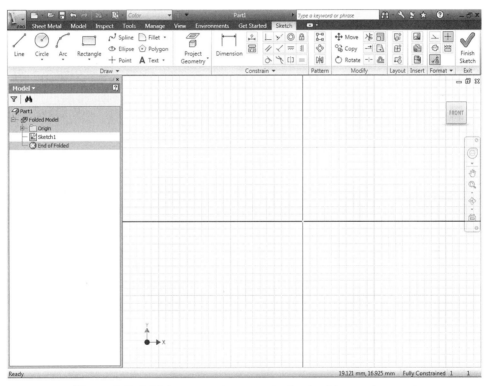

Figure 2-8 Initial screen appearance in the sketching environment

SETTING UP THE SKETCHING ENVIRONMENT

It is very important to first set up the sketcher environment. This has to be done before you start drawing a sketch. Setting up the sketcher environment includes modifying the grids of a drawing. It is unlikely that the designs that you want to create consist of small dimensions. You will come across a number of designs that are large. Therefore, before starting a drawing, you need to modify the grid settings. These settings will depend on the dimensions of the design. The process of modifying the grid settings of a drawing is discussed next.

Modifying the Document Settings of a Sketch

Before sketching, you may need to modify the setting of the sketching environment as per your requirement. You can change the snapping distance, grid spacing, and various attributes related to line display of the sketching environment. You must have noticed that the drawing window in the sketching environment consists of a number of light and dark lines that are normal to each other. These normal lines are called grid lines. The grid lines help you locate an entity, thereby helping you to draw a sketch correctly or modify an existing sketch precisely.

You can modify the document settings of a sketch. To do so, choose the **Document Settings** tool from the **Options** panel of the **Tools** tab; the **Document Settings** dialog box will be displayed. In this dialog box, choose the **Sketch** tab to display the options related to the sketching environment, see Figure 2-9. The options under this tab are discussed next.

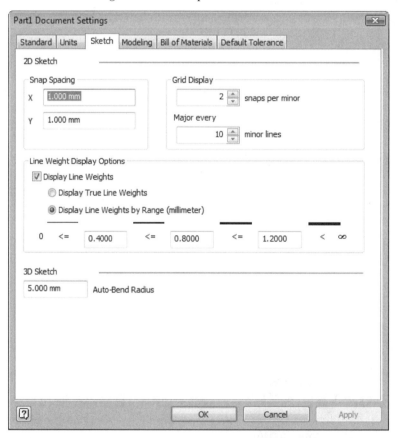

*Figure 2-9 The **Sketch** tab of the **Document Settings** dialog box*

Snap Spacing Area

The options under this area are used to specify the snap distances.

X

This edit box is used to specify the snap spacing in the X direction.

Y

This edit box is used to specify the snap spacing in the Y direction.

Grid Display Area

The options in this area are used to control the number of major and minor lines. The minor lines are the light lines that are displayed inside the dark gray lines. The dark gray lines are called the major lines.

snaps per minor

This spinner is used to specify the number of snap points between each minor line.

Major every minor lines

This spinner is used to specify the number of minor lines between two major lines.

Line Weight Display Options Area

The options in the **Line Weight Display Options** area allow you to control the line weight in the sketching environment. The **Display Line Weights** check box is selected by default and displays the sketches with the set line weights. If this check box is cleared, then the differences in the line weights will not be displayed in the sketch. The **Display True Line Weights** radio button, if selected, displays the line weights on screen as they would appear on paper when printed. The **Display Line Weights by Range (millimeter)** radio button, if selected, displays the line weights according to the values entered.

Note

You will have to increase the drawing display area after increasing the grid spacing. The options to do so are discussed next.

Tip. *You can also turn off the display of the major and minor grid lines and the axes. To turn off the display of the grid line and the axes, choose the **Application Options** tool from the **Options** panel; the **Application Options** dialog box will be displayed. Next, choose the **Sketch** tab and clear the **Grid lines**, **Minor grid lines**, and **Axes** check boxes from the **Display** area.*

UNDERSTANDING THE DRAWING DISPLAY TOOLS

The drawing display tools or navigation tools are an integral part of any design software. These tools are extensively used during the design process. These tools are available in the **Navigation Bar** located on the right in the graphics window and in the **Navigate** panel of the **View** tab. Some of the drawing display tools in Autodesk Inventor are discussed next. The rest of these tools will be discussed in the later chapters.

Zoom All

Ribbon:	View > Navigate > Zoom drop-down > Zoom All
Navigation Bar:	Zoom flyout > Zoom All

 The **Zoom All** tool is used to increase the drawing display area to display all the sketched entities in the current display.

Zoom Window

Ribbon:	View > Navigate > Zoom drop-down > Zoom Window
Navigation Bar:	Zoom flyout > Zoom Window

 The **Zoom Window** tool is used to define an area to be magnified and viewed in the current drawing. The area is defined using two diagonal points of a box (called window) in the drawing window. The area inscribed inside the window will be magnified and displayed on the screen.

 Tip. *The size of the dimension text always remains constant even if you magnify the area that includes some dimensions.*

To switch to the previous view, right-click in the drawing window and then choose ***Previous View*** *from the shortcut menu or press the F5 key. You can restore nine previous views in the current sketching environment by using this option.*

Zoom

Ribbon:	View > Navigate > Zoom drop-down > Zoom
Navigation Bar:	Zoom flyout > Zoom

The **Zoom** tool is used to interactively zoom in and out of the drawing view. When you choose this tool, the default cursor is replaced by the zoom cursor. You can zoom into the drawing by pressing the left mouse button and dragging the cursor down. Similarly, you can zoom out of the drawing by pressing the left mouse button and then dragging the cursor up. You can exit this tool by choosing another tool or by pressing ESC. You can also choose **Done** from the shortcut menu, which is displayed on right-clicking. You can also zoom into the drawing by rolling the scroll wheel of the mouse in the reverse direction. Similarly, you can zoom out of the drawing by rolling the scroll wheel in the forward direction.

 Tip. *You need to increase the drawing display area by zooming out from the drawing using the* ***Zoom*** *tool after increasing the grid spacing.*

Zoom Selected

Ribbon:	View > Navigate > Zoom drop-down > Zoom Selected
Navigation Bar:	Zoom flyout > Zoom Selected

 When you choose the **Zoom Selected** tool, you will be prompted to select an entity to zoom. Select an entity from the drawing area; it will magnified to maximum extent and placed at the center of the drawing window. This tool can also be invoked by pressing the END key.

Pan

Ribbon: View > Navigate > Pan
Navigation Bar: Pan

The **Pan** tool is used to drag the current view in the drawing window. This option is generally used to display the contents of the drawing that are outside the display area, without actually changing the magnification of the current drawing. It is similar to holding the drawing and dragging it across the drawing window. You can also invoke the **Pan** tool by pressing and holding the middle scroll wheel of the mouse.

SKETCHING ENTITIES

Getting acquainted with the sketching entities is an important part of learning Autodesk Inventor. A major part of the design is created using the sketched entities. Therefore, this section can be considered as one of the most important sections of the book. In Autodesk Inventor, the sketched entities are of two types: **Normal** and **Construction**. The normal entities are used to create a feature and become a part of it, but the construction entities are drawn just for reference and support, and cannot become a part of the feature. By default, all drawn entities are normal entities. To draw construction entities, choose the **Construction** tool from the **Format** panel of the **Sketch** tab. All entities drawn after choosing the **Construction** tool will be the construction entities. Deselect this tool by choosing it again to draw normal entities.

SPECIFYING THE POSITION OF ENTITIES DYNAMICALLY BY USING THE DYNAMIC INPUT

With this release of Autodesk Inventor, you can specify the position of sketching entities dynamically by using the Pointer Input and the Dimension Input. The Pointer Input is displayed when you invoke the sketching tools such as **Line**, **Rectangle**, **Arc**, and it displays the coordinates of the current location of the cursor. As you move the cursor, the coordinates change dynamically. When you specify the first point, the Pointer Input is displayed. The Pointer Input is displayed in the form of Cartesian Coordinates (X and Y). If you specify the second point or the subsequent points of entities, the Dimension Input will be displayed. The Dimension Input is displayed in the form of polar coordinates (Length and Angle).

To specify the position of sketching entities dynamically, invoke the required sketching tool and then move the cursor in the drawing window; the location of the cursor will be displayed in the cartesian coordinate in the Pointer Input. Press the TAB key and enter the X and Y coordinate values in the Pointer Input to specify the first point; you will be prompted to specify the endpoint or second point of the entity. Alternatively, you can specify the first point of the entity by clicking in the drawing window. On doing so, the Pointer Input will be modified to the Dimension Input and the polar coordinate input fields will be displayed. To specify the endpoint or second point of the entity, enter the length and angle values in the input fields. To toggle between the length and angle input fields, use the TAB key. If you specify input values by using the Dimension Input and then use the TAB key, lock icons will be displayed on the right of the input fields. The lock icons indicates that the values defined are constrained. Figure 2-10 shows the Pointer Input of a line and Figure 2-11 shows the Dimension Input of the endpoint of a line of length 20 mm at an angle of 45-degree.

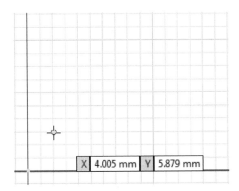

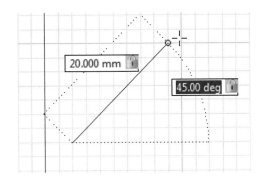

Figure 2-10 *Pointer input of a line*   **Figure 2-11** *Dimension input of the endpoint of a line of length 20 mm at 45-degree*

If some sketched entities exist in the drawing window and you start creating new entities in the drawing window, an appropriate constraint symbol will be displayed near the cursor. You can control the display of the Pointer Input and Dimension Input by using the **Application Options** dialog box. This dialog box can be invoked by choosing the **Application Options** tool from the **Options** panel. To control the display of Pointer Input and Dimension Input, choose the **Sketch** tab in the **Application Options** dialog box. Clear the **Enable the Heads-Up Display (HUD)** check box from the **Sketch** tab and choose the **OK** button from this dialog box. As a result, the display of Pointer Input and Dimension Input will be turned off and now you cannot enter the input values of the entities dynamically.

The sketcher entities in Autodesk Inventor are discussed next.

Drawing Lines

Ribbon:	Sketch > Draw > Line
Toolbar:	2D Sketch Panel > Line drop-down > Line

Lines are the basic and one of the most important entities in the sketching environment. As mentioned earlier, you can draw either normal lines or construction lines. A line is defined as the shortest distance between two points. The two points are the start point and the endpoint of the line. Therefore, to draw a line, you need to define these two points. The parametric nature of Autodesk Inventor allows you to draw the initial line of any length or at any angle by just picking the points on the screen. After drawing the line, you can drive it to a new length or angle by using parametric dimensions. You can also create the line of actual length and angle directly by using the **Inventor Precise Input** toolbar. Both these methods of drawing the lines are discussed next.

Drawing Lines by Picking Points in the Drawing Window

This is a very convenient method to draw lines and is used extensively while sketching. When you invoke the **Line** tool from the **Draw** panel, the cursor (which was initially an arrow) is replaced by crosshairs with a yellow circle at the intersection. Also, you are prompted to select the start point of the line or drag off the endpoint for the tangent arc. In addition, the coordinates of the current location of the cursor are displayed in the Pointer Input and also at the lower right corner of the Autodesk Inventor window. The point of intersection of the X and Y axes (black lines among grid lines) is the origin point. If you move the cursor close to the origin, it will snap to the origin automatically. To draw a line, specify a point anywhere in the drawing window; the Pointer Input will display both length and angle values as zero. Move the cursor; a rubber-band line will start from the specified point and the length and angle values will change accordingly in the Pointer Input. One end of this rubber-band line is fixed at the point specified in the drawing window and the other end is attached to the yellow circle in crosshairs. As you move the cursor after specifying the start point of the line, the Pointer Input will display the length and angle of the current location of the line. Click at the required position in the drawing window. Alternatively, enter the required length and angle values in the Pointer Input to specify the endpoint of the line. You can use the TAB key to toggle between the length and angle values in the Pointer Input. After specifying the endpoint of the line, a line is drawn and a new rubber-band line starts. The start point of the new rubber-band line is the endpoint of the last line and you are again prompted to specify the endpoint of the line. You can continue specifying the endpoints to draw continuous lines.

When you draw entities in Autodesk Inventor, valid constraints are applied automatically to entities. Therefore, when you draw continuous lines, the horizontal, vertical, perpendicular, and parallel constraints are applied automatically to them. The symbol of the applied constraint is displayed on the line while drawing it. You can exit the **Line** tool by pressing the ESC key. You can also right-click in the drawing window, and then choose **Done** from the shortcut menu displayed. Figures 2-12 and 2-13 display the **Perpendicular Constraint** and **Parallel Constraint** being applied to the lines while they are being drawn.

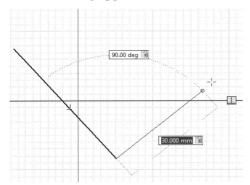

Figure 2-12 *Drawing a line using the* **Perpendicular Constraint**

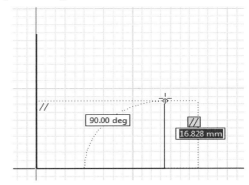

Figure 2-13 *Drawing a line using the* **Parallel Constraint**

Note

*The default screen appearance in the sketcher environment has been modified for clarity. To change the screen appearance, choose the **Application Options** tool from the **Options** panel; the **Application Options** dialog box will be displayed. Choose the **Colors** tab and then select the **Presentation** option from the **Color scheme** list box. Select **1 Color** from the **Background** drop-down list. Next, choose the **Apply** button from the **Application Options** dialog box to change the default appearance of the screen in the sketcher environment.*

Tip. *While drawing a sketch, constraints are displayed dynamically and are applied to it. To turn off the display of these constraints, press and hold the CTRL key and draw the sketch.*

With this release of Autodesk Inventor, you can close a sketch that has two or more than two lines. To do so, create two or more than two continuous lines and then right-click in the drawing window; a shortcut menu will be displayed. Choose the **Close** option from the shortcut menu; a line joining the endpoint of the current line and the start point of the first line will be created and the sketch will be closed. Figure 2-14 shows the **Close** option being chosen from the shortcut menu to close the sketch and Figure 2-15 shows the closed sketch created.

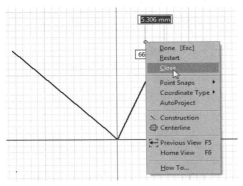

*Figure 2-14 Choosing the **Close** option from the shortcut menu*

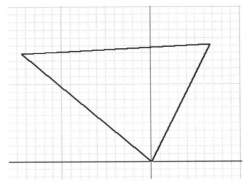

Figure 2-15 Closed sketch created

Drawing Lines by Specifying Exact Values

This is another method of drawing lines in Autodesk Inventor. In this method, you use the **Inventor Precise Input** toolbar to define the coordinates of the start point and the endpoint of lines. To display the **Inventor Precise Input** toolbar for the line, first invoke the **Line** tool. Next, click on the down arrow displayed at bottom of the **Draw** panel in the **Sketch** tab; the **Draw** panel will expand. Choose the **Precise Input** tool from this panel. As mentioned earlier, the origin of the drawing lies at the intersection of the X and Y axes. The X and Y coordinates of this point are 0, 0. You can take the reference of this point to draw lines. There are two methods to define the coordinates using this toolbar. Both the methods are discussed next.

Specifying Coordinates with respect to the Origin

The system of defining the coordinates with respect to the origin of the drawing is termed as the **absolute coordinate system**. By default, the origin lies at the intersection of the X and Y axes. All the points in this system are defined with respect to this origin. To define the points, you can use the following four methods.

Defining the Absolute X and Y Coordinates. In this method, you will define the X and Y coordinates of the new point with respect to the origin. To invoke this method, select the **Indicate a point location by typing X and Y values** option from the drop-down list in the **Inventor Precise Input** toolbar. The exact X and Y coordinates of the point can be entered in the **X** and **Y** edit boxes provided in this toolbar.

Defining the Absolute X Coordinate and the Angle from the X Axis. In this method, you will define the absolute X coordinate of a point with respect to the origin and the angle that this line makes with the positive X axis. The angle will be measured in the counterclockwise direction from the positive X axis. To invoke this method, select the **Specify a point using X coordinate and angle from X axis** option from the drop-down list. The X coordinate of the new point and the angle can be defined in the respective edit boxes in the **Inventor Precise Input** toolbar.

Defining the Absolute Y Coordinate and the Angle from the X Axis. In this method, you will define the absolute Y coordinate of a point with respect to the origin and the angle that this line makes with the positive X axis. To invoke this method, select the **Specify a point using Y coordinate and angle from X axis** option from the drop-down list. The Y coordinate of the new point and the angle can be defined in the respective edit boxes in the **Inventor Precise Input** toolbar.

Specifying the Distance from the Origin and the Angle from the X Axis. In this method, you will define the distance of the point from the origin and the angle that this line makes with the X axis. To invoke this method, select the **Specify a point using distance from the origin and angle from X axis** option from the drop-down list. The distance and the angle can be defined in the respective edit boxes.

Specifying Coordinates with respect to the Last Point

This system of specifying the coordinates with respect to the previous point is termed as the **relative coordinate system**. Note that this system of defining the points cannot be used for specifying the first point (the start point of the line). All absolute coordinate methods for specifying a point with respect to the origin can also be used with respect to the last specified point by choosing the **Precise Delta** button along with the respective method. This button will be available only after you specify the start point of the first line.

Note

While drawing continuous lines, when you move the cursor close to the start point of the first line, the yellow circle changes to green and the cursor snaps to the start point. On selecting the point at this stage the loop will be closed and you will exit the current line chain.

*To draw centerlines, first choose the **Centerline** tool from the **Format** panel and then create the line. Alternatively, select the required entities from the drawing window and then choose the **Centerline** tool; the selected entities will become centerlines.*

Restarting a Line

To restart a line, right-click and choose **Restart** from the shortcut menu. The start point of the line is canceled and you are prompted to select the start point of the line.

Drawing Circles

In Autodesk Inventor, you can draw circles using two methods. You can draw a circle by defining the center and the radius of the circle or draw a circle that is tangent to three specified lines. Both these methods of drawing the circle are discussed next.

Drawing Circles by Specifying the Center Point and Radius

Ribbon:	Sketch > Draw > Circle drop-down > Circle Center Point
Toolbar:	2D Sketch Panel > Circle drop-down > Center Point Circle

Circle

This is the default method of drawing circles. In this method, you need to define the center point and radius of a circle. To draw a circle using this method, choose the **Circle Center Point** tool from the **Draw** panel, see Figure 2-16; you will be prompted to select the center of the circle. Specify the center point of the circle in the drawing window; you will be prompted to specify a point on the circle. Click at the required location in the drawing window to specify a point on the circumference of the circle. This point will define the radius of the circle. Alternatively, enter the required value in the Pointer Input to specify the diameter of the circle. You can also specify the center and the radius using the **Inventor Precise Input** toolbar. Figure 2-17 shows a circle drawn by using the center and the radius.

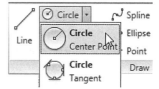

Figure 2-16 Tools in the Circle drop-down

Drawing Circles by Specifying Three Tangent Lines

Ribbon:	Sketch > Draw > Circle drop-down > Circle Tangent
Toolbar:	2D Sketch Panel > Circle drop-down > Tangent Circle

Circle

This is the second method of drawing circles and is used to draw a circle tangent to three selected lines. To draw a circle using this method, choose the **Circle Tangent** tool from the **Draw** panel, see Figure 2-16; you will be prompted to select the first, second, and third line, sequentially. As soon as you specify the third line, a circle tangent to all the three specified lines will be drawn, as shown in Figure 2-18.

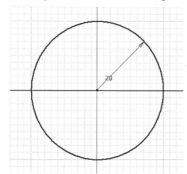

Figure 2-17 Circle drawn using the center point and the radius of the circle

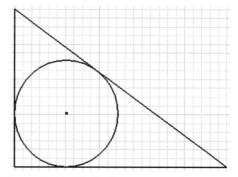

Figure 2-18 Circle drawn using three tangent lines

Drawing Ellipses

Ribbon:	Sketch > Draw > Ellipse
Toolbar:	2D Sketch Panel > Circle drop-down > Ellipse

Ellipse

To draw an ellipse, choose the **Ellipse** tool from the **Draw** panel; you will be prompted to specify the center of the ellipse. Select a point to specify the center of the ellipse; you will be prompted to specify the first axis point. Specify a point to define the first axis of the ellipse; you will be prompted to select a point on the ellipse. Select a point on the ellipse; the ellipse will be created. You can also specify these points using the **Inventor Precise Input** toolbar. However, remember that you cannot use the relative options for defining the points of the ellipse. Therefore, if you use the **Inventor Precise Input** toolbar for drawing the ellipse, all the values will be specified from the origin. However, you can redefine the origin by choosing the **Precise Redefine** button and placing it at the point that you want to define as the origin. Figure 2-19 shows an ellipse.

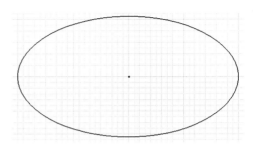

Figure 2-19 An ellipse drawn in the sketching environment

Drawing Arcs

Autodesk Inventor provides three methods for drawing arcs, which are discussed next.

Drawing an Arc by Specifying Three Points

Ribbon:	Sketch > Draw > Arc drop-down > Arc Three Point
Toolbar:	2D Sketch Panel > Arc drop-down > Three Point Arc

This is the default method of drawing arcs. To create an arc with three points, choose the **Arc Three Point** tool from the **Draw** panel, see Figure 2-20, and then specify three points. The first point is the start point of the arc, the second point is the endpoint of the arc, and the third point is a point on the arc. You can define these points by specifying them in the drawing window or by using the **Inventor Precise Input** toolbar. You can also use the Pointer Input for specifying the second and the third point of the arc. Figure 2-21 shows an arc drawn using this method.

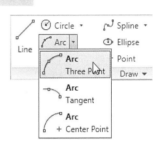

*Figure 2-20 Tools in the **Arc** drop-down*

Drawing an Arc Tangent to an Existing Entity

Ribbon:	Sketch > Draw > Arc drop-down > Arc Tangent
Toolbar:	2D Sketch Panel > Arc drop-down > Tangent Arc

This method is used to draw an arc that is tangent to an existing open entity. The open entity can be an arc or a line. To draw an arc using this method, choose the **Arc Tangent** tool from the **Draw** panel (see Figure 2-20); you will be prompted to select the start point of the arc. The start point of the arc must be the start point or endpoint of an existing open entity. Once you specify the start point, a rubber-band arc will start from it. Note that this arc is tangent to the selected entity. Now, you will be prompted to specify the endpoint of the arc. Click on the drawing window to specify the endpoint of the arc. Alternatively, enter the radius and the angle values in the Pointer Input to specify the endpoint of the arc. Here, it is very important to mention that the **Inventor Precise Input** toolbar or the Pointer Input cannot be used to select the start point of this arc. However, you can use this toolbar to specify the endpoint of this arc. Figure 2-22 shows an arc drawn tangent to the line.

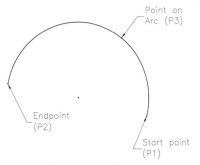

Figure 2-21 *Drawing the three points arc*

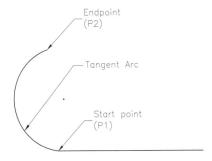

Figure 2-22 *Drawing the tangent arc*

Drawing Tangent/Normal Arcs Using the Line Tool

You can also draw a tangent or a normal arc when you are inside the **Line** tool. At least a line or an arc should be drawn before drawing an arc using this method. To draw an arc using the **Line** tool, draw a line or an arc and then invoke the **Line** tool. When you are prompted to select the start point of the line, move the cursor close to the point from where you want to start the tangent or normal arc; the yellow circle in the cursor turns green. Select the point at this stage; the green circle in the cursor turns gray. Press the left mouse button and drag the mouse; four construction lines appear at the start point displaying the normal and tangent directions. If you drag along the tangent direction, a tangent arc is drawn. But if you drag along the normal direction, an arc normal to the selected entity is drawn.

Drawing an Arc by specifying the Center, Start, and Endpoint

Ribbon:	Sketch > Draw > Arc drop-down > Arc Center Point
Toolbar:	2D Sketch Panel > Arc drop-down > Center Point Arc

This method is used to draw an arc by specifying the center point, start point, and endpoint of the arc. To draw an arc using this method, choose the **Arc Center Point** tool from the **Draw** panel (see Figure 2-20). On doing so, you will be prompted to specify the center point of the arc. Once you specify the center point of the arc, you will be prompted to specify the start point and then the endpoint of the arc, see Figure 2-23. You can also specify the start point and endpoint of the arc by using the Pointer Input. In case of start point, you need to specify the radius and angle of the arc from the center point. Whereas, in case of endpoint, you need to specify the arc length in terms of angle value. You can use the TAB key to toggle between the input values of the Pointer Input. As you define the center point and the start point, the radius of the arc will be defined automatically. So, the third point is just used to define the arc length. An imaginary line is drawn from the cursor to the center of the arc. The point at which the arc intersects the imaginary line will then be taken as the endpoint of the arc, see Figure 2-24. You can also use the **Inventor Precise Input** toolbar to specify these three points of the arc.

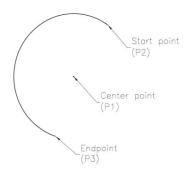

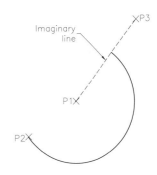

Figure 2-23 *The arc created by specifying the center point, start point, and endpoint*

Figure 2-24 *The imaginary line created while drawing the center point arc*

Drawing Rectangles

In Autodesk Inventor, rectangles can be drawn by using two methods that are discussed next.

Drawing Rectangles by Specifying Two Opposite Corners

Ribbon:	Sketch > Draw > Rectangle drop-down > Rectangle Two Point
Toolbar:	2D Sketch Panel > Rectangle drop-down > Two Point Rectangle

This is the default method used to draw a rectangle by specifying its two opposite corners. To draw a rectangle by using this method, choose the **Rectangle Two Point** tool from the **Draw** panel, see Figure 2-25; you will be prompted to specify the first corner of the rectangle and the Pointer Input will be displayed. Click at the required location to specify the first corner of the rectangle. Once you specify the first corner, you will be prompted to specify the opposite corner of the rectangle and the Pointer Input will be modified. Click to specify the second corner or enter the length and height of the rectangle in the Pointer Input. Figure 2-26 shows a rectangle drawn using the **Rectangle Two Point** tool.

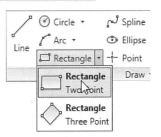

Figure 2-25 *Tools in the* **Rectangle** *drop-down*

Drawing Rectangles by Specifying Three Points on a Rectangle

Ribbon:	Sketch > Draw > Rectangle drop-down > Rectangle Three Point
Toolbar:	2D Sketch Panel > Rectangle drop-down > Three Point Rectangle

You can draw a rectangle by specifying its three points. In this method, the first two points are used to define the length and angle of one of the sides of the rectangle and the third point is used to define the length of the other side. To create a rectangle by using this method, choose the **Rectangle Three Point** tool from the **Draw** panel of the **Sketch** tab, see Figure 2-25; you will be prompted to specify the first corner of the rectangle. Once you specify it, you will be prompted to specify the second corner of the rectangle. Both these corners are along the same direction. As a result, you can use these points to define the length of one side of the rectangle. After specifying the second corner, you will be prompted to specify the third corner. This corner is used to define the length of the other side of the rectangle. Note that if you specify the second corner at a certain angle, then the resultant rectangle will also be inclined. You can also specify the first, second, and third points of the rectangle by using the Pointer Input. In case of second point, you need to specify the length and angle of rectangle in the input value fields of the Pointer Input. Whereas, in case of endpoint, you need to specify the height of the rectangle. You can use the TAB key to toggle between the input values of the Pointer Input. You can also specify the three points for drawing the rectangle using the **Inventor Precise Input** toolbar. Figure 2-27 shows an inclined rectangle drawn by using the **Three Point Rectangle** tool.

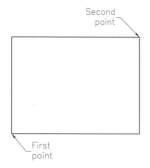

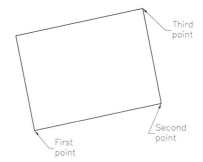

Figure 2-26 *Drawing a rectangle using two points*   ***Figure 2-27*** *Drawing the three-point rectangle at an angle*

Drawing Polygons

Ribbon:	Sketch > Draw > Polygon
Toolbar:	2D Sketch Panel > Polygon

The polygons drawn in Autodesk Inventor are regular polygons. A regular polygon is a multi-sided geometric figure in which the length of all sides and the angle between them are the same. In Autodesk Inventor, you can draw a polygon with the number of sides ranging from 3 to 120. When you invoke the **Polygon** tool, the **Polygon** dialog box will be displayed, as shown in Figure 2-28, and you will be prompted to select the center of the polygon. The options in this dialog box are discussed next.

Figure 2-28 *The **Polygon** dialog box*

Inscribed

This is the first button in the **Polygon** dialog box and is chosen by default. This option is used to draw an inscribed polygon. An inscribed polygon is the one that is drawn inside an imaginary circle such that its vertices touch the circle. Once you have specified the polygon center, you will be prompted to specify a point on the polygon. In case of an inscribed polygon, the point on the polygon specifies one of its vertices, see Figure 2-29.

Circumscribed

This is the second button in the **Polygon** dialog box and is used to draw a circumscribed polygon. A circumscribed polygon is the one that is drawn outside an imaginary circle such that its edges are tangent to the imaginary circle. In case of a circumscribed polygon, the point on the polygon is the midpoint of one of the polygon edges, see Figure 2-30.

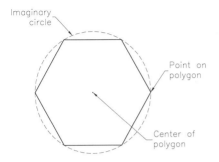

Figure 2-29 Drawing a six-sided inscribed polygon

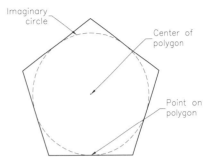

Figure 2-30 Drawing a five-sided circumscribed polygon

Number of Sides

This edit box is used to specify the number of sides of the polygon. The default value is 6. You can enter any value ranging from 3 to 120 in this edit box.

Note
The rectangles and polygons are a combination of individual lines. All the lines can be separately selected or deleted. However, when you select one of the lines and drag, the entire rectangle or polygon will be considered as a single entity. As a result, the entire object will be moved or stretched.

Placing Points

Ribbon:	Sketch > Draw > Point
Toolbar:	2D Sketch Panel > Point, Center Point

In Autodesk Inventor, you can place the sketched points in a sketch using the **Point** tool. To place a point, choose the **Point** tool from the **Draw** panel; you will be prompted to select the center point. Specify the center point; a point will be placed. You can specify the location of a point in the sketch by picking a point from the graphics window or by entering the value in the **Inventor Precise Input** toolbar.

Creating Fillets

Ribbon:	Sketch > Draw > Fillet/Chamfer drop-down > Fillet
Toolbar:	2D Sketch Panel > Fillet/Chamfer drop-down > Fillet

Filleting is defined as the process of rounding the sharp corners of a sketch. This is done to reduce the stress concentration in the model. Using the **Fillet** tool, you can round the corners of the sketch by creating an arc tangent to both the selected entities. The portions of the selected entities that comprise the sharp corners are trimmed when the fillet is created. When you invoke this tool from the **Fillet/Chamfer** drop-down, refer to Figure 2-31, the **2D Fillet** dialog box will be displayed with the default fillet radius, as shown in Figure 2-32, and you will be prompted to select the lines or the arcs to be filleted. If you have already created some fillets, their radius values will be stored as preset values. You can select these preset values from the list that is displayed when you choose the arrow provided on the right of the edit box.

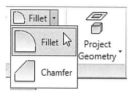

Figure 2-31 *Tools in the* ***Fillet/*** ***Chamfer*** *drop-down*

Figure 2-32 *The* ***2D*** ***Fillet*** *dialog box*

You can create any number of fillets of similar or dissimilar radii. If the **Equal** button in the **2D Fillet** dialog box is chosen, the dimension of the fillet will be placed only on the first fillet and not on the other fillets created by using the same sequence, see Figure 2-33. On modifying the dimension of the first fillet, all instances of fillet will be modified. To create fillets of independent radii values, deactivate the **Equal** button before creating fillets. The fillets thus created will show individual dimensions, see Figure 2-34. As a result, you can modify the dimension of one fillet without affecting the other. You can fillet two parallel or perpendicular lines, intersecting lines or arcs, non-intersecting lines or arcs, and a line and an arc.

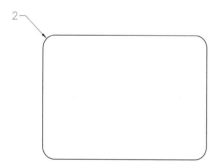

Figure 2-33 *Rectangle filleted using the same radius with the* ***Equal*** *button chosen*

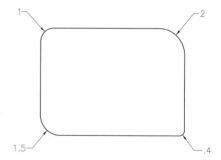

Figure 2-34 *Rectangle filleted using different radii with the* ***Equal*** *button deactivated*

Creating Chamfers

Ribbon:	Sketch > Draw > Fillet/Chamfer drop-down > Chamfer
Toolbar:	2D Sketch Panel > Fillet/Chamfer drop-down > Chamfer

Chamfering is defined as the process of beveling the sharp corners of a sketch. This is the second method of reducing stress concentration. To chamfer sketched entities, choose the **Chamfer** tool from the **Draw** panel (see Figure 2-31); the **2D Chamfer** dialog box will be displayed, as shown in Figure 2-35. Also, you will be prompted to select the lines to be chamfered. Select the lines; the chamfer will be created. The options in the **2D chamfer** dialog box are discussed next.

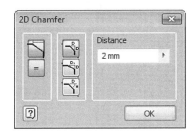

Create Dimensions

The **Create Dimensions** button is chosen to show the dimensions of the chamfer on the sketch. When you chamfer two lines, the dimensions of the chamfer are shown in the sketch. If you choose this button again, the chamfer dimensions will not be displayed in the sketch when you create another chamfer.

Figure 2-35 The 2D Chamfer dialog box

Equal

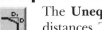
The **Equal** button is chosen to create multiple chamfers with the same parameters. This button is enabled only if the **Create Dimensions** button is chosen.

Equal Distance

The **Equal Distance** button is chosen to create an equal distance chamfer. The distance of the vertex along the two selected edges is the same. As a result, a 45-degree chamfer is created using this method. The distance value is specified in the **Distance** edit box. If the **Create Dimension** button is chosen, two dimensions of the same value will be shown in the sketch, as shown in Figure 2-36.

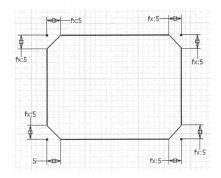

Figure 2-36 Chamfer with dimension values

Unequal Distances

The **Unequal Distances** button is chosen to create a chamfer with two different distances. The distance values are specified in the **Distance1** and **Distance2** edit boxes. The distance value specified in the **Distance1** edit box is measured along the edge selected first. Similarly, the value in the **Distance2** edit box is measured along the edge selected next. Figure 2-37 shows a chamfer created by using the **Unequal Distances** method.

Distance and Angle

The **Distance and Angle** button is chosen to create a chamfer by specifying a distance and an angle. On choosing this button, the distance needs to be specified in the **Distance** edit box and the angle in the **Angle** edit box. The specified angle is measured from the first edge selected to chamfer, see Figure 2-38.

Tip. *If multiple chamfers are created with same values, the dimension value is displayed only at the first instance. At the remaining chamfers, the dimension will be displayed as fx of the value, which means the function of the original value.*

You can also select the vertex to create a fillet or chamfer. The two entities forming the selected vertex will be filleted or chamfered using the current parameters.

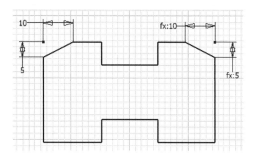

Figure 2-37 *The unequal distances chamfer crteated*

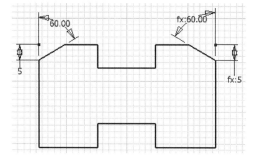

Figure 2-38 *The distance and angle chamfer created*

Drawing Splines

Ribbon:	Sketch > Draw > Spline drop-down > Spline
Toolbar:	2D Sketch Panel > Line drop-down > Spline

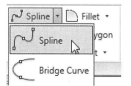

Figure 2-39 *Tools in the **Spline** drop-down*

To draw a spline, choose the **Spline** tool from the **Draw** panel, see Figure 2-39; you will be prompted to specify the first point of the spline. Specify the start point; you will be prompted to specify the next point of the spline. This process will continue until you terminate the spline creation. To end the spline at the current point, double-click in the drawing window or right-click to display the shortcut menu and choose **Create**. Note that if you choose **Done** from the shortcut menu, the spline will not be drawn. You can also end the spline creation by pressing the ENTER key. Note that after creating a spline, the square and diamond points will be displayed on the spline along with the tangent handles, as shown in Figure 2-40. You can drag these square and diamond points to modify the shape of the spline.

You can undo the last drawn spline segment while drawing a spline. This can be done by choosing the **Back** option from the shortcut menu that is displayed when you right-click.

You can also draw a spline tangent to an existing entity. To draw the tangent spline, select the point where the spline should be tangent. Next, hold the left mouse button and drag it; a construction line will be drawn, which displays the possible tangent directions for the spline. Drag the mouse in the required direction to draw the tangent spline and release the left mouse button. Figure 2-40 shows a spline drawn by specifying different points and Figure 2-41 shows a spline drawn tangent to an existing line.

Tip. *Autodesk Inventor allows you to invoke the last used tool by right-clicking anywhere in the drawing window. For example, create a line using the **Line** tool. If you want to create another line, right-click anywhere in the drawing window and choose the **Repeat Line** option from the shortcut menu. Alternatively, you can invoke the last used tool by pressing the SPACEBAR key.*

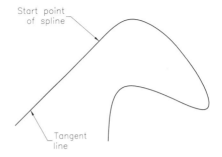

Figure 2-40 *A spline drawn by specifying different points*

Figure 2-41 *A spline drawn tangent to a line*

Creating a Smooth Curve between Two Existing Curves

Ribbon:	Sketch > Draw > Spline drop-down > Bridge Curve

In Autodesk Inventor, you can create a smooth (G2) continuous curve between two existing curves. The existing curves can be arcs, lines, splines, or projected curves. To create a smooth curve, choose the **Bridge Curve** tool from the **Draw** panel (see Figure 2-39); you will be prompted to select the curves one after the other. Select the two curves; a smooth G2 continuous curve, known as bridge curve, will be created between the selected curves. The profile of the bridge curve depends on the position where two existing curves are selected. Figure 2-42 shows the point of selection of two curves and the resulting bridge curve. Figure 2-43 shows different points of selection of the same curve and the resulting bridge curve.

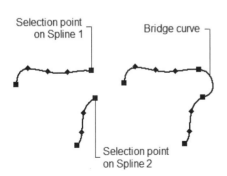

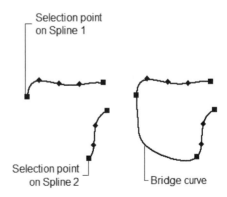

Figure 2-42 *Bridge curve created between curves at the selection points*

Figure 2-43 *Bridge curve created between curves at different selection points*

DELETING SKETCHED ENTITIES

To delete the sketched entity, first ensure that no drawing tool is active. If it is, press the ESC key. Now, select the entity you want to delete using the left mouse button and then right-click to display the shortcut menu. Choose the **Delete** option from this shortcut menu. You can also press the DELETE key to delete the selected entities. To delete more than one entity, you can use a window or a crossing. Deleting entities using these methods are discussed next.

Deleting Entities by Using a Window

A window is defined as a box created by pressing and holding the left mouse button and dragging the cursor from the left to the right in the drawing window. The window has a property that all the entities that lie completely inside the window will be selected. The box defined by the window consists of continuous lines. All the selected entities will be displayed in cyan color. After selecting the entities, right-click and choose **Delete** from the shortcut menu or press the DELETE key to delete all the selected entities.

Deleting Entities by Using a Crossing

A crossing is defined as a box created by pressing and holding down the left mouse button and dragging the cursor from the right to the left in the drawing window. The crossing has a property that all entities that lie completely or partially inside the crossing or the entities that touch the crossing will be selected. The box defined by the crossing consists of dashed lines. Once the entities are selected, right-click and choose **Delete** from the shortcut menu.

 Tip. *You can add or remove an entity from the selection set by pressing the SHIFT or the CTRL key and then selecting the entity by using the left mouse button. If the entity is already in the current selection set, it will be removed from the selection set. If not, it will be added to set.*

FINISHING A SKETCH

After creating the required sketch, you need to save it. But before you save the sketch, you need to finish the sketch and come out of the sketching environment. To do so, choose the **Finish Sketch** tool from the **Exit** panel of the **Sketch** tab; the sketch will be finished and you will switch to the **Home** view. This view enables you to view and create the modeling features with ease. After switching to the **Modeling** environment, you can save the document.

TUTORIALS

Although Autodesk Inventor is parametric in nature, in this chapter you will use the **Inventor Precise Input** toolbar and the dynamic input method to draw objects. This is to make you comfortable with various drawing options in Autodesk Inventor. From the next chapter onward, you will use the parametric feature of Autodesk Inventor to size or draw the entities as per the desired dimension values.

Although the sketches for the tutorials in this chapter are to be drawn on the other sketching planes, you will draw them on the default XY plane. In the later chapters, you will learn how to change a sketching plane.

Tutorial 1

In this tutorial, you will draw the sketch of the model shown in Figure 2-44. The sketch to be drawn is shown in Figure 2-45. Do not dimension it, as the dimensions are given only for reference. **(Expected time: 30 min)**

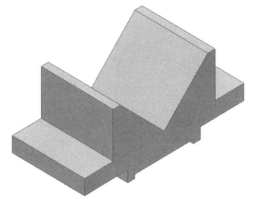

Figure 2-44 *Model for Tutorial 1*   *Figure 2-45* *Sketch of the model*

The following steps are required to complete this tutorial:

a. Start a new Autodesk Inventor session and then start a new metric part file.
b. Invoke the **Line** tool and draw the sketch by specifying the coordinates of the points in the **Inventor Precise Input** toolbar.
c. Save the sketch with the name *Tutorial1* and close the file.

Starting Autodesk Inventor

1. Start Autodesk Inventor by double-clicking on its shortcut icon on the desktop of your computer. Alternatively, choose **Start > Programs > Autodesk > Autodesk Inventor 2011 > Autodesk Inventor Professional 2011** from the taskbar; a new session of Autodesk Inventor is started.

2. Choose the **New** tool from the **Launch** panel of the **Get Started** tab; the **New File** dialog box is displayed.

3. Choose the **Metric** tab and then double-click on the **Standard (mm).ipt** icon to start a standard metric template; a new metric standard part file is started in the **Sketching** environment.

The major and minor grid lines are also displayed in the drawing window, along with the X and Y axes.

Note
*You can also open a standard metric template by selecting **Standard.ipt** from the **Default** tab of the **New File** dialog box.*

Drawing the Sketch

As mentioned earlier, Autodesk Inventor is parametric in nature. Therefore, you can draw the sketch from any point in the drawing window. However, it is recommended that you initially use the **Inventor Precise Input** toolbar to specify the points. Once you are conversant with this design tool, you can specify the points directly in the drawing window.

1. Choose the **Line** tool from the **Draw** panel in the **Sketch** tab. Next, choose **Precise Input** from the **Draw** panel in the **Sketch** tab; the **Inventor Precise Input** toolbar is displayed. Double-click on the title bar of this toolbar to dock it. If you want, you can also leave this toolbar floating on the screen.

    Initially, the **Precise Input** button is not enabled. This button is enabled only when you invoke a sketching tool. Since all initial settings are configured, you can now start drawing the sketch.

    When you invoke the **Line** tool, the cursor is replaced by the drawing cursor that has a yellow circle at the intersection of crosshairs. This circle is used to snap to the points in the drawing window.

2. Specify **0** as the start point of the sketch in both the **X** and **Y** edit boxes of the **Inventor Precise Input** toolbar and then press ENTER; you are prompted to specify the endpoint of the line.

3. In the **Inventor Precise Input** toolbar, enter **-3** and **3** in the **X** and **Y** edit boxes, respectively and then press ENTER to define the endpoint of the line. On doing so, the first line of the sketch is drawn and you are prompted to select the endpoint of the line or drag off to create a tangent arc.

    You will notice that the line is very small because the dimensions of the sketch are very small and the drawing display area is large. Therefore, you need to modify the drawing display area by using the drawing display tools. To modify this area, you can use the **Zoom** tool.

4. Choose the **Zoom** tool from the **Navigation Bar**; the drawing cursor is changed to an arrow cursor.

5. Move the cursor to the top of the drawing window, press and hold the left mouse button and then drag the cursor downward. Stop dragging the cursor once you notice that the display is adjusted.

6. Right-click to display the shortcut menu, and then choose **Done** to exit the **Zoom** tool.

    You will notice that the creation of line is resumed and you are prompted to specify the endpoint of the next line.

7. The coordinates of the remaining points (see Figure 2-46) in the sketch are given next.

Point	Coordinates (X, Y)
3	-3.5,3
4	-3.5,0
5	-5.5,0
6	-5.5,-1
7	-2.5,-1
8	-2.5,-1.75
9	-2,-1.75
10	-2,-1.5
11	2,-1.5
12	2,-1.75
13	2.5,-1.75
14	2.5,-1
15	5.5,-1
16	5.5,0
17	3.5,0
18	3.5,3
19	3,3
20	0,0

Tip. *You can use the TAB key to switch from the X edit box to the Y edit box and vice versa in the **Inventor Precise Input** toolbar.*

8. After specifying all points, right-click to display the shortcut menu. Choose **Done** from the shortcut menu or press ESC to exit the **Line** tool. The final sketch for Tutorial 1 is shown in Figure 2-46. However, the points in the final sketch in this figure have been numbered for reference only.

While specifying various points, you will notice that some of the constraints are applied automatically to the lines. These constraints help you reduce the number of dimensions to be specified to complete the sketch.

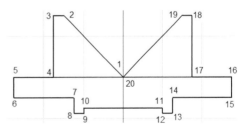

Figure 2-46 *Final sketch for Tutorial 1*

Note

The method of applying additional constraints and using them to fully constrain the sketch will be discussed in Chapter 3.

Saving the Sketch

Remember that you cannot save a sketch in the sketching environment. This is because the sketching environment is just a part of the **Part** module in Autodesk Inventor. This environment is used only for drawing the sketches of features. Therefore, you need to exit the sketching environment to save the sketch for further use. The sketches in the **Part** module are saved in the *.ipt* format.

1. Choose the **Finish Sketch** button from the **Exit** panel; the **Sketching** environment is closed and you will switch to the **Home** view of the part modeling environment. Also, notice that the **Model** tab is activated in place of the **Sketch** tab. The options in the **Model** tab are used to create features. The options under this tab will be discussed in later chapters.

2. Choose **Save** from the **Quick Access Toolbar**; the **Save As** dialog box is displayed.

    Whenever you invoke the **Save As** dialog box for the first time, all files are saved in the *My Documents* folder, by default.

3. Create a new folder with the name *Inventor_2011* in the C drive of your computer. In this folder, create a folder with the name *c02*.

4. Enter *Tutorial1* as the file name in the **File name** edit box, refer to Figure 2-47, and then choose the **Save** button from the **Save As** dialog box to save the sketch.

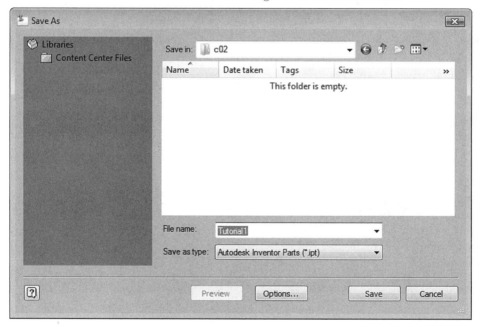

*Figure 2-47 The **Save As** dialog box*

5. Choose **Close > Close** from the **Application Menu** to close this file.

Tutorial 2

In this tutorial, you will draw the sketch for the model shown in Figure 2-48. The sketch to be drawn is shown in Figure 2-49. Do not dimension it, as the dimensions are given only for reference.   **(Expected time: 30 min)**

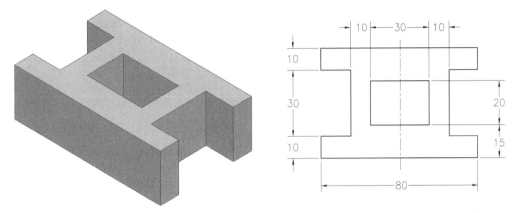

Figure 2-48 *Model for Tutorial 2*   **Figure 2-49** *Dimensionsed sketch for Tutorial 2*

The following steps are required to complete this tutorial:

a. Start a new metric standard part file.
b. Draw the outer loop by specifying the length and angle lines by using the dynamic input method.
c. Draw the inner closed loop by using the dynamic input method, refer to Figure 2-51.
d. Save the sketch with the name *Tutorial2.ipt* and close the file.

Starting a New File

1. Choose the **New** tool from **Launch** panel of the **Get Started** tab to display the **New File** dialog box. In this dialog box, choose the **Metric** tab and then double-click on the **Standard (mm).ipt** icon to start a standard metric template.

Drawing the Sketch

As evident from Figure 2-49, the sketch consists of two nested loops: inner loop, and outer loop. While extruding a nested loop, the inner loop can be subtracted from the outer loop. In this way, a cavity will be created automatically in the model when you extrude the sketch. This reduces the time and effort required in creating the inner cavity as another feature. Therefore, you can draw both the loops together for this tutorial.

The **Inventor Precise Input** toolbar was invoked in the previous tutorial; and therefore, it is available on the screen. You need to close it before drawing the sketch.

1. Close the **Inventor Precise Input** toolbar and then choose the **Line** tool from the **Draw** panel; you are prompted to specify the start point of the line or drag off an endpoint to create a tangent arc. Also, the coordinates of the current location of the cursor are displayed in the Pointer Input.

2. Move the cursor and click when the cursor displays -40 and -25 in the Pointer Input or enter the X and Y coordinate values in the Pointer Input. As you specify the first point, you are prompted to specify the endpoint of the line and the Pointer Input is changed to Dimension Input.

3. Enter **80** in the length input field of the Dimension Input and press the TAB key; the angle input field becomes active. Enter **0** and then press ENTER; the first line is created and the Dimension Input is displayed again.

4. Move the cursor up and then enter **10** in the length input field of the Dimension Input. Next, press the TAB key and enter **90** in the angle input field and then press ENTER; the second line is created and the Dimension Input is displayed again.

5. Move the cursor toward left and then enter **15** in the length input field. Next, press the TAB key and enter **90** in the angle input field. Then, press ENTER; the third line is created and the Dimension Input is displayed again.

6. Move the cursor up and then enter **30** in the length input field. Next, press the TAB key and enter **90** in the angle input field. Then, press ENTER; the fourth line is created and the Dimension Input is displayed again.

7. Move the cursor toward right and then enter **15** in the length input field. Next, press the TAB key and enter **90** in the angle input field. Then, press ENTER; the fifth line is created and the Dimension Input is displayed again.

8. Move the cursor up and then enter **10** in the length input field. Next, press the TAB key and enter **90** in the angle input field. Then, press ENTER; the sixth line is created and the Dimension Input is displayed again.

9. Move the cursor toward left and then enter **80** in the length input field. Next, press the TAB key and enter **90** in the angle input field. Then, press ENTER; the seventh line is created and the Dimension Input is displayed again.

10. Move the cursor down and then enter **10** in the length input field. Next, press the TAB key and enter **90** in the angle input field. Then, press ENTER; the eighth line is created and the Dimension Input is displayed again.

11. Move the cursor toward right and then enter **15** in the length input field. Next, press the TAB key and enter **90** in the angle input field. Then, press ENTER; the ninth line is created and the Dimension Input is displayed again.

12. Move the cursor down and then enter **30** in the length input field. Next, press the TAB key and enter **90** in the angle input field. Then, press ENTER; the tenth line is created and the Dimension Input is displayed again.

13. Move the cursor toward left and then enter **15** in the length input field. Next, press the TAB key and enter **90** in the angle input field. Then, press ENTER; the eleventh line is created and the Dimension Input is displayed again.

14. Move the cursor down and then enter **10** in the length input field. Next, press the TAB key and enter **90** in the angle input field. Then, press ENTER; the twelfth line is created and the Dimension Input is displayed again.

15. Right-click to display the shortcut menu. Choose **Done** from the shortcut menu to exit the **Line** tool. The sketch of the outer loop is shown in Figure 2-50. You need to arrange the position of dimensions in the sketch by dragging them to view the sketch clearly.

    Next, you need to draw the inner loop. You can draw the loop by using the **Two Point Rectangle** tool.

16. Choose the **Rectangle Two Point** tool from **Sketch > Draw > Rectangle** drop-down; you are prompted to specify the first corner of the rectangle.

17. Press the TAB key and then enter **-15** and **-10** in the Pointer Input. Alternatively, move the cursor and click when the cursor displays **-15** and **-10** in the Pointer Input. As you click to specify the first corner, you are prompted to specify the opposite corner of the rectangle and the Pointer Input is changed to Dimension Input.

18. Move the cursor diagonally upward in the right direction and enter **30** and **20** in the horizontal and vertical input fields of the Dimension Input, respectively. Press ENTER and right-click; a shortcut menu is displayed.

19. Choose **Done** from the shortcut menu; the sketch is created, as shown in Figure 2-51.

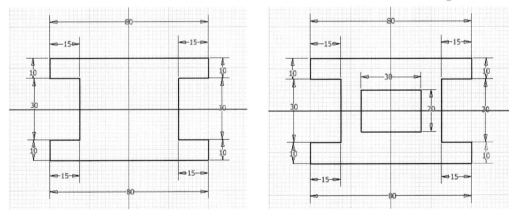

Figure 2-50 *Sketch of the outer loop*   ***Figure 2-51*** *Completed sketch for Tutorial 2*

Note

The angular dimensions have not been shown in Figures 2-50 and 2-51 for clarity of sketches. You can control the display of the linear and angular dimensions of the sketch by using the **Sketch** *tab of the* **Application Options** *dialog box. This dialog box is displayed when you choose the* **Application Options** *tool from the* **Options** *panel. Alternatively, choose* **Options** *from the* **Application Menu** *to invoke the* **Application Options** *dialog box. In the* **Sketch** *tab of the* **Application Options** *dialog box, choose the* **Settings** *button; the* **Heads-Up Display Settings** *dialog box is displayed. Clear the* **Create dimensions when inputting dimension value** *check box in the* **Persistent Dimensions** *area of the* **Heads-Up Display Settings** *dialog box and then choose* **OK**. *Next, choose the* **Apply** *and* **Close** *buttons from the* **Application Options** *dialog box to turn off the visibility of the dimension during sketching.*

Saving the Sketch

Next, you need to save the sketch. As mentioned earlier, you cannot save the sketch in the sketching environment. First, you need to exit the sketching environment and then save it.

1. Choose the **Finish Sketch** button from the **Exit** panel; the sketching environment is closed and you will switch to the **Home** view of the part modeling environment.

2. Choose the **Save** tool and save the sketch with the name Tutorial2 at the location given below:

   C:\Inventor_2011\c02

3. Choose **Close > Close** from the **Application Menu** to close this file.

Tutorial 3

In this tutorial, you will draw the sketch for the model shown in Figure 2-52. The sketch of the model is shown in Figure 2-53. Do not dimension the sketch as the dimensions are given only for reference. **(Expected time: 30 min)**

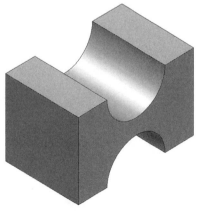

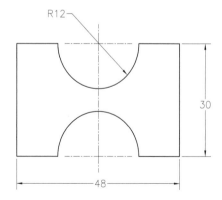

Figure 2-52 *Model for Tutorial 3*   ***Figure 2-53*** *Sketch for Tutorial 3*

The following steps are required to complete this tutorial:

a. Start a new metric standard part file.
b. Draw the sketch by using the **Arc** and **Line** tools, refer to Figure 2-55.
c. Save the sketch with the name *Tutorial3* and close the file.

Starting a New File

1. Choose the **New** tool from the **Launch** panel of the **Get Started** tab to invoke the **New File** dialog box.

2. Start a new metric standard part file by double-clicking on **Standard (mm).ipt** in the **Metric** tab.

Drawing the Sketch

The upper arc of the sketch can be drawn by specifying the center point, start point, and endpoint of the arc. Therefore, you need to use the **Center Point Arc** tool to draw this arc.

1. Choose the **Arc Three Point** tool from **Sketch > Draw > Arc** drop-down; you are prompted to specify the center of the arc.

2. Enter **0, 15** in the **Inventor Precise Input** toolbar and press ENTER; you are prompted to specify the start point of the arc.

3. Enter **-12,15** in the **Inventor Precise Input** toolbar and press ENTER.

Next, you need to define the endpoint of the arc. The arc drawn after you specify the endpoint, can be in the clockwise or counterclockwise direction.

4. Move the mouse from the start point of the arc to a small distance in the counterclockwise direction. Now, enter **12,15** as the endpoint in the **Inventor Precise Input** toolbar and press ENTER; the upper arc is drawn.

Next, you need to draw lines in the sketch.

5. Choose the **Line** tool from the **Draw** panel; you are prompted to specify the start point of the line.

It is evident from Figure 2-53 that the lines start from the endpoints of the arc. You can specify the coordinates of the start point of the arc in the **Inventor Precise Input** toolbar or select the start point of the line in the drawing window.

6. Move the cursor close to the start point of the arc; the yellow circle snaps to the endpoint of the arc and turns green. When the yellow circle turns green, it indicates that the cursor has snapped to the endpoint of the arc. Press the left mouse button to select this point as the start point of the line.

As it is easier to define the points by using relative coordinates, it is recommended that you use the **Precise Delta** button in the **Inventor Precise Input** toolbar to draw lines. Choose the **Precise Delta** button, if it is not already chosen.

7. If the **Precise Delta** button is not chosen automatically, you need to specify the start point of the line and then choose this button. Next, press the ESC key to exit the **Line** tool. Now, invoke the **Line** tool again; a triad is placed at the origin (0,0). Enter **-12, 15** as the start point of the line in the **Inventor Precise Input** toolbar. Next, enter **-12, 0** as the endpoint of the line in the **Inventor Precise Input** toolbar.

8. Enter **0, -30** as the second point and **12, 0** as the third point in the **Inventor Precise Input** toolbar. As mentioned earlier, Autodesk Inventor provides you with the option to draw tangent or normal arcs while drawing lines. This is done by dragging the cursor from the point where you want to start the arc. You can directly draw it within the **Line** tool.

9. Move the cursor close to the endpoint of the last line until the yellow circle snaps to that point. When the yellow circle snaps to the endpoint, it turns gray. However, you will not be able to view the gray circle because of the triad. Now, press and hold the left mouse button and drag the mouse through a small distance in the upward direction.

    You will notice that four imaginary lines are displayed, showing the four directions in which you can draw the arc.

10. As you need to draw the arc normal to the line, drag the cursor vertically upward in the direction of the vertical imaginary line to a small distance and then drag the cursor toward the right. While drawing the arc by dragging the cursor, you cannot use the **Inventor Precise Input** toolbar.

    To specify the endpoint of the arc precisely, you can use the temporary tracking option. The temporary tracking option allows you to select a point by using two different points. For example, in this case, the right endpoint of the lower arc has to be vertically in the same line as that of the right endpoint of the upper arc, and horizontally in the same line as that of the start point of the lower arc. Now, assume a vertical imaginary line drawn from the endpoint of the upper arc and a horizontal imaginary line drawn from the start point of the lower arc. Both these imaginary lines intersect at a point that is essentially the endpoint of the lower arc. The temporary tracking option is used to draw these imaginary lines and to remove them after the point has been selected.

11. With the left mouse button pressed to define the endpoint of the arc, drag the cursor close to the right endpoint of the upper arc; the cursor snaps to the endpoint of the arc and turns green. Now, move the cursor vertically downward.

    You will notice that a vertical imaginary line appears at the right endpoint of the upper arc. You do not need to snap to the horizontal point, because this point was automatically selected when you started drawing the lower arc. As you move the cursor downward, you will notice a point where both the vertical and horizontal imaginary lines intersect each other, see Figure 2-54. This point is the endpoint of the lower arc. The cursor automatically snaps to the point where both the imaginary lines intersect. Do not release the left mouse button until the entire process is completed.

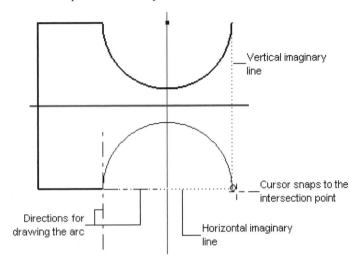

Figure 2-54 Use of the temporary tracking option to draw an arc

Note
In Figure 2-54, the major and minor grid lines and triad have not been displayed for a better display of the sketch and the imaginary lines.

12. When the cursor snaps to the intersection of the imaginary lines, release the mouse button to complete the lower arc.

13. Enter **12,0** as the coordinates of the next point in the **Inventor Precise Input** toolbar.

14. For the next point, you can enter coordinates in the **Inventor Precise Input** toolbar or use the temporary tracking option. To use this option, move the cursor close to the endpoint of the upper arc. Once the cursor snaps to this point and turns green, move it horizontally toward the right. As a result, a horizontal imaginary line is drawn. Using the left mouse button, select the point at which the vertical line becomes perpendicular to the horizontal imaginary line. This point is the endpoint of the right vertical line.

Note
While using the temporary tracking option to draw lines, you do not need to press the left mouse button and drag it. You need to press the left mouse button once to select the endpoint of the line after you get the intersection point of the imaginary lines.

15. Complete the sketch by snapping to the endpoint of the upper arc as the endpoint of the line. Next, right-click to display the shortcut menu, and then choose **Done** from it to exit the **Line** tool.

16. The final sketch for Tutorial 3 is shown in Figure 2-55.

Saving the Sketch

1. Choose the **Finish Sketch** button from the **Exit** panel; the sketching environment is closed and you will switch to the **Home** view of the part modeling environment.

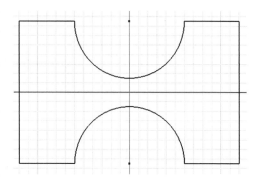

Figure 2-55 *Final sketch for Tutorial 3*

2. Choose the **Save** button and save the sketch with the name *Tutorial3* at the location given below:

   C:\Inventor_2011\c02

3. Choose **Close > Close** from the **Application Menu** to close this file.

Tutorial 4

In this tutorial, you will draw the basic contour of the revolved solid model shown in Figure 2-56. The contour that you will draw for creating this revolved solid is shown in Figure 2-57. Do not dimension the sketch as the dimensions are given only for reference.

(Expected time: 30 min)

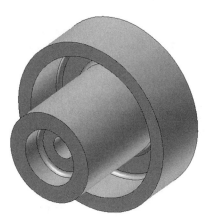

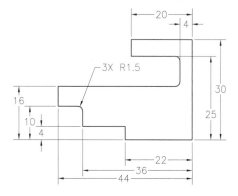

Figure 2-56 *Revolved model for Tutorial 4*   *Figure 2-57* *Sketch for the revolved model*

The following steps are required to complete this tutorial:

a.   Start a new metric standard part file.
b.   Invoke the **Line** tool and draw the sketch by specifying the coordinates of points in the **Inventor Precise Input** toolbar, refer to Figure 2-57.
c.   Save the sketch with the name *Tutorial4* and close the file.

Starting a New File

1.   Choose the **New** tool from the **Quick Access Toolbar** to display the **New File** dialog box.

2.   Choose the **Metric** tab to display the standard metric templates. Double-click on **Standard (mm).ipt** to start a new metric part file.

Drawing the Sketch

1.   Choose the **Line** tool from the **Draw** panel; you are prompted to specify the start point of the line. Enter **22,0** as the coordinates of the start point in the **Inventor Precise Input** toolbar and press ENTER; you are prompted to specify the endpoint of the line. You can specify the coordinates of the next point relative to the previous point, as it becomes easier to define points.

If the same session of Autodesk Inventor is used, the **Precise Delta** button is chosen automatically in the **Inventor Precise Input** toolbar. However, if you use a new session, you need to choose this button to invoke this toolbar.

2.   Choose the **Precise Delta** button, if it is not chosen automatically and then press the ESC key. Invoke the **Line** tool and enter **22, 0** as the start point of the line in the **Inventor Precise Input** toolbar. Next, enter the following coordinates of the remaining points in the **Inventor Precise Input** toolbar.

Point	Coordinates (X, Y)
2	0,30
3	-20,0
4	0,-5
5	16,0
6	0,-9
7	-40,0
8	0,-6
9	8,0
10	0,-6
11	14,0
12	0,-4
13	22,0

3. Right-click to display the shortcut menu, and then choose **Done** from it to complete the sketch. The sketch should look similar to the one shown in Figure 2-58. For your reference, the lines in the sketch are numbered.

    You will create the arcs at the end of lines 4 and 5, 5 and 6, and 8 and 9 by using the **Fillet** tool. This tool draws the arcs at the point of intersection of the lines and removes sharp corners.

4. Choose the **Fillet** tool from **Sketch > Draw > Fillet/Chamfer** drop-down; the **2D Fillet** dialog box is displayed with some default fillet radius. Enter **1.5** in the **Radius** edit box of this dialog box. Do not press ENTER.

5. Select line 4 and then line 5, refer to Figure 2-58; a fillet is created between these lines and the radius of the fillet is displayed in the sketch.

6. Similarly, select lines 5 and 6 and then lines 8 and 9 to create a fillet between these lines. Right-click, and then choose **Done** from the shortcut menu to exit the **Fillet** tool after creating all fillets.

    As all lines are filleted with the same radius value, the radius of the fillet is not displayed on other fillets. This completes the sketch. The final sketch for this tutorial after filleting is shown in Figure 2-59.

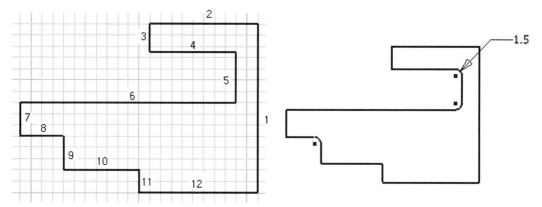

Figure 2-58 Sketch after drawing the lines   *Figure 2-59* Final sketch after filleting

Note
In Figures 2-58 and 2-59, the display of axes has been turned off for a better visibility of the lines of the sketch.

Saving the Sketch

1. Choose the **Finish Sketch** button from the **Exit** panel.

2. Choose the **Save** button and save this sketch with the name *Tutorial4* at the location given below:

   C:\Inventor_2011\c02

3. Choose **Close > Close** from the **Application Menu** to close this file.

Self-Evaluation Test

Answer the following questions and then compare them to those given at the end of this chapter:

1. Most designs created in Autodesk Inventor are a combination of sketched features and placed features. (T/F)

2. Whenever you start a new file in the **Part** module, the sketching environment is invoked by default. (T/F)

3. You cannot turn off the display of grid lines. (T/F)

4. You cannot draw an arc within the **Line** tool. (T/F)

5. In Autodesk Inventor, the two types of sketching entities that can be drawn are _____ and _____.

6. In the sketching environment, the _____ tool is used to place a sketch point or a center point.

7. Filleting is defined as the process of _____ the sharp corners and sharp edges of models.

8. You can also delete sketched entities by pressing the _____ key.

9. In Autodesk Inventor, rectangles are drawn as the combination of _____ entities.

10. You can undo the last drawn spline segment when you are still inside the spline drawing option by choosing _____ from the shortcut menu displayed.

Review Questions

Answer the following questions:

1. In most designs, generally the first feature or the base feature is the placed feature. (T/F)

2. You can invoke the options related to sheet metal parts from the **.ipt** file. (T/F)

3. You can change the current project directory and the project files by choosing **Projects** from the **Open** dialog box. (T/F)

4. You can specify the position of entities dynamically by using the Dynamic Input. (T/F)

5. In Autodesk Inventor, you can save a file in the sketching environment. (T/F)

6. In Autodesk Inventor, you can start a new file by using the **Open** dialog box. (T/F)

7. Which of the following tools in the **Tools** tab is used to invoke additional toolbars?

    (a) **Application Options**   (b) **Customize**
    (c) **Document Setting**   (d) None of these

8. Which of the following drawing display options is used to interactively zoom in and out a drawing?

    (a) **Zoom All**   (b) **Pan**
    (c) **Zoom**   (d) **Zoom Window**

9. Which of the following keys is used to restore the previous view?

    (a) F5   (b) F6
    (c) F7   (d) F4

10. Which of the following drawing display options prompts you to select an entity whose magnification has to be increased?

    (a) **Zoom**   (b) **Pan**
    (c) **Zoom Selected**   (d) None of these

Exercises

Exercise 1

Draw the basic sketch of the model shown in Figure 2-60. The sketch to be drawn is shown in Figure 2-61. Do not dimension it, as the dimensions are given only for reference.

(Expected time: 30 min)

Figure 2-60 Model for Exercise 1

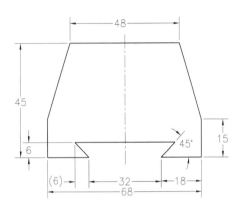

Figure 2-61 Sketch for Exercise 1

Exercise 2

Draw the basic sketch of the model shown in Figure 2-62. The sketch to be drawn is shown in Figure 2-63. Do not dimension it, as the dimensions are given only for reference.

(Expected time: 45 min)

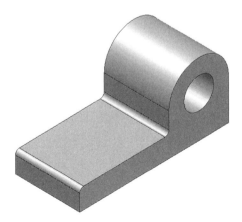

Figure 2-62 Model for Exercise 2

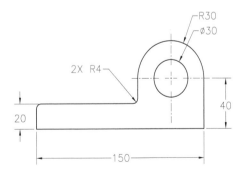

Figure 2-63 Sketch for Exercise 2

Exercise 3

Draw the sketch of the model shown in Figure 2-64. The sketch to be drawn is shown in Figure 2-65. Do not dimension it, as the dimensions are given only for reference.

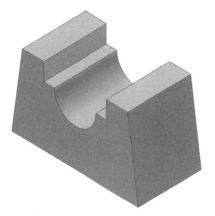

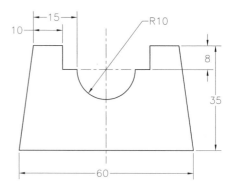

Figure 2-64 *Model for Exercise 3*   ***Figure 2-65*** *Sketch for Exercise 3*

(Expected time: 45 min)

Answers to Self-Evaluation Test
1. T, **2.** T, **3.** F, **4.** F, **5.** normal, construction, **6. Point**, **7.** rounding, **8.** DELETE, **9.** individual, **10. Back**

Chapter 3

Adding Constraints and Dimensions to Sketches

Learning Objectives

After completing this chapter, you will be able to:

- *Add geometric constraints to a sketch.*
- *Control the constraint inference.*
- *View and delete constraints from a sketch.*
- *Dimension a sketch.*
- *Modify the dimensions of a sketch.*
- *Measure distances, angles, loops, and areas in a sketch.*

ADDING GEOMETRIC CONSTRAINTS TO A SKETCH

Constraints are applied to the sketched entities to define their size and position with respect to other elements. Also, they are useful for capturing the design intent. As mentioned in Chapter 1, there are twelve types of geometric constraints that can be applied to the sketched entities. These constraints restrict their degrees of freedom and make them stable. Most of these constraints are automatically applied to the entities while drawing. However, sometimes you may need to apply some additional constraints to the sketched entities. These constraints are discussed next.

Perpendicular Constraint

Ribbon:	Sketch > Constrain > Perpendicular Constraint
Toolbar:	2D Sketch Panel > Constraints drop-down > Perpendicular

The **Perpendicular Constraint** forces the selected entity to become perpendicular to the specified entity. To apply this constraint, choose the **Perpendicular Constraint** tool from the **Constrain** panel; you will be prompted to select the first line or an ellipse axis. After you select an entity, you will be prompted to select the second line or ellipse axis. On selecting the second entity, the selected entities will become perpendicular. Figure 3-1 shows two lines before and after adding this constraint.

Parallel Constraint

Ribbon:	Sketch > Constrain > Parallel Constraint
Toolbar:	2D Sketch Panel > Constraints drop-down > Parallel

The **Parallel Constraint** forces the selected entity to become parallel to the specified entity. The entities to which this constraint can be applied are lines and ellipse axes. To apply this constraint, choose the **Parallel Constraint** tool from the **Constrain** panel; you will be prompted to select the first line or ellipse axis. After you select an entity, you will be prompted to select the second line or ellipse axis. On selecting the second entity, the two entities will become parallel. Figure 3-2 shows two lines before and after adding this constraint.

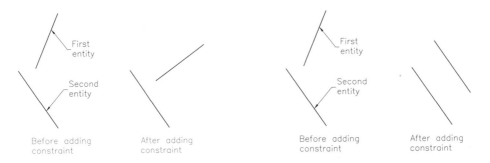

Figure 3-1 *Applying the* ***Perpendicular*** *constraint*

Figure 3-2 *Applying the* ***Parallel*** *constraint*

Tangent Constraint

Ribbon:	Sketch > Constrain > Tangent
Toolbar:	2D Sketch Panel > Constraints drop-down > Tangent

The **Tangent** constraint forces the selected line segment or curve to become tangent to another curve. To apply this constraint, choose the **Tangent** tool from the **Constrain** panel; you will be prompted to select the first curve. After you select the first curve, you will be prompted to select the second curve. The curves that can be selected are lines, circles, ellipses, or arcs. Figures 3-3 and 3-4 show the use of the **Tangent** constraint.

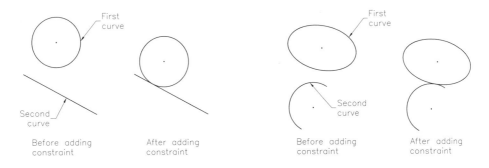

Figure 3-3 *Applying the **Tangent** constraint*   ***Figure 3-4*** *Applying the **Tangent** constraint*

Coincident Constraint

Ribbon:	Sketch > Constrain > Coincident Constraint
Toolbar:	2D Sketch Panel > Constraints drop-down > Coincident

The **Coincident Constraint** is used to force two points or a point and a curve to become coincident. To apply this constraint, choose the **Coincident Constraint** tool from the **Constrain** panel; you will be prompted to select the first curve or point. After you select the first curve or point, you will be prompted to specify the second curve or point. Note that either the first or the second entity selected should be a point. The points include sketch points, endpoints of a line or an arc, or center points of circles, arcs, or ellipses.

Concentric Constraint

Ribbon:	Sketch > Constrain > Concentric Constraint
Toolbar:	2D Sketch Panel > Constraints drop-down > Concentric

The **Concentric Constraint** is used to force two curves to share the same location of center points. The curves that can be made concentric include arcs, circles, and ellipses. When you invoke this constraint, you will be prompted to select the first arc, circle, or ellipse. After making the first selection, you will be prompted to select the second arc, circle, or ellipse. Select the second entity to be made concentric with the first entity.

Note

*If you apply a constraint that over-constrains a sketch, the **Autodesk Inventor 2011 - Create Constraint** message box will be displayed, informing that adding this constraint will over-constrain the sketch, see Figure 3-5. A sketch is said to be over-constrained if the number of dimensions or constraints in it exceed the number that can be applied to the sketch.*

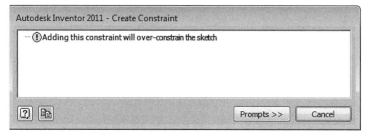

*Figure 3-5 The **Autodesk Inventor 2011 - Create Constraint** message box*

Collinear Constraint

Ribbon:	Sketch > Constrain > Collinear Constraint
Toolbar:	2D Sketch Panel > Constraints drop-down > Collinear

The **Collinear Constraint** forces the selected line segments or ellipse axes to be placed in the same line. When you invoke this constraint, you will be prompted to select the first line or ellipse axis. After making the first selection, you will be prompted to select the second line or ellipse axis. Select the entity to be made collinear with the first entity.

Tip. *To select an ellipse axis, move the cursor close to the ellipse. Depending on whether the cursor is close to the major axis or the minor axis, the particular axis will be highlighted. When the required axis is highlighted, select it using the left mouse button.*

Horizontal Constraint

Ribbon:	Sketch > Constrain > Horizontal Constraint
Toolbar:	2D Sketch Panel > Constraints drop-down > Horizontal

The **Horizontal Constraint** forces the selected line segment, ellipse axis, or two points to become horizontal, irrespective of their original orientation. When you invoke this constraint, you will be prompted to select a line, an ellipse axis, or the first point. If you select a line or an ellipse axis, it will become horizontal. If you select a point, you will be prompted to select a second point. The points, in this case, can also include the center points of arcs, circles, or ellipses.

Vertical Constraint

Ribbon:	Sketch > Constrain > Vertical Constraint
Toolbar:	2D Sketch Panel > Constraints drop-down > Vertical

The **Vertical Constraint** is similar to the **Horizontal Constraints**, with the difference that this constraint forces the selected entities to become vertical.

Tip. *You can use the **Horizontal** or **Vertical** constraint to line up arcs, circles, or ellipses in the same horizontal or vertical direction by selecting their center points.*

Equal Constraint

Ribbon:	Sketch > Constrain > Equal
Toolbar:	2D Sketch Panel > Constraints drop-down > Equal

The **Equal** constraint can be used for line segments or curves. If you select two line segments, this constraint will force the length of one of the selected line segments to become equal to the length of the other selected line segment. In case of curves, this constraint will force the radius of one of the selected curves to become equal to that of the other selected curve. Note that if the first selection is a line, also the second selection has to be a line. Similarly, if the first selection is a curve, also the second selection also has to be a curve.

Fix Constraint

Ribbon:	Sketch > Constrain > Fix
Toolbar:	2D Sketch Panel > Constraints drop-down > Fix

This constraint is used to fix the orientation or location of the selected curve or point with respect to the coordinate system of the current drawing. If you apply this constraint to a line or an arc, you cannot move them from their current locations. However, you can change their length by selecting one of their endpoints and then dragging it. If you apply this constraint to a circle or an ellipse, you cannot edit either of these entities by dragging. Once you apply this constraint to an entity, its color changes from black to blue.

Symmetric Constraint

Ribbon:	Sketch > Constrain > Symmetric
Toolbar:	2D Sketch Panel > Constraints drop-down > Symmetric

This constraint is used to force two selected sketched entities to become symmetrical about a single sketched line segment. On invoking this constraint, you will be prompted to select the first sketched entity. Note that you can select only one entity at a time to apply this constraint. Once you have selected the first sketched entity, you will be prompted to select the second sketched entity. Select the second sketched entity; you will be prompted to select the symmetry line. Select the symmetry line (a line about which the selected entities need to be symmetric); the second selected entity will become symmetric to the first entity. After you have applied this constraint to one set of entities, you will again be prompted to select the first and second sketched entities. However, this time you will not be prompted to select the line of symmetry. The last line of symmetry will be automatically selected to add this constraint. Similarly, you can apply this constraint to other entities.

If the line of symmetry is different for applying the symmetric constraint to different entities in the sketch, you will have to restart the process of applying this constraint by right-clicking and choosing the **Restart** option from the shortcut menu. This is because the first symmetry line is used to apply this constraint to all the sets of entities you select. However, if you restart applying this constraint, you will be prompted to select the line of symmetry again.

Smooth Constraint

Ribbon:	Sketch > Constrain > Smooth (G2)
Toolbar:	2D Sketch Panel > Constraints drop-down > Smooth (G2)

 This constraint is used to apply curvature continuity between a spline and an entity connected to it. The entities that can be selected to apply this constraint include a line, arc, or another spline. Note that these entities should be connected to the spline.

VIEWING THE CONSTRAINTS APPLIED TO A SKETCHED ENTITY

Ribbon:	Sketch > Constrain > Show Constraints
Toolbar:	2D Sketch Panel > Show Constraints

You can view all constraints that are applied to the entities of a sketch by choosing the **Show Constraints** tool from the **Constrain** panel. When you invoke this tool and move the cursor close to any sketched entity, it will be highlighted and boxes will be displayed after a pause. These boxes show the symbols of all constraints that are applied to the entity. The symbols of the constraints will be highlighted in yellow box. Select the entity to retain the constraint box; the constraint box will be displayed with the constraints in a white background. Figure 3-6 shows the constraint boxes along with the constraints applied to the lines. You can move this box by selecting it and dragging. To close a box, choose the cross (X) on the extreme right of the box. In the case of **Coincident Constraint**, the constraint applied on a point is highlighted in yellow, instead of a box. To view symbols, move the cursor over the highlighted yellow point; the yellow point will be highlighted in red border and the symbols will be displayed in boxes, refer to Figure 3-6.

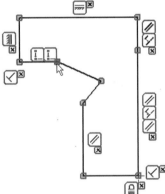

Figure 3-6 *The constraint boxes showing the constraints applied to the sketch*

If you move the cursor close to a constraint in the constraint box, it will be highlighted in yellow and the entities to which the constraint is applied are highlighted in red. For example, if you take the cursor close to the perpendicular constraint, the vertical line will also be highlighted along with the horizontal line, suggesting that the horizontal line is perpendicular to the vertical line.

Tip. *You can also display the constraints applied to all the entities in the drawing. To display all the constraints, right-click to display the shortcut menu and choose the **Show All Constraints** option; separate boxes will be displayed showing the constraints on all the entities. Similarly, to hide all constraints, right-click and choose the **Hide All Constraints** option from the shortcut menu.*

CONTROLLING CONSTRAINTS AND APPLYING THEM AUTOMATICALLY WHILE SKETCHING

You can control and select the constraints that need to be applied automatically as well as select the geometry to which they will be applied. The tools and the procedure of selecting the constraints and the geometry are discussed next.

Selecting Constraints

Ribbon:	Sketch > Constrain > Constraint Inference

By default, all possible constraints will be applied automatically on the sketching entities while drawing the sketches. However, you can also specify the constraints that need to be applied automatically and also the geometry to which they will be applied while sketching. To do so, choose the **Constraint Inference** tool from the **Constrain** panel and right-click anywhere in the drawing window; a shortcut menu will be displayed. Choose **Constraint Options** from the shortcut menu; the **Constraint Options** dialog box will be displayed, as shown in Figure 3-7. The options in this dialog box are discussed next.

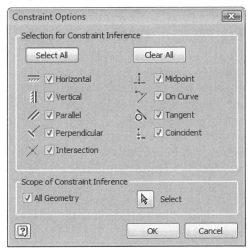

*Figure 3-7 The **Constraint Options** dialog box*

Selection for Constraint Inference Area

In this area, nine types of constraints and two buttons are available. All the constraints in this area are selected by default. However, if you need to clear all the constraints, choose the **Clear All** button. You can manually select or clear the required constraint by selecting the corresponding check box provided on the right of the constraint symbols. The selected constraints will be applied automatically to the geometry while sketching.

Scope of Constraint Inference Area

This area is used to set the geometry to which constraint is applied while drawing. By default, the **All Geometry** check box is selected to apply the constraint to all the active sketches. If you clear this check box, the **Select** button will be activated automatically. You can use this button to select the geometry to which the constraints will be applied.

Applying Constraints

Ribbon:	Sketch > Constrain > Constraint Persistence

 To apply the constraints selected in the **Constraint Options** dialog box, you need to choose the **Constraint Persistence** button from the **Constrain** panel. This is a toggle button and if you choose it, the **Constraint Inference** button will be activated and all the constraints selected earlier in the **Constraint Options** dialog box will be applied to the sketches while drawing them. You can also switch off the inference of the constraint by choosing this button again.

 Tip. *The remaining three constraints **Coincident**, **Fix**, and **Symmetric** are not provided in the **Constraint Options** dialog box. By default, the **Coincident** constraint is applied whenever it is possible. You can apply the **Fix** and **Symmetric** constraints manually according to your requirement.*

DELETING GEOMETRIC CONSTRAINTS

Autodesk Inventor allows you to delete the constraints applied to the selected entities. To delete constraints, first you need to invoke the constraint box by using the **Show Constraints** tool. Once the constraints are displayed, exit the **Show Constraints** tool by pressing the ESC key. Now, move the cursor over the constraint that you want to delete; it will be highlighted in yellow. Click the left mouse button to select the constraint; a red box will appear around the constraint. Now, move the cursor away and right-click, and then choose **Delete** from the shortcut menu, see Figure 3-8.

*Figure 3-8 Choosing the **Delete** option from the shortcut menu*

The selected constraint will be deleted and removed from the constraint box. Similarly, you can delete all unwanted constraints from the sketch.

 Tip. *When you move the cursor close to the constraint in the constraint box, its references will be highlighted in the sketch. For example, if you move the cursor over the **Perpendicular** constraint, the lines on which this constraint is applied will be highlighted. This allows you to confirm that the constraint selected is correct.*

Note
The total number of constraints and dimensions required to fully constrain a sketch is displayed at the lower right corner of the drawing window.

ADDING DIMENSIONS TO SKETCHES

Ribbon: Sketch > Constrain > Dimension
Toolbar: 2D Sketch Panel > General Dimension

Dimension

After drawing a sketch and adding constraints to it, dimensioning is the next most important step in creating a design. As mentioned earlier, Autodesk Inventor is a parametric solid modeling package. The parametric property ensures that irrespective of its original size, the selected entity is driven by the specified dimension value. Therefore, whenever you modify or apply dimension to an entity, it is forced to change its size with respect to the specified dimension value. The type of dimension to be applied varies according to the type of entity selected. For example, if you select a line segment, linear dimensions will be applied and if you select a circle, diameter dimensions will be applied. Note that all these types of dimensions can be applied using the same dimensioning tool. While dimensioning, you can set the priority for editing a dimension value as soon as you place it. To set the priority, choose the **Dimension** tool from the **Constrain** panel and then right-click; a shortcut menu will be displayed. Choose **Edit Dimension** from this menu, see Figure 3-9. As soon as you place the dimension, the **Edit Dimension** toolbar will be displayed, see Figure 3-10. This toolbar is used to modify the dimensions of an entity. The selected entity will be driven to the dimension value defined in this toolbar.

Figure 3-9 *Setting the priority for editing dimensions*

Figure 3-10 *The **Edit Dimension** toolbar*

You can enter a new value for the dimension or choose the button on the right of this toolbar to accept the default value.

If you do not want to edit the dimensions after you place them, invoke the **Dimension** tool and then right-click to display the shortcut menu. Clear the check mark on the left of the **Edit Dimension** option by choosing it again. When you place a dimension now, the **Edit Dimension** toolbar will not be displayed. To edit the dimension value in this case, click on it after placing, if the **Dimension** tool is still active. If the tool is not active, double-click on the dimension; the **Edit Dimension** toolbar will be displayed. Enter the new dimension value in this toolbar. The dimensioning techniques available in Autodesk Inventor are discussed next.

Linear Dimensioning

The linear dimensions are defined as the dimensions that specify the shortest distance between two points. You can apply linear dimensions directly to a line or select two points or entities to apply the linear dimension between them. The points that you can select include the endpoints of lines, splines, or arcs, or the center points of circles, arcs, or ellipses. You can dimension a vertical or a horizontal line by directly selecting it. As soon as you select it, the dimension will be attached to the cursor. You can place the dimension at any desired location. If the priority for editing the dimensions is set, the **Edit Dimension** toolbar will be displayed as soon as you place the dimension. To place the dimension between two points, select the points one by one. After selecting the second point, right-click to display the shortcut menu, as shown in Figure 3-11. In this menu, choose the dimension type. If you choose **Horizontal**, the horizontal dimension will be placed between the two selected points. If you choose **Vertical**, the vertical dimension will be placed between the two selected points. If you choose **Aligned**, the aligned dimension will be placed between the two selected points. Figure 3-12 shows the linear dimensioning of lines and Figure 3-13 shows the linear dimensioning of two points.

Figure 3-11 *Shortcut menu displaying various options to dimension two points*

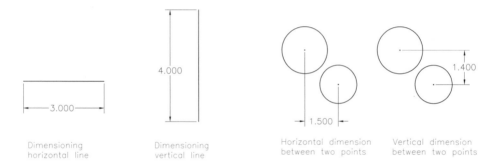

Figure 3-12 *Linear dimensioning of lines*   *Figure 3-13* *Linear dimensioning of two points*

You can also apply a horizontal or vertical dimension to an inclined line, see Figure 3-14. To apply these dimensions, select the inclined line and then right-click; a shortcut menu similar to the one shown in Figure 3-11 will be displayed. In this menu, choose **Horizontal** to place the horizontal dimension and **Vertical** to place the vertical dimension.

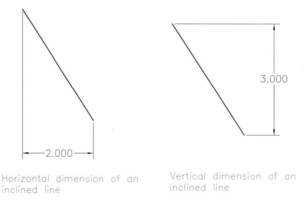

Figure 3-14 *Linear dimensioning of an inclined line*

Aligned Dimensioning

The aligned dimensions are used to dimension lines that are not parallel to the X or Y-axis. This type of dimension measures the actual distance of the aligned lines or the lines drawn at a certain angle. To apply the aligned dimension, select the inclined line and then right-click; a shortcut menu will be displayed, refer to Figure 3-11. Choose the **Aligned** option from the shortcut menu; the aligned dimension of the selected line will be attached to the cursor. Next, click in the drawing window to specify the location of the aligned dimension. You can also apply aligned dimension between two points. The points include the endpoints of lines, splines, or arcs or the center points of arcs, circles, or ellipses. To apply the aligned dimension between two points, invoke the **Dimension** tool. Next, select the two points and right-click; a shortcut menu will be displayed. Choose the **Aligned** option from the shortcut menu. Figures 3-15 and 3-16 show the aligned dimensions applied to various objects.

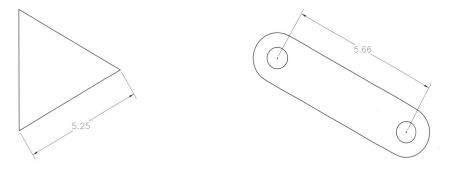

Figure 3-15 *Aligned dimension of a line*   *Figure 3-16* *Aligned dimension between two points*

Angular Dimensioning

The angular dimensions are used to dimension angles. You can select two line segments or use three points to apply the angular dimensions. You can also use angular dimensioning to dimension an arc. All these options of angular dimensioning are discussed next.

Angular Dimensioning Using Two Line Segments

You can directly select two line segments to apply angular dimensions. Invoke the **Dimension** tool and then select a line segment using the left mouse button. Instead of placing the dimension, select the second line segment. Now, place the dimension to measure the angle between the two lines. While placing the dimension, you need to be careful about the point where you place the dimension. This is because depending on the location of the placement of dimension, the vertically opposite angles will be displayed. Figure 3-17 shows the angular dimension between two lines and Figure 3-18 shows the dimension of the vertically opposite angle between two lines. Also, depending on the location of the dimension, the major or minor angle value will be displayed. Figure 3-19 shows the major angle dimension between two lines and Figure 3-20 shows the minor angle dimension between the same set of lines.

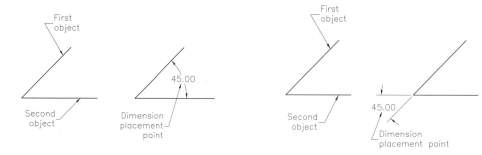

Figure 3-17 *Angular dimensioning*   **Figure 3-18** *Vertically opposite angle*

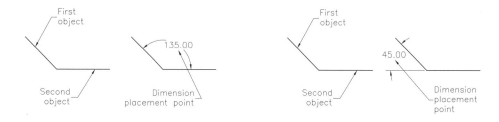

Figure 3-19 *Major angle dimension*   **Figure 3-20** *Minor angle dimension*

Angular Dimensioning Using Three Points

You can also apply angular dimensions using three points. Remember that the three points should be selected in the clockwise or counterclockwise sequence. The points that can be used to apply the angular dimensions include the endpoints of lines or arcs, or the center points of arcs, circles, and ellipses. Figure 3-21 shows angular dimensioning using three points.

Angular Dimensioning of an Arc

You can use angular dimensions to dimension an arc. In case of arcs, the three points are the endpoints and the center point of the arc. Note that the points should be selected in the clockwise or counterclockwise sequence, but the center point should always be the second selection point. Figure 3-22 shows the angular dimensioning of an arc.

Diameter Dimensioning

Diameter dimensions are applied to dimension a circle or an arc to specify its diameter. In Autodesk Inventor, when you select a circle to dimension, the diameter dimension is applied to it by default. However, if you select an arc to dimension, the radius dimension will be applied to it. You can also apply the diameter dimension to an arc by invoking the **Dimension** tool and selecting the arc. Next, right-click to display the shortcut menu, see Figure 3-23. Choose **Diameter** from this shortcut menu to apply the diameter dimension. Figure 3-24 shows a circle and an arc with diameter dimensions.

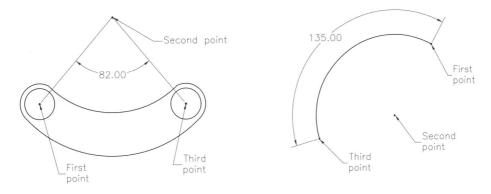

Figure 3-21 *Angular dimensioning using three points*

Figure 3-22 *Angular dimensioning of an arc*

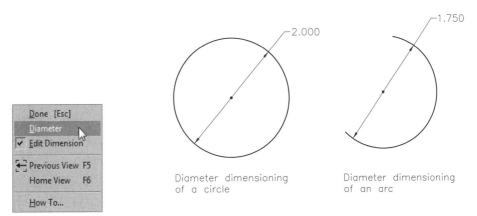

Figure 3-23 *Shortcut menu to apply a diameter dimension to an arc*

Figure 3-24 *Diameter dimensioning of a circle and an arc*

Radius Dimensioning

Radius dimensions are applied to dimension an arc or a circle to specify its radius. As mentioned earlier, by default, circles are assigned diameter dimensions and arcs are assigned radius dimensions. However, you can also apply the radius dimension to a circle. To do so, invoke the **Dimension** tool and then select the circle. Now, right-click to display the shortcut menu, as shown in Figure 3-25. In the shortcut menu, choose **Radius** to apply the radius dimension. Figure 3-26 shows an arc and a circle with radius dimensions.

Figure 3-25 *Shortcut menu to apply the radius dimension to a circle*

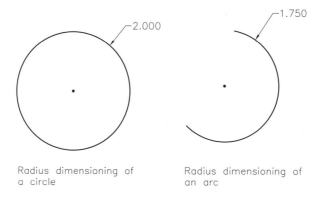

Radius dimensioning of
a circle

Radius dimensioning of
an arc

Figure 3-26 Radius dimensioning of a circle and an arc

Tip. *After invoking the **Dimension** tool, as you move the cursor close to the sketched entities, a small symbol will be displayed close to the cursor. This symbol displays the type of dimension that will be applied. For example, if you select a line, the linear dimensioning or aligned dimensioning symbol will be displayed. If you move the cursor close to another line after selecting the first, the symbol of angular dimensioning will be displayed. These symbols help you in determining the type of dimensions that will be applied.*

*In Autodesk Inventor, the ellipses are dimensioned as half of the major and minor axes distances. To dimension an ellipse, invoke the **Dimension** tool and then select the ellipse. Now, if you move the cursor in the vertical direction, the axis of the ellipse along the X-axis will be dimensioned in terms of its half length. Similarly, if you move the cursor in the horizontal direction, the axis of the ellipse along the Y axis will be dimensioned equal to its half-length.*

To distinguish whether the dimension applied to an arc or a circle is a radius or a diameter, try to locate the number of arrowheads in the dimension. If there are two arrowheads in the dimension and the dimension line is placed inside the circle or the arc, it is a diameter dimension. The radius dimension has one arrowhead and the dimension line is placed outside the circle or the arc.

Linear Diameter Dimensioning

Linear diameter dimensioning is used to dimension the sketches of the revolved components. The sketch for a revolved component is drawn using simple sketcher entities. For example, if you draw a rectangle and revolve, it will result in a cylinder. Now, if you dimension the rectangle using the linear dimensions, the same dimensions will be displayed when you generate the drawing views of the cylinder. Also, the same dimensions will be used while manufacturing the component. But these linear dimensions will result in a confusing situation in manufacturing. This is because while manufacturing a revolved component, the dimensions have to be specified as the diameter of the revolved component. The linear dimensions will not be acceptable in manufacturing a revolved component. To resolve this problem, the sketches for the revolved features are dimensioned using the linear diameter dimensions. These dimensions display the distance between the two selected line segments as a diameter, that is, double the original length. For example, if the original dimension between two entities is 10 mm, the linear diameter dimension will display it as 20 mm. This is because when you revolve a rectangle with 10 mm width, the diameter of the resultant cylinder will be 20 mm. In this type of dimension, if you select two lines, the line selected first will act as the axis of revolution for the sketch and the line selected last will result in the outer surface of the revolved feature. It means the line selected last will be the one that will be dimensioned. But, if one of these lines is a centerline drawn by choosing the **Centerline** tool from the **Format** panel, the centerline will be considered as the axis of revolution.

To apply linear diameter dimensions, invoke the **Dimension** tool; you will be prompted to select the first geometry to dimension. Select the first line; you will be prompted to select the second geometry to dimension. Select the second line with reference to which you want to apply the linear diameter dimensions. If the first line selected is a centerline, the linear diameter dimension will be displayed. Else, right-click and choose **Linear Diameter** from the shortcut menu, see Figure 3-27. You will notice that the distance between the two lines is displayed as twice the distance. Also, the dimension value is preceded by the **Ø** symbol, indicating that it is a linear diameter dimension. Figures 3-28 and 3-29 show the use of linear diameter dimensioning.

Figure 3-27 Choosing the Linear Diameter option

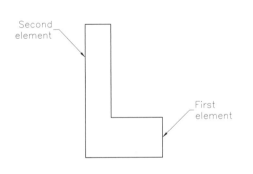

Figure 3-28 Selecting elements for linear diameter dimension

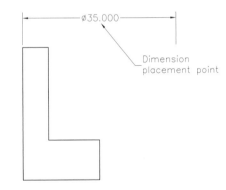

Figure 3-29 The linear diameter dimension

CREATING DRIVEN DIMENSIONS

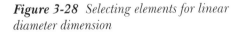

| **Ribbon:** | Sketch > Format > Driven Dimension |

  This toggle button is used to switch between the driven dimension and the sketch (driving) dimension. A dimension is called as a sketch (driving) dimension, if it forces an entity to change its length and orientation. A driven dimension is the one whose value depends on the value of the sketch (driving) dimension. The driven dimensions are enclosed within parenthesis and display the current value of the sketched geometry. This value cannot be modified. If you change the value of the sketch (driving) dimension, the value of the driven dimension will change automatically, as shown in Figures 3-30 and 3-31. All dimensions applied after choosing the **Driven Dimension** button will be the driven dimensions. To convert sketch (driving) dimensions into driven dimensions, select the required sketch (driving) dimension and choose the **Driven Dimension** button from the **Format** panel.

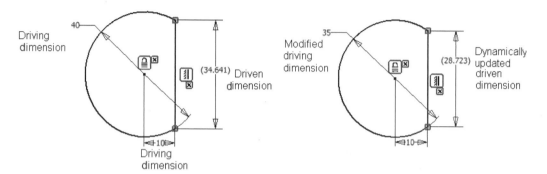

Figure 3-30 *Driving dimension and driven dimension in a sketch*

Figure 3-31 *Modified driving dimension and dynamically updated driven dimension*

UNDERSTANDING THE CONCEPT OF FULLY-CONSTRAINED SKETCHES

A fully-constrained sketch is the one whose all entities are completely constrained to their surroundings using constraints and dimensions. In a fully-constrained sketch, all degrees of freedom of the sketch are constrained. A fully-constrained sketch cannot change its size, location, or orientation unexpectedly. Whenever you draw a sketched entity, it will be black in color. If you add dimensions and constraints to fully constrain it, the entities will turn blue. There is one more method to understand whether the sketched entities are fully-constrained or not. In this method, you need to right-click in the graphic window and choose the **Show All Degrees of Freedom** option from the shortcut menu; the entities will display the available degrees of freedom such as horizontal, vertical, angular, or rotational. Note that while creating the base sketch in Autodesk Inventor, you need to dimension it with respect to a fixed point in order to fully constrain it. Therefore, you need to use some extra steps to fully constrain the sketch. These steps are given next.

1. Draw a sketch point at the origin. You can use the **Inventor Precise Input** toolbar or the Pointer Input to ensure that the point is placed exactly at the origin.
2. Apply the **Fix** constraint to the point.
3. Use this point to dimension the original sketch. You can add horizontal and vertical dimensions to the sketch from this point. You can also add a **Coincident** constraint between the point and the endpoints of one of the entities in the sketch.

MEASURING SKETCHED ENTITIES

Autodesk Inventor allows you to measure various parameters of the sketched entities. The parameters that you can measure are distances, angles, loops, and area. Measuring these parameters is discussed next.

Measuring Distances

Ribbon:	Tools / Inspect > Measure > Distance
Shortcut Menu:	Measure > Measure Distance

Autodesk Inventor allows you to measure the length of a line segment, radius of an arc, diameter of a circle, minimum distance between two entities, or coordinates of a point. All these distances can be measured by using the **Distance** tool from the **Measure** panel. On invoking this tool, the **Measure Distance** dialog box will be displayed and you will be prompted to select the first item. The **Measure Distance** dialog box is modified depending upon the type of entities selected to be measured. The methods of measuring distances between various entities are discussed next.

Measuring the Length of a Line Segment

When you invoke the **Distance** tool, the **Measure Distance** dialog box will be displayed and you will be prompted to select the first entity. Select a line segment, the **Measure Distance** dialog box will be changed to the **Length** dialog box and the length of the selected line segment will be displayed in this dialog box, see Figure 3-32.

*Figure 3-32 The **Length** dialog box displaying the length of a line segment*

 Tip. *To restart measuring the distances, right-click to display the shortcut menu and choose **Restart**; you will be prompted to select the first element to be measured.*

Measuring the Distance between a Point and a Line Segment

To measure the distance between a point and a line segment, invoke the **Distance** tool and then select the point. The **Measure Distance** dialog box will be modified to the **Position** dialog box, which shows the X, Y, and Z coordinates of the point, and you will be prompted to select the next entity. Select the line; the **Position** dialog box will change to the **Minimum Distance** dialog box. This dialog box will display the minimum distance between the point and the line, and the length of the line, see Figure 3-33.

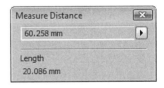

*Figure 3-33 The **Minimum Distance** dialog box displaying the distance between the lines*

Measuring the Coordinates of a Point

To measure the coordinates of a point with respect to the current coordinate system, invoke the **Distance** tool; you will be prompted to select the first element. Select the point whose coordinates you want to know. The selectable points include the endpoints of lines, arcs, or splines, center point of arcs, circles, or ellipses, or hole centers. If you select a hole center or the center point, the **Measure Distance** dialog box will change into the **Position** dialog box and the X, Y, and Z coordinates of the selected point with respect to the current coordinate system will be displayed, see Figure 3-34. However, if you select an endpoint, the coordinates will be specified in the **Measure Distance** dialog box.

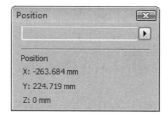

*Figure 3-34 The **Position** dialog box displaying the coordinates of a point*

Measuring the Distance between Two Points

To measure the distance between two points, invoke the **Distance** tool and then select the first point; the coordinates of the selected point will be displayed in the **Position** dialog box. You will be prompted to select the second element. Select the second point; the **Position** dialog box will be changed to the **Minimum Distance** dialog box. This dialog box will display the distance between the two points. This dialog box will also display the coordinates of the second point. You will also notice the **Delta X**, **Delta Y**, and **Delta Z** values in this dialog box, see Figure 3-35. These values are the distances between the two selected points along the X, Y, and Z axes. Note that if you move the cursor after selecting the second point, the **Position** dialog box will be replaced by the **Measure Distance** dialog box.

*Figure 3-35 The **Minimum Distance** dialog box*

Tip. *You would have noticed that the Z coordinates or the Z distances are zero at all places. This is because by default, when you start a new drawing, the sketches are drawn in the XY plane. You can also draw the sketches on other planes. You will learn more about these sketching planes in the later chapters.*

Measuring the Radius of an Arc or the Diameter of a Circle

You can also measure the radius of an arc or the diameter of a circle by using the **Distance** tool. When you invoke this tool, the **Measure Distance** dialog box will be displayed and you will be prompted to select the first item. If you select an arc or move the cursor over the arc, this dialog box will be momentarily changed to the **Radius** dialog box and will display the radius of the arc, see Figure 3-36. If you select a circle or move the cursor over the circle, this dialog box will momentarily change into the **Diameter** dialog box and will display the diameter of the circle, see Figure 3-37. Note that if you select an arc or a circle, you will not be prompted to select the second element because you cannot calculate any value other than their radius or diameter.

*Figure 3-36 The **Radius** dialog box displaying the radius of the arc*

*Figure 3-37 The **Diameter** dialog box displaying the diameter of the circle*

Measuring Angles

Ribbon:	Tools / Inspect > Measure > Angle
Shortcut Menu:	Measure > Measure Angle

To measure an angle, right-click in the drawing window and choose **Measure > Measure Angle** from the shortcut menu; the **Measure Angle** dialog box will be displayed. Alternatively, choose the **Angle** tool from the **Measure** panel. This tool is used to measure the angle between two line segments or among three points. Both these methods for measuring angles are discussed next.

Measuring the Angle between Two lines

To measure the angle between two lines, invoke the **Angle** tool; the **Measure Angle** dialog box will be displayed and you will be prompted to select the first item. Select the first line; you will be prompted to select the second line. Select the second line; the **Measure Angle** dialog box will change momentarily into the **Angle** dialog box and the angle between the selected line segments will be displayed, see Figure 3-38.

Figure 3-38 The **Angle** dialog box displaying the angle between two lines

Measuring the Angle Using Three Points

You can also measure the angle using three points. When you invoke the **Angle** tool, you will be prompted to select the first item. Select the first point; you will be prompted to select the next point. After you select the second point, you will again be prompted to select the next point. Select the third point. Once you have selected the three points, Autodesk Inventor draws imaginary lines between the first and second points as well as between the second and third points. The angle between these two imaginary lines will be measured and displayed in the dialog box, as shown in Figures 3-39 and 3-40.

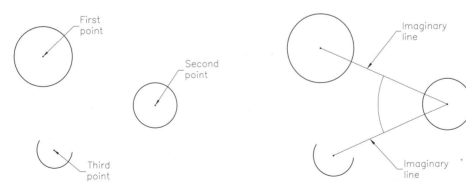

Figure 3-39 Selecting three points   *Figure 3-40* Angle between imaginary lines

Tip. Autodesk Inventor allows you to switch from one measuring tool to another. This is done using the flyout that is displayed on choosing the arrow on the right of the dialog box of any measuring tools. When you choose this arrow, the flyout will be displayed with the options for invoking other measuring tools.

Measuring Loops

Ribbon:	Tools / Inspect > Measure > Loop
Shortcut Menu:	Measure > Measure Loop

Autodesk Inventor allows you to measure closed loops. To measure closed loops, right-click in the drawing window and choose **Measure > Measure Loop** from the shortcut menu; the **Measure Loop** dialog box will be displayed. Alternatively, choose the **Loop** tool from the **Measure** tab; you will be prompted to select a face or a loop. Select the loop to be measured; the **Measure Loop** dialog box will be momentarily changed to the **Loop Length** dialog box and the measurement will be displayed in it. Figure 3-41 shows the **Measure Loop** dialog box with the measurement of a loop.

Measuring the Area

Ribbon:	Tools / Inspect > Measure > Area
Shortcut Menu:	Measure > Measure Area

To measure the area of closed loops, right-click in the drawing window and choose **Measure > Measure Area** from the shortcut menu; the **Measure Area** dialog box will be displayed and you will be prompted to select a face or a loop. Select the closed loop to measure the area; the **Measure Area** dialog box will change momentarily to the **Area** dialog box and the area of the loop will be displayed in it. Figure 3-42 shows the **Area** dialog box with the area of a closed loop.

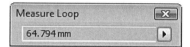

*Figure 3-41 The **Measure Loop**
dialog box*

*Figure 3-42 The **Area** dialog
box*

Tip. *You can also measure the loop or the area defined by a face of an existing feature. You will learn more about features in the later chapters.*

Adding Linear Measurements

Shortcut Menu:	Measure > Measure Distance

You can calculate the total measurement of several linear measurements by adding their values. To do so, invoke the **Distance** or **Angle** tool. Next, select the geometry or the distance to be measured; the measurement will be displayed in the **Measure Distance** dialog box. Next, click the arrow on right side of the display box; a flyout will be displayed. Choose the **Add to Accumulate** option from the flyout and again choose the same arrow; the same flyout will be displayed. Choose the **Restart** option from the flyout. Next, choose another measurement and follow the same procedure till you add all the desired measurements. Then click on the arrow and choose the **Display Accumulate** option from the flyout; the sum of the measurements will be displayed in the dialog box.

Clearing Accumulated Dimensions

Shortcut Menu:	Measure > Measure Distance

On choosing this option, you can clear all the accumulated measurements and reset the sum to zero. This option is located below the **Add to Accumulate** option.

Evaluating Region Properties

Ribbon:	Tools / Inspect > Measure > Region
Shortcut Menu:	Measure > Region Properties

This tool is used to evaluate the properties of the closed sketch loop such as area, perimeter, and display the region properties of the sketch such as Area and Moment of Inertia by taking measurements from the sketch coordinate system. To invoke this tool, right-click in the drawing window and choose **Measure > Region Properties** from the shortcut menu; the **Region Properties** dialog box will be displayed, as shown in Figure 3-43. Alternatively, invoke the **Region Properties** tool by choosing the **Region** tool from the **Measure** panel. The options in this dialog box are discussed next.

Selections

When you invoke the **Region Properties** dialog box, this option is chosen by default and you will be prompted to select one or more closed sketch loops. Select one or more closed sketch loops from the drawing window.

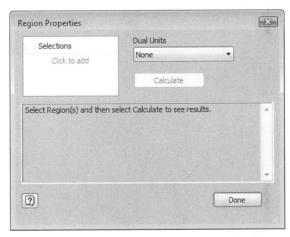

Dual Units

You can select the required unit of measurement from this drop-down list to display the results of measurements in the selected unit. You can view the results in two different units.

*Figure 3-43 The **Region Properties** dialog box*

Calculate

After setting the options in the **Selections** and the **Dual Units** area, choose the **Calculate** tool; the results will be displayed in the display box. In case you add or remove a closed loop in the **Selections** area or change the unit in the **Dual Units** drop-down list, the recalculation will occur and the updated results will be displayed in the display box.

TUTORIALS

From this chapter onward, you will use the parametric feature of Autodesk Inventor for drawing and dimensioning sketches. The following tutorials will explain the method of drawing sketches with some arbitrary dimensions and then driving them to the dimension values required in the model.

Tutorial 1

In this tutorial, you will draw the sketch shown in Figure 3-44. This sketch is the same as the one drawn in Tutorial 2 of Chapter 2. In this tutorial, you will not use the **Inventor Precise Input** toolbar while drawing the initial sketch. After drawing the sketch, you will add the required constraints and then dimension it. Also, you will place a point at the origin and fix it at that location. Then, you will dimension the sketch and fully constrain it by using this point.

(Expected time: 30 min)

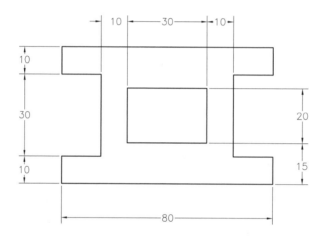

Figure 3-44 Dimensioned sketch for Tutorial 1

The following steps are required to complete this tutorial:

a.   Start a new metric standard part file.
b.   Draw the initial sketch by using the **Line** and **Two point rectangle** tools, refer to Figure 3-45.
c.   Add the required constraints and dimensions to complete the sketch, refer to Figure 3-47.
d.   Place a sketch point at the origin(0,0) and add the **Fix** constraint to it.
e.   Dimension the sketch by using the sketch point to fully constrain it, refer to Figure 3-48.
f.   Save the sketch with the name *Tutorial1.ipt* and then close the file.

Starting Autodesk Inventor

1.   Start Autodesk Inventor by double-clicking on its shortcut icon on the desktop of your computer or by using the **Start** menu.

2. Choose the **New** tool from the **Quick Access Toolbar** and start a new metric standard part file by using the **Metric** tab of the **New File** dialog box.

Drawing the Initial Sketch

1. Using the **Line** tool and the **Two point rectangle** tool, draw the required sketch similar to the one shown in Figure 3-44. You do not need to draw the sketch to the exact length. Use the temporary tracking option for drawing the sketch. For your reference, all lines in the sketch are numbered, see Figure 3-45.

Note that in this sketch, the display of the X and Y axes is turned off.

Adding Constraints to the Sketch

It is evident from Figure 3-45 that some of the lines need to be of the same length. For example, lines 1 and 7, lines 2 and 6, lines 8 and 12, and so on need to be of the same length. You can do so by using two options. In the first option, you can assign dimensions to all these lines. However, this will increase the number of dimensions in the sketch. In the second option, you can apply constraints that will force the lines to maintain an equal length. You can apply the **Equal** constraint to

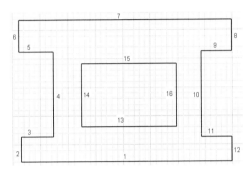

Figure 3-45 *Initial sketch drawn using the sketching tools*

all lines that have the same length. This constraint will relate the length of one of the lines with respect to the other. Now, if you dimension any one of the related lines, all other lines related to it will be forced to acquire the same dimension value. The **Equal** constraint is applied in pairs.

1. Choose the **Equal** tool from the **Constrain** panel of the **Sketch** tab to invoke the **Equal** constraint.

When you invoke this constraint, you are prompted to select the first line, circle, or arc.

2. Select line 2; the color of this line is changed to blue and you are prompted to select the second line, circle, or arc. Select line 6; the **Equal** constraint is applied to lines 2 and 6. Again, you are prompted to select the first line, circle, or arc. Select line 6 as the first line and then line 8 as the second line.

While applying any of these constraints, if the **Autodesk Inventor 2011 - Create Constraint** warning message box is displayed, choose **Cancel** to exit that box.

3. Similarly, select lines 8 and 12, 1 and 7, 3 and 5, 5 and 9, 9 and 11. The **Equal** constraint is applied to all these pairs of lines. Next, right-click in the drawing window, and then choose **Done** from the shortcut menu.

4. If needed, apply the **Horizontal** and **Vertical** constraints to the horizontal and vertical lines of the sketch, respectively.

Dimensioning the Sketch

Once all required constraints are applied to the sketch, you can dimension it. As mentioned earlier, when you add dimensions to a sketch and modify their values, an entity is forced to the specified dimension values.

1. Choose the **Dimension** tool from the **Constrain** panel of the **Sketch** tab; you are prompted to select the geometry to be dimensioned. Select line 1.

    As soon as you move the cursor close to line 1, it turns red and a small symbol is displayed, indicating that a linear dimension will be applied to this line. It is important to modify the value of the dimension after it is placed so that geometries are driven to the values that you require. Therefore, after selecting line 1, right-click to display the shortcut menu. In this menu, choose **Edit Dimension**. If it has already been chosen, press ESC once. This ensures that the **Edit Dimension** toolbar is displayed whenever you place the dimension. This toolbar allows you to modify the dimension value.

2. Place the dimension below line 1; the **Edit Dimension** toolbar is displayed. Enter **80** as the length of line 1 in this toolbar and then choose the check mark on the right of this toolbar.

    You will notice that the length of this line is modified to 80 units. Also, the length of line 7 is also modified because of the **Equal** constraint (refer to Figure 3-47).

3. As the **Dimension** tool is still active, you are prompted again to select the geometry to dimension. Select line 2 and place the dimension on the left of this line; the **Edit Dimension** toolbar is displayed. Change the length of this line to **10** in this toolbar and press ENTER.

    You will notice that the length of lines 6, 8, and 12 is also forced to 10 units. This is because the **Equal** constraint is applied to all these lines.

4. Select line 4 and place it along the previous dimension. Modify the dimension value in the **Edit Dimension** toolbar to **30** and press ENTER. Notice that the length of line 10 is also modified.

5. Select line 16 and place the dimension outside the sketch on the right. Modify the dimension value in the **Edit Dimension** toolbar to **20** and press ENTER.

6. Select line 15 and place the dimension outside the sketch on the top. Modify the dimension value to **30** in the **Edit Dimension** toolbar and press ENTER.

7. Now, to dimension the distance between lines 4 and 14, select them one by one. Place the dimension outside the sketch on the top and then change the dimension value to **10** in the **Edit Dimension** toolbar and press ENTER.

8. Similarly, select lines 16 and 10 to dimension the distance between these two lines and place the dimension outside the sketch on the top. Change the dimension value to **10** in the **Edit Dimension** toolbar and press ENTER. You will notice that the length of lines 5, 9, 3, and 11 is automatically adjusted because the **Equal** constraint is applied to them.

9. To locate the inner rectangle vertically from the outer loop, select lines 1 and 13, and then place the dimension on the right of the sketch. Next, modify the dimension value in the **Edit Dimension** toolbar to **15** and press ENTER.

    With this, you have applied all required constraints and dimensions to the sketch. Now the sketch is ready to be converted into a feature. If you try to add more constraints or dimensions to this sketch, Autodesk Inventor will display an error message box, informing that adding this dimension or constraint will over-constrain the sketch, see Figure 3-46. If you still want this dimension to be displayed, choose the **Accept** button from this message box. The dimension will be added as a driven dimension. A driven dimension is placed inside parentheses and is not used during the manufacturing process. This dimension is used only for reference. Note that you cannot edit the value of a driven dimension.

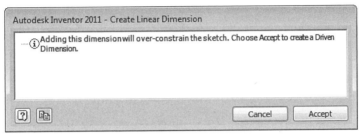

Figure 3-46 The Autodesk Inventor - 2011 message box

The sketch after applying all dimensions and constraints should look similar to the one shown in Figure 3-47.

Even after adding all dimensions, the color of entities in the sketch is still black. This is because the sketch is not fully constrained. As mentioned in the tutorial description, you need to place a sketch point at the origin and then use it to fully constrain the sketch.

10. Place a sketch point at the origin by using the **Inventor Precise Input** toolbar.

11. Choose the **Fix** tool from the **Constrain** panel of the **Sketch** tab; you are prompted to select a curve or a point to be fixed.

12. Select the sketch point that you placed at the origin; the point is fixed at the origin. Now, you can use this point to fully constrain the initial sketch.

13. Choose the **Coincident Constraint** tool from the **Constrain** panel of the **Sketch** tab; you are prompted to select the first curve or point.

14. Select the intersection point of lines 1 and 2, which is the lower left vertex of the sketch; you are prompted to select the second curve or point.

15. Select the sketch point placed at the origin. The entire sketch shifts itself such that the lower left vertex of the sketch is now at the origin. In spite of its shift, the sketch is not completely visible in the drawing window.

16. Choose the **Zoom All** tool from **Navigation Bar > Zoom** flyout to fit the sketch into the drawing window. You will notice that all entities in the sketch are turned blue, indicating that the sketch is fully constrained. Next, press ESC to exit the **Coincident Constraint** tool.

Figure 3-48 shows the fully constrained sketch for Tutorial 1.

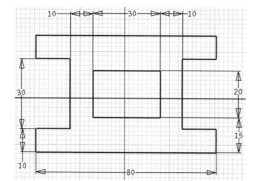

Figure 3-47 *Sketch after adding dimensions*   **Figure 3-48** *Fully constrained sketch for Tutorial 1*

Saving the Sketch

1. Choose the **Finish Sketch** button from the **Exit** panel of the **Sketch** tab to exit the sketching environment.

2. Choose the **Save** tool from the **Quick Access Toolbar** or the **Application Menu** and save this sketch with the name *Tutorial1* at the location given below:

   C:\Inventor_2011\c03

3. Choose **Close > Close** from the **Application Menu** to close the file.

Tutorial 2

In this tutorial, you will draw the sketch shown in Figure 3-49. This sketch is the same as the one drawn in Tutorial 4 of Chapter 2. In this tutorial, you will not use the **Inventor Precise Input** toolbar to draw the initial sketch. After drawing it, you will apply the required constraints and dimensions to fully constrain it.   **(Expected time: 30 min)**

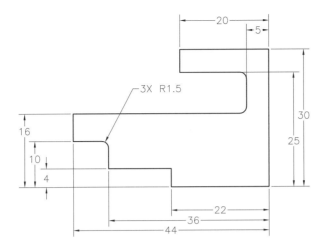

Figure 3-49 *Sketch for Tutorial 2*

The following steps are required to complete this tutorial:

a. Start a new metric standard part file and draw the initial sketch by using the **Line** tool, refer to Figure 3-50.
b. Place a point at the origin and fix it by using the **Fix** constraint.
c. Add linear diameter dimensions to the sketch by using the **Dimension** tool.
d. Apply **Coincident Constraint** between the fixed sketch point and the lower left vertex of the sketch to make it a fully constrained sketch, refer to Figure 3-51.
e. Add fillets, save the sketch with the name *Tutorial2.ipt*, and then close the file.

Starting a New File

1. Choose the **New** tool from the **Quick Access Toolbar** and start a new metric standard part file by using the **Metric** tab of the **New File** dialog box.

Drawing the Initial Sketch

1. Draw the initial sketch, as shown in Figure 3-50, using the **Line** tool. The lines in the sketch are numbered for your reference.

2. Place a sketched point at the origin by using the **Inventor Precise Input** toolbar.

Dimensioning and Constraining the Sketch

The dimensions shown in Figure 3-49 are linear dimensions. As the sketch is for a revolved feature, you need to add linear diameter dimensions to it. It is recommended that you first apply all dimensions and then add fillets to the sketch. This is because the size of a sketch is generally changed after dimensioning. Before adding dimensions to a revolved section, it is important to determine which line segment of the sketch will act as the axis for revolving the sketch. If you refer to Figure 2-58 in Chapter 2, you will notice that line

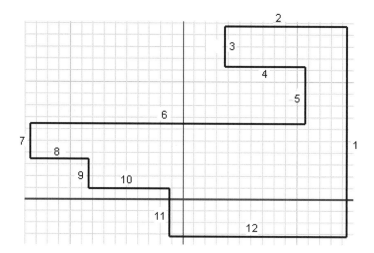

Figure 3-50 *Lines numbered in the sketch*

12 acts as the axis to revolve the sketch for the model. Therefore, while applying linear diameter dimensions, line 12 should be selected first.

1. Choose the **Dimension** tool from the **Constrain** panel of the **Sketch** tab; you are prompted to select the geometry to be dimensioned. Right-click to display the shortcut menu, and then choose **Edit Dimension** from it, if it has not already been chosen. If it has already been chosen, press the ESC key once to exit the shortcut menu.

2. Select line 12; you are prompted again to select the geometry to be dimensioned. Select line 10 and then right-click; a shortcut menu is displayed. In this menu, choose **Linear Diameter**.

    You will notice that the dimension is twice as double of its actual length. Also, the dimension value is preceded by the Ø symbol, indicating that it is a linear diameter dimension.

3. Place the dimension on the left of the sketch; the **Edit Dimension** toolbar is displayed.

    Figure 3-49 shows the value to be specified as 4 because the linear diameter dimensions are placed twice the original length.

4. Enter **8** in the **Edit Dimension** toolbar and press ENTER; the vertical distance between lines 12 and 10 is automatically adjusted to the value entered.

5. As the **Dimension** tool is still active, you are prompted again to select the geometry to be dimensioned. Select line 12 and line 8. Next, right-click; a shortcut menu is displayed. Choose **Linear Diameter** from the shortcut menu; the linear dimension is changed to the linear diameter dimension. Place the dimension on the left of the previous dimension. Next, modify its value in the **Edit Dimension** toolbar to **20** and press ENTER.

6. Select lines 12 and 6. Right-click to display the shortcut menu, and then choose **Linear Diameter** from it. Place the dimension on the left of the previous dimension and change its dimension value in the **Edit Dimension** toolbar to **32** and press ENTER.

> **Tip**. *Autodesk Inventor allows you to invoke the drawing display options even when a sketching environment tool is active. This is done using the combination of hot keys and the left mouse button. For example, if the **Dimension** tool is active, you can use the **Pan** option by holding the F2 key and then pressing the left mouse button and dragging the cursor. Similarly, you can dynamically zoom in and out the sketch by holding the F3 key and then pressing the left mouse button and dragging the cursor.*

7. Select lines 12 and 4, and then right-click; a shortcut menu is displayed. In the shortcut menu, choose **Linear Diameter**. Place the dimension on the right of the sketch and change its value in the **Edit Dimension** toolbar to **50** and then press ENTER.

8. Select lines 12 and 2, and then right-click to display the shortcut menu. In this menu, choose **Linear Diameter**. Place the dimension on the right of the previous dimension and change its value in the **Edit Dimension** toolbar to **60** and then press ENTER.

   Now, you need to add linear dimensions to the sketch

9. Select lines 1 and 5, and then place the dimension above the sketch. Modify its value in the **Edit Dimension** toolbar to **5** and press ENTER.

10. Select line 2 and then place the dimension above the previous dimension. Modify its value in the **Edit Dimension** toolbar to **20** and press ENTER.

11. Select line 12 and then place the dimension below the sketch. Modify its value in the **Edit Dimension** toolbar to **22** and press ENTER.

12. Select lines 1 and 9, and then place the dimension below the previous dimension. Modify its value in the **Edit Dimension** toolbar to **36** and press ENTER.

13. Select lines 1 and 7, and then place the dimension below the previous dimension. Modify its value in the **Edit Dimension** toolbar to **44** and press ENTER.

   With this, all dimensions are added to the sketch. However, entities in the sketch are still displayed in black, indicating that the sketch is not fully constrained. Therefore, you need to add more dimensions or constraints to make the sketch fully constrained. In this sketch, first you will add the **Fix** constraint to the sketched point placed at the origin and then add the **Coincident Constraint** to the sketched point and the intersection point of lines 11 and 12.

> **Tip**. *Sometimes while dimensioning a sketch, some existing dimensions move from the location where they have been placed. In this case, you need to exit the **Dimension** tool and then drag the existing dimensions back to their original locations. To resume dimensioning, invoke the **Dimension** tool again.*

14. Invoke the **Point** tool and place the point at the origin.

15. Invoke the **Fix** constraint from the **Constrain** panel of the **Sketch** tab and select the sketches point placed at the origin to fix it at the origin.

16. Invoke the **Coincident Constraint** tool; you are prompted to select the first curve or point. Select the intersection point of lines 11 and 12, which is the lower left vertex of the sketch; you are prompted to select the second curve or point.

17. Select the sketched point placed at the origin; the entire sketch shifts from its original location and is relocated such that the lower left vertex of the sketch now lies at the origin. Also, all entities in the sketch are displayed in blue, indicating that the sketch is fully constrained.

Note

*If the entities of the sketch are not fully constrained, you need to apply the **Vertical Constraint** to the vertical lines on the right of the sketch.*

18. Choose the **Zoom All** tool from the **Navigation Bar > Zoom** flyout to fit the sketch into the drawing window. The fully constrained sketch after adding all dimensions is shown in Figure 3-51.

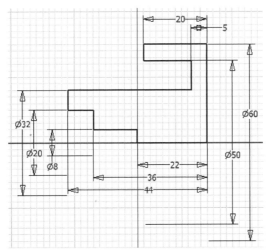

Figure 3-51 Fully constrained sketch for Tutorial 2

Adding Fillets to the Sketch

After dimensioning the sketch, you need to add fillets to it.

1. Choose the **Fillet** tool from **Sketch > Draw > Fillet/Chamfer** drop-down; the **2D Fillet** dialog box is displayed. In this dialog box, set the value of fillet to **1.5**. Now, select lines 8 and 9; the fillet is automatically added between these two lines and the dimension of the fillet is displayed.

2. Similarly, select lines 5 and 6 as well as lines 4 and 5 to add fillets between these lines. Exit the **2D Fillet** dialog box. The final sketch after adding fillets is shown in Figure 3-52.

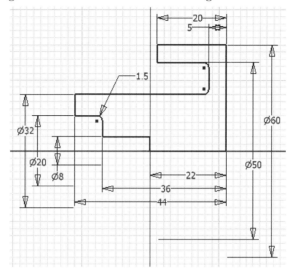

Figure 3-52 *Fully dimensioned sketch after adding fillets*

Note

*To modify the radius of the fillet, double-click on it; the **Edit Dimension** toolbar is displayed. Modify the value in this toolbar and press ENTER.*

Saving the Sketch

1. Choose the **Finish Sketch** button from the **Exit** panel of the **Sketch** tab to exit the sketching environment.

2. Save this sketch with the name *Tutorial2* at the location *C:\Inventor_2011\c03*.

3. Choose **Close > Close** from the **Application Menu** to close the file.

Tutorial 3

In this tutorial, you will draw the sketch for the model shown in Figure 3-53. After drawing the sketch, you will add the required constraints to it and then dimension it. The dimensioned sketch required for this model is shown in Figure 3-54. The solid model shown in Figure 3-53 is only for reference. **(Expected time: 30 min)**

The sketch shown in Figure 3-54 is the combination of multiple closed loops: the outer loop and inner circles. As the numbers of loops increase, so does the complexity of the sketch. This is because the numbers of constraints and dimensions in a sketch increase in case of multiple loops. Now, to draw sketches without using the **Inventor Precise Input** toolbar, it is recommended that you first draw the outer loop of the sketch and then add constraints and dimensions to it. This is because once the outer loop is constrained and dimensioned, the inner circles can be constrained and dimensioned easily with reference to the outer loop.

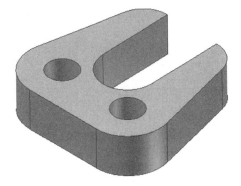

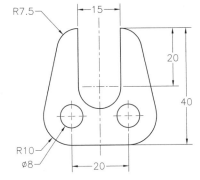

Figure 3-53 Model for Tutorial 3   *Figure 3-54* Dimensioned sketch for the model

The following steps are required to complete this tutorial:

a. Start a new metric template and draw the outer loop of the sketch, refer to Figure 3-55.
b. Add the required dimensions and constraints to the outer loop, refer to Figure 3-57.
c. Draw inner circles and add constraints and dimensions to them, refer to Figure 3-58.
d. Save the sketch with the name *Tutorial3.ipt* and close the file.

Starting a New File
1. Choose the **New** button from the **Quick Access Toolbar** and start a new metric standard part file using the **Metric** tab of the **New File** dialog box.

Drawing the Outer Loop
1. Using the **Line** tool, draw the profile, as shown in Figure 3-55.

You can draw the tangent arcs within the **Line** tool. This can be done by pressing the left mouse button and then dragging in the required direction (refer to Tutorial 3 of Chapter 2 to learn more about drawing this type of arc.)

For your reference, all geometries in the sketch are numbered. You will draw inner holes in the sketch after dimensioning the outer loop.

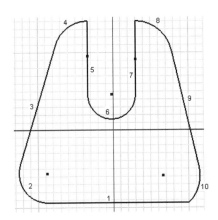

Figure 3-55 Profile with geometries numbered

Adding Constraints to Sketched Entities
As evident from Figure 3-55, some of the constraints such as tangent and equal are missing in the sketch. Therefore, you need to add these constraints manually to the sketch. You can view the constraints applied on various geometries by using the **Show Constraints** tool.

1. In Figure 3-55, the **Tangent** constraint is missing between line 1 and arc 10. To add this constraint, choose the **Tangent** tool from the **Constrain** panel of the **Sketch** tab; you are prompted to select the first curve. Select arc 10 as the first curve; you are prompted to select the second curve. Select line 1 as the second curve. Similarly, add this constraint to all places in the sketch wherever it is missing.

    The geometries 5 and 7, and 3 and 9 are the lines that must be of equal length. Also, the geometries 2 and 10, and 4 and 8 are the arcs that must be of equal radii. Therefore, you need to add the **Equal** constraint between the respective pairs of all these geometries.

2. Choose the **Equal** tool from the **Constrain** panel of the **Sketch** tab.

3. Select line 5 as the first line and then line 7 as the second line to apply the **Equal** constraint to them; you are prompted again to select the first entity.

4. Select line 3 and then line 9 to apply the **Equal** constraint to these lines; you are prompted to select the first entity again.

5. Select arc 2 and then arc 10 to apply the **Equal** constraint to these arcs. Applying this constraint to arcs or circles forces their radii or diameters to be equal.

6. Similarly, apply the **Equal** constraint to arcs 4 and 8.

7. Apply the **Coincident Constraint** between the center points of arc 4 and line 5, and the center points of arc 8 and line 7, if it is not applied automatically.

8. Choose the **Fix** tool from the **Constrain** panel and then select the sketched point; the point is fixed at the origin.

9   Choose the **Coincident Constraint** tool from the **Constrain** panel; you are prompted to select the first curve or point.

10. Select the sketched point; you are prompted to select the second curve or point.

11. Select the center point of arc 6; the entire sketch moves to make the sketched point coincident with the center point of the arc. The sketch after applying all constraints is shown in Figure 3-56.

Note
The shape of the sketch that you have drawn may be a little different at this stage because of the difference in specifying points while drawing the sketch. However, once all dimensions are applied, the shape of the sketch will be the same. Also, you may need to add vertical constraint to lines 5 and 7 to fully constrain the sketch.

Dimensioning the Sketch

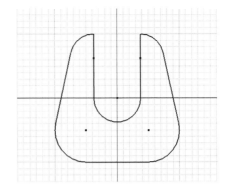

1. Choose the **Dimension** tool from the **Constrain** panel of the **Sketch** tab. Next, right-click to display the shortcut menu. In this shortcut menu, choose **Edit Dimension** if the check mark is not available on the left of the **Edit Dimension** option. If it shows the check mark, press the ESC key once to exit the shortcut menu. On doing so, you are prompted to select the geometry to be dimensioned. Select line 1 and place the dimension below the sketch. Modify the value of this dimension in the **Edit Dimension** toolbar to **20**.

Figure 3-56 The sketch after applying all constraints

2. Select arc 4 and place the dimension on the left of the sketch; the radius dimension of the sketch is placed. Modify the dimension value in the **Edit Dimension** toolbar to **7.5**. The size of arc 8 is also modified because of the **Equal** constraint applied between these two entities.

Note

As discussed in the previous tutorial, you may need to use the combination of hot keys to zoom or pan the model.

3. Select arc 2 and place the radius dimension on the left of the sketch. Modify the dimension value in the **Edit Dimension** toolbar to **10** and press ENTER. The size of arc 10 is also modified because of the **Equal** constraint applied between these two entities.

4. Select line 5 and then line 7, and then place the dimension above the sketch. Modify the value of this dimension in the **Edit Dimension** toolbar to **15** and press ENTER.

5. Select line 7 and place the dimension on the right of the sketch. Modify the value of this dimension in the **Edit Dimension** toolbar to **20** and press ENTER.

6. Select the upper endpoint of line 7 and select line 1, and then place the dimension on the right of the previous dimension. Modify the value of this dimension to **40** and press ENTER. Next, exit the **Dimension** tool.

   With this, all dimensions are applied to the sketch (see Figure 3-57), except the horizontal dimension between the center points of arcs 4 and 6 or arcs 8 and 6. The need of these dimensions depends on the constraints and dimensions assumed while drawing the sketch. If the sketch gets over-constrained, the **Autodesk Inventor 2011** message box is displayed. Choose **Cancel** from the message box. In this case, this dimension has already been assumed.

Drawing Circles

Once all the required dimensions and constraints are applied to the sketch, you need to draw circles. Figure 3-54 indicates that circles are concentric with arcs 2 and 10.

1. To draw concentric circles, choose the **Circle Center Point** tool from the **Draw** panel; you are prompted to select the center of the circle. Move the cursor close to the center of arc 2. Specify the center point when the cursor snaps to the center point of arc 2 and turns green. Now, move the cursor away from the center and specify a point to size the circle.

2. Similarly, draw the other circle taking the reference of the center of arc 10.

Adding Constraints to Circles

As both the circles have the same diameter, you can apply the **Equal** constraint to them. So, you need to apply the dimension to just one of them. On applying the dimension, the other circle will automatically be forced to the specified diameter value because of the **Equal** constraint.

1. Invoke the **Equal** constraint from the **Constrain** panel. Select the first circle and then the second circle to apply the **Equal** constraint.

Dimensioning the Circles

1. Choose **Dimension** from the **Constrain** panel and select the left circle. Place the dimension on the left of the sketch. In the **Edit Dimension** toolbar, change the value of the diameter of the circle to **8** and press ENTER.

Dimension

Notice that the size of the right circle is automatically modified to match the dimension of the left circle. This is because the **Equal** constraint is applied between the two circles. The final sketch for Tutorial 3 after drawing and dimensioning circles is shown in Figure 3-58.

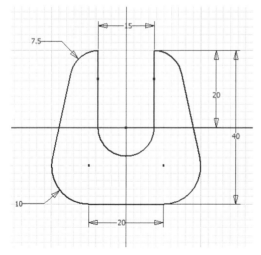

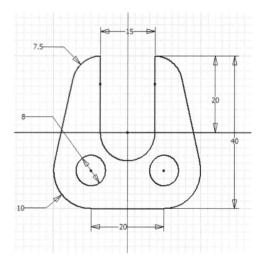

Figure 3-57 Dimensioned sketch for Tutorial 3

Figure 3-58 The final dimensioned sketch for Tutorial 3

Saving the Sketch

1. Choose the **Return** tool from the **Quick Access Toolbar** to exit the sketching environment. Save this sketch with the name *Tutorial3* at the location given below:

   C:\Inventor_2011\c03.

   Note
   *If the **Return** tool is not available in the **Quick Access Toolbar**, you need to add this tool to this toolbar. To do so, choose the down arrow on right of the **Quick Access Toolbar**; a flyout is displayed. Next, choose the **Return** option from the flyout.*

2. Choose **Close > Close** from the **Application Menu** to close the file.

Tutorial 4

In this tutorial, you will draw the sketch of the model shown in Figure 3-59. The dimensions of the sketch are shown in Figure 3-60. After drawing the sketch, add constraints and then dimension it. The solid model is given for reference only. **(Expected time: 30 min)**

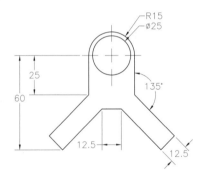

Figure 3-59 *Model for the sketch of Tutorial 4*   **Figure 3-60** *Dimensions of the sketch*

The following steps are required to complete this tutorial:

a. Start a new metric standard part file and draw the outer loop of the sketch.
b. Add the required dimensions and constraints to the sketch.
c. Add the inner circle to the sketch and dimension it.
d. Save the sketch with the name *Tutorial4.ipt* and close the file.

Starting a New File

1. Choose the **New** tool from the **Quick Access Toolbar** to display the **New File** dialog box. Start a new metric standard part file from the **Metric** tab of this dialog box.

Drawing the Outer Loop

1. Choose **Line** from the **Draw** panel of the **Sketch** tab to draw the outer loop, as shown in Figure 3-61. As mentioned earlier, you should draw the inner loop after drawing and dimensioning the outer loop. This is because once the outer loop is dimensioned, you can draw the inner loop by taking the reference of the outer loop.

You can draw the arc within the **Line** tool. You can also use the temporary tracking option for drawing this sketch. For your reference, the geometries in the sketch are numbered, see Figure 3-61.

Adding Constraints to the Outer Loop

1. Add the **Equal** constraint to lines 1 and 9, lines 2 and 8, lines 3 and 5, lines 5 and 7, and lines 4 and 6.

2. Add the **Perpendicular Constraint** to lines 2 and 3, and lines 7 and 8.

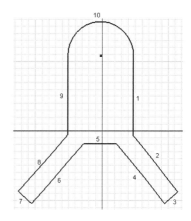

Figure 3-61 *Initial sketch with the geometries numbered*

3. Add the **Horizontal Constraint** to the lower endpoints of lines 4 and 6.

4. Add the **Tangent** constraint to lines 1 and 9 with arc 10, if it is missing.

Dimensioning the Outer Loop

1. Choose the **Dimension** tool from the **Constrain** panel of the **Sketch** tab; you are prompted to select the geometry to dimension. Select line 9 and place the dimension on the left of the sketch. Modify the dimension value in the **Edit Dimension** toolbar to **25** and press ENTER.

2. Select the center of the arc and then select the lower endpoint of line 6. Place the dimension on the left of the previous dimension. Modify the dimension value in the **Edit Dimension** toolbar to **60** and press ENTER.

3. Select line 3 and then right-click to display the shortcut menu. Choose **Aligned** from the shortcut menu and then place the dimension below the sketch. Modify the dimension value in the **Edit Dimension** toolbar to **12.5** and press ENTER.

   Notice that the length of lines 5 and 7 is also modified because of the **Equal** constraint.

4. Select lines 1 and 2 and then place the angular dimension on the right of the sketch. Modify the value of the angular dimension in the **Edit Dimension** toolbar to **135** and press ENTER.

5. Select arc 10 and then place the radius dimension above the sketch. Modify the value of the radius of the arc in the **Edit Dimension** toolbar to **15** and press ENTER.

   With this, the required dimensions are applied to the outer loop. Even after adding all dimensions, the color of entities in the sketch is still black. To fully constrain the sketch, you need to place a sketch point at the origin and then constrain it.

6. Choose the **Point** tool from the **Draw** panel of the **Sketch** tab and place the point at the origin.

7. Choose the **Fix** tool from the **Constrain** panel of the **Sketch** tab; you are prompted to select a curve or a point to be fixed.

8. Select the sketch point that you have placed at the origin; the point is fixed at the origin. Now, you can use this point to fully constrain the initial sketch.

9. Choose the **Coincident Constraint** tool from the **Constrain** panel; you are prompted to select the first curve or point.

10. Select the center of the arc; you are prompted to select the second curve or point.

11. Select the sketch point that you have placed at the origin. The entire sketch shifts itself such that the center of arc of the sketch is now at the origin. But, the sketch may not be visible completely in the drawing window.

12. Choose the **Zoom All** tool from the **Navigation Bar > Zoom** flyout to fit the sketch into the drawing window. You will notice that all entities in the sketch are turned blue, indicating that the sketch is fully constrained. Press the ESC key to exit the **Coincident Constraint** tool.

Drawing the Circle

1. Choose **Circle Center Point** from the **Draw** panel of the **Sketch** tab; you are prompted to select the center of the circle.

2. Move the cursor close to the center of the arc; the cursor snaps to the center point and turns green. Select this point as the center of the circle and then move the cursor away from the center to size the circle. Specify a point to give it an approximate size.

Dimensioning the Circle

1. Choose **Dimension** from the **Constrain** panel of the **Sketch** tab and select the circle. Place the diameter dimension below the arc dimension. Enter **25** in the **Edit Dimension** toolbar as and press ENTER. This completes the sketch for Tutorial 4. The final dimensioned sketch is shown in Figure 3-62.

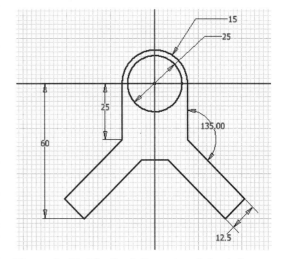

Figure 3-62 *The final dimensioned sketch for Tutorial 4*

Saving the Sketch

1. Choose the **Finish Sketch** button from the **Exit** panel of the **Sketch** tab to exit the sketching environment. Save the sketch with the name *Tutorial4* at the location given below:

C:\Inventor_2011\c03

2. Choose **Close > Close** from the **Application Menu** to close the file.

Self-Evaluation Test

Answer the following questions and then compare them to those given at the end of this chapter:

1. The **Perpendicular Constraint** forces a selected entity to become perpendicular to a specified entity. (T/F)

2. The **Coincident Constraint** can be applied to two line segments. (T/F)

3. The **Collinear Constraint** can only be applied to line segments. (T/F)

4. If an unnecessary constraint is applied to a sketch, Autodesk Inventor displays a message box informing that adding this constraint will over-constrain the sketch. (T/F)

5. The _____ nature of Autodesk Inventor ensures that a selected entity is driven to a specified dimension value irrespective of its original size.

6. When you select a circle to be dimensioned, the _____ dimension is applied to it by default.

7. The _____ dimension has one arrowhead and is placed outside a circle or an arc.

8. The _____ dimension displays the distance between two selected line segments in terms of diameter and the distance shown is twice the original length.

9. The _____ tool is used to measure the radius of an arc.

10. A _____ constrained sketch is the one whose all entities are completely constrained to their surroundings using constraints and dimensions.

Review Questions

Answer the following questions:

1. You cannot apply the **Concentric Constraint** between a point and a circle. (T/F)

2. You can use the **Horizontal Constraint** or **Vertical Constraint** to line up arcs, circles, or ellipses in the same horizontal or vertical direction. (T/F)

3. You can view all, or some of the constraints applied to a sketch. (T/F)

4. There are twelve types of geometric constraints that can be applied to sketched entities. (T/F)

5. The linear dimensions are the dimensions that define the shortest distance between two points. (T/F)

6. A situation where the number of dimensions or constraints exceeds the required number of dimensions or constraints in a sketch is called

    (a) Fully-constrained   (b) Under-constrained
    (c) Over-constrained   (d) None of these

7. To which of the following toolbars does the **Measure Distance** toolbar change when you invoke the **Distance** tool and select two lines?

    (a) **Length**   (b) **Distance**
    (c) **Minimum Distance**   (d) None of these

8. Which of the following dimensions is applied to the arc by default whenever you select an arc to be dimensioned?

    (a) **Radius**   (b) **Diameter**
    (c) **Linear**   (d) **Linear Diameter**

9. In addition to lines, which of the following entities can be selected to apply the **Collinear** constraint?

    (a) Arc   (b) Circle
    (c) Ellipse   (d) Ellipse axis

10. Which of the following combination of entities cannot be used to apply the **Tangent** constraint?

    (a) Line, line   (b) Line, arc
    (c) Circle, circle   (d) Arc, circle

Exercises

Exercise 1

Draw the sketch of the model shown in Figure 3-63. The sketch is shown in Figure 3-64. After drawing the sketch, add the required constraints to it and then dimension it.

(Expected time: 30 min)

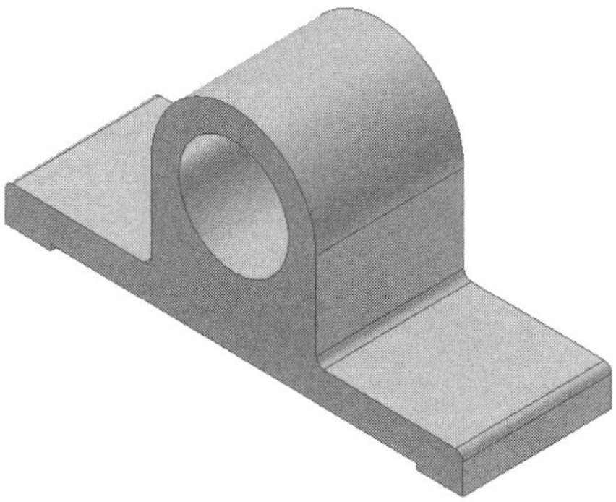

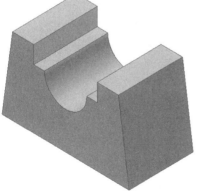

Figure 3-63 *Model for Exercise 1*

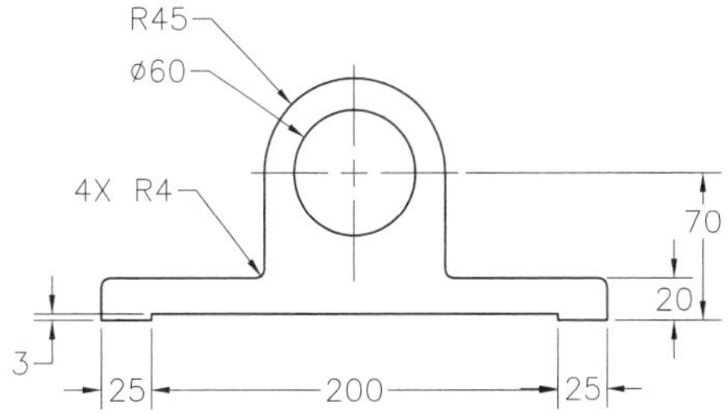

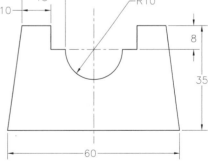

Figure 3-64 *Sketch for Exercise 1*

Exercise 2

Draw the sketch of the model shown in Figure 3-65. The sketch is shown in Figure 3-66. After drawing the sketch, add the required constraints to it and then dimension it.

(Expected time: 30 min)

Figure 3-65 *Model for Exercise 2*

Figure 3-66 *Sketch for Exercise 2*

Exercise 3

Redraw the sketch of Exercise 1 of Chapter 2 without using the **Inventor Precise Input** toolbar. After drawing the sketch, add the required constraints to it and then dimension it. The dimensioned sketch is shown in Figure 3-67. **(Expected time: 30 min)**

Exercise 4

Redraw the sketch of Exercise 2 of Chapter 2 without using the **Inventor Precise Input** toolbar. After drawing the sketch, add the required constraints to it and then dimension it. The dimensioned sketch is shown in Figure 3-68.   **(Expected time: 30 min)**

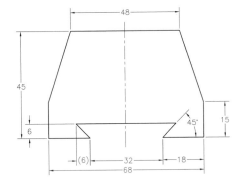

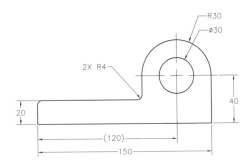

Figure 3-67 *Dimensioned sketch for Exercise 3*   **Figure 3-68** *Dimensioned sketch for Exercise 4*

Exercise 5

Draw the sketch of the model shown in Figure 3-69. The sketch to be drawn is shown in Figure 3-70. After drawing the sketch, add the required constraints to it and then dimension it.
                                                                        (Expected time: 30 min)

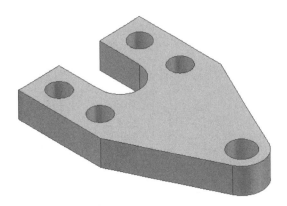

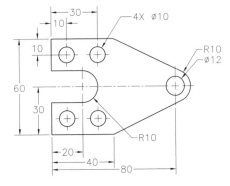

Figure 3-69 *Model for Exercise 5*   **Figure 3-70** *Sketch for Exercise 5*

Answers to Self-Evaluation Test
1. T, **2.** F, **3.** F, **4.** T, **5.** parametric, **6.** diameter, **7.** radius, **8.** linear diameter, **9. Measure Distance**, **10.** fully

Chapter 4

Editing, Extruding, and Revolving the Sketches

Learning Objectives

After completing this chapter, you will be able to:

- *Edit sketches using various editing tools.*
- *Create rectangular and circular patterns.*
- *Write text in the sketching environment and convert it into a feature.*
- *Insert external images, Word documents, and Excel spreadsheets in the sketching environment.*
- *Convert sketches into base features using the Extrude tool.*
- *Convert sketches into base features using the Revolve tool.*
- *Manipulate features by using the mini toolbar.*
- *Dynamically change the view of a model using Free Orbit, ViewCube, and SteeringWheels.*

EDITING SKETCHED ENTITIES

Autodesk Inventor provides you with a number of tools that can be used to edit the sketched entities. These tools are discussed next.

Extending Sketched Entities

Ribbon:	Sketch > Modify > Extend
Toolbar:	2D Sketch Panel > Extend

This tool is used to extend or lengthen the selected sketched entity up to a specified boundary. Therefore, to use this tool, you should have at least two entities such that when extended, they meet at a point. Taking the reference of one of the entities, the other will be extended. The entities that can be extended using this tool are lines, splines, and arcs. On invoking this tool, you will be prompted to select the curve to be extended. As you move the cursor close to the curve to be extended, the original curve will be displayed in red and the portion that will be extended will be displayed in black. While extending the arcs, the point where you select the arc will determine the side that will be extended. Figures 4-1 and 4-2 show the curves before and after extending them.

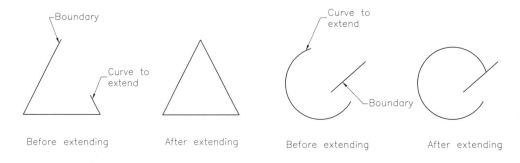

Figure 4-1 Line before and after extending it   *Figure 4-2* Arc before and after extending it

Trimming Sketched Entities

Ribbon:	Sketch > Modify > Trim
Toolbar:	2D Sketch Panel > Trim

This tool can be considered as the opposite of the **Extend** tool and is used to chop the selected sketched entity by using an edge (also called the knife-edge). The knife-edge, in its current form, may or may not actually intersect the entity to be trimmed. However, when extended, the knife-edge must intersect the entity to be trimmed. On invoking this tool, you will be prompted to select the portion of the curve to be trimmed or press and hold the CTRL key. As you move the cursor close to the curve to be trimmed, the entity will be highlighted in red color and the portion of the entity to be trimmed will be displayed as a dashed line. Once you select the portion of the entity to be trimmed by clicking on it, the selected portion will be trimmed to the nearest intersection point with the next closest entity. Figure 4-3 shows the curves to be selected for trimming and Figure 4-4 shows the sketch after trimming the curves. If you use this tool on an isolated entity, it will work as the **Delete** tool and will delete the isolated entity.

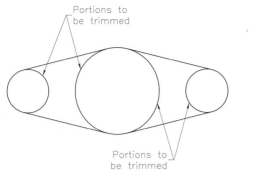

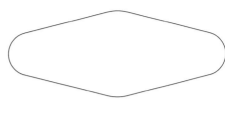

Figure 4-3 *Selecting the curves for trimming*   **Figure 4-4** *Sketch after trimming the curves*

To trim the entities within a boundary, press and hold the CTRL key after invoking the **Trim** tool; you will be prompted to select the geometry used for trimming. Select the geometry to be used as boundary for trimming. Next, release the CTRL key; you will be prompted to select the portion of the curve to be trimmed. Select the portion by clicking on it; the portion within the boundary will be trimmed.

Tip. *If you are using the **Extend** or **Trim** tool while editing, you can also temporarily switch between these tools by pressing and holding the SHIFT key. For example, if the active tool is **Trim** and you press and hold the SHIFT key, then this tool will act as the **Extend** tool, but on releasing the SHIFT key, the original tool will resume its function.*

Splitting Sketched Entities

Ribbon:	Sketch > Modify > Split
Toolbar:	2D Sketch Panel > Split

The **Split** tool is used to break a sketched entity into two or more entities at the intersection point(s) with another sketched entity. On invoking this tool, you will be prompted to select a curve to split. As you move the cursor close to the sketched entity, it is highlighted in red and a red cross-mark will be displayed at the nearest intersection point or the apparent intersection point. The intersection point will be selected depending on the selection point on the sketched entity. It means that the intersection point nearest to the point of selection will be selected as the point of break for the sketched entity. Click on the entity highlighted in red; the entity will split into two parts. Each part of the split entity will now act an individual sketched entity and can be modified or deleted independent of the other part. However, the broken parts will be joined through the **Coincident** constraint. As a result, if you drag the broken entity to a new position, the entire entity will also move.

Tip. *If you are editing sketched entities using the **Trim** tool, you can switch to the **Extend** or **Split** tool. To do so, right-click in the drawing area; a shortcut menu will be displayed. You will observe a check mark on the left of the active tool. Select the editing tool as per your requirement to switch to that tool.*

Offsetting Sketched Entities

Ribbon:	Sketch > Modify > Offset
Toolbar:	2D Sketch Panel > Offset

Offsetting is one of the easiest methods of drawing parallel lines, concentric arcs and circles. You can select the entire loop as a single entity or select the individual entities to be offset. When you invoke the **Offset** tool, you will be prompted to select the curve to offset. If you right-click at this point, a shortcut menu will be displayed, as shown in Figure 4-5. The **Loop Select** option is chosen by default in this shortcut menu, see Figure 4-5. This option allows you to select the entire loop as a single entity. However, if this option is cleared, the entire loop will be considered as a combination of individual segments and you will be allowed to select individual entities. The **Constrain Offset** option applies the constraints automatically when the loop or the individual entity is offset.

Figure 4-5 The offset shortcut menu

If you choose the **Loop Select** option from the shortcut menu, you will be prompted to specify the offset position for the new loop immediately after selecting the original loop. If you specify the location inside the original loop, the new loop will be smaller than the original loop. If you specify the location outside the original loop, the new loop will be bigger.

In case of individual entities, once you have selected the entity to be offset, right-click to display the shortcut menu and choose **Continue**, or press the ENTER key to continue. You will be prompted to specify the location for the new entity. If the selected entity is a line segment, its length will remain the same and if it is an arc or a circle, the size of the new entity will depend on the location of the new point. Figure 4-6 shows the offset of a complete loop and Figure 4-7 shows the offset of an individual entity of a loop.

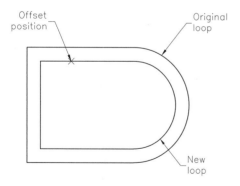

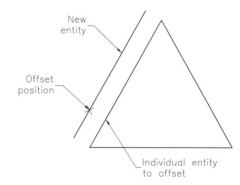

Figure 4-6 *Creating a new loop by offsetting the original loop*

Figure 4-7 *Offsetting an individual line segment to a new location*

Mirroring Sketched Entities

Ribbon:	Sketch > Pattern > Mirror
Toolbar:	2D Sketch Panel > Mirror

The **Mirror** tool is used to create a mirror image of the selected entities. The entities are mirrored about a straight line segment. This tool is used to draw sketches that are symmetrical about a line or sketches that have some portion symmetrical about a line. When you invoke this tool, the **Mirror** dialog box will be displayed, as shown in Figure 4-8. The **Select** button will be chosen by default and you will be prompted to select

*Figure 4-8 The **Mirror** dialog box*

the geometry to be mirrored. You can select multiple entities to be mirrored. Once you have selected the entities, choose the **Mirror line** button; you will be prompted to select the line about which the entities should be mirrored. After selecting the mirror line, choose the **Apply** button; the selected entities will be mirrored about the mirror line. If the mirror line is at an angle, the resultant entities that will be created upon mirroring will also be at an angle. After mirroring the entities, choose the **Done** button to exit this dialog box.

Figure 4-9 shows various sketched entities selected for mirroring and the mirror line that will be used to mirror the entities. Figure 4-10 shows the sketch after mirroring the entities. Figure 4-11 shows the entities selected to be mirrored about an inclined mirror line and Figure 4-12 shows the sketch after mirroring the entities.

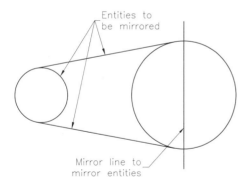
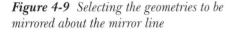
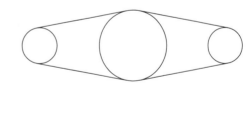

Figure 4-9 Selecting the geometries to be mirrored about the mirror line

Figure 4-10 Sketch after mirroring the geometries and deleting the mirror line

Moving Sketched Entities

Ribbon:	Sketch > Modify > Move
Toolbar:	2D Sketch Panel > Move

The **Move** tool is used to move one or more selected sketched entities from one point to the other. The points that can be used to move the entities include the sketched points/hole centers, endpoints of lines, arcs, splines, and the center

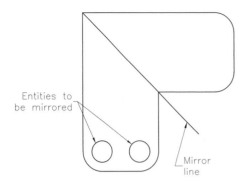

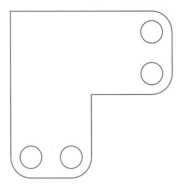

Figure 4-11   *Selecting the geometries to be mirrored about an inclined mirror line*

Figure 4-12   *Sketch after mirroring the geometries and deleting the mirror line*

points of arcs, circles, and ellipses. When you invoke this command, the **Move** dialog box will be displayed, as shown in Figure 4-13. You can also use this dialog box to create copies of the selected entities.

Note
Remember that while moving the selected entities, their behavior is also governed by the constraints that are applied to them. If the selected entities are constrained with some other entities, the constrained entities will also move. However, if the other entities have a Fix constraint applied to them, because of which they cannot move from their location, the original entities will also not be able to move.

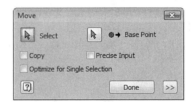

Figure 4-13   *The Move dialog box*

Options in the Move Dialog Box

The options in the **Move** dialog box are discussed next.

Select

This button is used to select the entities to be moved. When you invoke the **Move** tool, this button is automatically chosen. You can select more than one object using the Window or Crossing options or by selecting them one by one using the left mouse button.

Base Point

This button is chosen to specify the point that will act as the base point for moving the selected entities. Once you have selected all the entities to be moved, choose this button to select the point from where the movement will start.

Copy

This check box is selected to create a copy of the selected entities as they are moved. If this check box is selected, a copy of the selected entities will be created and placed at the destination point, keeping the original entities intact at their original location.

Precise Input

This check box, if selected, allows you to specify the coordinates for the base point and the destination point using the **Inventor Precise Input** toolbar.

Optimize for Single Selection

If this check box is selected, the **Base Point** button will be activated automatically after making a single selection or the window selection of geometry. But if you clear this check box, you can make multiple geometry selections before choosing the **Base Point** button.

Autodesk Inventor allows you to control the geometric and dimensional constraints of the entity being moved. To do this, choose the **> >** button at the lower right corner of the **Move** dialog box; the **Move** dialog box will expand, as shown in Figure 4-14.

The radio buttons in the **Relax Dimensional Constraints** area are used to control the behavior of the dimensional constraints that are applied to the sketched entities. Different radio buttons in this area are discussed next.

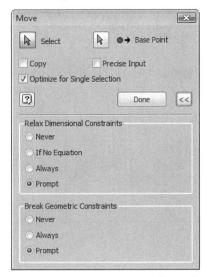

Never

If this radio button is selected, the dimensional constraints applied to the sketched entities will not be ignored while moving them. If moving the sketched entities conflicts with the constraints applied to them earlier, then the **Autodesk Inventor 2011** message box will be displayed warning about the conflicts.

Figure 4-14 *The expanded form of the* **Move** *dialog box*

If No Equation

This radio button, if selected, modifies the dimensions that are not a function of any other dimension, while the move operation is being performed.

Always

This radio button, if selected, modifies the dimensions of the entities that are outside the selection box, after moving the selected entities to a new position.

Prompt

This radio button is selected by default, and if the move operation cannot be performed with the existing dimensions and constraints, a dialog box offering possible solutions will be displayed.

Similarly, the radio buttons in the **Break Geometric Constraints** area control the behavior of the geometric constraints that are applied to the sketched entities. These radio buttons are discussed next.

Never

This radio button, if selected, will not ignore the geometric constraints that are applied to the sketched entities while moving them.

Always

This radio button, if selected, deletes only the geometric constraints that are associated with the selected entity.

Prompt

This radio button is selected by default and will display the possible solutions for moving the sketched entities.

Figures 4-15 through 4-18 show moving and copying of various sketched entities from one specified point to the other specified point.

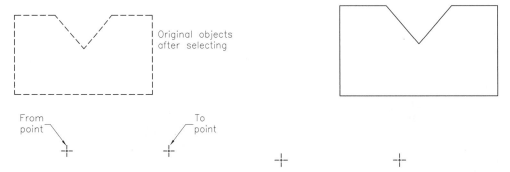

Figure 4-15 *Moving the entities using the sketch points*

Figure 4-16 *Objects after moving*

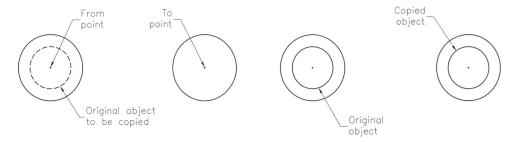

Figure 4-17 *Moving and copying the entities using the center points of circles*

Figure 4-18 *Objects after moving and copying*

Rotating Sketched Entities

Ribbon:	Sketch > Modify > Rotate
Toolbar:	2D Sketch Panel > Rotate

*Figure 4-19 The **Rotate** dialog box*

The **Rotate** tool is used to rotate the selected sketched entities about a specified center point. You can also use this tool to create a copy of the selected entities while rotating them. When you invoke this tool, the **Rotate** dialog box will be displayed, as shown in Figure 4-19.

Options in the Rotate Dialog Box

The options in the **Rotate** dialog box are discussed next.

Select

This button is chosen to select the entities to be rotated. When you invoke the **Rotate** tool, the **Rotate** dialog box will be displayed and the **Select** button will be automatically chosen. You can use any object selection technique to select one or more objects.

Center Point Area

The **Select** button in the **Center Point** area helps you to specify a center point for rotation. The **Precise Input** check box, if selected, allows you to input the coordinates for the center point of rotation.

Angle

This edit box is used to define the value of the angle through which the selected entities will be rotated. You can enter the value in this edit box or choose the arrow on the right of this edit box to specify the predefined angle values. Remember that a positive angle will rotate the selected entities in the counterclockwise direction and a negative angle will rotate the selected entities in the clockwise direction.

Copy

This check box is selected to create a copy of the selected entities as they are rotated. If this check box is selected, a copy of the selected entities will be created and placed at the angle that you have specified in the **Angle** edit box. The original entities will be intact at their original location.

Optimize for Single Selection

If this check box is selected, then as soon as you select a geometry, the **Select** button of the **Center Point** area will be activated automatically. But if you clear this check box, you can select multiple geometries before choosing the **Select** button from the **Center Point** area.

Autodesk Inventor allows you to control the dimensional and geometrical constraints that are applied to the sketched entities while rotating them. These options are available when you choose the **>>** button at the lower right corner of the **Rotate** dialog box. These options are the same as discussed in the previous section on moving the sketched entities. Figure 4-20 shows the rotation of the selected entities at various angles.

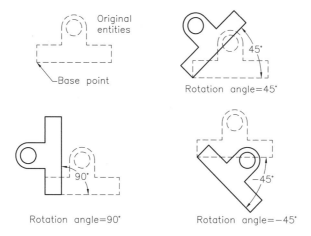

Figure 4-20 *Rotating the entities at various angles*

 Tip. *You can also create a copy of the sketched entities using the shortcut menu. Select the sketched entities and right-click to display a shortcut menu. In this menu, choose* **Copy**. *Again, right-click to display a shortcut menu and choose* **Paste** *to paste the selected entities, thus creating a copy of the selected entities.*

CREATING PATTERNS

Generally, in the mechanical industry, you come across various designs that consist of multiple copies of a sketched feature arranged in a particular fashion. For example, it can be multiple grooves around an imaginary circle. It can also be along the edges of an imaginary rectangle, such as the grooves in the pedestal bearing. Drawing the sketches for such features again and again is a very tedious and time-consuming process. To avoid this lengthy process, Autodesk Inventor provides you with an option of creating patterns of the sketched entities during the sketching stage itself. The patterns are defined as the sequential arrangement of the copies of the selected entities. You can create the patterns in a rectangular fashion or a circular fashion. Both these types of patterns are discussed next.

Creating Rectangular Patterns

Ribbon:	Sketch > Pattern > Rectangular Pattern
Toolbar:	2D Sketch Panel > Rectangular Pattern

 Rectangular patterns are the patterns that arrange the copies of the selected entities in rows and columns. When you invoke this tool, the **Rectangular Pattern** dialog box will be displayed, as shown in Figure 4-21. The options in this dialog box are discussed next.

Geometry

This button is chosen by default and is used to select the entities to be patterned. You can select one or more entities to be patterned using any object selection technique.

Direction 1 Area

This area provides the option for defining the first direction of pattern creation, the number of copies to be created in this direction, and the spacing between the entities. These options are discussed next.

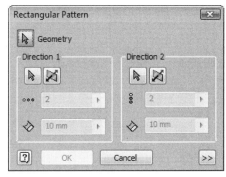

Figure 4-21 *The **Rectangular Pattern** dialog box*

Direction

This is the button with an arrow and is chosen to select the first direction of the rectangular pattern. The other options in the **Direction 1** area will be available only after you define the first direction of the pattern creation. The direction can be defined by selecting a line segment, which can be at any angle. The resultant pattern will also be created at an angle, if the line selected to specify the direction is at an angle. As you define the first direction, you can preview the pattern created using the current values in the drawing window. The pattern in the preview will be modified dynamically on changing the values in this dialog box.

Flip

This button is available on the right of the **Direction** button and is chosen to reverse the first direction of the pattern creation. When you define the first direction using the **Direction** button, an arrow appears on the sketch. This arrow displays the direction in which the items of the pattern will be created. If you choose this button, the direction will be reversed and the arrow will point in the opposite direction.

Count

This edit box is used to specify the number of items in the pattern along the first direction. Remember that this value includes the original selected item. On increasing the value in this edit box, you can dynamically preview the increased items in the pattern in the drawing window. You can also select a predefined number of items by choosing the arrow on the right of this edit box. However, if you are using this tool for the first time in the current session of Autodesk Inventor, this arrow will not provide any value.

Spacing

This edit box is used to define the distance between the individual items of the pattern in the first direction. You can enter a value or choose the arrow on the right of this edit box to use the **Measure** or **Show Dimension** options to define this value. The **Measure** option allows you to select a line segment, the length of which will specify the distance between the individual items. The **Show Dimension** option allows you to use an existing dimension to specify the distance between the individual items of the pattern. The selected dimension will automatically appear in the edit box. You need to delete the existing value in this edit box to use the measured value.

Direction 2 Area

This area provides the option for defining the second direction of the pattern creation, the number of copies to be created in this direction, and the spacing between the entities. All these options are discussed next.

Direction

This button is chosen to select the second direction for arranging the items of the rectangular pattern.

Flip

This button is available on the right of the **Direction** button and is chosen to reverse the second direction of pattern creation.

Count

This edit box is used to specify the number of items in the pattern along the second direction.

Spacing

This edit box is used to define the distance between the individual items of the pattern in the second direction. Similar to the **Spacing** edit box in the **Direction 1** area, you can directly enter a value in this edit box or use the **Measure** or the **Show Dimension** options to define this value.

Figure 4-22 shows various parameters involved in creating a rectangular pattern with three items along direction 1 and four items along direction 2.

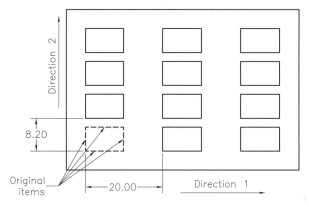

Spacing between items along direction 1=20
Spacing between items along direction 2=8.2

Figure 4-22 Creating a rectangular pattern

More

 This button is provided on the lower right corner of the **Rectangular Pattern** dialog box. When you choose this button, the **Rectangular Pattern** dialog box expands, providing you with more options for creating the pattern, see Figure 4-23. These options are discussed next.

Figure 4-23 *More options in the* ***Rectangular Pattern*** *dialog box*

Suppress

This button is chosen to suppress the selected item from the pattern. When you select any item of the pattern using this button, it will change into dashed lines. The items that are suppressed will be displayed on the screen, but will not participate in the feature creation when you finish the sketch. You can unsuppress these items later, if required.

Note
The process of editing the sketches of features will be discussed in the later chapters.

Associative

This check box is selected so that all items of the pattern are associated with each other. All the items of the associative pattern are automatically updated, if any one of the entity is modified. For example, if you modify the dimension of any of the items of the pattern, the dimensions of all the other items will also be modified. However, if you clear this check box before creating the pattern, all the items will be individual entities and you can modify them individually.

Fitted

This option works in combination with the **Spacing** option in the **Direction 1** and **Direction 2** areas. If you select this option, the specified number of items will be created in the distances specified in the **Spacing** edit boxes in the **Direction 1** and **Direction 2** areas. Figure 4-24 shows the pattern created by clearing this check box (spacing is incremental) and Figure 4-25 shows the pattern created by selecting this check box (included spacing between all the items).

Creating Circular Patterns

Ribbon:	Sketch > Pattern > Circular Pattern
Toolbar:	2D Sketch Panel > Circular Pattern

Circular patterns are the patterns created around the circumference of an imaginary circle. To create the circular pattern, you will have to define the center of that imaginary circle. When you invoke this tool, the **Circular Pattern** dialog box will be displayed, as shown in Figure 4-26. The options provided in this dialog box are discussed next.

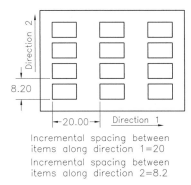

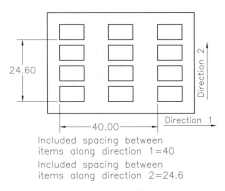

*Figure 4-24 Pattern created with the **Fitted** check box cleared*

*Figure 4-25 Pattern created with the **Fitted** check box selected*

Geometry

This button is chosen to select the entities to be patterned. As you select the individual entities, they turn blue, indicating that they are selected.

Axis

This is the button with an arrow and is provided on the right of the **Geometry** button. This button is chosen to select the center of the imaginary circle around which the circular pattern will be created. The points that can

*Figure 4-26 The **Circular Pattern** dialog box*

be used to define the center of the pattern creation are the endpoints of lines, splines, and arcs, center points of arcs, circles, and ellipses, and the points/hole centers. Most of the options in the **Circular Pattern** dialog box are enabled only after you select the axis of rotation. You can dynamically preview the pattern using the current values. If you modify the other values in this dialog box, the preview of the pattern will also be modified.

Tip. *If you select an arc or a circle to define the axis of the circular pattern, its center will be automatically selected as the center of the circular pattern. However, this is not possible in case of an ellipse. You cannot select an ellipse to define the center of the circular pattern. In such cases, you will have to select the center of ellipse.*

Flip

This button provided on the right of the **Axis** button and when chosen, reverses the direction of pattern creation. By default, the circular pattern will be created in the counterclockwise direction. If you choose this button, the circular pattern will be created in the clockwise direction.

Tip. *If the circular pattern is created through 360-degree, you cannot notice the difference in the change of the direction of the pattern creation from counterclockwise to clockwise. However, if the pattern is created through an angle less than 360-degree, you will notice this difference.*

Count

This edit box is used to specify the number of items in the circular pattern. You can enter a value in this edit box or choose the arrow provided on the right of this dialog box for using the predefined values or for using the **Measure** or **Show Dimension** options. These options are the same as those discussed in the rectangular pattern.

Angle

This edit box is used to define the angle for creating the circular pattern. You can directly enter an angle in this edit box or use the predefined values by choosing the arrow on the right of this edit box. You can also use the **Measure** or the **Show Dimension** options to define the angle. Figures 4-27 and 4-28 show the circular patterns created using various angles.

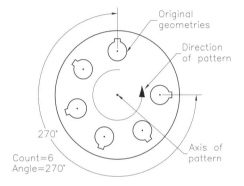

Figure 4-27 *Circular pattern with 6 items and a 270-degree angle*

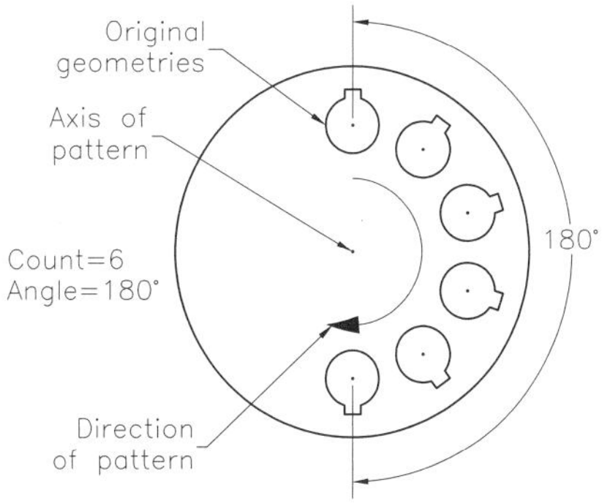

Figure 4-28 *Circular pattern with 6 items and a 180-degree angle*

>> (More)

This button is available on the lower right corner of the **Circular Pattern** dialog box. When you choose this button, the **Circular Pattern** dialog box expands, providing more options, see Figure 4-29. These options are discussed next.

Figure 4-29 *More options in the* **Circular Pattern** *dialog box*

Suppress

This button is chosen to suppress the selected item from the pattern. Similar to the rectangular pattern, when you select any item of the circular pattern, it will change into dashed lines. Although the items that are suppressed will be displayed in the drawing window, they will not participate in the feature creation when you finish the sketch. However, you can unsuppress these items later, if you need them.

Associative

This check box is selected so that all the items of the pattern are associated with each other. All the items of the associative pattern are automatically updated if any entity of the pattern is modified. If you clear this check box before creating the pattern, all items will become individual entities and you can modify them individually.

Fitted

This option works in combination with the **Angle** edit box. If you select this check box, the specified number of items will be created such that the angle specified in the **Angle** edit box defines the included angle between all the items. This check box is selected by default in the **Circular Pattern** dialog box. If you clear this check box, the angle that you specify in the **Angle** edit box will be considered as the incremental angle between each item. Figure 4-30 shows the pattern created by selecting this check box (included angle between all the items) and Figure 4-31 shows the pattern created by clearing this check box (angle is incremental).

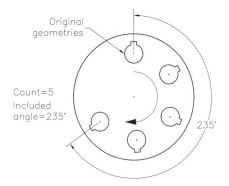
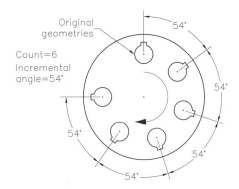

Figure 4-30 *Pattern created with the **Fitted** check box selected*

Figure 4-31 *Pattern created with the **Fitted** check box cleared*

Tip. *If you create a circular pattern through an angle of 360-degree and clear the **Fitted** check box, you will see only one item in the drawing window. This is because the incremental angle between the individual items is 360-degree and all the items will be arranged on top of each other, displaying only one copy.*

WRITING TEXT IN THE SKETCHING ENVIRONMENT

Autodesk Inventor allows you to write text in the sketching environment. The text behaves like other sketched entities and can be converted into features using the modeling tools of Autodesk Inventor. There are two methods to write the text. These methods are discussed next.

Writing Regular Text

Ribbon:	Sketch > Draw > Text drop-down > Text
Toolbar:	2D Sketch Panel > Text drop-down > Text

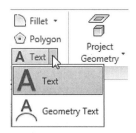

To write text, choose the **Text** tool from the **Draw** panel (see Figure 4-32); you will be prompted to select the location of the text. You can also drag a window to define the text box. Specify a point in the drawing window to start the text or press and hold the left mouse button and drag the mouse to define a window; the **Format Text** dialog box will be displayed, as shown in Figure 4-33. The options in this dialog box are discussed next.

Figure 4-32 *Tools in the **Text** drop-down*

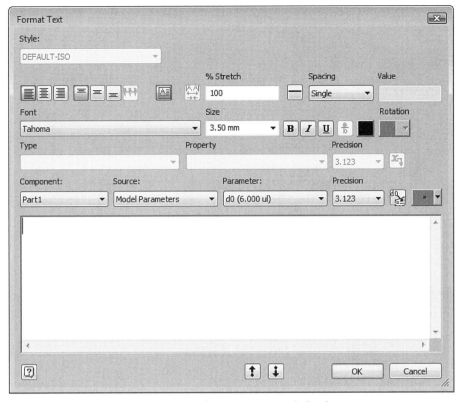

*Figure 4-33 The **Format Text** dialog box*

Text Justification

You can select the justification for writing the text by choosing the buttons in the upper left portion of this dialog box. The justification of a text is defined using a combination of two buttons. By default, the **Left Justification** and **Top Justification** buttons are chosen. As a result, the justification for the text is top left. You can select other justifications by choosing their respective buttons. The **Baseline Justification** button is activated only when you choose the **Single Line Text** button on the left of the **Spacing** drop-down list.

Text Box

If this button is chosen, a construction line box is placed around the text.

Fit Text

This button is activated only when you choose the **Single Line Text** button and is used to fit the text in a single line inside the window that you defined by dragging the mouse.

Stretch

You can define the percentage of text stretching in the **% Stretch** edit box. The default value in this edit box is 100. As a result, there is no stretching of the text. If you enter a value more than 100, the text width will be increased. If you enter a value less than 100, the width of the text will be reduced.

Spacing

You can select an option to define the spacing between the text lines using the **Spacing** drop-down list. If you select the **Multiply** option from this drop-down list, the **Value** edit box will be enabled and you can enter the multiplication factor for the line spacing in this edit box.

Font

The **Font** drop-down list is located below the justification buttons. You can select the font for the text using this drop-down list.

Size

The **Size** edit box is used to specify the height of the text. You can enter the height in this edit box or select the standard values using the down arrow on the right of this edit box.

Text Style

You can define the text style by choosing the **Bold**, **Italic**, and **Underline** buttons on the right of the **Size** drop-down list.

Color

The default color of the text is black. You can change the color of the text by choosing the **Color** button on the right of the **Underline** button. When you choose this button, the **Color** dialog box is displayed. You can specify the color of the text using this dialog box.

Rotation

The **Rotation** flyout is activated only when the **Text Box** button is not chosen. This flyout is used to specify the orientation of the text.

Insert symbol

Autodesk Inventor provides you with some standard symbols that you can insert in the text. To insert the symbols, choose the down arrow on the right of the **Insert symbol** button; the standard symbols in Autodesk Inventor are displayed, as shown in Figure 4-34.

Text Window

You can enter the text in the **Text Window**. This is the area provided in the **Format Text** dialog box. You can also paste the text copied from any other source. The text written in this window will appear on the screen.

Figure 4-34 *Default symbols*

Zoom In/Zoom Out

You can zoom in and out of the text in the **Text Window** by choosing the **Zoom In** and **Zoom Out** buttons provided at the bottom of this dialog box.

Note
*The remaining options in the **Format Text** dialog box are used in the **Drawing** module and therefore, they are not discussed here.*

Writing Text Aligned to a Geometry

Ribbon:	Sketch > Draw > Text drop-down > Geometry Text
Toolbar:	2D Sketch Panel > Text drop-down > Geometry-Text

In Autodesk Inventor 2011, you can write a text aligned to a line, arc, or circle. To do so, choose the arrow on the right of the **Text** tool and invoke the **Geometry Text** tool from the **Draw** panel (see Figure 4-32); you will be prompted to select a geometry. Select the required line, circle, or arc; the **Geometry-Text** dialog box will be displayed, as shown in Figure 4-35. Most of the options in this dialog box are similar to the **Format Text** dialog box. The remaining options are discussed next.

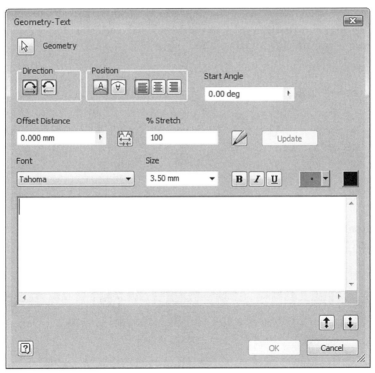

*Figure 4-35 The **Geometry-Text** dialog box*

Geometry
To change the geometry selected by default, choose this button and select the new geometry.

Direction Area
In this area, there are two buttons, **Clockwise** and **Counterclockwise**. These buttons are used to specify the orientation of the text.

Position Area
This area is used to specify the position of the text. Choose the **Outside** button to place the text outside the geometry. Choose the **Inside** button to place the text inside the geometry.

Start Angle
This edit box is used to specify the angle between the left quadrant point of the selected geometry and the starting point of the text.

Offset Distance
This edit box is used to specify the offset distance between the text and the selected geometry.

Figure 4-36 shows the text created using the **Outside** and **Clockwise** options. Figure 4-37 shows the text created using the **Inside** and **Counterclockwise** options. Note that in Figure 4-37, the text is created at an offset from the circle.

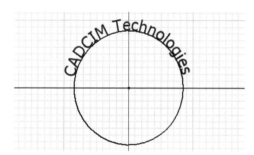

Figure 4-36 *Geometry text created using the* **Outside** *and* **Clockwise** *options*

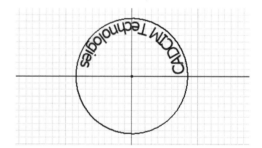

Figure 4-37 *Geometry text created using the* **Inside**, **Offset Distance**, *and* **Counterclockwise** *options*

INSERTING IMAGES AND DOCUMENTS IN SKETCHES

Ribbon:	Sketch > Insert > Insert Image
Toolbar:	2D Sketch Panel > Insert Image

The **Insert Image** tool allows you to insert the external images such as JPG, BMP, PCX, TIFF, TGA, and so on in the sketch. You can also insert Word documents or Excel spreadsheets using this tool. To insert an image, invoke this tool; the **Open** dialog box will be displayed, as shown in Figure 4-38.

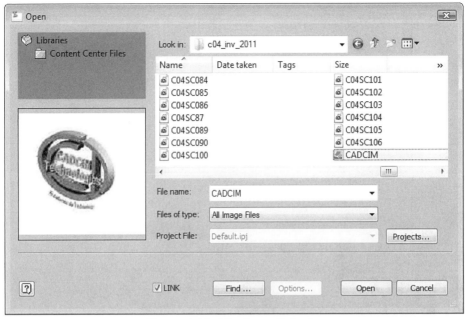

*Figure 4-38 The **Open** dialog box*

Select the image or document using this dialog box and then choose the **Open** button; the dialog box will be closed and you will be prompted to select the sketch point. The point you specify on the screen will be taken as the insertion point for the image. After inserting the image, right-click and choose **Done** from the shortcut menu to exit this tool.

Note
*You may need to modify the drawing display area using the **Zoom All** tool to view the image on the screen.*

Tip. *To modify the size of the image inserted in the sketch, drag it by holding one of its four edges. Depending on the direction in which you drag it, the size will increase or decrease. To rotate the image, hold it at one of the corners and drag. The image will be rotated in the direction in which you drag the cursor. To move the image, press and hold the left mouse button anywhere on the image and drag the cursor.*

EDITING SKETCHED ENTITIES BY DRAGGING

Autodesk Inventor allows you to edit the sketched entities by dragging them. Depending on the type of entity selected and the point of selection, the object will be moved or stretched. For example, if you select a circle at its center and drag, it will be moved. However, if you select the same at a point on its circumference, it will be stretched to a new size. Similarly, if you select a line at its endpoints, it will be stretched and if you select a line at a point other than its endpoints, it will be moved. Therefore, editing the sketched entities by dragging is entirely based on the selection points. The table given next will give you the details of the operation that will be performed when you drag various objects.

Object	Selection point	Operation
Circle	On circumference	Stretch/Shrink
	Center point	Move
Arc	On circumference	Stretch/Shrink
	Center point	Move
Polygon	Any of the edges	Move
	Endpoints	Move
	Center point	Stretch/Shrink
Single line	Any point other than the endpoints	Move
	Endpoints	Stretch/Shrink
Rectangle	All lines selected together	Move
	Any one line or any endpoint	Stretch/Shrink

TOLERANCES

In simple words, tolerance is defined as the permissible variation from the actual value. As it is an allowed variation, you can vary the dimension of the component through the specified value while manufacturing.

Adding Tolerances to the Dimensions in the Sketching Environment

In Autodesk Inventor, tolerances are added to the sketch after dimensioning it. To add tolerance to a dimension, right-click on the dimension and choose **Dimension Properties** from the shortcut menu; the **Dimension Properties** dialog box will be displayed. You can use the options in the **Dimension Settings** tab of this dialog box to add tolerances, see Figure 4-39.

By default, the **Default** option is selected in the **Type** drop-down list of the **Tolerance** area. As a result, no tolerance is added to the dimension.

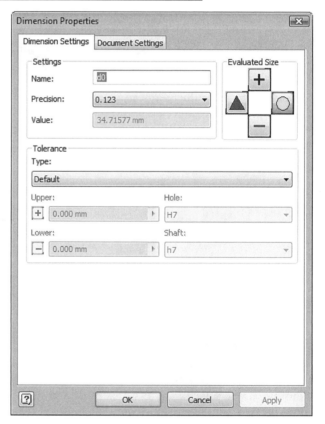

*Figure 4-39 The **Dimension Settings** tab of the **Dimension Properties** dialog box*

To add tolerance, select the required tolerance type from this drop-down list. Next, specify the value of the upper and lower limits in the **Upper** and **Lower** edit boxes. However, note that you can specify the upper and lower limits only if you select the **Deviation**, **Limits-Stacked**, or **Limits-Linear** option from the **Type** drop-down list. If you select any fit tolerance from this drop-down list, you can select the values of the hole fit and the shaft fit from the **Hole** and **Shaft** drop-down lists.

Once you have defined all the tolerance values, choose the **Apply** button in the **Dimension Properties** dialog box. You will notice that the tolerance is applied to the selected dimension. Now, choose **OK** to exit this dialog box. Figure 4-40 shows a sketch with the tolerance applied to the dimensions.

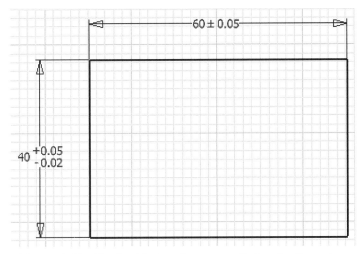

Figure 4-40   Sketch with the tolerance applied to the dimensions

In this figure, the vertical dimension is applied the deviation tolerance type. The upper deviation value for this tolerance is 0.05 mm and the lower deviation value is 0.02 mm. The horizontal dimension in the same figure is applied the symmetric tolerance of 0.05 mm.

CONVERTING THE BASE SKETCH INTO A BASE FEATURE

As mentioned earlier, any 3D design is a combination of various sketched, placed, and work features. The first feature, generally, is a sketched feature. You have already learned to draw the sketches and to dimension them. After you have finished drawing and dimensioning the sketch, choose the **Finish Sketch** button from the **Exit** panel of the **Sketch** tab. On choosing this button, you will exit the sketching environment and enter the **Part** module. You will also notice that the **Sketch** tab is replaced by the **Model** tab. Autodesk Inventor provides you with a number of tools such as **Extrude**, **Revolve**, **Loft**, **Sweep**, and so on to convert these sketches into base features. However, in this chapter, you will learn the use of the **Extrude** and **Revolve** tools for converting the sketch into a base feature. The remaining tools will be discussed in the later chapters.

Note
With this release of Inventor, on exiting from the Sketching environment, the sketch will be displayed in the Isometric view. Now, if you create any feature, you can dynamically preview the result while specifying the required options in the respective dialog boxes.

EXTRUDING THE SKETCH

Ribbon:	Model > Create > Extrude
Toolbar:	Part Features > Extrude

Extrude

The **Extrude** tool is one of the most extensively used tools for creating a design. Extrusion is a process of adding or removing material defined by a sketch, normal to the current sketching plane. If you create the first feature, the options available to you will be for adding the material and not for removing it. This is because there is no existing feature from which you can remove the material. When you invoke this tool, the **Extrude** dialog box will be displayed, as shown in Figure 4-41. In addition to this dialog box, a mini toolbar will be displayed in the drawing window. The mini toolbar is a new user interface that provides you with different options to control the extrusion process. The options in this toolbar will be discussed later. The tabs in the **Extrude** dialog box are discussed next.

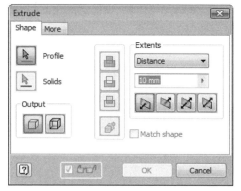

*Figure 4-41 The **Extrude** dialog box*

Shape Tab

The options in this tab are discussed next.

Profile

This button is used to select the sketch to be extruded. If the sketch consists of a single loop, it will be automatically selected. In this case, because the sketch is already selected, the **Profile** button will not be chosen. However, if the sketch consists of more than one loop, this button will be chosen and you will be prompted to select the profile that you want to extrude. As you move the cursor close to one of the loops, it will be highlighted. After you have selected the sketch to be extruded, the preview of the resultant solid will be displayed in the drawing window. Also, the **Profile** selection tag attached to the preview of the solid feature will be displayed in the drawing window. The selection tag will be discussed later in this chapter. Note that if you select any of the inner loops, only that loop will be extruded. Also, after the extrusion of the selected inner loops, the remaining loops will no more be displayed on the screen. But, if you select the profile by specifying a point inside the outer loop but outside the inner loops, the sketch will be extruded such that the resultant solid will have the inner loops subtracted from the outer loop, refer to Figures 4-42 and 4-43.

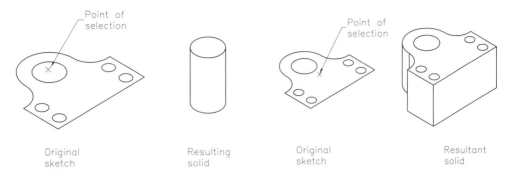

Figure 4-42 *Specifying the selection point inside the inner loop*

Figure 4-43 *Specifying the selection point between the inner and outer loops*

Solids

The **Solid** button is used to select a body in a multi-body environment so that the resultant extruded feature becomes a portion of the body. You can join, cut, or intersect the resultant extruded feature to the selected body. This button will be active only when there are multiple bodies in the drawing window. The procedure to create multiple bodies will be discussed later in Chapter 5.

Output Area

The buttons in the **Output** area are used to specify the type of resulting feature. If you select a closed sketch to extrude, the **Solid** button is chosen automatically. As a result, a solid feature will be created. If you choose the **Surface** button, the resultant feature will be a surface. Remember that the sketches for surface models do not need to be closed loops. If you select an open sketch to extrude, the Surface button is chosen automatically in the **Extrude** dialog box.

Operation Area

This area is provided on the left of the **Extents** area and has four buttons. As the first feature created will be essentially a protrusion feature, no buttons except the **New solid** button will be enabled in this area. However, if a feature already exists in the drawing window and you want to extrude another sketch, the buttons namely **Join**, **Cut**, and **Intersect** will be enabled. These buttons are discussed in Chapter 5.

Extents Area

You can select the method of terminating the extruded feature using the options in the drop-down list available in the **Extents** area or mini toolbar. These options are discussed next.

Distance

By default, the **Distance** option is selected in this drop-down list. This option is used to define the extrusion depth by specifying its numeric value. The value of extrusion can be specified in the **Depth** edit box available below this drop-down list. If this feature termination option is selected, four buttons will be displayed below the **Depth** edit box.

These buttons are used to specify the direction of extrusion. The current direction will be displayed by the first button. You can reverse the direction of feature creation by choosing the second button. The third button is used to extrude the feature equally in both directions of the current sketching plane. This button is also called the **Symmetric** button. For example, if the specified extrusion depth is 20 mm, the resultant feature will have extrusion depth of 10 mm above the current sketch plane and 10 mm below the current sketch plane. With this release of Autodesk Inventor, you can extrude a sketch asymmetrically about the sketching plane. You can do so by using the **Asymmetric** button. After choosing this button, two edit boxes and two drop-down lists will be displayed in the **Extents** area of the **Extrude** dialog box. Also, two arrows will be displayed on the preview of the extruded model. Enter the required extrusion depths in the edit boxes or drag the arrows on the sides of the sketching plane to specify the depths of extrusion. You can interchange the extrusion depths of feature on two sides by choosing the **Flip** button. You can also specify the extrusion depth by using the mini toolbar.

Note

*You can also select **Measure**, **Show Dimensions**, or a predefined distance value by choosing the arrow on the right of the **Depth** edit box to specify the depth of extrusion.*

Tip. *You can dynamically modify the depth of asymmetric extrusion by using the manipulators. These manipulators are displayed as arrows pointing in opposite directions on the preview of the extrusion. Drag the required manipulator arrow to change the extrusion depth dynamically in the corresponding direction.*

To

This is the second option in the **Distance** drop-down list and is used to define the termination of the extruded feature using an extended face, a work plane or planar face. When you select this option, all other options in the **Extents** area are removed and only the **Select surface to end the feature creation** button is displayed. If you select a plane or a face that does not intersect the extruding feature to terminate the extrusion, the **Check to terminate feature on the extended face** check box is displayed. This check box is selected to terminate the feature on the plane or the planar face as if it was extended.

Between

This is the third option in the **Distance** drop-down list. This option uses two planes to define a feature. The first plane defines the plane from which the feature will start and the second plane defines the plane for terminating the feature. When you select this option, all the remaining options in the **Extents** area are replaced by two buttons. The upper button is the **Select surface to start the feature creation** button and is used to define the plane where the feature starts. The lower button is the **Select the surface to end the feature creation** button and is used to define the plane where the feature terminates.

Note

*The methods of creating work planes will be discussed in the later chapters. The **Distance** drop-down list will display more options once you have created the base feature. These options will be discussed in Chapter 5.*

More Tab

The **Taper** option in the **More** tab (Figure 4-44) is discussed next. The remaining options will be discussed in later chapters.

Taper

This edit box is used to define the taper angle for the resulting solid model. Taper angles are generally provided to solid models for their easy withdrawal from the molds. A negative taper angle will force the solid to taper inwards, thus creating a negative taper. A positive taper angle will force the resultant solid to taper outwards, thus creating a positive taper. When you define a taper angle, an arrow will be displayed in the preview of the solid model in the drawing window. Depending on the positive or negative value of the taper angle, this arrow will point inwards or outwards from the sketch. Figures 4-45 and 4-46 show the model created using the negative and positive taper angles. Figure 4-47 shows a model extruded with a positive taper angle using the **Symmetric** option.

Figure 4-44 *The **More** tab of the **Extrude** dialog box*

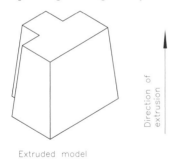

Figure 4-45 *Extruding the model with a negative taper angle*

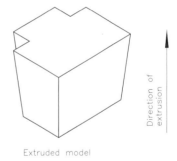

Figure 4-46 *Extruding the model with a positive taper angle*

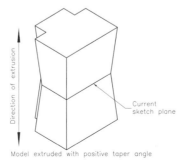

Figure 4-47 *Model extruded with a positive taper angle using the **Symmetric** option*

REVOLVING THE SKETCH

Ribbon:	Model > Create > Revolve
Toolbar:	Part Features > Revolve

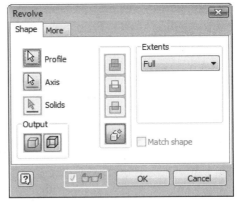

The **Revolve** tool is used to create circular features like shafts, couplings, pulleys, and so on. You can also use this tool for creating cylindrical cut features. A revolved feature is created by revolving the sketch about an axis. You can use a normal line segment, a center line, or a construction line of a sketch as the axis for revolving the sketch. On invoking this tool, the **Revolve** dialog box, as shown in Figure 4-48, and a mini toolbar will be displayed in the drawing window. This mini toolbar provides you with different options to control the revolution of sketches and will be discussed later. The options in the **Revolve** dialog box are discussed next.

Figure 4-48 The Revolve dialog box

Shape Tab

The buttons in this tab are used to select the sketch to be revolved and the axis of revolution. These buttons are discussed next.

Profile

This button is chosen to select the sketch to be revolved. If there is only one loop in the drawing window, the sketch will be automatically selected and the **Profile** button will not be chosen. However, if there are more than one loops, this button will be chosen and you will be prompted to select the profile to be revolved. Also, two selection tags, **Profile** and **Axis**, will be displayed near the profile in the drawing window. The selection tag will be discussed later in this chapter.

Axis

This button is chosen to select the axis for revolving the sketch. As mentioned earlier, you can select a line segment in the sketch as the axis for creating the revolved feature. When you select the axis, the preview of the feature that will be created using the current values will be displayed in the drawing window.

Solids

The **Solids** button is used to select a body in a multi-body environment so that the resultant revolved feature becomes a portion of the body. You can join, cut, or intersect the resultant revolved feature to the selected body. This button will be active only when there are multiple bodies in the graphic window.

Output Area

The buttons in the **Output** area are used to specify the type of output for the revolved feature.

If you choose the **Solid** button, the resulting feature will be a solid. However, if you choose the **Surface** button, the resulting feature will be a surface. The sketch for the surface may or may not be closed. But for a solid feature, the sketch needs to be closed.

Operation Area

This area is provided on the left of the **Extents** area and has four buttons, namely **New solid**, **Join**, **Cut**, and **Intersect**. As the first feature created will essentially be a new revolved feature, no button except the **New solid** button will be available in this area. However, if a feature already exists in the drawing window and you want to extrude another sketch, all four buttons will be available. These buttons are discussed in Chapter 5.

Extents Area

The drop-down list provided under this area is used to specify the method of termination of a revolved feature. You can also specify the termination option by using the mini toolbar. These options are discussed next.

Full

This option is selected to create a feature by revolving the sketch through 360-degree. This is the default option.

Angle

This option is used to terminate the revolved feature at the specified angle. You can specify the angle of revolution by first selecting the **Angle** option and then entering the value in the edit box displayed below this drop-down list. Alternatively, you can specify the angle in the mini toolbar. You can also use a predefined value by choosing the arrow provided on the right side of this edit box. You can also use the **Measure** and **Show Dimensions** options to define the angle of revolution.

When you select the **Angle** option, four buttons will be displayed in this area. These buttons are used to define the direction of rotation. You can also revolve the sketch equally in both directions by choosing the **Symmetric** button. Figures 4-49 and 4-50 show the features created by revolving the sketches through different angles.

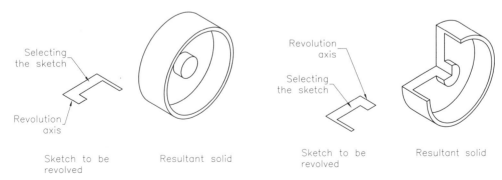

Figure 4-49 *Revolving the sketch through 360-degree*

Figure 4-50 *Revolving the sketch through 270-degree*

With this release of Autodesk Inventor, you can revolve a sketch asymmetrically about the sketching plane. You can do so by using the **Asymmetric** button. After choosing this button, two edit boxes and two drop-down lists will be displayed in the **Extents** area of the **Extrude** dialog box. Also, two arrows will be displayed in the preview of the revolved feature. Enter the values for the revolution angle in the edit boxes or drag the arrows on the sides of the sketching plane to specify the angle on the respective sides. You can interchange the angle values of the feature by choosing the **Flip** button. You can also specify the revolution angle values by using the mini toolbar.

To

This is the third option in the **Extents** drop-down list and is used to define the termination of the revolved feature using an extended face, a work plane, or a planar face. When you select this option, the **Select surface to end the feature creation** button will be displayed. If you select a plane or a face that does not intersect the revolved feature to terminate revolution, the **Check to terminate feature on the extended face** check box will be displayed. This check box is selected to terminate the feature on the plane or the planar face as if it was extended toward it.

Between

This is the fourth option in the **Extents** drop-down list and uses two planes to create a revolved feature. The first plane defines the plane from which the feature will start and the second plane defines the plane for terminating the feature. When you select this option, the **Select surface to start the feature creation** and **Select surface to end the feature creation** buttons are displayed. The **Select surface to start the feature creation** button is used to define the plane where the feature starts and the **Select surface to end the feature creation** button is used to define the plane where the feature terminates.

DIRECT MANIPULATION OF FEATURES BY USING THE MINI TOOLBAR

With this release, Autodesk Inventor has introduced a new interface tool, known as mini toolbar. This toolbar is actually a user interface with combination of selection tags, command options, and manipulators. It allows you to directly manipulate or modify a feature by specifying values or options of the feature creation tools, such as **Extrude**, **Revolve**, **Hole**, **Fillet**, **Chamfer**, as well as different work feature tools. Figures 4-51 and 4-52 show the mini toolbars that are displayed on selecting the sketches for the extrude and revolved operations, respectively. Different components of the mini toolbar, shown in Figure 4-53, are discussed next.

Selection tag

The selection tags appear like callouts and prompt you to select entities for a particular operation. The selection tags prompt you to select the axis, profile, and faces of the model. For example, in case of extrusion, the **Profile** selection tag will be displayed, and in case of revolve feature, the **Profile** and **Axis** selection tags will appear on the graphics window.

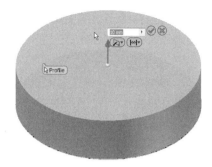

Figure 4-51 Mini toolbar for the extrude feature

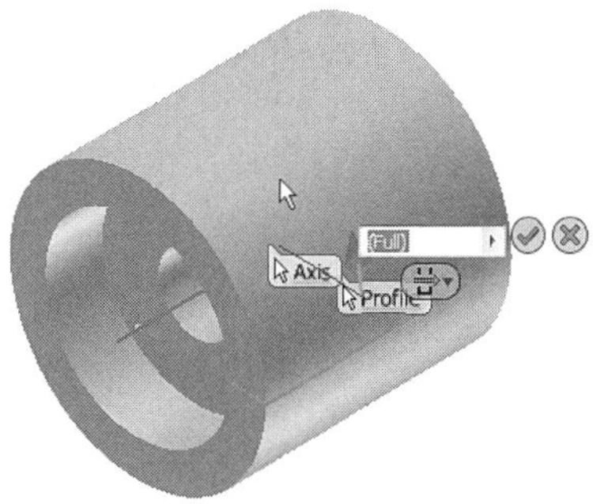

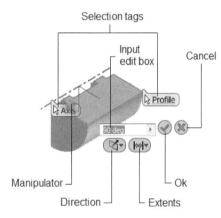

Figure 4-52 Mini toolbar for the revolve feature

Command Options

The options that define the extent, direction, and value for the feature to be created are called command options. For example, in case of revolved feature, the extent options such as **Angle**, **To selected face/plane**, **Between two faces/planes**, and **Full**, and the direction options such as **Direction1**, **Direction2**, **Symmetric**, and **Asymmetric** are available. You can also enter the angle of revolution in the edit box provided in the mini toolbar. After setting these options, choose **OK** to finish the creation of revolve feature; else, choose **Cancel**.

Figure 4-53 Components of the mini toolbar

Manipulators

The manipulators appear in the form of arrows. The manipulators for the **Extrude**, **Revolve**, and **Hole** tools are represented by a straight arrow, a curved arrow, and a sphere, respectively.

With the help of these manipulators, you can specify the extrusion depth of an extruded feature, revolution angle for a revolved feature, and the location of the hole dynamically.

The function of the mini toolbar differs based on the selection of the feature. If you have not invoked any tool and you click on the face of a model, the mini toolbar displays the options that can be used to create or edit sketches and edit the feature, as shown in Figure 4-54. Similarly, if a command is not active and you select an edge, the mini toolbar will provide you with options to create

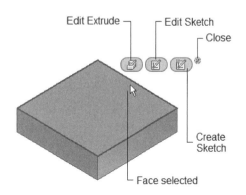

Figure 4-54 Mini toolbar displayed on selecting a face

a fillet or a chamfer feature, as shown in Figure 4-55. Similarly, if you select a sketch without invoking any command, the mini toolbar displays the options to create extruded feature, revolved feature, and hole as well as the option to edit a sketch, as shown in Figure 4-56.

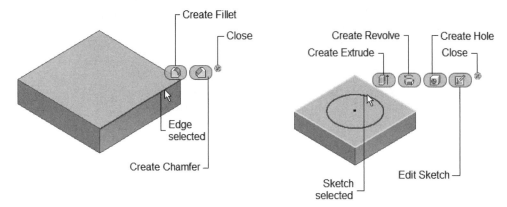

Figure 4-55 *Mini toolbar displayed on selecting an edge*

Figure 4-56 *Mini toolbar displayed on selecting a sketch*

ROTATING THE VIEW OF A MODEL IN 3D SPACE

Autodesk Inventor 2011 provides three different tools to rotate the view of the model. These tools are discussed next.

Rotating the View of a Model Using the Orbit

Ribbon:	View > Navigate > Orbit drop-down > Free Orbit
Toolbar:	2D Sketch Standard > Orbit drop-down > Free Orbit

     Autodesk Inventor provides you with an option to rotate the view of a solid model freely in 3D space. This allows you to visually maneuver the solid model and view it from any direction. To invoke this option, choose the **Free Orbit** tool from the **Navigate** panel of the **View** tab (see Figure 4-57). When you choose this tool, a circle will be displayed with small lines at all four quadrant points and a cross at the center of the circle. The circle is called the rim, the small lines at four quadrants are called handles, and the cross at the center is called the center point. Also, when you invoke this tool, the shape of the cursor changes and the new shape thus created will depend on its current position. For example, if the cursor is inside the rim, it will show two elliptical arrows, suggesting that the model can be freely rotated in any direction. If you move the cursor close to the horizontal handles, the cursor will change to a horizontal elliptical arrow. The methods to rotate the view of a model are discussed next.

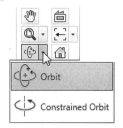

Figure 4-57 *Tools in the **Orbit** drop-down*

Rotating the View of a Model Freely in 3D Space

To freely rotate the view of a model, move the cursor inside the rim; the cursor will be replaced by two elliptical arrows. Click inside the rim and then drag it anywhere in the drawing window. The model will dynamically rotate as you drag the cursor around the drawing window.

Rotating the View of a Model Around the Vertical Axis

 To rotate the view of a model around the vertical axis, move the cursor close to one of the horizontal handles; the cursor will be replaced by a horizontal elliptical arrow. Next, click and drag the cursor to rotate the model along the vertical axis.

Rotating the View of a Model Around the Horizontal Axis

To rotate the view of a model around the vertical axis, move the cursor close to one of the vertical handles; the cursor will be replaced by a vertical elliptical arrow. Now, click and drag the cursor to rotate the model along the horizontal axis.

Rotating the View Around the Axis Normal To the View

 To rotate the view of a model around an axis normal to the current view, move the cursor close to the rim; the cursor will be replaced by a circular arrow. Now, press and hold the left mouse button down and drag the cursor; the model will be rotated around the center point.

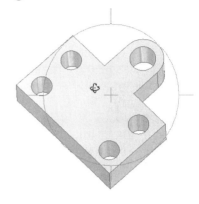

Figure 4-58 shows the view of a model being rotated freely in 3D space. To exit this tool, right-click to display the shortcut menu and choose **Done**.

Figure 4-58 Rotating the view of a model freely in 3D space

 Tip. *You can press and hold the F4 key on the keyboard to invoke the* **Free Orbit** *tool.*

Changing the View Using the ViewCube

| **Ribbon:** | View > Windows > User Interface drop-down > ViewCube |
| **Toolbar:** | 2D Sketch Standard > ViewCube |

Autodesk Inventor 2011 provides you with an option to change the view of a solid model freely in 3D space using the ViewCube. A ViewCube is a 3D navigation tool, which allows you to switch between the standard and isometric views in a single click. ViewCube is a toggle tool and is used to hide or unhide the ViewCube. If you choose this tool, the ViewCube will be displayed at the top right corner of the graphics window. By default, it is in the inactive state, as shown in Figure 4-59. When you move the cursor closer to the ViewCube, it will get activated, as shown in Figure 4-60.

Figure 4-59 Inactive ViewCube

Figure 4-60 Active ViewCube

You can also control the visibility of the ViewCube by using the **Ribbon**. To do so, choose the **User Interface** tool from the **Windows** panel of the **View** tab; a drop-down will be displayed (see Figure 4-61). Select or clear the **ViewCube** check box from this drop-down to display or hide the ViewCube, respectively.

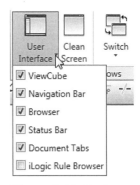

The faces, vertices, and the edges of the ViewCube are called clickable areas. If you place the cursor on any clickable area of the ViewCube, they will be highlighted. Click on the required area to orient the model such that the clicked area and the model become parallel to the screen. If you press and drag the left mouse button over the ViewCube, it will provide a visual feedback of the current viewpoint of the model. When you right-click on the ViewCube, a shortcut menu will be displayed, as shown in Figure 4-62. The options in this shortcut menu are discussed next.

Figure 4-61 *Options in the **User Interface** drop-down*

Go Home
It is used to display the default view of the model. On choosing this option, you can switch over to the home or isometric view of the model.

Orthographic
Choose this option to display the model in the orthographic view.

Perspective
Choose this option to display the model in the perspective view.

Perspective with Ortho Faces
Choose this option to display the model in the orthographic projection when one of the faces of the ViewCube is active.

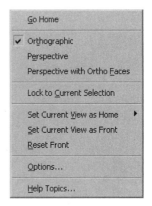

Figure 4-62 *The shortcut menu*

Lock to Current Selection
If you choose this option in a particular view, then that view gets locked and the further manipulation of the view of the object will occur with respect to the locked position.

Set Current View as Home
This option is used to set the current view as the default view. When you move the cursor over the **Set Current View as Home** option, a small flyout will be displayed. The options in this flyout are **Fixed Distance** and **Fit to View**.

Fixed Distance is used to set a Home view, which defines direction of the view as well as extent of the model that fills the view. **Fit to View** is used to set a Home view which defines direction of the view as well as extent of the model always taken as **Zoom All** or view all mode.

Set Current View as Front

This option is used to set the current view as the front view.

Reset Front

This option is used to reset the front view to the default setting.

Options

Choose this option to invoke the **ViewCube Options** dialog box, as shown in Figure 4-63. Alternatively, you can access this dialog box by choosing the **Tools** tab. To do so, choose the **Application Options** tool from the **Options** panel of the **Tools** tab; the **Application Options** dialog box will be displayed. Next, choose the **Display** tab from the **Application Options** dialog box and then choose the **ViewCube** tool; the **ViewCube Options** dialog box will be displayed, refer to Figure 4-63. The options in this dialog box are discussed next.

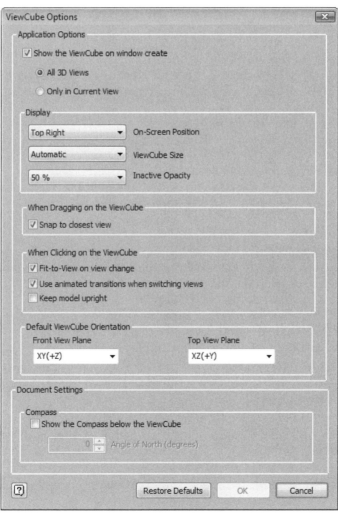

Figure 4-63 The ViewCube Options dialog box

Show the ViewCube on window create

By default, this check box is selected. As a result, the ViewCube will be displayed in the graphics window. Also, two radio buttons, **All 3D Views** and **Only in Current View** will be activated. By default, the **All 3D Views** radio button is selected and is used to display the ViewCube in all views. If you select the **Only in Current View** radio button, the ViewCube will be displayed in the current view only.

Display Area

This area is used to display the on-screen position of the ViewCube, its size, and its inactive opacity. Select the required option from the **On-Screen Position** drop-down list in this area to set the position of ViewCube at any corner of the window such as **Top Right**, **Bottom Right**, **Top Left**, or **Bottom Left**.

Select the required option from the **ViewCube Size** drop-down list; the size of the ViewCube will be set. You can also set the opacity of the ViewCube in the inactive state using the **Inactive Opacity** drop-down list in this area.

When Dragging on the ViewCube Area

If the **Snap to closest view** check box is selected in this area, the view point will snap to one of the fixed views when the model is rotated using the ViewCube.

When Clicking on the ViewCube Area

This area is used for setting the preferences while clicking on the ViewCube.

Default ViewCube Orientation Area

The options in this area are used to set the alignment of the front and top plane of the ViewCube with the model-space plane, when you create a new part or assembly from a template.

Document Settings Area

This area is used to set the preference for the default display of the Compass. If you select the **Show the Compass below the ViewCube** check box, the Compass will be displayed below the ViewCube in the graphics window, as shown in Figure 4-64. The **Angle of North (degrees)** spinner is used to set the angle between the **FRONT** face of the ViewCube and the **N** (North direction) of the Compass.

Figure 4-64 *The ViewCube with Compass*

Navigating the Model

Autodesk Inventor 2011 allows you to navigate the model using different navigating tools such as zoom, pan, track, and so on. Different navigating tools in Autodesk Inventor 2011 are discussed next.

SteeringWheels

Ribbon:	View > Navigate > SteeringWheels drop-down > Full Navigation Wheel
Toolbar:	2D Sketch Standard > SteeringWheels

 To invoke SteeringWheels, choose the **SteeringWheels** tool from the **2D Sketch Standard** toolbar. On choosing this tool, the SteeringWheels will be displayed, as shown in Figure 4-65. You can also invoke the SteeringWheels by using the **Navigate** panel of the **View** tab or by using the **Navigation Bar**. However, by using the **Navigate** panel or **Navigation Bar**, you can invoke different types of SteeringWheels depending upon your requirement. The **SteeringWheels** are the tracking tools that are divided into different wedges. Each wedge represents a single navigation tool such as **PAN**, **ORBIT**, **ZOOM**, **REWIND**, **LOOK**, **CENTER**, **WALK**, and **UP/DOWN**. You can activate any wedge of the SteeringWheels by pressing and holding the cursor over it. The SteeringWheels travels along with the cursor to provide a quick access to common navigation controls. Right-click on the SteeringWheels; a shortcut menu will be displayed. Different types of SteeringWheels are available in this shortcut menu. You can choose any type of SteeringWheels by clicking on it.

Figure 4-65 The SteeringWheels

Previous View

 The **Previous View** tool in the **Navigate** panel of the **View** tab is used to view the previous orientation of the model.

Next View

 The **Next View** tool in the **Navigate** panel of the **View** tab is used to activate the view that was current before you chose the **Previous View** tool. You can also switch to the previous view by pressing the F5 key and to the next view, by holding down the SHIFT key and then pressing the F5 key.

 Note
*The **Pan** and **Zoom All** options are the same as those discussed in Chapter 2.*

CONTROLLING THE DISPLAY OF MODELS

Autodesk Inventor allows you to control the display of the models by setting various display modes and setting the camera type for displaying them. You can also control the display of the shadows of the model. The options for controlling the display of the models are discussed next.

Setting the Visual Styles

Ribbon:	View > Appearance > Visual Style drop-down
Toolbar:	2D Sketch Standard > Visual Style drop-down

Visual style of a model determines the display of edges and face of a model in the graphics window. You can set the visual style for the solid models by using the **Visual**

Style drop-down provided in the **Appearance** panel of the **View** tab (see Figure 4-66). Various visual styles available in this drop-down are discussed next.

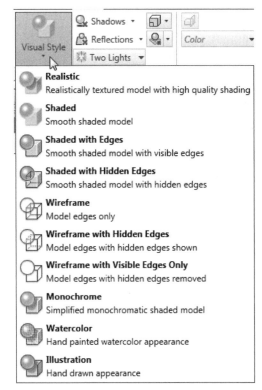

Realistic

The realistic visual style is used to shade the faces of a model with realistic materials. To apply this visual style, choose the **Realistic** tool from the **Appearance** panel. In this style, the visibility of the visible and hidden edges is turned off.

Shaded

This style is used to shade the faces of a model with standard materials and colors. To apply this visual style, choose the **Shaded** tool from the **Appearance** panel. In this style, the visibility of the visible and hidden edges is turned off.

Shaded with Edges

This is the default visual style. In this style, the model appears shaded with all external edges clearly visible. To

*Figure 4-66 Tools in the **Visual Style** drop-down*

apply this visual style, choose the **Shaded with Edges** tool from the **Appearance** panel. In this style, the standard materials and colors are assigned to the model.

Shaded with Hidden Edges

This style is used to shade a model with standard materials and colors keeping all the edges visible. To apply this visual style, choose the **Shaded with Hidden Edges** tool from the **Appearance** panel. In this style, the visibility of both the visible and hidden edges is turned on. The visible edges are displayed as solid lines and the hidden edges are displayed as dashed lines.

Wireframe

This style is used to display a model in wireframe with the shading turned off. To apply this visual style, choose the **Wireframe** tool from the **Appearance** panel. In this style, the visibility of both the visible and hidden edges is turned on and these edges are displayed as solid lines.

Wireframe with Hidden Edges

This style is used to display a model in wireframe with the shading turned off. To apply this visual style, choose the **Wireframe with Hidden Edges** tool from the **Appearance** panel. In this style, the visibility of the visible and hidden edges is turned on. In this style, all visible edges are displayed as solid lines, and all the hidden edges are displayed as dashed lines.

Wireframe with Visible Edges Only

 This style is used to display a model in wireframe with the shading turned off. To apply this visual style, choose the **Wireframe Visible Edges Only** tool from the **Appearance** panel. In this style, the visibility of visible edges is turned on, and the visibility of hidden edges is turned off.

Monochrome

 This style is used to give the model a simple monochromatic appearance. To apply this visual style, choose the **Monochromatic** tool from the **Appearance** panel. In this style, the visibility of both the visible and hidden edges is turned off.

Watercolor

 This style is used to give the visible components of a model a watercolor appearance. To apply this visual style, choose the **Watercolor** tool from the **Appearance** panel. In this style, the model appears to be hand-painted with water color. Also, the visibility of both the visible and hidden edges is turned off.

Illustration

 This style is used to give the visible components of the model a hand drawn appearance. To apply this visual style, choose the **Illustration** tool from the **Appearance** panel. Also, the visibility of the visible and hidden edges is turned off in this style.

Setting the Shadow Options

Ribbon:	View > Appearance > Shadows drop-down

In Autodesk Inventor, you can make your design look realistic by casting the shadows of objects. By default, the shadow option is turned off. You can cast three types of shadows. You can use the **Shadows** drop-down in the **Appearance** panel to cast different types of shadows (see Figure 4-67). The three types of shadows are discussed next.

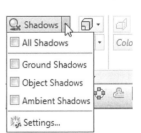

*Figure 4-67 Options in the **Shadows** drop-down*

Ground Shadow

A ground shadow is a flat shadow appearing below the model. To cast a flat shadow, select the **Ground Shadow** check box from the **Shadows** drop-down in the **Appearance** panel; the flat shadow of the model will appear below it, as shown in Figure 4-68.

Object Shadows

The object shadows, also known as self shadows, are those that cast on the object itself. These shadows depend on the shape of the object and the lighting arrangement surrounding it. To cast an object shadow, select the **Object Shadows** check box from the **Shadows** drop-down in the **Appearance** panel; the object shadow of the model will be casted, as shown in Figure 4-69.

Figure 4-68 *Model with the ground shadow*   ***Figure 4-69*** *Model with the object shadows*

Ambient Shadows

The ambient shadows are those that are cast on the transition regions of the model such as cavities, grooves, and corners. These shadows are significant for enhancing the visual display of these transition regions. To cast the ambient shadow, select the **Ambient Shadows** check box from the **Shadows** drop-down in the **Appearance** panel.

All Shadows

You can have an object with all above mentioned shadows cast on it. To do so, you need to select the **All Shadows** check box from the **Shadows** drop-down in the **Appearance** panel.

 Note
You can cast shadows only below the model and not on any other plane. The distance of the shadow from the model gets modified as you zoom the model.

Setting the Camera Type

By default, the models are displayed in the orthographic camera type. You can change the camera type from the default orthographic to the perspective camera. This is done by choosing the **Perspective** tool from the **Appearance** panel of the **View** tab. On doing so, the model will be displayed in the perspective camera. Figure 4-70 shows the view of the model when the perspective camera is on.

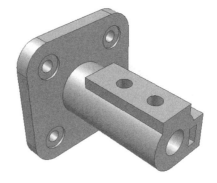

Figure 4-70 *Displaying a model in the perspective camera*

TUTORIALS

Tutorial 1

In this tutorial, you will open the sketch drawn in Tutorial 1 of Chapter 3. You will then convert this sketch into a solid model by extruding it to a distance of 20 mm. After creating the solid model, you will rotate its view in 3D space by using the **SteeringWheels** tool.

(Expected time: 30 min)

The following steps are required to complete this tutorial:

a. Save the sketch from the *c03* folder to the *c04* folder with another name.
b. Open the sketch from the *c04* folder and extrude it to a distance of 20 mm using the **Extrude** tool, refer to Figure 4-73.
c. Change the material of the model by using the **Color Override** drop-down list from the **Quick Access Toolbar**.
d. Rotate the model in 3D space using the **SteeringWheels** tool, refer to Figure 4-74.

Opening the Sketch Drawn in Chapter 3

1. Start Autodesk Inventor by double-clicking on its shortcut icon on the desktop of your computer or by using the **Start** menu. Next, choose the **Open** tool from the **Launch** panel of the **Get Started** tab; the **Open** dialog box is displayed.

2. Open the *c03* folder from the location *C:\Inventor_2011* and then open the *Tutorial1.ipt* file.

When you open an existing part drawing, by default, you get into the **Part** module even if the drawing is just a sketch. Also, the sketch is displayed in the isometric view, see Figure 4-71.

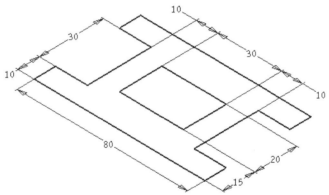

Figure 4-71 *Sketch displayed in the isometric view when opened*

Saving the Sketch with Another Name

After opening the sketch, you need to first save it with another name so that the original sketch drawn in Chapter 3 is not modified. Remember that in Autodesk Inventor, when you save a file with another name, a new file is created and saved, but the original file remains open. You need to close the original file and open the new file using the **Open** dialog box.

1. Choose **Save As > Save Copy As** from the **Application Menu**; the **Save Copy As** dialog box is displayed.

2. Browse to the location *C:\Inventor_2011\c04* from the **Save in** drop-down list.

3. Save the sketch with the name *Tutorial1.ipt*.

> **Tip**. *If you have not created a folder with the name c04, you can create it by using the **Save Copy As** dialog box. To do so, select the **Inventor_2011** folder from the **Save in** drop-down list. Next, choose the **Create New Folder** button and specify c04 as the name of the folder.*

4. Now, choose **Close > Close** from the **Application Menu** to close this file. If you are prompted to specify whether or not you want to save the changes in this file, choose **No**.

5. Choose the **Open** tool from the **Quick Access Toolbar** to display the **Open** dialog box. Open the *Tutorial1.ipt* file from the location *C:\Inventor_2011\c04*.

Extruding the Sketch

As mentioned earlier, when you open an existing part file, you are, by default, in the part modeling environment and the sketch is displayed in the isometric view. Sometimes when you open an existing sketch, the dimensions of the sketch are not displayed in the current view. In such a case, use the **Zoom All** tool to increase the drawing display area so that all dimensions are displayed in the current view. As you are in the part modeling environment, all tools of this module are available in the **Model** tab.

1. Choose the **Extrude** tool from the **Create** panel of the **Model** tab to invoke the **Extrude** dialog box.

As the sketch consists of two loops, the sketch is not automatically selected. Therefore, the **Profile** button in the **Shape** tab is chosen and you are prompted to select the profile to be extruded. Also, the **Profile** selection tag is displayed in the mini toolbar in the graphics window.

2. Move the cursor outside the inner loop but inside the outer loop; the profile will be highlighted, as shown in Figure 4-72.

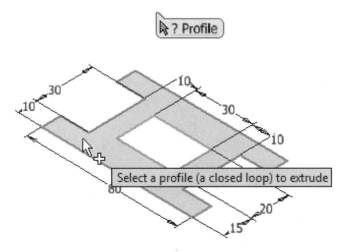

Figure 4-72 Selecting the profile to be extruded

As evident from Figure 4-72, the area inside the inner loop is not highlighted. This shows that the selected profile, when extruded, will have a cavity at the center. This cavity is defined by the inner loop.

3. Click inside the highlighted area as shown in Figure 4-72; the preview of the extruded model along with the mini toolbar interface is displayed in the drawing window.

4. Enter **20** in the **Depth** edit box available in the **Extents** area. Alternatively, enter **20** in the input edit box of the mini toolbar. You can also drag the extrude manipulator to specify the extrusion depth.

5. Choose **OK** from the dialog box to create the model and exit the **Extrude** tool. Alternatively, choose **OK** from the mini toolbar. The extruded model is shown in Figure 4-73.

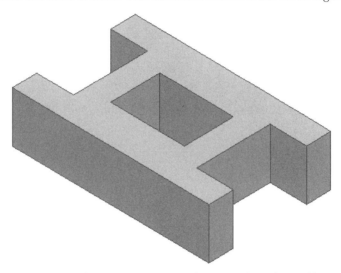

Figure 4-73 *The model created on extruding the profile*

Changing the Material of the Model

After extruding the sketch, you need to change the material of the extruded part.

1. Click on the down arrow on the right of the **Color Override** option in the **Quick Access Toolbar**; a drop-down list is displayed.

2. Select the **Metal-Brass** option from this drop-down list; the material of the extruded model changes to metallic brass. Also, the color of the model gets changed in the graphics window.

Rotating the View of the Model in 3D Space

1. Choose the **Full Navigation Wheel** tool from the **Navigation Bar** or the **Navigate** panel of the **View** tab; the SteeringWheel is attached to the cursor.

2. Move the cursor over the model and then move it inside the **Zoom** wedge, as shown in Figure 4-74.

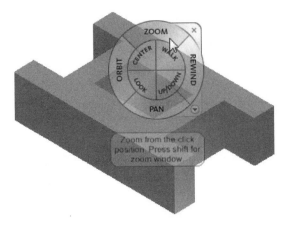

Figure 4-74 *Zooming the model freely in 3D space*

3. Press and hold the left mouse button; the **Zoom** tool is activated. Next, drag the cursor front and back to zoom the model in or out.

4. Move the cursor inside the **ORBIT** wedge and press and hold the left mouse button; the **Orbit** tool is activated. Drag the cursor; the model rotates about the **PIVOT** point.

5. Move the cursor inside the **PAN** wedge and press and hold the left mouse button; the **Pan** tool is activated. Drag the cursor; the model moves along the cursor.

6. Move the cursor inside the **REWIND** wedge and press and hold the left mouse button; the previous views are displayed in small boxes in a row. Drag the cursor along the row and select a view.

7. Move the cursor over the model and then move it inside the **CENTER** wedge. Next, press and hold the left mouse button on the **CENTER** wedge; a pivot will be attached to the model. Release the left mouse button; the pivot is moved to the center of the drawing area.

8. Click on the cross mark at the top right corner of the SteeringWheels to exit this tool. Alternatively, right-click to display the shortcut menu and choose **Close Wheel** from the shortcut menu to exit this tool.

9. Again, right-click and choose **Home View** from the shortcut menu; the current view is changed to the isometric view.

Saving the Model

1. Choose **Save > Save** from the **Application Menu** to save the changes made to the model. As the file is already saved once, the **Save As** dialog box is not displayed.

2. Choose **Close > Close** from the **Application Menu** to close this file.

Tutorial 2

In this tutorial, you will open the sketch drawn in Tutorial 2 of Chapter 3 and then convert it into a fully revolved model. Next, you will change the projection type to perspective and then view the model.   **(Expected time: 30 min)**

The following steps are required to complete this tutorial:

a. Open the sketch from the *c03* folder and save it in the *c04* folder.
b. Open the sketch from the *c04* folder and revolve it through an angle of 360-degree by using the **Revolve** tool.
c. Change the projection type and view the model.

Opening the Sketch Drawn in Chapter 3

1. Choose **Open** from the **Application Menu** to display the **Open** dialog box.

2. Using the **Open** dialog box, open the *Tutorial2.ipt* file from the location *C:\Inventor_2011\c03*; the sketch is displayed in the **Part** module in the isometric view.

Saving the Sketch with another Name

1. Choose **Save As > Save Copy As** from the **Application Menu**; the **Save Copy As** dialog box is displayed.

2. Browse to the location *C:\Inventor_2011\c04* and save the sketch with the name *Tutorial2*.

    As the current file is the file taken from *c03* folder, you need to close it and then open the file that has been saved as *Tutorial2* in *c04* folder.

3. Choose **Close > Close** from the **Application Menu** to close this file. Now, choose the **Open** tool from the **Quick Access Toolbar** to display the **Open** dialog box and open the file *Tutorial2.ipt* from the location *C:\Inventor_2011\c04*.

    The dimensions of the sketch may not be displayed completely inside the current drawing display area. Therefore, you can increase the drawing display area using the **Zoom All** and **Pan** tools to fit the dimensions in the current view, see Figure 4-75.

Revolving the Sketch

As mentioned earlier, you need an axis of revolution to revolve a profile. This axis can be a sketched line segment.

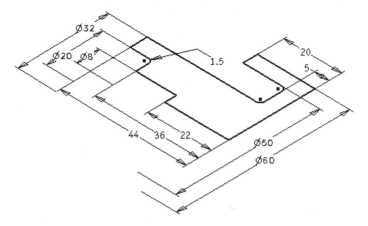

Figure 4-75 Sketch in the isometric view after zooming and panning

1. Choose the **Revolve** tool from the **Create** panel to display the **Revolve** dialog box. Since the sketch has just one loop, therefore it is automatically selected and highlighted. The **Axis** button is activated and you are prompted to select the axis. The **Profile** and **Axis** selection tags are also displayed in the graphics window.

2. Select the bottom horizontal line that measures 22 mm as the axis of revolution.

    When you move the cursor close to this line, it is highlighted in red. On selecting this line, the preview of the revolved model is displayed in the drawing window. Also, the mini toolbar with the **Full** option selected in the **Extents** drop-down list is displayed in the drawing window.

3. Accept the default values and choose **OK** from the mini toolbar to complete the process of creating the revolved model.

Changing the View of the Model

The current view, in which the model is displayed, does not show the model properly. Therefore, you will have to change the view of the model.

1. In case the ViewCube is hidden, choose the **ViewCube** tool from the **2D Sketch Standard** toolbar; the ViewCube is displayed in the drawing window. Alternatively, select the **ViewCube** check box from the **User Interface** drop-down in the **Windows** panel of the **View** tab.

2. To view the component in different direction, select the corner of the ViewCube, as shown in Figure 4-76.

3. Press and hold the left mouse button on the face of the ViewCube and drag the cursor; as the cursor moves, the model reorients to give you a better view of the model.

4. Choose the **Zoom All** tool from the **Navigate** panel of the **View** tab or from the **Navigation Bar** to modify the drawing display.

Changing the Camera Type

By default, the orthographic camera type is used to display the model. In this tutorial, you need to display the model in perspective camera or view. In this type of viewing, the lines in the model, when extended, meet at three points.

1. Choose the **Perspective** tool from the **Appearance** panel in the **View** tab; the perspective view of the model is displayed, see Figure 4-77.

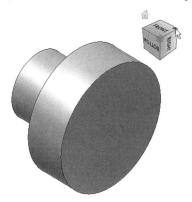

Figure 4-76 Selecting the corner of the ViewCube   *Figure 4-77 Model displayed using the perspective projection*

Saving the Model

1. Choose **Save > Save** from the **Application Menu** to save the model.

2. Now, choose **Close > Close** from the **Application Menu** to close this file.

Tutorial 3

In this tutorial, you will create the model shown in Figure 4-78. Its dimensions are shown in Figure 4-79. The extrusion height for the model is 10 mm. After extruding it, you will set the option to cast the X-ray ground shadow.   **(Expected time: 45 min)**

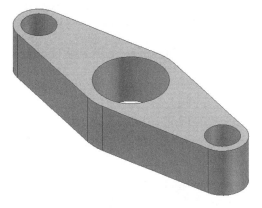

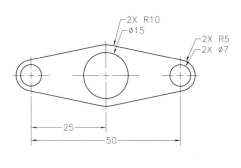

Figure 4-78 *Model for Tutorial 3*   **Figure 4-79** *Dimensions of the model*

The following steps are required to complete this tutorial:

a. Start a new metric standard part file. Draw the sketch of the outer loop and add constraints to it.
b. Draw the inner circles and add the required constraints. Dimension the complete sketch, refer to Figure 4-83.
c. Extrude the sketch to a distance of 10 mm using the **Extrude** tool, refer to Figure 4-84.
d. Cast the object and ambient shadows on the final model, refer to Figure 4-85.

Starting a New Part File

If you have installed Autodesk Inventor with millimeter as the unit of measurement, you can directly start a new metric standard part file, thus avoiding the use of the **New File** dialog box for opening a new part file.

1. Click on the down arrow on the right of the **New** tool in the **Quick Access Toolbar**; a flyout is displayed.

2. Choose the **Part** option from this flyout to start a new metric part file. If Autodesk Inventor was not installed with millimeter as the measurement unit, you need to choose the **Metric** tab of the **New File** dialog box to start the new metric standard part file.

Note
*You can change the units used in Inventor file by using the **Document Settings** dialog box. To invoke this dialog box, choose the **Document Settings** tool from the **Options** panel. Next, choose the **Units** tab in the **Document Settings** dialog box to display various options related to units. Select the required unit from the **Length** drop-down list in the **Units** area of this dialog box. Next, choose **Apply** and then **Close** to exit the dialog box.*

Creating the Sketch of the Model

As shown in Figure 4-79, the sketch is a combination of an outer loop and three circles. First, you will create the outer loop. This outer loop will be created by drawing three circles, two at the ends and one at the center, and then connecting the middle circle with the other two circles through tangent lines. Finally, you will trim the unwanted portions of the circles.

1. Draw the sketch, which is a combination of three circles and tangent lines. Add the **Tangent** constraint to the lines wherever it is missing. Also, add the **Equal** constraint to all four lines, and the circles on the left and the right sides. Finally, add the **Horizontal** constraint to the center points of the circles. The sketch, after drawing and adding constraints, should look similar to the one shown in Figure 4-80.

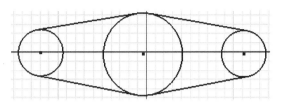

Figure 4-80 Sketch after drawing and adding constraints

Next, you need to remove the unwanted portions of the circles using the **Trim** tool.

2. Choose the **Trim** tool from the **Modify** panel of the **Sketch** tab; you are prompted to select the portion of the curves to be trimmed.

3. Move the cursor close to the right half of the left circle.

   As you move the cursor close to the circle, the color of the circle turns red and it appears as dashed on the right side.

4. Specify a point on the right half of the left circle; the right half of this circle is trimmed. Similarly, select portions of the other circles to trim, as shown in Figure 4-81.

5. Next, draw three circles concentric to the three trimmed arcs. Add the **Equal** constraint between the left and right circles. The sketch after drawing the circles and applying the **Equal** constraint to them should look similar to the one shown in Figure 4-82.

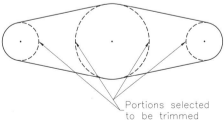

Figure 4-81 Selecting the portions to be trimmed

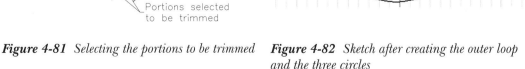

Figure 4-82 Sketch after creating the outer loop and the three circles

Dimensioning the Sketch

1. Dimension the sketch as required. The sketch, after it has been dimensioned, should look similar to the one shown in Figure 4-83.

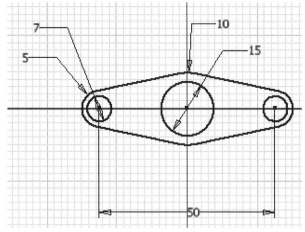

Figure 4-83 Sketch after adding dimensions

Extruding the Sketch

The sketch consists of four loops: the outer loop and the three circles. When you extrude this sketch, the three circles will be automatically subtracted from the outer loop. As a result, you will get the required model. However, this is possible only if the point specified for selecting the profile is inside the outer loop but outside all three circles.

1. Choose the **Finish Sketch** button from the **Exit** panel of the **Sketch** tab to exit the sketching environment. You will notice that the current view is changed to the Home (Isometric) view.

2. Choose the **Extrude** tool from the **Create** panel of the **Model** tab; the **Extrude** dialog box is invoked. As the sketch consists of more than one loop, the **Profile** button is chosen in the **Shape** tab of the **Extrude** dialog box and you are prompted to select the profile to be extruded. Also, the **Profile** selection tag is displayed in the drawing window.
Extrude

3. Move the cursor to a point anywhere inside the outer loop but outside all three circles; the profile is selected and highlighted. Notice that the area inside any of these circles is not shaded. This shows that the area inside these circles will not be extruded. This is also one of the methods to cross check whether the profile selected is the one you need to extrude or not.

4. Click inside the shaded profile; the preview of the model is displayed in the drawing window. Also, the mini toolbar is displayed in the drawing window.

5. Accept the default values and choose **OK** from the mini toolbar to extrude the profile to a depth of 10 mm.

You may need to change the camera type from perspective to orthographic if you are in that session of Autodesk Inventor in which you changed the camera type to perspective in Tutorial 2. To change the camera type, choose the **Orthographic** button from the **Appearance** panel of the **View** tab. The final model is shown in Figure 4-84.

Casting the Object Shadows and Ambient Shadow

Next, you need to cast the object shadow and ambient shadow of the model. You can cast these shadows using the options in the **Shadows** drop-down in the **Appearance** panel.

1. Click on the down arrow on right of **Shadows** in the **Appearance** panel; a drop-down is displayed.

2. Select the **Object Shadows** and **Ambient Shadows** check boxes from the drop-down; the object and ambient shadows are cast on the model, as shown in Figure 4-85.

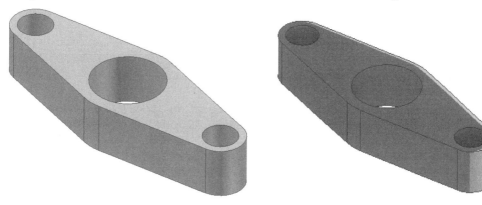

Figure 4-84 Final model for Tutorial 3   *Figure 4-85 Object and ambient shadows cast on the model*

Saving the Model

1. Choose the **Save** tool from the **Quick Access Toolbar**; the **Save As** dialog box is displayed.

2. Save the model with the name *Tutorial3* at the location given below:

   C:\Inventor_2011\c04

3. Choose **Close > Close** from the **Application Menu** to close the file.

Tutorial 4

In this tutorial, you will extrude the text and then change the visual style of the extruded text, as shown in Figure 4-86. The font size of the text is 5 mm and the height of extrusion of the text is 2.5 mm. **(Expected time: 15 min)**

Figure 4-86 Extruded text with the hand drawn appearance

The following steps are required to complete this tutorial:

a.   Start a new metric standard part file and write the text in the sketching environment.
b.   Extrude the text to a distance of 2.5 mm using the **Extrude** tool.
c.   Change the visual style of the extruded text.

Starting a New File and Writing the Text

1.   Start a new metric standard part file using the **Metric** tab of the **New File** dialog box.
      Also, ensure that the display of the shadow is turned off.

2.   Choose the **Text** tool from the **Draw** panel of the **Sketch** tab; you are prompted
      to click on the location of the text.

3.   Specify a point anywhere in the drawing window; the **Format Text** dialog box is
      displayed.

4.   Select the **Arial** font from the **Font** drop-down list and then set the font height to 5 mm
      in the **Size** edit box.

5.   Type the text **Autodesk Inventor** in the **Text Window** in two lines. Choose **OK** to exit the
      dialog box; the typed text is displayed in the drawing window, as shown in Figure 4-87.

Extruding the Text

Next, you need to exit the sketching environment and extrude the text.

1.   Choose the **Finish Sketch** button from the **Exit** panel of the **Sketch** tab and exit the
      sketching environment. Note that the current view is changed to the home or isometric view.

2. Choose the **Extrude** tool from the **Create** panel of the **Sketch** tab; the **Extrude** dialog box is invoked and the **Profile** selection tag is displayed in the drawing window. Also, you are prompted to select the profile to extrude.

3. Move the cursor over the text and select it when it turns red.

4. Specify **2.5** as the extrusion depth in the input edit box of the mini toolbar. Choose **OK** from the mini toolbar; the text is extruded to a distance of 2.5 mm, refer to Figure 4-88.

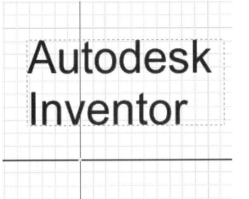

Figure 4-87 Text in the sketching environment   *Figure 4-88* Feature created on extruding the text

Changing the Visual Style

After extruding the text, you need to change its visual style.

1. Click the **Visual Style** in the **Appearance** panel of the **View** tab; a drop-down is displayed.

2. Choose the **Illustration** tool from this drop-down to give the extruded text a hand-drawn appearance. The final extruded text with the hand-drawn appearance is shown in Figure 4-89.

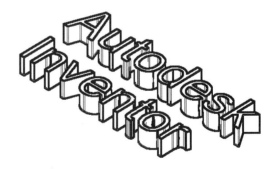

Figure 4-89 Text after changing the visual style

Saving the Sketch

1. Choose the **Save** tool from the **Quick Access Toolbar**; the **Save As** dialog box is displayed. Save the model with the name *Tutorial4* at the location given below:

C:\Inventor_2011\c04

2. Choose **Close > Close** from the **Application Menu** to close the file.

Self-Evaluation Test

Answer the following questions and then compare them to those given at the end of this chapter:

1. In Autodesk Inventor, you cannot reduce the length of a line once it is drawn. You will have to delete the line and then redraw a line of smaller length. (T/F)

2. The copies of the sketched entities can be arranged along the length and width of an imaginary rectangle using the **Circular Pattern** tool. (T/F)

3. When you select a profile by using a point that is inside the outer loop but outside the inner loops, the resultant solid will have the inner closed loops subtracted from the outer closed loop. (T/F)

4. The _____ tool allows you to switch between the standard and isometric views in a single click.

5. In the shortcut menu, you need to clear the _____ option if you want to select only one entity from a closed loop for offsetting.

6. To create a copy of an existing sketched entity by rotating it, select the _____ check box in the **Rotate** dialog box.

7. Autodesk Inventor allows you to create two types of patterns, namely _____ and _____.

8. The _____ option allows you to select a line segment whose length will define the distance between the individual items.

9. The _____ angles are generally provided to solid models so that the models can be easily taken out from the casting.

10. If the _____ button is chosen in the **Extrude** dialog box, the resulting feature will be a surface and not a solid.

Review Questions

Answer the following questions:

1. You can invoke the **Trim** tool from within the **Extend** tool by pressing the SHIFT key. (T/F)

2. Offsetting is one of the easiest methods of drawing parallel lines or concentric arcs and circles. (T/F)

3. If you select a circle by clicking on a point on its circumference and drag it, the circle will move from its location. (T/F)

4. Selecting a line at its endpoint and dragging it will stretch the line. (T/F)

5. You can move a rectangle by selecting and then dragging it. (T/F)

6. Which of the following tools can be used to reposition the sketched entity from one place to another place by using two points?

  (a) **Move** (b) **Rotate**
  (c) **Mirror** (d) **Extend**

7. Which of the following tools can be used to arrange multiple copies of sketched entities around an imaginary circle?

  (a) **Move** (b) **Rotate**
  (c) **Rectangular Pattern** (d) **Circular Pattern**

8. Which of the following options allows you to use an existing dimension to define the distance between individual items of a pattern.

  (a) **Dimension** (b) **Show Dimensions**
  (c) **Measure** (d) None of these

9. Which of the following check boxes should be selected to ensure that all items in the pattern are automatically updated, if any one of the entities is modified.

  (a) **Associative** (b) **Fitted**
  (c) **Suppress** (d) None of these

10. Which of the following options in the ViewCube shortcut menu is used to the display the isometric view of the model?

  (a) **Go Home** (b) **Reset Front**
  (c) **Options** (d) **Orthographic**

Exercises

Exercise 1

In this exercise, you will extrude the sketch drawn in Exercise 5 of Chapter 3, see Figure 4-90. The extrusion depth for the model is 15 mm. **(Expected time: 30 min)**

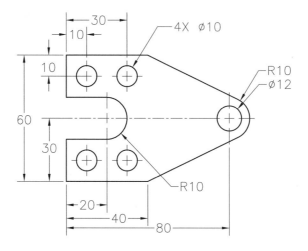

Figure 4-90 *Sketch for Exercise 1*

Exercise 2

In this exercise, you will extrude the sketch drawn in Exercise 1 of Chapter 3, see Figure 4-91. The extrusion depth for the model is 80 mm. **(Expected time: 30 min)**

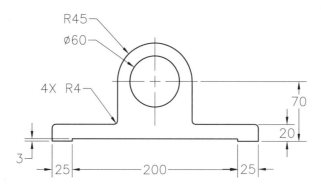

Figure 4-91 *Sketch for Exercise 2*

Exercise 3

In this exercise, you will extrude the sketch drawn in Exercise 3 of Chapter 2, see Figure 4-92.
The extrusion depth for the model is 40 mm. **(Expected time: 30 min)**

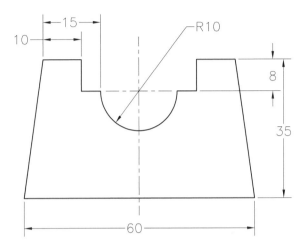

Figure 4-92 Sketch for Exercise 3

Exercise 4

In this exercise, you will extrude the sketch drawn in Exercise 3 of Chapter 3, see Figure 4-93.
The extrusion depth for the model is 35 mm. **(Expected time: 30 min)**

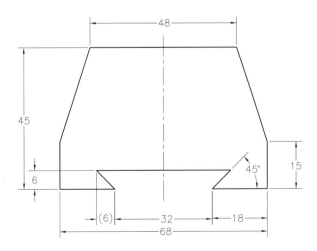

Figure 4-93 Sketch for Exercise 4

Exercise 5

In this exercise, you will extrude the sketch drawn in Exercise 4 of Chapter 3, see Figure 4-94. The extrusion depth for the model is 65 mm.   **(Expected time: 30 min)**

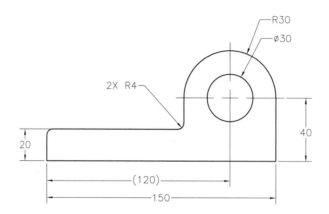

Figure 4-94 *Sketch for Exercise 5*

Note
When you extrude the sketches shown in Exercises 2, 3, 4, and 5, the models may not orient as given in the figures of exercises in Chapter 3. The reason for this is that these sketches are created on the default XY plane, which is horizontal. You will learn to draw sketches on other planes in the next chapter.

Answers to Self-Evaluation Test
1. F, **2.** F, **3.** T, **4. ViewCube**, **5. Loop Select**, **6. Copy**, **7.** Rectangular, Circular, **8. Measure**, **9.** taper, **10. Surface**

Chapter 5

Other Sketching and Modeling Options

Learning Objectives

After completing this chapter, you will be able to:

- *Create features on planes other than the default XY plane.*
- *Create work features such as work planes, work axes, and work points.*
- *Use other extrusion and revolution options for creating models.*

NEED FOR OTHER SKETCHING PLANES

All mechanical designs consist of a number of sketched, work, and placed features integrated together. The first feature in a model is the base feature and is generally a sketched feature. After creating the base feature, you need to add more features to it. By default, when you open a new file, the features are created on the XY plane. However, most of the times, the additional features are not created on the default plane on which the base feature is created. For example, refer to the model shown in Figure 5-1.

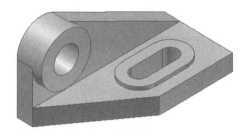

The base feature for this model is shown in Figure 5-2. Its sketch is drawn on the XY plane. After creating it, you need to create three join features, one cut feature, and a hole feature, see Figure 5-3. Now, the cut feature and all the join features are sketched features and, therefore, you require sketching planes to draw their sketches.

Figure 5-1 *Model created by combining various features*

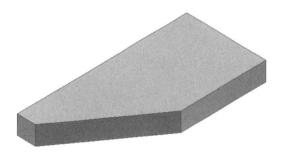

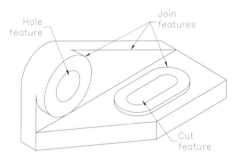

Figure 5-2 *Base feature for the model*

Figure 5-3 *Model after adding other features*

As evident from Figure 5-3, all these features are not created on the same plane as that of the base feature. Therefore, to draw the sketches of the sketched features, you need to define new sketching planes, which are different from the default XY plane. The method of specifying a new sketching plane is discussed next.

Defining a New Sketching Plane

In Autodesk Inventor, defining a new sketching plane is an easy process. You just need to specify the plane for drawing the sketch, the selected plane will automatically become the current sketching plane. Once you have finished creating the base feature, choose the **Create 2D Sketch** tool from the **Sketch** panel of the **Model** tab; you will be prompted to select a plane to create the sketch or edit an existing sketch. Select a plane to draw the sketch. When you move the cursor close to the plane, its boundary will be highlighted in red. As soon as you select the sketching plane, the sketching environment will be activated and the grid lines will be displayed on that plane. Also, you will be switched to the **Sketch** tab from the **Model** tab.

Note
*Generally, while creating a feature, the isometric view is used to view the object. Now, when you define a new sketching plane to draw the sketch for the next feature, the sketching environment is activated. However, the isometric view is still the current view. Before proceeding, you need to change the current view such that you can view the new sketch plane from the top. You can change the isometric view to the plane view by choosing the **View Face** tool from the **Navigate** panel. This tool is used to reorient the view using an existing plane or sketched entity. On invoking this tool, you will be prompted to select the entity to look at. Select the new sketching plane; the view will be changed to the plane view of the selected plane. You can also use the ViewCube to orient the sketching plane.*

WORK FEATURES

Work features are parametric features that are associated with a model. Autodesk Inventor has provided three types of work features to assist you in creating a design. The three types of work features are:

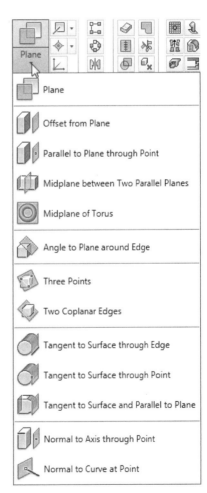

- Work Planes
- Work Axes
- Work Points

The methods of creating these work features are discussed next.

Creating Work Planes

Ribbon:	Model > Work Features > Plane drop-down

Work planes are similar to sketching planes and are used to draw sketches of sketched features or create placed features like holes. The reason for preferring work planes over sketching planes is that the sketching planes have some limitations. For example, it is not possible to define a sketching plane at an offset distance from an existing plane. Also, it is not possible to define a sketching plane that is tangent to a cylindrical feature. In such situations, you can define a work plane and use it as the sketching plane. In Autodesk Inventor, there are thirteen tools that can be used to create work planes. You can choose the desired tool from the **Plane** drop-down in the **Work Features** panel of the **Model** tab, see Figure 5-4. The procedures of creating work planes using these tools are discussed next.

*Figure 5-4 The **Plane** drop-down showing various tools for creating work planes*

Creating a Work Plane through Selected Objects

Ribbon:	Model > Work Features > Plane drop-down > Plane

You can create a work plane based on the reference objects selected and the sequence of their selection. To do so, choose the **Plane** tool from the **Work Features** panel (see Figure 5-4) and then select the required entity from the model in the drawing window. Figure 5-5 shows a planar face and point to be selected for creating a work plane and Figure 5-6 shows the resulting work plane.

Note

The new work plane will be displayed on the screen as a shaded plane. If required, you can turn off the display of this work plane. The procedure to do so will be discussed later in this chapter.

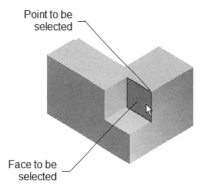

Figure 5-5 *The face and a point to be selected to define a work plane*

Figure 5-6 *Resulting work plane*

Creating a Work Plane Using Two Coplanar Edges, Axes, or Lines

Ribbon:	Model > Work Features > Plane drop-down > Two Coplanar Edges

You can create a work plane that passes through any two coplanar edges, axes, or lines. To do so, choose the **Two Coplanar Edges** tool from the **Work Features** panel (see Figure 5-4) and then select the two coplanar edges, axes, or lines from the model. Figure 5-7 shows the edges to be selected for creating a work plane and Figure 5-8 shows the resulting work plane.

Creating a Work Plane Using Three Vertices or Points

Ribbon:	Model > Work Features > Plane drop-down > Three Points

You can create a work plane that passes through three points. These points can be the vertices of the model or the point/hole center. To create such a plane, choose the **Three Points** tool from the **Work Features** panel (see Figure 5-4). Next, move the cursor close to a vertex; a yellow circle with a cross is snapped to it, suggesting that the vertex can be selected. Select any three vertices or points; the work plane will be created. Figure 5-9 shows three vertices selected to create a work plane and Figure 5-10 shows the resulting work plane.

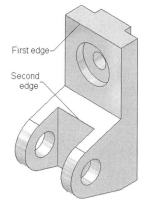

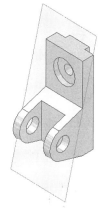

Figure 5-7 Edges to be selected   *Figure 5-8 Resulting work plane*

Tip. *You can also select work axes to define the work plane. You will learn more about work axes later in this chapter.*

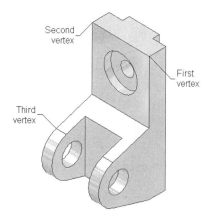

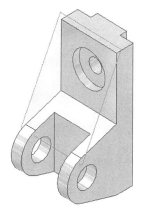

Figure 5-9 Vertices to be selected   *Figure 5-10 Resulting work plane*

Creating a Work Plane through an Edge/Axis and at an angle to a Plane/ Planar Face

Ribbon:	Model > Work Features > Plane drop-down > Angle to Plane around Edge

 You can create a work plane that passes through an edge or axis and lies at the specified angle to a plane or a planar face. To do so, choose the **Angle to Plane around Edge** tool from the **Work Features** panel (see Figure 5-4). Select the work plane or the planar face to which the resulting work plane will be at an angle. Next, select the edge through which the work plane will pass; the preview of the plane along with the mini toolbar will be displayed. Enter the required angle value in the edit box of the mini toolbar and then choose **OK**. You can also drag the manipulator arrow to specify the angle value of the plane. Figure 5-11 shows the edge and the planar face selected to create the work plane and Figure 5-12 shows the work plane created at an angle of -30 degrees. With the help of the mini toolbar, you can create a plane parallel or perpendicular to the selected plane/planar face. To create a plane parallel to the selected plane/planar face, enter **0** in the edit box of mini toolbar and then choose **OK**. Figure 5-13 shows a planar face and an edge selected for creating the work plane and Figure 5-14 shows the resulting work plane. To create a plane perpendicular to the selected plane/planar face, enter **90** in the edit box of the mini toolbar and then choose **OK**. Figure 5-15 shows a planar face and an edge selected for creating a work plane and Figure 5-16 shows the resulting work plane.

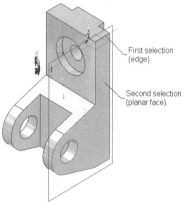

Figure 5-11 *An edge and a planar face selected to define a work plane at -30 degrees to the selected plane*

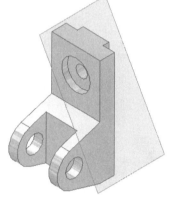

Figure 5-12 *Resulting work plane*

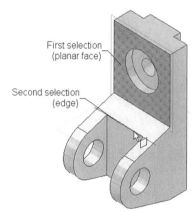

Figure 5-13 *A planar face and an edge selected to define a work plane parallel to the selected plane*

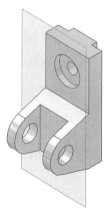

Figure 5-14 *Resulting work plane*

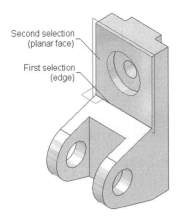
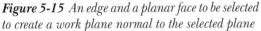

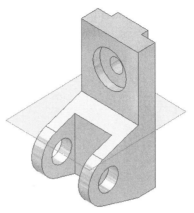

Figure 5-15 *An edge and a planar face to be selected to create a work plane normal to the selected plane*

Figure 5-16 *Resulting work plane*

Creating a Work Plane Passing through a Point and Parallel to a Plane/ Planar Face

Ribbon: Model > Work Features > Plane drop-down > Parallel to Plane through Point

You can create a work plane that passes through a specified point and is parallel to a plane or a planar face. To do so, choose the **Parallel to Plane through Point** tool from the **Work Features** panel (see Figure 5-4). Next, select the point and the plane or planar face in any sequence. You can select the point first and then the plane or the planar face to which the new work plane will be parallel and vice versa. Figure 5-17 shows a point and a planar face to be selected to define a work plane and Figure 5-18 shows the resulting work plane.

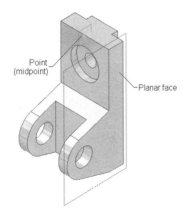

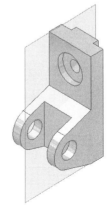

Figure 5-17 *A point and a planar face to be selected to define the work plane*

Figure 5-18 *Resulting work plane*

Creating a Work Plane Tangent to a Circular Face and Parallel to a Plane/Planar Face

Ribbon:	Model > Work Features > Plane drop-down > Tangent to Surface and Parallel to Plane

You can create a work plane that is tangent to a circular face and parallel to a plane or a planar face. To do so, choose the **Tangent to Surface and Parallel to Plane** tool from the **Work Features** panel (see Figure 5-4). Next, select the cylindrical face and then select the XY, YZ, or XZ plane or the planar face to which the resulting work plane should be parallel. Figure 5-19 shows a circular face to which the new work plane will be tangent and a planar face to which the resulting work plane will be parallel. Figure 5-20 shows the resulting work plane.

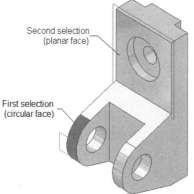

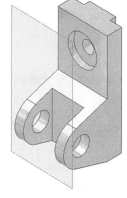

Figure 5-19 *Circular feature and a planar face to be selected to define a work plane*

Figure 5-20 *Resulting work plane*

Tip. *To select the XY, YZ, and XZ planes, click on the (+) sign located on the left of* **Origin** *node in the* **Browser Bar**. *The three default planes along with their three axes will be displayed. You can now select the required plane from the* **Browser Bar**.

Creating a Work Plane Normal to a Line Passing through a Point

Ribbon:	Model > Work Features > Plane drop-down > Normal to Axis through Point

You can create a work plane that is normal to an axis and passes through a point. The axis can be a line, an edge, or a work axis and the point can be any vertex in the model, a sketched point, hole center, or a work point. To create a work plane normal to an axis through a point, choose the **Normal to Axis through Point** tool from the **Work Features** panel (see Figure 5-4). Next, select the point and the edge in any sequence to create the plane. Figure 5-21 shows an edge and a point selected to create a work plane and Figure 5-22 shows the resulting work plane.

You can also use the **Normal to Axis through Point** tool to create a work plane that is normal to a line and passes through the intersection of the line with an arc or a circle. To do so, first you need to draw a circle or an arc and then a line or a centerline. Note that one endpoint of the line should lie on the circumference of the circle. After drawing the circle/arc and the line or the centerline, exit the sketching environment. Next, choose the **Normal to Axis through Point** tool from the **Work Features** panel (see Figure 5-4); you will be prompted to define the work plane by highlighting and selecting the geometry. Select the line or the centerline and then select the point of intersection of the line and the circle/arc; the work plane will be created at the intersection of the line/centerline and the circle/arc. Also, the new work plane will be normal to the centerline, see Figures 5-23 and 5-24.

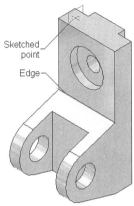

Figure 5-21 Selecting an edge and a point to define a work plane

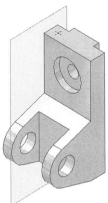

Figure 5-22 Resulting work plane

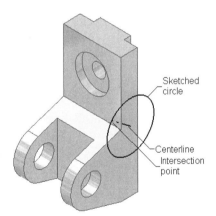

Figure 5-23 Selecting a centerline and an intersection point to define a work plane

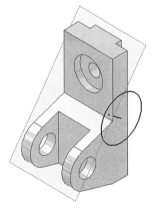

Figure 5-24 Resulting work plane

Note

The size of the work plane in Figure 5-24 has been modified to improve its clarity. The work planes are infinite features and their size displayed on the graphics screen is just for reference. To resize a work plane, move the cursor over one of its corners and then click on it. Next, drag the mouse when the cursor turns into a two-sided arrow. Note that the four-sided arrow cursor will move the work plane.

Creating a Work Plane Tangent to a Circular Face and Passing through an Edge/Axis

Ribbon:	Model > Work Features > Plane drop-down > Tangent to Surface through Edge

You can create a work plane that is tangent to a circular face and passes through the selected edge. To do so, choose the **Tangent to Surface through Edge** tool from the **Work Features** panel (see Figure 5-4). Next, select an edge or an axis and then select a circular face; a work plane passing though the selected edge and tangent to the circular face will be created. Figure 5-25 shows a circular face and an edge selected to create a work plane and Figure 5-26 shows the resulting work plane.

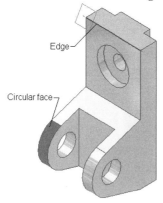

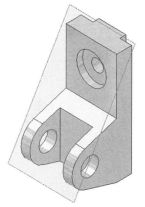

Figure 5-25 *Selecting a circular face and an edge to define a work plane*

Figure 5-26 *Resulting work plane*

Creating a Work Plane Parallel to a Plane/Planar Face and at an Offset

Ribbon:	Model > Work Features > Plane drop-down > Offset from Plane

You can create a work plane that is parallel to a plane or a planar face and is at some offset distance from the selected plane or planar face. To do so, choose the **Offset from Plane** tool from the **Work Features** panel (see Figure 5-4). Next, select the plane or planar face to which the resulting plane will be parallel; the preview of the work plane along with a mini toolbar will be displayed. Specify the offset distance in the edit box of the mini toolbar or drag the arrow manipulator to specify it. After specifying the offset distance, choose **OK** from the mini toolbar. If you specify a negative offset value, the work plane will be offset in the opposite direction. Figure 5-27 shows a plane selected to define the offset work plane and Figure 5-28 shows the new work plane created at an offset of 30 mm.

Note

*To create more than one work feature in succession, you can turn on the option of work feature to repeat the command. To invoke the **Repeat command**, first invoke any work feature tool and then right-click in the graphics window. From the shortcut menu, choose the **Repeat command** option. This option ensures that the previous work feature tool is repeated until you terminate it.*

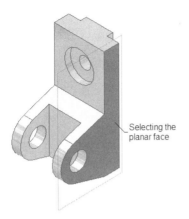

Figure 5-27 *Selecting a planar face to define the offset work plane*

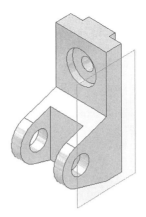

Figure 5-28 *Resulting work plane*

Creating a Work Plane in the Middle of Two Parallel Planes/Planar Faces

Ribbon: Model > Work Features > Plane drop-down > Midplane between Two Parallel Planes

 You can create a work plane in the middle of two parallel planes/planar faces. To do so, choose the **Midplane between Two Parallel Planes** tool from the **Work Features** panel (see Figure 5-4). Next, select two parallel planes/planar faces; a plane will be created in the middle of the selected planes/planar faces. Figure 5-29 shows two planar faces to be selected and Figure 5-30 shows the resulting work plane.

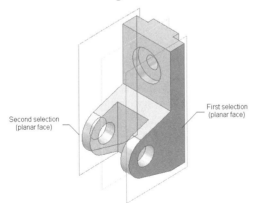

Figure 5-29 *Selecting two planar faces to define a work plane*

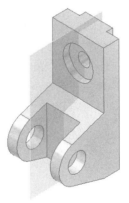

Figure 5-30 *Resulting work plane*

Creating a Work Plane Tangent to a Surface and Passing through a Point

Ribbon: Model > Work Features > Plane drop-down > Tangent to Surface through Point

You can create a work plane that is tangent to a surface and passes through a specified point. To do so, choose the **Tangent to Surface through Point** tool from the **Work**

Features panel (see Figure 5-4). Next, select a surface and then a point or a vertex; a work plane passing though the selected point and tangent to the surface will be created. Figure 5-31 shows a surface and a point to be selected to create a work plane and Figure 5-32 shows the resulting work plane.

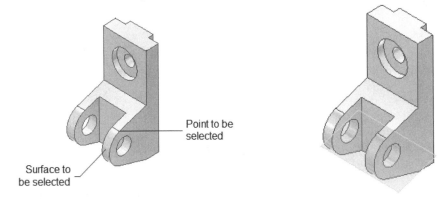

Figure 5-31 *A surface and a point to be selected to define a work plane*

Figure 5-32 *Resulting work plane*

Creating a Work Plane through the Center or the Midplane of a Torus

Ribbon: Model > Work Features > Plane drop-down > Midplane of Torus

You can create a work plane that passes through the center or the midplane of a torus. To do so, choose the **Midplane of Torus** tool from the **Work Features** panel (see Figure 5-4). Move the cursor to the torus; the preview of the plane will be displayed. Next, select the torus; the work plane will be created on its midplane. Figure 5-33 shows a torus to be selected and Figure 5-34 shows the resulting work plane.

Figure 5-33 *Torus to be selected to define the work plane*

Figure 5-34 *Resulting work plane*

Creating a Work Plane Normal to a Curve

Ribbon:	Model > Work Features > Plane drop-down > Normal to Curve at Point

You can create a work plane that is normal to a curve at the specified point. The curve can be a line, a spline, or an arc. The point can be any control vertex or the endpoint of the curve or spline. To create a work plane normal to a curve, choose the **Normal to Curve at Point** tool from the **Work Features** panel (see Figure 5-4). Next, select the curve and then the point. Figure 5-35 shows a curve and a point to be selected to create a work plane and Figure 5-36 shows the resulting work plane.

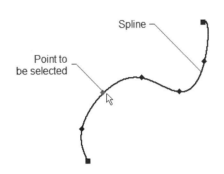

Figure 5-35 Spline (curve) and point to be selected to define the work plane

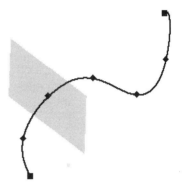

Figure 5-36 Resulting work plane

Creating Work Axes

Ribbon:	Model > Work Features > Work Axis drop-down

Work axes are parametric axes that pass through a model or feature. These axes are used as a reference to create work planes, work points, and circular patterns. The work axis is displayed in both the model and in the **Browser Bar**. In Autodesk Inventor, there are eight tools that can be used to create work axes. You can choose the desired tool from the **Work Axis** drop-down in the **Work Features** panel of the **Model** tab, see Figure 5-37. The procedures of creating work axes using these tools are discussed next.

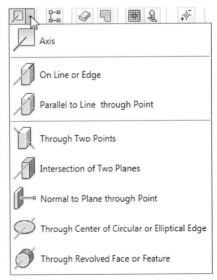

*Figure 5-37 The **Work Axis** drop-down showing various tools for creating work axes*

Creating a Work Axis through Selected Objects

Ribbon: Model > Work Features > Work Axis drop-down > Axis

 You can create work axis through selected objects depending upon the reference objects and the sequence in which they are selected. To do so, choose the **Axis** tool from the **Work Features** panel (see Figure 5-37) and then select the required entities from the model in the drawing window.

Creating a Work Axis passing through a Revolved or Cylindrical Feature

Ribbon: Model > Work Features > Work Axis drop-down > Through Revolved Face or
               Feature

You can create a work axis that passes through the center of a revolved or cylindrical feature. To do so, choose the **Through Revolved Face or Feature** tool from the **Work Features** panel (see Figure 5-37); you will be prompted to select a cylindrical or a revolved surface. Select a cylindrical or revolved feature from the drawing window; a work axis passing through the center of the selected feature will be created, see Figure 5-38.

Creating a Work Axis Normal to a Plane/Planar Face and Passing through a Point

Ribbon: Model > Work Features > Work Axis drop-down > Normal to Plane through Point

You can create a work axis that is normal to a plane or a planar face and passes through a specified point. To do so, choose the **Normal to Plane through Point** tool from the **Work Features** panel. Next, select a plane or a planar face to which the axis will be normal and then select the point through which the axis will pass, see Figure 5-39.

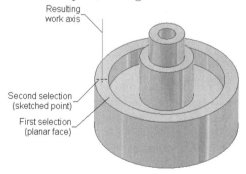

Figure 5-38 *Work axis passing through the center of a circular feature*

Figure 5-39 *Creating a work axis through a planar face and a sketched point*

Creating a Work Axis Passing through the Intersection of Two Planes/ Planar Faces

Ribbon: Model > Work Features > Work Axis drop-down > Intersection of Two Planes

You can create a work axis that passes through the intersection of two planes or planar faces. To do so, choose the **Intersection of Two Planes** tool from the **Work Features** panel. Next, select two intersecting planar faces; a work axis will be created at their intersection. If you select two planar faces that do not intersect in the model but intersect when extended, the resulting axis will pass through the extended intersection, see Figure 5-40.

Creating a Work Axis Passing through Two Points

Ribbon: Model > Work Features > Work Axis drop-down > Through Two Points

You can create a work axis that passes through two specified points. The points can be the vertices, midpoints of edges, sketched points, hole centers, or work points. To create a work axis passing through two points, choose the **Through Two Points** tool from the **Work Features** panel (see Figure 5-37). Next, select two points from the drawing window; an axis passing through the selected points will be created. Figure 5-41 shows a work axis created using the midpoints of two edges of a model.

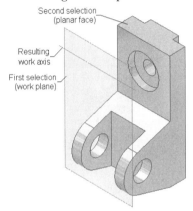

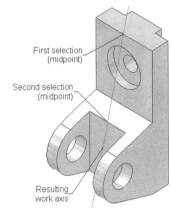

Figure 5-40 *Work axis passing through the intersection of two planes*

Figure 5-41 *Creating a work axis through the midpoints of two edges*

Creating a Work Axis along a Linear Edge/Sketch Line/3D Sketch Line

Ribbon: Model > Work Features > Work Axis drop-down > On Line or Edge

You can create a work axis along a linear edge/sketch line/3D sketch line. To do so, choose the **On Line or Edge** tool from the **Work Features** panel (see Figure 5-37) and select a linear edge, sketch line, or 3D sketch line of a model.

Creating a Work Axis Passing through a Point and along a Line/Edge

Ribbon: Model > Work Features > Work Axis drop-down > Parallel to Line through Point

You can create a work axis that is parallel to a linear edge or a line and passes through a point. To do so, choose the **Parallel to Line through Point** tool from the **Work Features** panel. Next, select a point and then a line or a linear edge; an axis parallel to the selected line or edge and passing through the selected point will be created. Figure 5-42 shows a work axis that is parallel to a line and passes through a specified point.

Creating a Work Axis Coincident with the Axis of the Circular, Elliptical, or Fillet Edge of a Feature

Ribbon:	Model > Work Features > Work Axis drop-down > Through Center of Circular or Elliptical Edge

You can create a work axis that is coincident with the axis of an elliptical, a circular, or a fillet edge of a feature. To do so, choose the **Through Center of Circular or Elliptical Edge** tool from the **Work Features** panel (see Figure 5-37). Next, select the circular, elliptical, or fillet edge from the feature; a work axis coincident with the axis of the selected edge will be created. Figure 5-43 shows a work axis created. This work axis coincides with the axis of the circular edge of the feature.

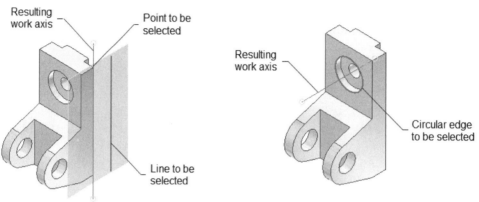

Figure 5-42 Creating a work axis parallel to a line passing through a point

Figure 5-43 Creating a work axis coincident with the axis of the circular edge

Creating Work Points

Ribbon:	Model > Work Features > Work Point drop-down

 Work points are parametric points that can be created on an existing model. These points help create work planes, work axes, or other features. In Autodesk Inventor, there are eight tools that can be used to create work points. You can choose the desired tool from the **Work Point** drop-down in the **Work Features** panel of the **Model** tab, see Figure 5-44. The procedure of creating work points using these tools are discussed next.

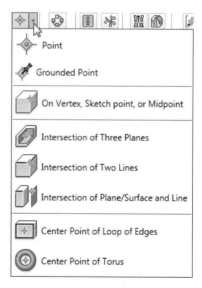

*Figure 5-44 The **Work Point** drop-down showing various tools for creating work points*

Creating a Work Point through Selected Objects

Ribbon: Model > Work Features > Work Point drop-down > Point

You can create various types of work points depending upon the reference objects selected and the sequence in which they are selected. To do so, choose the **Point** tool from the **Work Features** panel (see Figure 5-44) and then select the required entities from the model in the drawing window.

Creating a Work Point at a Vertex or at the Midpoint of an Edge

Ribbon: Model > Work Features > Work Point drop-down > On Vertex, Sketch point, or Midpoint

You can create a work point at any vertex of a model or at the midpoint of any of its edges. To do so, choose the **On Vertex, Sketch point, or Midpoint** tool from the **Work Features** panel (see Figure 5-44). Next, select a vertex of the model; a new work point will be created on the selected vertex. To create a work point at the midpoint of an edge, move the cursor close to the midpoint of the edge; the midpoint will be highlighted. Next, select the midpoint; the work point will be created. You can also right-click and choose **Select Other** from the shortcut menu to cycle through various entities and select the midpoint when it is displayed. Figure 5-45 shows work points created at the vertices and at the midpoints of the edges of the model.

Creating a Work Point at the Intersection of Two Edges/Axes

Ribbon: Model > Work Features > Work Point drop-down > Intersection of Two Lines

You can create a work point at the intersection or extended intersection of two edges or axes. To do so, choose the **Intersection of Two Lines** tool from the **Work Features** panel (see Figure 5-44). Select the two intersecting edges or axes; the work point will be created at the intersection point. Figure 5-46 shows two edges to be selected to create the work point and the resulting work point.

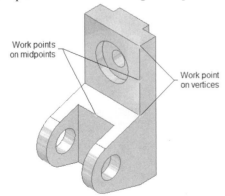

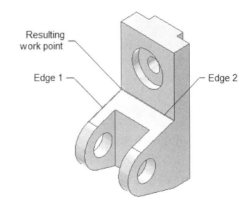

Figure 5-45 Work points on the vertices and on the midpoints of edges

Figure 5-46 Work point at the intersection of two edges

Creating a Work Point at the Intersection of a Plane/Planar Face and an Edge/Axis

Ribbon: Model > Work Features > Work Point drop-down > Intersection of Plane/ Surface and Line

 You can create a work point at the intersection of a plane or a planar face and an edge or axis. To do so, choose the **Intersection of Plane/Surface and Line** tool from the **Work Features** panel (see Figure 5-44). Next, select the plane or the planar face and then the line or linear edge normal to it in any sequence; a work point will be created at their intersection, see Figure 5-47.

Creating a Work Point at the Intersection of Three Planes/Planar Faces

Ribbon: Model > Work Features > Work Point drop-down > Intersection of Three Planes

You can create a work point at the intersection of three planes or planar faces. To do so, choose the **Intersection of Three Planes** tool from the **Work Features** panel (see Figure 5-44). Select the three planes or planar faces; a work point will be created at their intersection, see Figure 5-48.

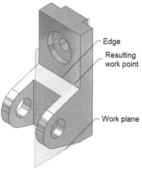

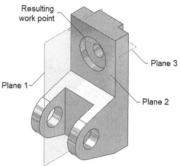

Figure 5-47 *Work point created at the intersection of an edge and a work plane*

Figure 5-48 *Work point created at the intersection of three planes*

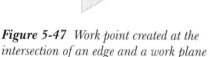 **Note**

*If you delete work features such as work planes, work axes, or work points, the features created with reference to these work features will also be deleted. To hide the work features, right-click on them in the **Browser Bar** and choose **Visibility** from the shortcut menu; the display of the selected work feature will be turned off. Choose this option again to turn the visibility on.*

Creating a Work Point at the Center Point of a Loop of Edges

Ribbon: Model > Work Features > Work Point drop-down > Center Point of Loop of Edges

You can create a work point at the center point of a closed loop of edges of a feature. To do so, choose the **Center Point of Loop of Edges** tool from the **Work Features** panel (see Figure 5-44). Next, select an edge that forms a closed loop with other edges; a work point will be created at the center point of the loop of the selected edges, see Figure 5-49. Note that before selecting the edge for creating a work point, you need to right-click and then choose the **Loop Select** option from the shortcut menu.

Creating a Work Point through the Center or Midplane of a Torus

Ribbon:	Model > Work Features > Work Point drop-down > Center Point of Torus

You can create a work point that passes through the center or midplane of a torus. To do so, choose the **Center Point of Torus** tool from the **Work Features** panel (see Figure 5-44). Move the cursor to the torus; the preview of the work point will be displayed. Next, select the torus; the work point will be created on its center or midplane. Figure 5-50 shows a torus with a work point created on its center.

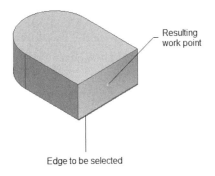

Figure 5-49 *Creating work point at the center point of an edge of a closed loop*

Figure 5-50 *Work point created on the center of a torus*

Creating a Grounded Point

Ribbon:	Model > Work Features > Work Point drop-down > Grounded Point

You can create a grounded point by using the **Grounded Point** tool. To create a grounded point, choose the **Grounded Point** tool from the **Work Features** panel (see Figure 5-44); you will be prompted to select a vertex or work point to specify the initial position of the point. Select a vertex or a work point; a triad will be placed at the selected vertex or point, as shown in Figure 5-51. Also, the **3D Move / Rotate** dialog box will be displayed, as shown in Figure 5-52. You can move the triad in the required direction by clicking on the corresponding axis and then dragging it. You can also rotate the triad about its axis. After specifying the position and orientation of the grounded point, choose the **OK** button; the grounded point will be placed at the specified position.

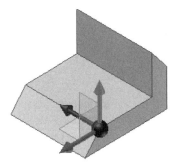

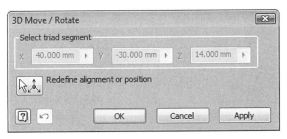

Figure 5-51 *Triad placed at the selected vertex*

Figure 5-52 *The **3D Move / Rotate** dialog box*

Tip. *1. To understand the geometrical dependency of an axis, work plane, or work point, select the* **Work Point**, **Work Axis**, *or* **Work Plane** *in the* **Browser Bar** *or in the graphic window and right-click; a shortcut menu will be displayed. Choose the* **Show Inputs** *option from the shortcut menu; the geometry that was used to create the work plane, work axis, or work point will be highlighted in the graphic window.*

2. The work features can also be created in-line. The in-line features are created while you are in the process of creating some other feature. For example, while creating a work axis, if you right-click, a shortcut menu will be displayed. This shortcut menu provides the options for creating a work plane and a work point as well. The work plane and the work point created using this shortcut menu will be the in-line work features. Note that all in-line features are dependent on the parent features.

OTHER EXTRUSION OPTIONS

As mentioned earlier, some of the options of the **Extrude** dialog box will not be available until you have created the base feature. Once the base feature is created, the remaining options in both the tabs of this dialog box will be available. These options are discussed next.

Shape Tab

The options in the **Shape** tab of the **Extrude** dialog box, shown in Figure 5-53, are discussed next.

Join

This is the first button on the left of the **Extents** area and is used to create an extruded feature by adding new material to an existing feature. This button will be activated only after you have created the base feature. You can also choose this option from the mini toolbar, refer to Figure 5-54.

Cut

This is the second button on the left of the **Extents** area. This button will be available only after you have created the base feature. The **Cut** option is used to create an extruded feature by removing material from the existing feature. You can also choose this option from the mini toolbar that is displayed on invoking the **Extrude** tool, as shown in Figure 5-54. The material to be removed will be defined by the sketch that you have drawn. Figure 5-55 shows a join feature created using a sketch and Figure 5-56 shows the cut feature created using the same sketch.

Intersect

This button is available below the **Cut** button and is used to create an extruded feature by using the material that is common to both the existing feature and the sketch, see Figure 5-57. You can also choose this option from the mini toolbar, refer to Figure 5-54.

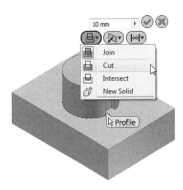

Figure 5-53 *The **Extrude** dialog box with the **Shape** tab chosen*

Figure 5-54 *Choosing the **Cut** option from the mini toolbar*

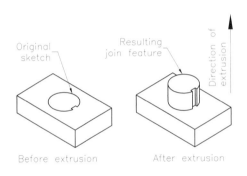

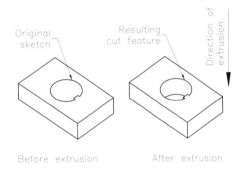

Figure 5-55 *Extruding the sketch using the **Join** option*

Figure 5-56 *Extruding the sketch using the **Cut** option*

New solid

 On choosing this button, the resultant feature will be a new body. The new body thus created will be independent of the existing body and will be listed in the **Solid Bodies** node of the **Browser Bar**. You can also choose this option from the mini toolbar, refer to Figure 5-54.

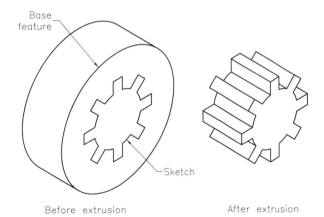

Figure 5-57 *Extruding the sketch using the **Intersect** option*

Extents Area

The **Extents** area is used to specify the termination options for the feature to be extruded. These options are also available in the mini toolbar, refer to Figure 5-58. Some of the options in this area were discussed in Chapter 4 and the rest of them are discussed next.

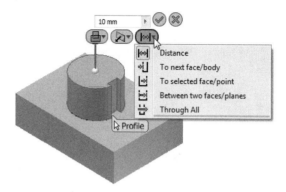

To Next

This option is used to terminate the extruded feature on the first plane or the first face that it comes across in the specified direction. On selecting this option, the **Terminator** button will

Figure 5-58 Invoking the extent options from the mini toolbar

appear in the **Extents** area. This button is used to define the end of the extruded feature. You can also invoke this option by choosing the **To next face/body** option from the mini toolbar, refer to Figure 5-58.

Note
*The **Symmetric** option will not be available with the **To Next** termination option because you cannot select planes or planar faces in both the directions of the current sketch plane in a single attempt.*

All

The **All** option is used to create a feature by extruding the sketch through all the features that it comes across. You can also invoke this option by choosing the **Through All** option from the mini toolbar, refer to Figure 5-58. You can extrude the sketch in either direction of the current sketching plane by using the direction buttons in the **Extents** area. You can also extrude the sketch in both the directions of the current sketch plane by choosing the **Symmetric** button.

Figure 5-59 shows a sketch drawn on an offset plane. Figures 5-60 and 5-61 show the profile extruded using the **To Next** and **All** options, respectively.

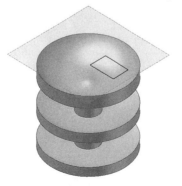

Figure 5-59 Sketch drawn on an offset plane

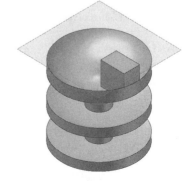

*Figure 5-60 Sketch extruded using the **To Next** option*

Match shape

This check box is available only when you are extruding an open sketch. If this check box is selected, the open sketch is extruded in such a way that it extends to the last face of the model that it comes across. The sketch fills the material in all the features up to the last face of the model. For example, refer to the open sketch shown in Figure 5-62. This sketch is drawn at a plane offset from the bottom face of the model.

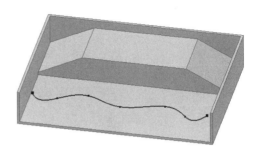

Figure 5-61 *Sketch extruded using the **All** option*

Figure 5-62 *Sketch drawn on the offset plane*

When you invoke the **Extrude** tool and select this open profile, you are allowed to extrude it on either of the two sides, as shown in Figures 5-63 and 5-64.

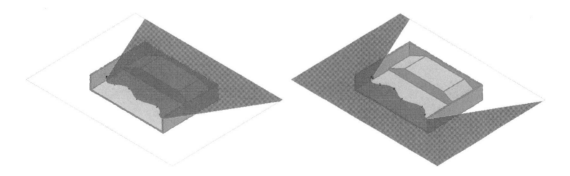

Figure 5-63 *First side for extruding the profile*   *Figure 5-64* *Second side for extruding the profile*

While selecting the side to be extruded, you need to be careful because the feature will be successful only when you extrude it in the direction in which the sketch will find faces to terminate the feature. In this case, the feature will not be created if you select the side shown in Figure 5-64. This is because the sketch cannot find any face to terminate the feature in the front direction.

After you select the side of the sketch to be extruded, you will be prompted to define the extent of the feature. You can select the type of termination from the **Distance** drop-down list and define the direction using the two buttons. If the **Match shape** check box is selected, the sketch will fill the model with the material and the feature will be created similar to that shown in Figure 5-65. But if the **Match shape** check box is cleared, the feature will be created similar to that shown in Figure 5-66. As evident in this figure, the shape of the sketch is not retained while creating the feature.

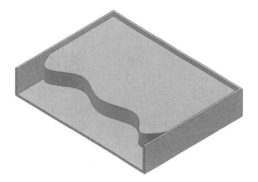

Figure 5-65 *Result with the* **Match shape** *check box selected*

Figure 5-66 *Result with the* **Match shape** *check box cleared*

More Tab

While creating a feature after creating the base feature, you can also use the remaining options of the **More** tab shown in Figure 5-67. These options are discussed next.

Alternate Solution Area

The options in the **Alternate Solution** area are used in combination with the **To** and the **From To** termination options. These options are used in creating those extruded features that terminate on the curved faces, resulting in more than one possible solution. These options are discussed next.

Figure 5-67 *The* **Extrude** *dialog box with the* **More** *tab chosen*

Flip
The **Flip** buttons are used to reverse the direction of the extruded features.

Minimum Solution
By default, in case of more than one solution, the extruded feature terminates at the face that is at the maximum distance from the sketch. Figure 5-68 shows the sketch and the face at which the extruded feature will terminate. Notice that the resulting feature in Figure 5-69 is created up to the face that is at the maximum distance from the sketch. However, if you select the **Minimum Solution** check box, the feature will terminate at the face that is at the minimum distance from the sketch, see Figures 5-70 and 5-71.

Note

In Figures 5-69 and 5-71, the visibility of work planes is turned off.

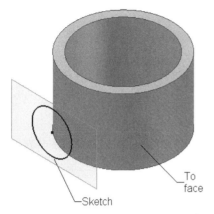

Figure 5-68 Sketch and termination face

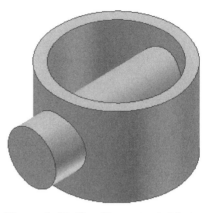

Figure 5-69 Resulting extruded feature

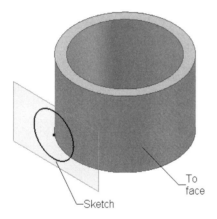

Figure 5-70 Sketch and termination face

Figure 5-71 Resulting extruded feature

Infer iMates

The **Infer iMates** check box in the **More** tab is selected to apply an iMate to an edge of the solid. Note that only the edge that is a full circle in shape can be selected for this purpose.

OTHER REVOLUTION OPTIONS

Most of the options in the **Revolve** dialog box were discussed in Chapter 4. The remaining options are discussed next.

Operations Area

Once you have created the base feature, the **Join**, **Cut** and **Intersect** buttons will be activated in the **Operations** area of the **Revolve** dialog box, see Figure 5-72. These options are also available in the mini toolbar. The functions of these options are discussed next.

*Figure 5-72 The **Revolve** dialog box*

Join

 This is the first button on the left of the **Extents** area and is used to create a revolved feature by adding new material to an existing feature. This button will be available only after you have created the base feature. You can also invoke this option from the mini toolbar, refer to Figure 5-73.

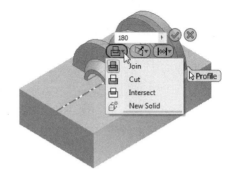

Figure 5-73 *Choosing an option from the mini toolbar*

Cut

 This is the second button on the left of the **Extents** area. This button will be available only after you have created the base feature. You can also choose this option from the mini toolbar, see Figure 5-73. The **Cut** option is used to create a revolved feature by removing material from the feature. This material to be removed is defined by the sketch you have drawn and the axis of revolution.

Intersect

 This button is available below the **Cut** button and is used to create a revolved feature by retaining the material common to the existing feature and the sketch. You can also choose the **Intersect** option from the mini toolbar, refer to Figure 5-73.

New Solid

 On choosing the **New solid** button, the resultant revolved feature will be a new body. The new body will be independent of the existing body and will be listed in the **Solid Bodies** node of the **Browser Bar**. You can also choose this option from the mini toolbar, refer to Figure 5-73.

Match shape

This check box is available only when you revolve an open sketch. Similar to the **Extrude** tool, in this case also, the **Match shape** check box is used to revolve the open sketch in such a way that it extends to the axis of revolution. On doing so, the sketch floods all features up to the last face of the model with material. Figure 5-74 shows the open sketch and Figures 5-75 and 5-76 show the revolved feature created by selecting this check box and clearing it.

Figure 5-74 *Open sketch for the revolved feature*

Infer iMates

This check box is selected to apply an iMate to a full circle edge of the solid feature.

Figure 5-75 *Revolve feature with the **Match** shape check box selected*

Figure 5-76 *Revolve feature with the **Match** shape check box cleared*

THE CONCEPT OF SKETCH SHARING

Generally, while creating a design, you will frequently come across situations where you have to use a consumed sketch for creating another feature in the same plane and along the same direction of extrusion. As mentioned at the start of this chapter, a consumed sketch is the one that has already been converted into a feature. For example, consider a case where you have to create a join feature by extruding the sketch to different distances in both the directions about the current sketch plane.

In some solid modeling programs, to use the consumed sketch, you will have to copy it to the new location. After placing the sketch, you will have to add the dimensions to locate it on its exact location. However, in Autodesk Inventor, you can directly use the same sketch by sharing it. This concept of using the consumed sketch again is termed as sharing the sketches. This concept has drawn a very distinct line between Autodesk Inventor and other solid modeling programs as it reduces the design time appreciably.

Sharing Sketches

As mentioned in Introduction, all operations that were used to create a model are displayed in the form of a tree view in the **Browser Bar**. All these operations will be arranged in the sequence in which they were performed. Also, once the sketch is converted into a feature, the sketch will be hidden and the feature will be displayed in the **Browser Bar**. For example, when you create the sketch for the base feature, the **Browser Bar** will display **Sketch1** below **Origin**. When this sketch is extruded and converted into the base feature, the **Browser Bar** will display **Extrusion1** below **Origin** and it will have a plus sign (+) located on the left. If you click on this plus sign, it will expand and will display **Sketch1**. Similarly, if you click on the plus sign of any sketched feature, it will expand and display the sketch.

Figure 5-77 *Sharing the sketch using the shortcut menu*

To share the sketch, right-click on the sketch that you want to share; a shortcut menu will be displayed, see Figure 5-77. In this shortcut menu, choose **Share Sketch**. Another sketch with the same name will be displayed in the **Browser Bar**. Also, the shared sketch will be displayed in the graphics window. You can now convert this sketch into a feature.

Note
*By default, the visibility of the shared sketch is set to ON. As a result, after converting into a feature, the sketch will also be displayed along with the new feature. You need to manually turn off the visibility of this sketch. This is done by using the shortcut menu that is displayed upon right-clicking on the sketch. In this shortcut menu, the **Visibility** option will have a check mark on its left. Choose this option again to turn off the visibility. You will notice that the sketch is no more visible on the screen. Similarly, right-click on any work feature and turn off its visibility using the **Visibility** option in the shortcut menu.*

TUTORIALS

Tutorial 1

In this tutorial, you will create the model of the Standard Bracket shown in Figure 5-78a. Its dimensions are shown in Figures 5-78b through 5-78d. **(Expected time: 30 min)**

Figure 5-78a Model for Tutorial 1

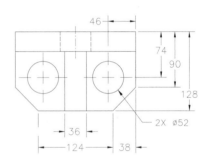

Figure 5-78b Top view of the model

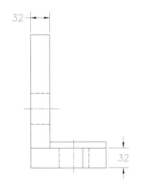

Figure 5-78c Left view of the model

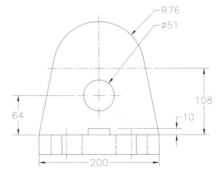

Figure 5-78d Front view of the model

The following steps are required to complete this tutorial:

a. On the XY plane, create the base feature with two holes, refer to Figures 5-79 and 5-80.
b. Define a new sketch plane on the back face of the base feature and create the join feature with a hole, refer to Figure 5-82.
c. Define a new sketch plane on the front face of the model and create the rectangular join feature, refer to Figure 5-85.

Creating and Dimensioning the Sketch of the Base Feature

1. Start Autodesk Inventor and then start a new metric standard part file.

    Whenever you start a new part file, by default, the XY plane is displayed as the sketching plane. In this tutorial, the base feature will be created on the XY plane. Therefore, you can directly start drawing the sketch on starting a new file.

2. Draw the sketch of the base feature using various sketching tools, see Figure 5-79.

3. Add the required constraints and dimensions to the sketch to make it fully constrained, as shown in Figure 5-79.

4. Choose the **Finish Sketch** button from the **Exit** panel of the **Sketch** tab; you will exit the Sketching environment and the current view is changed to the home view or isometric view.

Extruding the Base Sketch

After creating the sketch, you need to extrude it to create the base feature.

1. Using the **Extrude** tool, extrude the sketch to a distance of 32 mm.

    As the sketch has multiple loops, you need to specify the profile to be extruded. Make sure you define the profile to be extruded by specifying a point outside the circles but inside the outer loop. The model after creating the base feature is shown in Figure 5-80.

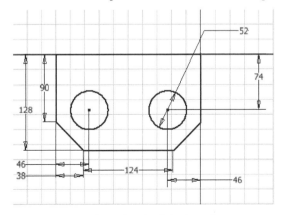

Figure 5-79 *Sketch of the base feature*

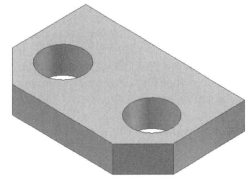

Figure 5-80 *Base feature of the model*

Creating a Feature on the Back Face of the Base Feature

To create a feature on the back face of the base feature, you first need to define the sketching plane on the back face.

1. Invoke the **Free Orbit** tool from the **Navigation Bar** and rotate the model such that the back face of the model becomes visible.

2. Choose the **Create 2D Sketch** tool from **Model > Sketch > Sketch** drop-down; you are prompted to select the plane on which the sketch will be created.

3. Select the back face of the base feature; the sketching environment is invoked and the grid lines are displayed in the drawing window. Note that the current view was invoked using the **Free Orbit** tool. This tool is used to rotate the view of the model to an arbitrary location but not to the exact location. Therefore, you need to reorient the current view using the ViewCube.

4. Invoke the **View Face** tool from the **Navigation Bar** and select the back face of the base feature; the selected face is reoriented parallel to the screen. Alternatively, you can select that face of the ViewCube which is facing toward the same direction as does the back face of the base feature.

   Sometimes, while reorienting the model, the X axis of the model (displayed red in the 3D Indicator) points vertically downward. You need to reorient the model again using the arrow on the top right of the ViewCube to make the X axis of the model horizontal.

5. In case the X axis points vertically downward, choose the arrow on the top right corner of the ViewCube to reorient the model. However, this step can be skipped if this axis points horizontally toward the left.

   Once you orient the model, you will notice that the red arrow in the 3D Indicator has become horizontal and is pointing toward the left. This shows that the X axis of the model is now in the horizontal direction.

   While defining a sketch plane to create a sketch on a planar face, you will notice that a sketch consisting of some sketcher entities is automatically drawn on the planar face. This sketch will define the contour of the planar face on which you define the sketching plane. In this case, the sketch is a rectangle defining the back face of the base feature. The entities that are used to create this sketch are called reference geometries. These entities can be used further for feature creation but cannot be dimensioned. You can use the entire sketch or some entities of this sketch and create a feature. The entities that are not required for feature creation can be deleted. Note that, if you do not delete these entities, they will become a part of the sketch.

6. Delete both vertical edges and the lower horizontal edge of the contour and then create the remaining portion of the sketch, refer to Figure 5-81.

7. Add the required constraints to the sketch and then dimension it to make it fully constrained. The sketch after dimensioning should look similar to the one shown in Figure 5-81.

8. Choose the **Finish Sketch** button from the **Exit** panel of the **Sketch** tab and exit the sketching environment.

Extruding the Sketch

1. Change the current view to isometric and then extrude the sketch to a distance of 32 mm using the **Extrude** tool. You need to reverse the direction of extrusion using the second button available below the **Depth** edit box in the **Extents** area of the **Extrude** dialog box. The model after creating the feature on the back face should look similar to the one shown in Figure 5-82.

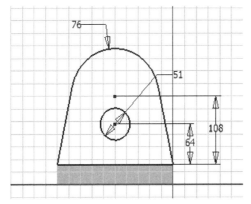

Figure 5-81 Sketch of the feature on the back face

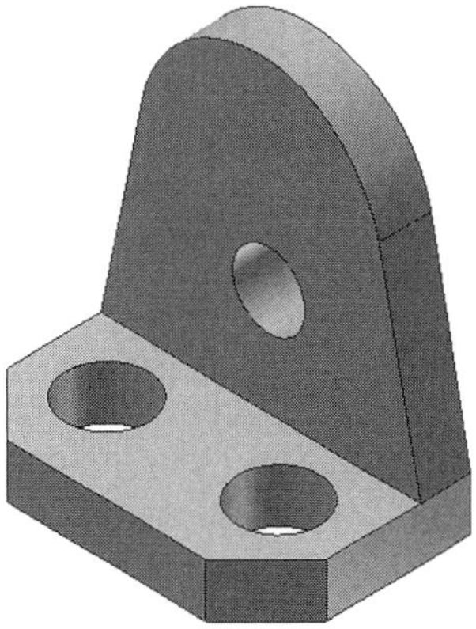

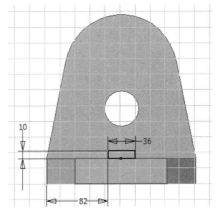

Figure 5-82 Model after creating the feature

Creating the Sketch on the Front Face of the Base Feature

1. Choose the **Create 2D Sketch** tool from the **Sketch** panel of the **Model** tab; you are prompted to select the plane on which the sketch will be created.

2. Select the front face of the base feature; the sketching environment is invoked and a rectangle defining the contour of the front face is created.

3. Choose the **View Face** tool from the **Navigation Bar** and then select the front face of the base feature; the model is reoriented such that its front face is parallel to the screen and the X axis of the model is in the horizontal direction. Next, choose the **Zoom All** tool to increase the drawing display area.

4. Delete the reference geometries and draw a rectangle as the sketch for the next feature, refer to Figure 5-83. Add the **Collinear Constraint** between the lower edge of the rectangle and the upper edge of the front face of the base feature.

Figure 5-83 Dimensioned sketch for the feature on the front face

5. Add the required dimensions to the sketch; refer to Figure 5-83.

6. Exit the sketching environment and then change the current view to the isometric view.

 Tip. *Whenever you apply the* **Collinear Constraint** *between a sketched line and an edge, another line will be created. It is recommended that you do not delete this line. If you delete this line, the* **Collinear Constraint** *will also be deleted.*

Extruding the Sketch

1. Choose the **Extrude** tool from the **Create** panel of the **Model** tab to invoke the **Extrude** dialog box. Select the rectangle as the profile to be extruded.

2. Choose the **To selected face/point** option from the mini toolbar, as shown in Figure 5-84. Alternatively, select **To** from the **Distance** drop-down list in the **Extents** area of the **Extrude** dialog box; the **Select surface to end the feature creation** button is displayed below the drop-down list. This button is chosen by default.

3. Select the front face of the second feature as the face where the current feature will terminate; the **Check to terminate feature on the extended face** check box is displayed on the right of the **Select surface to end the feature creation** button in the **Extrude** dialog box. This check box is selected by default. As the current feature will terminate on the selected face, you need to clear this check box.

4. Clear the **Check to terminate feature on the extended face** check box and then choose the **OK** button. Alternatively, choose **OK** from the mini toolbar. The final model for Tutorial 1 is shown in Figure 5-85.

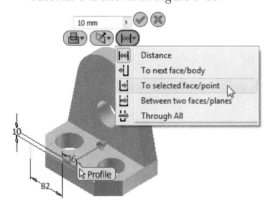

Figure 5-84 *Choosing the termination option*   ***Figure 5-85*** *Final model for Tutorial 1*

Saving the Model

1. Save the model with the name *Tutorial1* at the location given below and then close the file.

C:\Inventor_2011\c05

Note

*The holes shown in the model for Tutorial 1 can also be created directly using the **Hole** tool. The use of this tool will be discussed in the later chapters.*

Tutorial 2

In this tutorial, you will create the model shown in Figure 5-86a. Its dimensions are shown in Figures 5-86b through 5-86d.   **(Expected time: 30 min)**

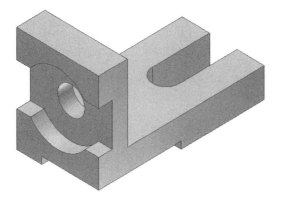

Figure 5-86a *Model for Tutorial 2*

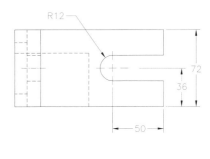

Figure 5-86b *Top view of the model*

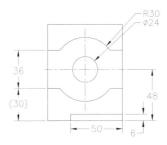

Figure 5-86c *Left view of the model*

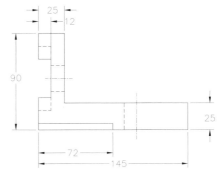

Figure 5-86d *Front view of the model*

The following steps are required to complete this tutorial:

a.   Create the base feature on the YZ plane by defining a new sketch plane on it, refer to Figures 5-87 and 5-88.

b.   Define a new sketch plane on the front face of the model and create a cut feature, refer to Figures 5-89 and 5-90.

c.   Create the next cut feature by defining a new sketch plane on the back face of the model, refer to Figures 5-91 and 5-92.

d.   Define a new sketch plane on the new face that is exposed by creating the last cut feature and create a circular cut feature, refer to Figure 5-93.

e.   Create the final cut feature on the top face of the horizontal base of the first feature, refer to Figure 5-93.

Changing the Sketch Plane

The base feature for this model is an L-shaped feature. You cannot create the L-shaped base feature on the XY plane. This feature will be created on the YZ plane. Therefore, you need to change the sketching plane before you start drawing the sketch.

1.   Start a new metric standard part file. Choose the **Finish Sketch** button from the **Exit** panel of the **Sketch** tab to exit the current sketching environment.

     This is needed to avoid drawing the sketch on the current sketching plane, which is the XY plane. You need to draw the sketch on the YZ plane.

2.   Click on the plus sign (+) on the left of the **Origin** folder in the **Browser Bar**; the folder expands and displays the YZ, XZ, and XY planes as well as the X, Y, and Z axes. The center point is also displayed.

3.   Choose the **Create 2D Sketch** tool from the **Sketch** panel of the **Model** tab; you are prompted to select the plane on which you want to create the sketch.

4.   Select the **YZ Plane** from the **Browser Bar**; the sketching environment is invoked.

     However, the isometric view is still the current view. Therefore, you need to change the current view such that the sketching plane becomes parallel to the screen.

5.   Choose the **View Face** tool from the **Navigation Bar** and then select the **YZ Plane** from the **Browser Bar**; the YZ plane becomes parallel to the screen. Now, you can draw the sketch on this plane.

Creating and Dimensioning the Sketch of the Base Feature

1.   Draw the L-shaped sketch for the base feature and add the required constraints to it.

2.   Add dimensions to the sketch. The sketch after adding the dimensions is shown in Figure 5-87.

3. Choose the **Finish Sketch** button from the **Exit** panel of the **Sketch** tab to exit the sketching environment. Change the current view to the isometric view.

Extruding the Sketch

1. Choose the **Extrude** tool from the **Create** panel of the **Model** tab to invoke the **Extrude** dialog box. Next, extrude the sketch to a distance of 72 mm using the **Symmetric** button. You can also choose the **Symmetric** option from the mini toolbar. Choose **OK** to exit the **Extrude** dialog box. The base feature is created, as shown in Figure 5-88.

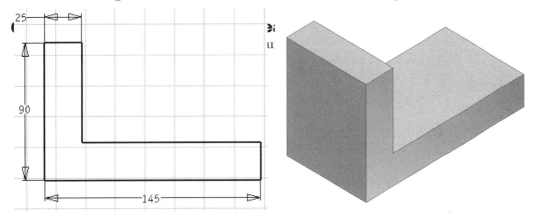

Figure 5-87 *Sketch for the base feature*   *Figure 5-88* *Base feature*

2. Choose the **Create 2D Sketch** tool from the **Sketch** panel of the **Model** tab; you are prompted to select the sketching plane. Select the front face of the base feature as the sketching plane; the sketching environment is invoked.

3. Reorient the model by using the ViewCube, see Figure 5-89. Also, delete the reference geometries that were created when you defined the sketch plane.

4. Draw the sketch for the cut feature and then add the required constraints and dimensions to it. The dimensioned sketch is shown in Figure 5-89.

5. Choose the **Finish Sketch** button from the **Exit** panel of the **Sketch** tab and then change the current view to the isometric view.

Creating the Cut Feature on the Front Face of the Model

1. Extrude the profile defined by the rectangle to a distance of 50 mm using the **Cut** operation. The isometric view of the model with the cut feature is shown in Figure 5-90.

Creating the Sketch for the Cut Feature on the Left Face

The next feature is a cut feature and is to be created on the left face of the model.

1. Choose the **Create 2D Sketch** tool from the **Sketch** panel of the **Model** tab; you are prompted to select a plane for creating the sketch. Select the left face of the model; the sketching environment is activated.

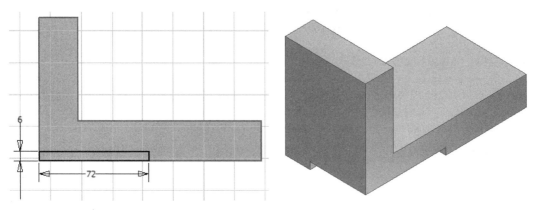

Figure 5-89 *Sketch for the cut feature*

Figure 5-90 *Model after creating the cut feature on the front face*

2. Choose the **View Face** tool from the **Navigation Bar** and then select the left face of the model; the model is reoriented such that the left face becomes parallel to the screen.

3. Delete all reference geometries and then draw the sketch for the cut feature. Add the required constraints and dimensions to the sketch, as shown in Figure 5-91.

4. Exit the sketching environment and then change the current view to the isometric view.

Extruding the Sketch to Create the Cut Feature

1. Extrude the profile to a distance of 12 mm using the **Cut** operation. The model after creating the cut feature on the left face is shown in Figure 5-92.

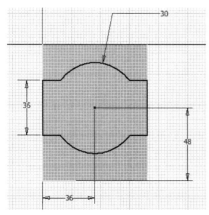

Figure 5-91 *Sketch for the cut feature*

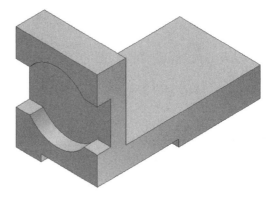

Figure 5-92 *Model after creating the cut feature on the left face*

Creating a Hole

1. Define a new sketch plane on the face that is exposed after creating the cut feature in the previous step.

2. Draw a circle on this face and then add dimensions to it, refer to Figure 5-86c for dimensions.

3. Invoke the **Extrude** tool and extrude the circle using the **Cut** operation. Note that to create this cut feature, you need to select the **All** option from the **Distance** drop-down list in the **Extents** area.

Creating the Last Cut Feature

1. Define a sketch plane on the horizontal face of the base feature and then reorient the model using the ViewCube.

2. Delete all reference geometries and then create the sketch for the cut feature, refer to Figure 5-86b for dimensions. Add the required constraints and dimensions to the sketch.

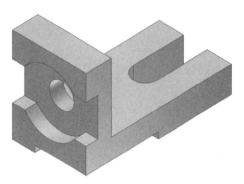

3. Extrude the sketch using the **Cut** operation. Use the **All** option from the **Distance** drop-down list in the **Extents** area. The final model for Tutorial 2 is shown in Figure 5-93.

Figure 5-93 *Solid model for Tutorial 2*

Saving the Model

1. Save the sketch with the name *Tutorial2* at the location given below.

    C:\Inventor_2011\c05

2. Choose **File > Close** from the menu bar to close this file.

Tutorial 3

In this tutorial, you will create the model shown in Figure 5-94a. Its dimensions are shown in Figures 5-94b through 5-94d.   **(Expected time: 45 min)**

Figure 5-94a Model for Tutorial 3

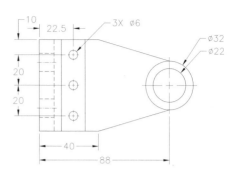

Figure 5-94b Top view of the model

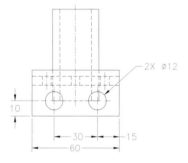

Figure 5-94c Left view of the model

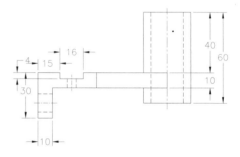

Figure 5-94d Front view of the model

The model for this tutorial is a combination of a base feature, two join features, and six cut features (Holes).

The following steps are required to complete this tutorial:

a. Create the base feature on the YZ plane, refer to Figures 5-95 and 5-96.
b. Create a join feature on the top face of the base feature, refer to Figure 5-98.
c. Create a work plane at an offset of 10 mm from the bottom face of the join feature and then create a cylindrical join feature on it, refer to Figure 5-100.
d. Create a hole in the cylindrical feature by defining a new sketch plane on its top face, refer to Figure 5-101.
e. Create two holes by defining a sketch plane on the left face of the model, refer to Figure 5-101.
f. Define a new sketch plane on the top face of the groove which is on the top face of the model. Then, create three holes on it, refer to Figure 5-101.

Creating the Base Feature

1. Start a new metric standard part file and choose the **Finish Sketch** button from the **Exit** panel of the **Sketch** tab to exit the sketching environment.

2. Click on the plus sign (+) to the left of the **Origin** folder in the **Browser Bar**; the default planes, axes, and center point are displayed.

3. Choose the **Create 2D Sketch** tool from the **Sketch** panel of the **Model** tab; you are prompted to select the plane to create the sketch. Select the **YZ Plane**; the sketcher environment is invoked.

4. Choose the **View Face** tool from the **Navigation Bar** and then select the **YZ Plane** from the **Browser Bar**; the current view is reoriented such that the YZ plane becomes parallel to the screen.

5. Create the sketch for the base feature and then add the required constraints and dimensions to it. The dimensioned sketch for the base feature is shown in Figure 5-95.

6. Exit the sketching environment and then change the current view to the isometric view. Choose the **Extrude** tool from the **Create** panel of the **Model** tab; the **Extrude** dialog box is displayed.

   As the sketch has a single loop, it is automatically selected.

7. Extrude the sketch to a distance of 60 mm using the **Symmetric** option. The base feature is created, as shown in Figure 5-96.

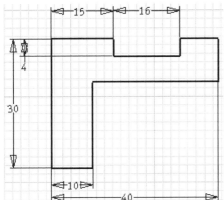
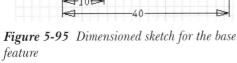

Figure 5-95 Dimensioned sketch for the base feature

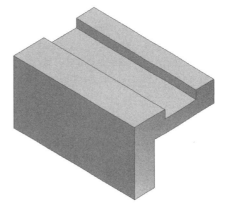

Figure 5-96 Base feature

Creating the First Join Feature on the Top Face

1. Choose the **Create 2D Sketch** tool from the **Sketch** panel of the **Model** tab and select the top face of the base feature as the new sketching plane.

2. Reorient the view using the ViewCube, see Figure 5-97. Draw the sketch for the first join feature and add the required constraints and dimensions to it, as shown in Figure 5-97.

3. Exit the sketching environment and change the current view to the isometric view.

4. Extrude the sketch in the downward direction to a distance of 10 mm, see Figure 5-98.

Note
If the join feature is extruded in the opposite direction, reverse its direction by choosing the **Direction 2** *button from the mini toolbar or from the* **Extents** *area of the* **Extrude** *dialog box.*

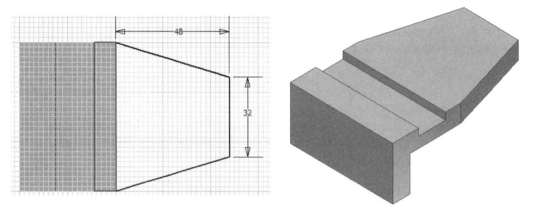

Figure 5-97 *Sketch for the first join feature*   **Figure 5-98** *Model after extruding*

Creating the Cylindrical Feature

As shown in Figure 5-94d, the cylindrical feature starts at a distance of 10 mm below the bottom face of the feature you just created. Therefore, you first need to define a work plane offset at a distance of 10 mm from the bottom face of the first join feature. But first, you need to change the orientation of the model such that the bottom face of the first join feature is visible.

1. Reorient the model using the **Free Orbit** tool such that the bottom face of the first join feature is visible.

2. Choose the **Offset from Plane** tool from **Model > Work Features > Plane** drop-down. Click on the bottom face of the first join feature; the mini toolbar is displayed.

3. Enter **10** in the edit box available in the mini toolbar and make sure the arrow manipulator in the mini toolbar points downward. Next, press ENTER; a work plane is created at an offset of 10 mm from the bottom face of the first join feature.

4. Choose the **Create 2D Sketch** tool from the **Sketch** panel of the **Model** tab and select the work plane as the plane for drawing the sketch of the cylindrical feature. Next, reorient the model using the ViewCube, see Figure 5-99. Increase the drawing display area using the scroll wheel of the mouse, if required.

5. Draw a circle and then add the required constraints and dimensions to it, see Figure 5-99.

6. Exit the sketching environment and then change the current view to the isometric view.

7. Extrude the sketch to a distance of 60 mm in the upward direction and then increase the drawing display area.

    After extruding the sketch, you will notice that the work plane is still visible in the drawing window. As the work plane is not required, you need to turn off its visibility. This is done using the **Browser Bar**.

8. Right-click on **Work Plane1** in the **Browser Bar** to display the shortcut menu.

    In the shortcut menu, you will notice that there is a check mark beside the **Visibility** option. This indicates that the work plane is visible in the drawing window.

9. Choose the **Visibility** option from the shortcut menu; the check mark is cleared making the work plane invisible. Figure 5-100 shows the model after turning off the visibility of the work plane and changing the current view to the isometric view.

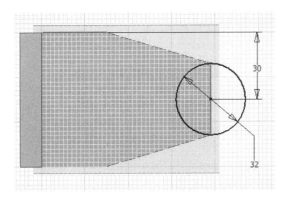

Figure 5-99 Sketch for the cylindrical feature

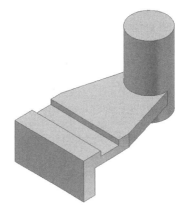

Figure 5-100 Model after creating the cylindrical feature

Creating the Remaining Cut Features

1. Create the remaining cut features by creating their respective sketches on the sketching planes. The final model after creating all cut features is shown in Figure 5-101.

Saving the Model

1. Save the model with the name *Tutorial3* at the location given below and then close the file.

C:\Inventor_2011\c05

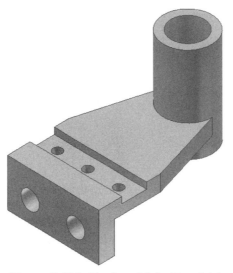

Figure 5-101 *Final model for Tutorial 3*

Self-Evaluation Test

Answer the following questions and then compare them to those given at the end of this chapter:

1. In mechanical designs, all features are created on the XY plane. (T/F)

2. As you select a sketching plane, the sketching environment is activated. (T/F)

3. You cannot define a sketch plane on the circular face of a cylindrical feature. (T/F)

4. The visibility of the shared sketches is turned off by default. (T/F)

5. The work axes are the _____ lines passing through the model or the feature.

6. When you select a vertex after invoking the _____ tool, a triad is displayed on the selected vertex.

7. When you select a planar face or a plane for defining a work plane and then drag it, the _____ toolbar is displayed.

8. All operations that have been used to create a model are displayed in the form of _____ in the **Browser Bar**.

9. The _____ check box in the **More** tab is selected to apply an iMate to an edge of the solid body.

10. The _____ planes are not visible on the screen, but the _____ planes are visible both on the screen and in the **Browser Bar**.

Review Questions

Answer the following questions:

1. Whenever you open a new file, by default you start drawing in the XY plane. (T/F)

2. You can create a work plane tangent to a cylinder by selecting its cylindrical face and then the XY, YZ, or XZ plane to which the resulting work plane should be parallel. (T/F)

3. You can create a work axis on a cylindrical feature by directly selecting it. (T/F)

4. The **All** option in the **Distance** drop-down list of the **Extents** area in the **Extrude** dialog box cannot be combined with the **Join** operation. (T/F)

5. A consumed sketch can be used again for creating another feature. (T/F)

6. Which of the following features is not a work feature?

    (a) Work line   (b) Work axis
    (c) Work plane   (d) Work point

7. How many planes are displayed when you click on the plus sign on the left of the **Origin** folder in the **Browser Bar**?

    (a) 2   (b) 3
    (c) 4   (d) 1

8. Which of the following options of the shortcut menu is used to turn off the display of the work features?

    (a) **Display**   (b) **Show**
    (c) **Visible**   (d) **Visibility**

9. Which of the following operations is used to create a feature by retaining the material common to the existing feature and the sketch?

    (a) **Cut**   (b) **Join**
    (c) **Intersect**   (d) None of these

10. In Autodesk Inventor, which option displays the geometrical dependency of a selected work point, work axis, or work plane.

    (a) **Show Inputs**   (b) **Visibility**
    (c) **Adaptive**   (d) **Show dimensions**

Exercises

Exercise 1

Create the model shown in Figure 5-102. Its dimensions are also given in the same figure.
(Expected time: 45 min)

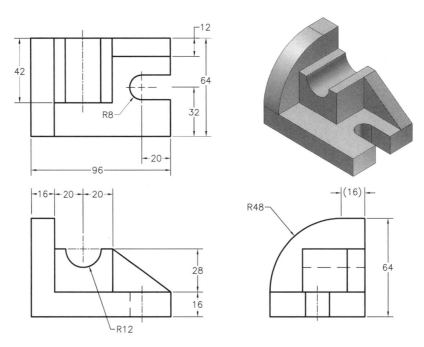

Figure 5-102 Model and its dimensions for Exercise 1

Exercise 2

Create the model shown in Figure 5-103. Its dimensions are given in Figures 5-104a and
5-104b.   **(Expected time: 30 min)**

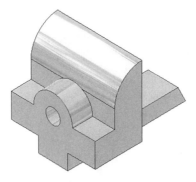

Figure 5-103 Solid model for Exercise 2

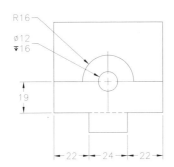

Figure 5-104a *Left view of the model*

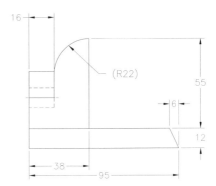

Figure 5-104b *Front view of the model*

Exercise 3

Create the model shown in Figure 5-105. Its dimensions are also given in the same figure.

(Expected time: 30 min)

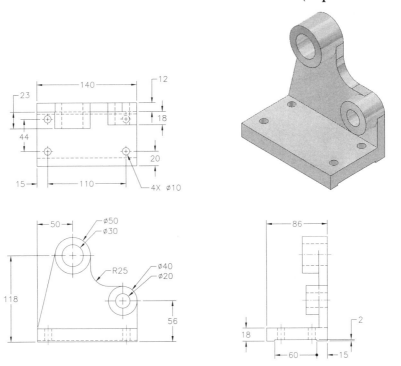

Figure 5-105 *Model and its dimensions for Exercise 3*

Exercise 4

Create the model shown in Figure 5-106. Its dimensions are given in the views shown in Figure 5-107.   **(Expected time: 45 min)**

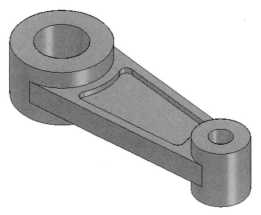

Figure 5-106 *Model for Exercise 4*

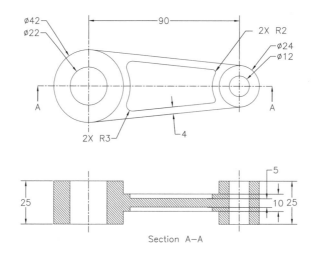

Figure 5-107 *Dimensions of the model for Exercise 4*

Answers to Self-Evaluation Test

1. F, **2.** T, **3.** T, **4.** F, **5.** parametric, **6. Grounded Point**, **7. Offset**, **8.** tree view, **9. Infer iMates**, **10.** sketch, work

Chapter 6

Advanced Modeling Tools-I

Learning Objectives

After completing this chapter, you will be able to:
- *Create various types of holes.*
- *Create fillets on a model.*
- *Chamfer the edges of a model.*
- *Mirror features.*
- *Create rectangular patterns of features.*
- *Create circular patterns of features.*
- *Create rib features.*
- *Thicken or offset faces or surfaces.*
- *Emboss or engrave sketched entities on a feature.*
- *Use the Decal tool to apply an image on a feature.*
- *Assign different colors/styles to a model.*

ADVANCED MODELING TOOLS

Autodesk Inventor has a number of advanced modeling tools to assist you in creating a design. These advanced modeling tools appreciably reduce the time taken in creating the features in the models, thus reducing the designing time. For example, to create a hole in a cylindrical feature, one option is that while sketching the cylindrical feature, you sketch the hole also. But, to edit the dimensions of the hole, you will have to edit the complete sketch. Also, if the hole is drawn along with the sketch of the cylindrical feature, it will be extruded to the same distance. However, if you want the hole to terminate before the end of the cylindrical feature, you will have to draw another sketch. But, if you create the hole using the **Hole** tool, you can specify its depth and other parameters. The advanced modeling tools used in Autodesk Inventor are listed below.

1. Hole
2. Fillet
3. Chamfer
4. Mirror
5. Rectangular Pattern
6. Circular Pattern
7. Rib
8. Thicken/Offset
9. Emboss
10. Decal
11. Sweep
12. Loft

13. Coil
14. Thread
15. Shell
16. Face Draft
17. Split
18. Boundary Patch
19. Trim and Extend Surface
20. Stitch Surface
21. Replace Face
22. Delete Face
23. Move Face
24. Sculpt

In this chapter, the first ten advanced modeling tools will be discussed. The remaining tools will be discussed in the later chapters.

Tip. *To display toolbars, choose the **Customize** tool from the **Options** panel; the **Customize** dialog box will be displayed. Choose the **Toolbars** tab and then select the required toolbar from the **Toolbars** list box in this dialog box. Next, choose the **Show** button; the selected toolbar will be displayed on the screen.*

Note
All features created using the advanced modeling tools are parametric in nature and can be modified at any time.

Creating Holes

Ribbon:	Model > Modify > Hole
Toolbar:	Part Feature > Hole

Hole

Holes are circular cut features that are created on an existing feature. Holes are generally provided to accommodate fasteners in an assembly. You can create drilled, counterbore, spotface, or countersink holes using the **Hole** tool. On invoking this tool, the **Hole** dialog box will be displayed, as shown in Figure 6-1. Alternatively, select the sketch created on an existing feature; a mini toolbar will be displayed in the graphics window. Choose the **Create Hole** tool from the mini toolbar to invoke the **Hole** tool. You can also specify whether a hole is a simple, tapped, taper tapped, or clearance hole using the options in the **Hole** dialog box. The options in this dialog box are discussed next.

Placement Area

The options in this area are used to specify the placement of a hole. These options are discussed next.

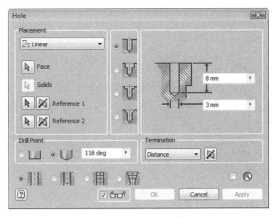

*Figure 6-1 The **Hole** dialog box*

Linear

If there is no unconsumed sketch in the model, this option is selected by default in the drop-down list in the **Placement** area. This option is used to place a hole by defining its location from two linear edges in the model. When you select this option, the **Face** button will be enabled and chosen. As a result, you will be prompted to select a planar face or a work plane as the placement plane. As soon as you select the placement plane, the preview of the hole along with the hole manipulator (sphere) will be displayed on the selected face. Also, the **Reference 1** button will be chosen and you will be prompted to select a linear edge to reference the dimension. You can change the location of the hole dynamically by dragging the hole manipulator. If you select a linear edge, the **Dimension** edit box and the lock icon will be displayed. Using this edit box, you can specify the distance from the center of the hole to the selected edge. After specifying the distance value, lock this value by clicking the lock icon; the **Reference 2** button will be chosen and you will be prompted to select a linear edge to reference the dimension. When you select the second linear edge, the **Dimension** edit box and the lock icon will be displayed. Using this edit box, you can specify the distance from the center of the hole to the selected edge. Figure 6-2 shows the preview of a hole placed using two linear edges.

From Sketch

This option is used to select points/hole centers, endpoints, or center points in an unconsumed sketch to place the hole and is selected by default if there is an unconsumed sketch in the model. When you select this option, the **Centers** button will be automatically chosen in the **Placement** area. If the sketch has a hole center, it will be automatically selected as the center of the hole. But to use endpoints or sketched points, you need to select them manually. Figure 6-3 shows the preview of a hole with a center point as its center.

Tip. *In case the **From Sketch** option is selected, you need to press the SHIFT key and select the hole centers once again to exclude them from being selected. You will notice that the preview of the hole is not displayed. It suggests that the hole center is removed from the selection set and no hole will be created on it.*

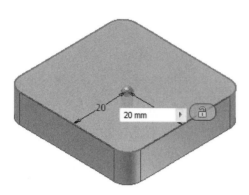

Figure 6-2 *Hole placed using two linear edges*   *Figure 6-3* *Hole placed on a center point*

Concentric

This option is used to place the hole
concentric to a circular feature. When
you select this option, the **Plane** button
will be chosen in the **Placement** area and
you will be prompted to select a planar
face or work plane as the reference plane.
This is the plane where the hole will be
placed. On selecting the placement plane,
the **Concentric Reference** button will be
chosen and you will be prompted to select
a circular edge or a cylindrical face to
reference the hole center. Select the circular
edge. Figure 6-4 shows the preview of a hole
placed concentric to the cylindrical face of
the fillet feature.

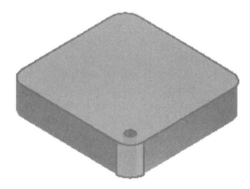

Figure 6-4 *Preview of a hole placed concentric
to the fillet*

On Point

This option is used to place the hole on a work point. The work point can be created by
using the **Grounded Point** option from the **Work Features** panel in the **Model** tab. When
you invoke this option, you will be prompted to select a work point for the hole placement.
After selecting the work point, the **Direction** button will be chosen in the **Placement**
area and you will be prompted to select a planar face, work plane, edge, or axis. Select
the required direction; the preview of the hole to be created will be displayed, as shown
in Figure 6-5. Figure 6-6 shows the preview of the hole at the same work point but the
direction is defined by the side planar face.

Drilled

This is the first radio button in the area to the right of the **Placement** area. This
radio button is selected by default and is used to create a drilled hole. A drilled hole
is the one that has a uniform diameter throughout its length. The hole diameter and depth
have to be specified in the preview window on the right side of this dialog box. Figure 6-7 shows
the section view of a drilled hole.

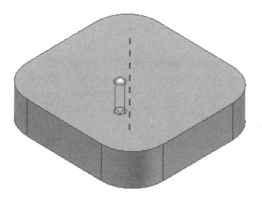

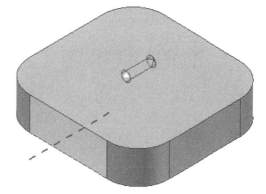

Figure 6-5 *Direction defined using the top plane*

Figure 6-6 *Direction defined using the side plane*

Note

*The end condition of a hole depends on the option selected from the **Termination** drop-down list. If you select the **Through All** option from this drop-down list, the end of the hole will be flat (refer to Figures 6-7 and 6-8). If you select the **Distance** option from it, the end of the hole will have a drill point (refer to Figures 6-9 and 6-11).*

Counterbore

 This radio button is available below the **Drilled** radio button and is used to create a counterbore hole. A counterbore hole is a stepped hole and has two diameters: a bigger diameter and a smaller diameter. The bigger diameter is called the counterbore diameter and the smaller diameter is called the drill diameter. In this type of hole, you also have to specify two depths. The first depth is the counterbore depth. The counterbore depth is the depth up to which the bigger diameter will be defined. The second depth is the depth of the hole, including the counter depth. All these values are defined in the preview window on the right side of the **Hole** dialog box. Figure 6-8 shows the section view of a counterbore hole.

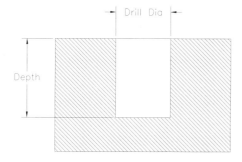

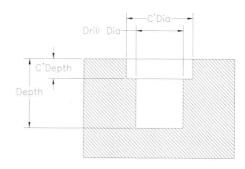

Figure 6-7 *Section view of a drilled hole*

Figure 6-8 *Section view of a counterbore hole*

Spotface

This radio button is available below the **Counterbore** radio button and is selected to create spotfaced holes. Spotfacing provides a seat or a flat surface at the entrance and the surrounding area of a hole. It also allows a cap screw or bolt to seat squarely with the material, even if the clearance hole is not normal to the surrounding material. Spotfacing is generally carried out on castings that have irregular surfaces. The cross-section of a spotfaced hole is similar to that of a counterbore hole. Figure 6-9 displays the section view of a spotface hole.

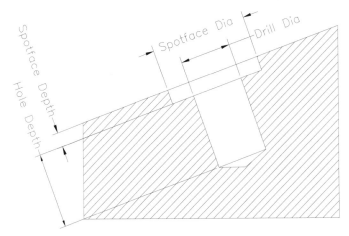

Figure 6-9 *Section view of a spotface hole*

Countersink

This radio button is provided below the **Spotface** radio button and is used to create a countersink hole. A countersink hole also has two diameters, but the transition between the bigger diameter and the smaller diameter is in the form of a cone. You need to define the countersink diameter, drill diameter, depth of the hole, and the countersink angle. Figure 6-10 shows the section view of a countersink hole.

Drill Point Area

The options in the **Drill Point** area are used to specify whether the end of the hole will be a flat or a tapered face. These options are discussed next.

Flat

If this radio button is selected, the end of the hole will be a flat plane.

Angle

If this radio button is selected, the end of the hole will be tapered and will converge to a point. The angle of the taper can be defined in the **Drill Point Angle** edit box provided on the right of this radio button. Figure 6-11 shows a countersink hole with a tapered end.

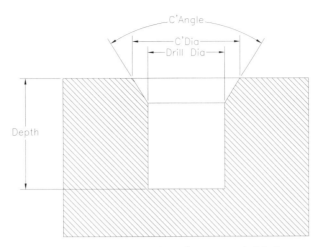

Figure 6-10 *Section view of a countersink hole*

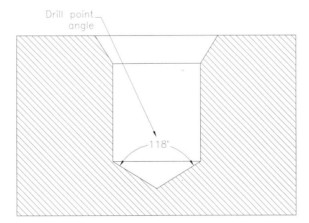

Figure 6-11 *Countersink hole with a tapered end*

Termination Area

The drop-down list under this area is used to define the termination of the holes. The options available in this drop-down list are discussed next.

Distance

This option is used to create a hole by defining its depth up to a certain distance. The depth of the hole is defined in the preview window. You can reverse the direction of hole creation by choosing the **Flip** button available on right of this drop-down list.

Through All

The **Through All** option is used to create a hole through all features that it comes across. The direction of the hole creation can be reversed by using the **Flip** button. When you select this option, the depth of the hole is no more displayed in the preview window because the hole will be created automatically by cutting through all features in the specified direction. Also, the **Drill Point** area will be deactivated.

To

The **To** option is used to terminate the hole feature at a specified plane, planar face, or an extended face. When you select this option, the **Flip** button is replaced by the **Select surface to end the feature creation** button. Using this button, you can select the face to terminate the hole feature.

Simple Hole

This radio button is selected by default and is used to create simple holes.

Clearance Hole

The **Clearance Hole** radio button is selected to create clearance holes to accommodate standard fasteners. When you select this radio button, the **Hole** dialog box expands and displays the **Fastener** area, as shown in Figure 6-12. This area provides the options to create a tapped hole. These options are discussed next.

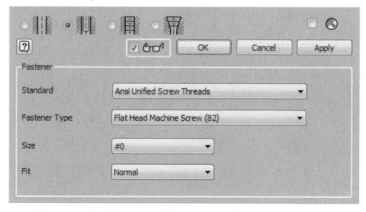

*Figure 6-12 The expanded portion of the **Hole** dialog box*

Standard

The **Standard** drop-down list is used to select the standard of the fastener to be accommodated in the hole.

Fastener Type

The **Fastener Type** drop-down list is used to select the type of fastener to be accommodated in the hole.

Size

This drop-down list is used to select the size of the fastener.

Fit

This drop-down list is used to specify the type of hole fit.

Tapped Hole

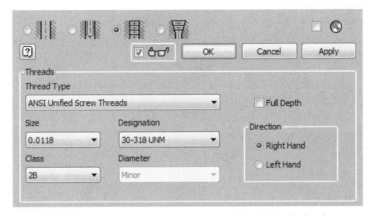

The **Tapped Hole** radio button is selected to create threaded holes. When you select this radio button, the **Hole** dialog box expands and displays the **Threads** area, as shown in Figure 6-13. This area provides the options to create a tapped hole. These options are discussed next.

Figure 6-13 The expanded portion of the **Hole** *dialog box*

Thread Type

The **Thread Type** drop-down list is used to select the type of threads. You can select the default type of threads in this drop-down list.

Size

This drop-down list is used to select the nominal size of the threads. The designation and the class value will be different for different nominal sizes.

Designation

This drop-down list is used to specify the designation of the thread profile.

Class

The **Class** drop-down list is used to select the class of threads. Also, higher the numeric value in this drop-down list, the more accurate is the fitting.

Diameter

The **Diameter** drop-down list is used to specify whether the diameter defined for creating the threads is the major, minor, pitch, or drill diameter. Note that you can change this value only by using the **Modeling** tab of the **Document Settings** dialog box. This dialog box can be invoked by choosing the **Document Settings** tool from the **Options** panel.

Full Depth

If the **Full Depth** check box is selected, the threads will run through the length of the hole. If this check box is not selected, you will have to specify the depth up to which the threads will be created. This depth is defined in the preview window on the right side of the **Hole** dialog box.

Direction Area

The options in the **Direction** area are used to specify the direction of the threads. These options are discussed next.

Right Hand

The **Right Hand** radio button is used to create right-handed threads. A right-handed thread enters a nut when you turn it in the clockwise direction.

Left Hand

The **Left Hand** radio button is used to create left-handed threads. A left-handed thread enters a nut when you turn it in the counterclockwise direction.

Figure 6-14 shows a hole without threads and Figure 6-15 shows a hole with threads.

Figure 6-14 *A counterbore hole without threads*   ***Figure 6-15*** *A counterbore hole with threads*

Taper Tapped Hole

The **Taper Tapped Hole** radio button is selected to create taper threaded holes. When you select this radio button, the **Hole** dialog box expands and displays the **Threads** area, as shown in Figure 6-16. This area provides the options to create different types of taper threaded holes. These options are discussed next.

Thread Type

The **Thread Type** drop-down list is used to select the type of threads. You can select the default type of threads in this drop-down list.

Size

This drop-down list is used to select the nominal size of the threads. The designation and the class value will be different for different nominal sizes.

Designation

This drop-down list is used to specify the designation of the thread profile.

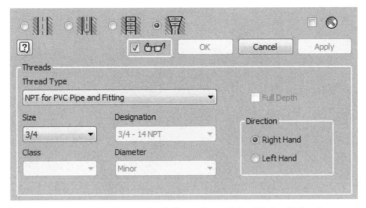

Figure 6-16 *The expanded portion of the* **Hole** *dialog box*

Class

The **Class** drop-down list is used to select the class of threads. Also, higher the numeric value in this drop-down list, more accurate is the fitting.

Diameter

The **Diameter** drop-down list is used to specify whether the diameter defined for creating the threads is the major, minor, pitch, or drill diameter of the original hole.

Direction Area

The options in the **Direction** area are used to specify the direction of the threads. These options are discussed next.

Right Hand

The **Right Hand** radio button is used to create right-handed threads. A right-handed thread enters a nut when you turn it in the clockwise direction.

Left Hand

The **Left Hand** radio button is used to create left-handed threads. A left-handed thread enters a nut when you turn it in the counterclockwise direction.

Figure 6-17 shows the section view of a straight hole with threads and Figure 6-18 shows the section view of a tapered hole with threads.

Infer iMates

This check box is available below the **Termination** area and is selected to create an iMate on the hole feature.

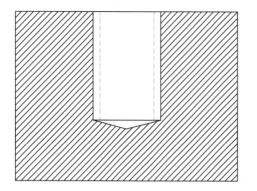

Figure 6-17 Section view of a straight hole with threads

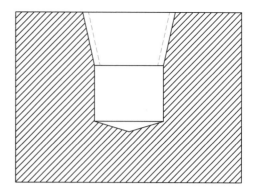

Figure 6-18 Section view of tapered hole with threads

CREATING FILLETS

| **Ribbon:** | Model > Modify > Fillet |
| **Toolbar:** | Part Features > Fillet |

Fillet

In Autodesk Inventor, you can add fillets or rounds using the **Fillet** tool. Fillets are generally used to apply curves on the interior edges of a model and result in concave surfaces by adding material. Rounds are generally used to apply curves on the exterior edges and result in convex surface by removing the material.

Autodesk Inventor allows you to create different types of fillets. You will learn about these fillets in the following topics.

Creating Edge Fillets

To create edge fillets, choose the **Fillet** tool; the **Fillet** dialog box will be displayed, as shown in Figure 6-19. Alternatively, invoke the **Fillet** dialog box by choosing the **Create Fillet** tool from the mini toolbar that is displayed when you select the edge to be filleted. By default, the **Edge Fillet** button is chosen in the **Fillet** dialog box. As a result, the options to create edge fillet are displayed. Also, the preview of the fillet along with the modified mini toolbar will be displayed on the selected edge, as shown in Figure 6-20. You can enter the radius of the fillet in the edit box of the mini toolbar and choose **OK** to create the fillet. The options available under various tabs of the **Fillet** dialog box are discussed next.

Constant Tab

The options under this tab are used to fillet the selected edges such that they have a constant radius throughout their length. However, different edges can have a different fillet radius.

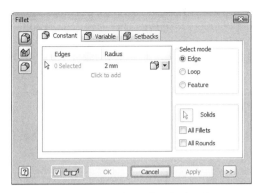

Figure 6-19 The **Fillet** *dialog box*

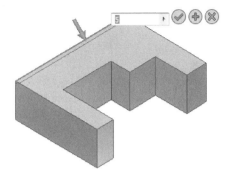

Figure 6-20 Mini toolbar displayed on invoking the **Fillet** tool

Edges

When you invoke the **Fillet** tool, the **Fillet** dialog box will be displayed and you will be prompted to select an edge to fillet. The number of edges you select will be displayed under this column. However, note that all the edges selected will have the same fillet radius. If you want to specify a different fillet radius to some edges, click on the text **Click to add**; another row will be added. Now, if you select an edge, it will be displayed in the second row. The second row can be assigned a different fillet radius.

Radius

In this column, you can specify the fillet radius for the selected edges. Different rows can have different radii. You can also specify the fillet radius for the selected edges by entering the radius value in the edit box of the mini toolbar or by dragging the arrow manipulator.

Continuity

This drop-down list is available on the right of the **Radius** column. You can select the option to apply a tangent continuity or smooth continuity by selecting the options in this drop-down list.

Select Mode Area

The options under this area are used to set the priorities of selection for filleting.

Edge: If the **Edge** radio button is selected, you can select the individual edges of a model for filleting. As you move the cursor close to any of the edges, it will be highlighted.

Loop: The **Loop** radio button is used to select all the edges of a face of the model. To use this option, select the **Loop** radio button and move the cursor close to an edge of the face; all its edges will be highlighted. Click at this stage to select all the edges of the face. Remember that edges selected using this option will have the same fillet radius.

Feature: If the **Feature** radio button is selected, all edges in the selected feature will be selected for filleting. In this case, all the selected edges will also be applied with the same fillet radius.

Solids

The **Solids** button is used to select a body in a multi-body environment so that the resultant fillet feature becomes a portion of the body. When you choose this button, you can create rounds or fillets on all edges of the selected body.

All Fillets

The **All Fillets** check box is selected to create concave-shaped fillets at all possible edges. Note that the fillet radius is same at all places. Figure 6-21 shows a model with fillets.

All Rounds

The **All Rounds** check box is selected to create convex-shaped fillets at all possible edges. All exterior corners will also be curved if you select this check box. The radius for all rounds will be the same. Figure 6-22 shows a model with rounds.

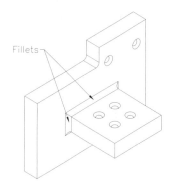

Figure 6-21 Model with fillets

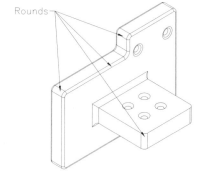

Figure 6-22 Model with rounds

Enable/Disable feature preview

This check box is used to enable or disable the preview of a fillet feature. If this check box is selected, the preview of the fillet will be displayed in the drawing window.

Variable Tab

The options in the **Variable** tab, as shown in Figure 6-23, are used to fillet the selected edges such that they can be applied different radii along their length. If you select a linear or a curved edge, there will be two points on the edge, one at the start point and the other at the end point. However, if you select a circular edge, no point will be defined. You can add points by specifying their desired location on the edge.

Edges

This column displays the number of edges selected to be filleted. You can select more edges by clicking on **Click to add**.

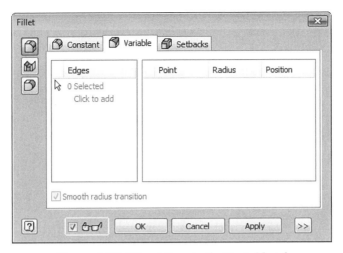

Figure 6-23 *The options in the* ***Variable*** *tab*

Point

This column displays the points selected on the edge. By default, there will be only two points, **Start** and **End**, at the start point and the endpoint of a linear or a curved edge, respectively. To add a point, move the cursor on the edge; the preview of the point is displayed. Click to place the point. As soon as you add a point by specifying its location on the edge, it will be added in this column. Similarly, you can add as many points as required on the edge. As mentioned earlier, if you select a circular edge for adding a variable fillet, no point will be added by default. You need to add all the points manually by clicking on the edge.

Radius

The **Radius** column displays the radius at a point selected on an edge. When you click on a value field in this column, it changes to an edit box. Also, the point selected on the edge is displayed under the **Point** column. You can change the radius value of a point by selecting its corresponding value field in the **Radius** edit box and entering a new value in it.

Position

This edit box is used to define the position of the point specified on an edge. Remember that the position is defined in terms of the percentage of the selected edge. This edit box will not be available until you select a point other than the default points on an edge. The length of the selected edge is taken as 1 (100 percent) and the position of the new point will be defined anywhere between 0 and 1. For example, a value of 0.5 will suggest that the point is placed at the midpoint of the edge.

Figures 6-24 and 6-25 show the variable fillets on the edges of a model.

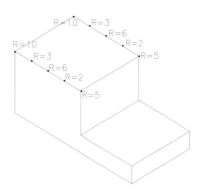

Figure 6-24 Defining the fillet radius

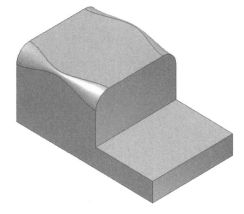

Figure 6-25 Model after creating the fillet

Smooth radius transition

This check box is selected to allow a smooth transition between all the points defined in an edge. If this check box is selected, there will be a smooth blending between all points, as shown in Figure 6-26. If it is cleared, the blending will be linear, as shown in Figure 6-27.

Figure 6-26 Smooth transition

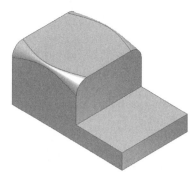

Figure 6-27 Linear transition

Setbacks Tab

The options in the **Setbacks** tab are used to specify the setbacks of the transition between the three edges that comprise a vertex. The setback smoothly blends the transition surfaces between the selected edges and the vertex that you define to fillet. To add a setback fillet, first you need to select the three edges that intersect at a corner by using the **Constant** tab and then choose the **Setbacks** tab, refer to Figure 6-28. The options in this tab are discussed next.

Vertex

After you have selected three edges using the **Constant** tab, invoke the **Setbacks** tab; you will be prompted to select the common vertex to add the setback. Select the vertex common to the three selected edges. The selected vertex will be displayed in this column. You can also add more vertices by clicking on **Click to add**.

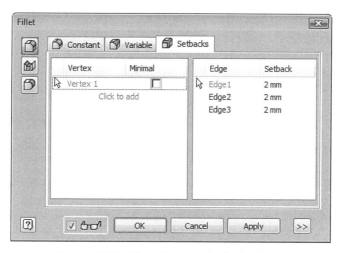

Figure 6-28 The options in the **Setbacks** tab

Minimal

This check box is selected to define the minimum allowable setback for a given vertex. You can solve difficult vertex fillets with smoothest transition by using this option.

Edge

This column displays the edges common to the vertex selected on a model. The edge that will have the arrow in front will be highlighted in the drawing window.

Setback

This column displays the setback value for the transition along the edge selected. You can modify this value by clicking on it.

Figures 6-29 and 6-30 show the fillets created using different setback values.

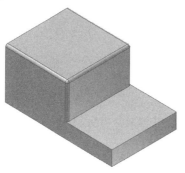

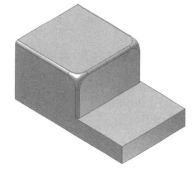

Figure 6-29 Fillet with setback =2   *Figure 6-30* Fillet with setback =10

Note

*You cannot set the radius of a fillet by using the **Setbacks** tab. It will be set in the **Constant** tab where you have selected the edges.*

>> (More)

This button is available at the lower right corner of the **Fillet** dialog box. When you choose this button, the **Fillet** dialog box will expand and display some more options, see Figure 6-31. All these options are discussed next.

*Figure 6-31 More options of the **Fillet** dialog box*

Roll along sharp edges

This check box is selected to modify the radius of the fillet in order to retain the shape and the sharpness of the edges of the adjacent faces. If this check box is cleared, the adjacent faces will extend in case the fillet radius is more than what can be adjusted in the current face. Figure 6-32 shows the fillet created with the **Roll along sharp edges** check box cleared and Figure 6-33 shows the fillet created with this check box selected.

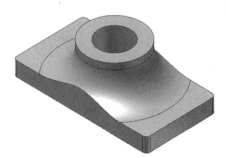

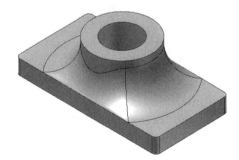

*Figure 6-32 Fillet created with the **Roll along sharp edges** check box cleared*

*Figure 6-33 Fillet created with the **Roll along sharp edges** check box selected*

Rolling ball where possible

This check box is selected to create a rolling ball fillet, wherever it is possible. If this check box is cleared, the transition at the sharp corners will be continuously tangent. Figure 6-34 shows the rolling ball fillet created by selecting this check box and Figure 6-35 shows the tangent fillet created by clearing the check box. Note that you need to select all the edges in a single fillet sequence to use this option.

Automatic Edge Chain

If this check box is selected, all tangent edges will also be selected on selecting an edge to fillet.

Preserve All Features

This check box is selected to calculate the intersection of all the features that intersect with the fillet. If this check box is cleared, the intersection of only the edges that are a part of the fillet will be calculated.

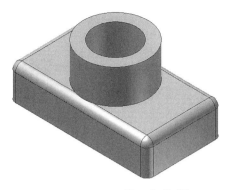

Figure 6-34 *Rolling ball fillet*

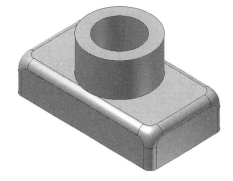

Figure 6-35 *Tangent fillet*

Creating Face Fillets

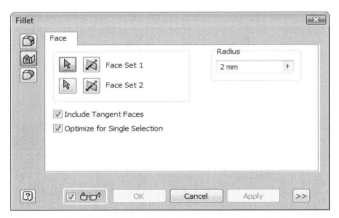

To create a fillet between two faces, choose the **Face Fillet** button provided below the **Edge Fillet** button of the **Fillet** dialog box. The **Face Fillet** button is used to blend the first face with the second face. When you create a fillet with this tool, the material is added or removed according to the geometric conditions. It can also remove the faces completely or partially to accommodate the fillet. When you choose the **Face Fillet** button from the **Fillet** dialog box, the dialog box will be modified, as shown in Figure 6-36 and you will be prompted to select faces to blend. The options used to create a face fillet are discussed next.

Figure 6-36 *The **Fillet** dialog box for creating the face fillet*

Face Set 1

This button is chosen by default and is used to select the first face to create the face fillet. You can choose the **Flip** button on the right of this button to reverse the direction in which the fillet will be created. The **Flip** button will be activated only if you are creating the face fillet between two surfaces. As soon as you select the first face, it will be highlighted in blue and the **Face Set 2** button will be chosen. If you have to select multiple faces to create the fillet, you need to clear the **Optimize for Single Selection** check box available in this dialog box.

Face Set 2

This button is used to select the second face to create the face fillet. You can choose the **Flip** button on the right of this button to reverse the direction in which the fillet will be created. The face that you select as the second face to blend will be highlighted in green.

Radius Area

The edit box available in this area is used to specify the face fillet radius. If the default value specified in this edit box is valid to create the fillet, the preview of the fillet will also be displayed as soon as you select the face set 2.

Include Tangent Faces

If this check box is selected, all faces tangent to the selected face sets will also be selected to create the fillet.

Optimize for Single Selection

If this check box is selected, the **Face Set 2** button is automatically chosen after you select the first face to fillet. If this check box is cleared, you can select multiple faces.

>> (More)

This button is available at the lower right corner of the **Fillet** dialog box. When you choose this button, the **Fillet** dialog box will expand and display some more options, see Figure 6-37. The **Help Point** area in the **More** option is discussed next.

Figure 6-37 *More option for creating the face fillet*

Help Point Area

This area is available when you choose the **More** button from the **Fillet** dialog box. When you select this check box, the **Point** button will be enabled. This button allows you to place help point on one of the faces selected to be filleted if there are multiple fillet solutions.

Figure 6-38 shows the faces selected to create the face fillet and Figure 6-39 shows the resulting face fillet.

Creating Full Round Fillets

A full round fillet is a semicircular fillet created between two side faces that are separated by a centre face. In this case, the system determines the required radius value, based on the side faces and center face. To create this type of fillet, choose the **Full Round** button available below the **Face Fillet** button of the **Fillet** dialog box; the options for creating the full round fillet will be displayed in the dialog box, as shown in Figure 6-40. Also, you will be prompted to select the faces to blend. The options used for creating a full round fillet are discussed next.

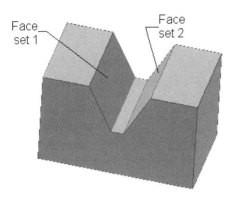

Figure 6-38 *Faces selected to create a face fillet*

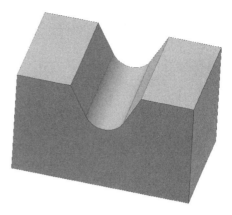

Figure 6-39 *Resulting face fillet*

Side Face Set 1

This button is chosen by default and is used to select the first side face. As soon as you select the first side face, the **Center Face Set** button is chosen. The side face 1 is highlighted in blue.

Center Face Set

This button is chosen to specify the center face for the full round fillet. Note that this face will be removed from the fillet. As soon as you select the center side face, the **Side Face Set 2** button is chosen. The center face is highlighted in green.

Figure 6-40 *The options in the **Fillet** dialog box to create the full round fillet*

Side Face Set 2

This button is chosen to specify the second side face. As soon as you select the second side face, the preview of the fillet will be displayed. The side face 2 is highlighted in purple.

Figure 6-41 shows the faces to be selected to create the full round fillet and Figure 6-42 shows the resulting fillet.

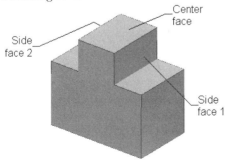

Figure 6-41 *Faces to be selected to create the fillet*

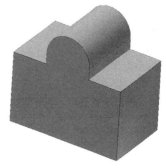

Figure 6-42 *Resulting face fillet*

Note
The remaining options to create the full round fillet are the same as those discussed while creating the face fillet.

Creating Chamfers

Ribbon:	Model > Modify > Chamfer
Toolbar:	Part Features > Chamfer

Chamfering is a process of beveling the sharp edges of a model to reduce stress concentration. In Autodesk Inventor, chamfers are created using the **Chamfer** tool.

To create a chamfer, choose the **Chamfer** tool from the **Modify** panel of the **Model** tab; the **Chamfer** dialog box will be displayed, as shown in Figure 6-43. Alternatively, choose the **Create Chamfer** tool from the mini toolbar that is displayed on selecting the edge to be filleted. In the **Chamfer** dialog box, the **Edges** button will be active by default. As a result, you will be prompted to select an edge. Select the required edge(s); the preview of the chamfer along with the modified mini toolbar will be displayed on the selected edge(s), refer to Figure 6-44. You can enter the chamfer value(s) either in the edit box(es) of the mini toolbar or in the **Distance** edit box(es) of the **Chamfer** dialog box. Next, specify the chamfer option and then choose **OK** to create the chamfer with the specified options.

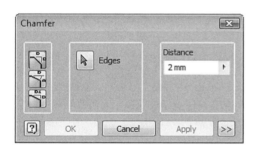

*Figure 6-43 The **Chamfer** dialog box*

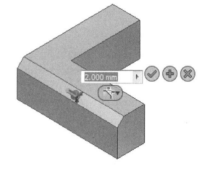

*Figure 6-44 Mini toolbar displayed on the selected edge on invoking the **Chamfer** tool*

The options in the **Chamfer** dialog box are discussed next.

Distance

This is the first button in the dialog box and is provided on the upper left corner of the **Chamfer** dialog box. This button is chosen to create a chamfer such that the selected edge is equidistant from both the faces. The chamfer thus created will be at 45-degree angle. Since both the distance values are the same, therefore, there will be only one edit box in the **Distance** area. You can specify the chamfer distance in it. You can also invoke the **Distance** option from the mini toolbar and specify the chamfer distance by dragging the arrow head manipulator.

Distance and Angle

This is the second method of creating chamfers. This option is used to create a chamfer by defining the chamfer distance and angle. On choosing this button, you will be prompted to select the face to be chamfered. This is the face from which the angle will be calculated. After selecting the face, you will be prompted to select an edge. Select the edge to be chamfered. The distance value and the angle value can be specified in their respective edit boxes in the dialog box. You can also invoke the **Distance and Angle** option from the mini toolbar and then specify the chamfer distance and the angle by dragging the corresponding manipulators in it.

Two Distances

This button is chosen to create a chamfer by using two different distances. You can also invoke this option from the mini toolbar. The distance values can be specified in the **Distance1** and **Distance2** edit boxes. These edit boxes are displayed when you choose this button. You can also specify the chamfer distances by dragging the corresponding manipulators in the mini toolbar. The distance values can be interchanged by choosing the **Flip** button available below the **Edge** button.

Figure 6-45 shows the model before chamfering and Figure 6-46 shows the model after chamfering.

Figure 6-45 Model before chamfering

Figure 6-46 Model after chamfering

>> (More)

This button is available at the lower right corner of the dialog box. When you choose this button, the **Chamfer** dialog box will expand and display some more options, see Figure 6-47. These options are discussed next.

Figure 6-47 More options in the **Chamfer** dialog box

Edge Chain Area

The buttons in this area are used to set the priorities for selecting the edges to be chamfered. If you select the **All tangentially connected edges** button, all the edges that are tangent to the selected edge will also be selected for chamfering. If you choose the **Single edge** button, the tangent edges will be ignored.

Setback Area

The buttons in this area are used to specify whether or not a setback will be applied to the model. If you choose the **Setback** button, the setback will be applied and the vertex will be flattened. However, if you choose the **No setback** button, the setback will not be applied and the vertex will be pointed. Figure 6-48 shows the chamfer created with a setback and Figure 6-49 shows the chamfer without a setback.

Figure 6-48 *Chamfer with a setback*   *Figure 6-49* *Chamfer without a setback*

Note
*The **Preserve All Features** check box is the same as that discussed in the **Fillet** dialog box.*

Mirroring Features and Models

Ribbon:	Model > Pattern > Mirror
Toolbar:	Part Features > Mirror

This tool is used to create the mirrored copies of selected features or to mirror the entire model by using a mirror plane. The plane that can be used to mirror the features can be a planar face or a work plane. An exact replica of the selected entities will be created at a distance from the mirror plane. This distance will be equal to the distance between the original selected entities and the mirror plane. On choosing the **Mirror** tool, the **Mirror** dialog box will be displayed, as shown in Figure 6-50, and you will be prompted to select the feature to be patterned. The options in the **Mirror** dialog box are discussed next.

Figure 6-50 *The **Mirror** dialog box*

Mirroring Features

To mirror features, choose the **Mirror individual features** button from the **Mirror** dialog box. The **Features** button will be chosen and you will be prompted to select the feature to be patterned. Select the features that you want to mirror. Next, choose the **Mirror Plane** button and select the mirror plane about which the selected features will be mirrored; the preview of the mirrored features will be displayed. Figure 6-51 shows the features selected to mirror and Figure 6-52 shows the model created by mirroring the features.

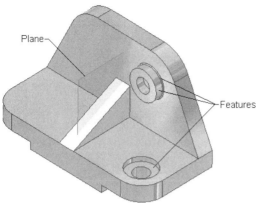

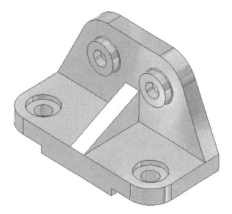

Figure 6-51 *The features to be mirrored and the mirror plane*

Figure 6-52 *Model after mirroring the features and hiding the work plane*

Mirroring Models

To mirror the entire model, choose the **Mirror a solid** button from the **Mirror** dialog box; the entire model will be selected and highlighted. Also, the **Mirror Plane** button will be chosen and you will be prompted to select a plane to mirror about. You can choose the **Include Work Features** button to select the work features that you want to mirror. Selecting the **Remove Original** check box allows you to remove the original model after it has been mirrored. You can select one body from a set of multiple bodies to pattern by choosing the **Solid** button from the **Mirror** dialog box. Choose the **Join** button to merge the selected solid body to the pattern. Figure 6-53 shows the model selected to be mirrored, the highlighted mirror plane, and the preview of the mirrored model. Figure 6-54 shows the mirrored model.

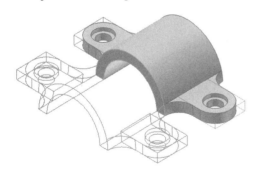

Figure 6-53 *Selecting a model to be mirrored and the mirror plane*

Figure 6-54 *The model after mirroring the entire model*

>> (More)

This button is available at the lower right corner of the **Mirror** dialog box. If you choose this button, the **Mirror** dialog box will expand and display some other options, see Figure 6-55. These options are discussed next.

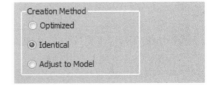

Figure 6-55 *Other options in the **Mirror** dialog box*

Optimized

This radio button is selected to mirror the model as the direct copy of the original model without any overlapping.

Identical

This radio button is selected to create a mirrored feature that is exactly similar to the original feature, even if it intersects other features.

Adjust to Model

This radio button is available only when you mirror features and is selected if the feature to be mirrored terminates on a face of the model. In this case, the mirror feature will modify its termination such that it adjusts in the model.

Creating Rectangular Patterns

Ribbon:	Model > Pattern > Rectangular Pattern
Toolbar:	Part Features > Rectangular Pattern

 You can use the **Rectangular Pattern** tool to create a rectangular pattern of the selected features or surfaces, or the entire model. When you invoke this tool, the **Rectangular Pattern** dialog box will be displayed, as shown in Figure 6-56.

Figure 6-56 The Rectangular Pattern dialog box

Pattern individual features

 This button is chosen to create a pattern of the selected features. You can select the features using the **Features** button that is available on the right of this button.

Pattern a solid

 This button is chosen to select the entire model to create a pattern. You can choose the **Include Work Features** button on the right of this button to select the work features that you want to include in the pattern of the model.

Direction 1/Direction 2 Area

Most of the options in the **Direction 1** and **Direction 2** areas are similar to those discussed in the **Rectangular Pattern** dialog box in the sketching environment. However, there are certain additional options and these are discussed next.

Midplane

This check box is selected to place the items symmetrically on both sides of the original feature. If there is even number of items in the pattern, the additional item is placed on the side in which the direction arrow points.

Spacing

The **Spacing** option, which is the default option, is used to specify the distance between the items in terms of the spacing between individual items.

Distance

The **Distance** option is used to specify the gap between the items in terms of the total distance between all the items along the current direction. The value entered in the **Spacing** edit box will be taken as the total distance between all the items.

Curve Length

The **Curve Length** option is used to select the length of the edge selected to define direction 1 or 2 as the distance between all the items in the array. When you select this option, the **Spacing** edit box is not enabled.

Figure 6-57 shows the hole to be selected for creating a rectangular pattern and Figure 6-58 shows the model after creating a rectangular pattern.

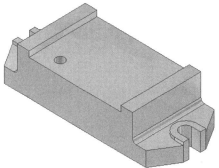

Figure 6-57 Hole to be patterned

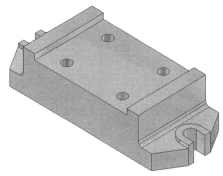

Figure 6-58 Model after creating the pattern

If you choose the **> > (More)** button at the lower right corner of the dialog box, the dialog box expands and displays other options, as shown in Figure 6-59. These options are discussed next.

Direction 1/Direction 2 Area

The **Start** buttons in these areas are used to specify the start point of the path along the first or second direction. You can use this option in association with the **Curve Length** option. For example, when you define the first and second directions using the edges,

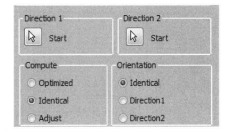

Figure 6-59 Other options in the *Rectangular Pattern* dialog box

two green points are displayed at their corners. These points specify the start points of the path along both the directions. Now, select the **Curve Length** option from the drop-down list available in the **Direction 1** and **Direction 2** areas and then select the start points in direction 1 and direction 2. You will notice that the selected feature starts patterning from the start points specified.

Compute Area

The options under this area are discussed next.

Optimized

The **Optimized** radio button is used to create optimized pattern instances for a lesser calculation time. This option is not useful while working on complex patterns such as when the pattern instances are intersected by some other features.

Identical

The **Identical** radio button is selected, if you want the patterned features to be exactly similar to the original feature, even if they intersect other features.

Adjust

The **Adjust** radio button is selected if any of the patterned features terminate at a face of the model. In this case, the patterned features will be modified such that they adjust in the model. But the pattern calculation time in such cases is longer.

Orientation Area

The options under this area are discussed next.

Identical

The **Identical** radio button is selected to specify the orientation of the patterned items to be the same as that of the original item.

Direction 1

The **Direction 1** radio button is selected to orient the items with reference to the first direction.

Direction 2

The **Direction 2** radio button is selected to orient the items with reference to the second direction.

Note

*All instances of the rectangular pattern are displayed under the heading **Rectangular Pattern** in the **Browser Bar**. Click on the plus sign (+) located on the left of the pattern feature in the **Browser Bar** to expand the tree view. You can select any of the instances and right-click and choose the **Suppress** option from the shortcut menu to turn off the display of that instance in the model. The remaining options in the **Rectangular Pattern** dialog box are similar to those discussed under the **Rectangular Pattern** dialog box in Chapter 4.*

For a better understanding of the **Orientation** options, create a pattern only in the first direction and use a circular edge to define the first direction. Now, one by one, set the orientation to Identical and Direction 1 and notice the difference in the orientation of the items. For example, Figure 6-60 shows the preview of the rectangular pattern oriented using the **Identical** option and Figure 6-61 shows the preview of the rectangular pattern oriented using the **Direction1** option. Note that in both these options, the first direction of the pattern is defined using the circular edge.

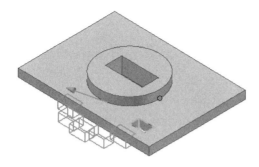

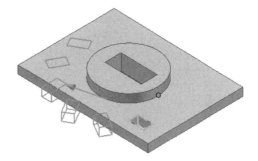

Figure 6-60 *Preview of the pattern oriented using the **Identical** option*

Figure 6-61 *Preview of the pattern oriented using the **Direction1** option*

Note
In Figures 6-60 and 6-61, the pattern is created only along one direction that is defined by the circular edge of the cylindrical feature.

Creating Circular Patterns

Ribbon:	Model > Pattern > Circular Pattern
Toolbar:	Part Features > Circular Pattern

In the Part module, you can use the **Circular Pattern** tool to arrange the selected features around an imaginary cylinder, thereby creating a circular pattern. When you invoke this tool, the **Circular Pattern** dialog box will be displayed. If you choose the **>>** button from this dialog box; this dialog box will expand, as shown in Figure 6-62.

Most options in the **Placement** and **Positioning Method** areas are similar to those discussed in the sketching environment. The remaining options of this dialog box are discussed next.

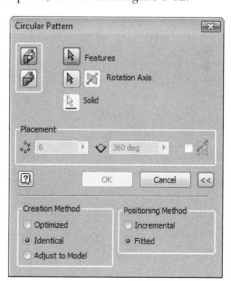

Pattern individual features

This button is chosen by default and is used to select the individual features to create the circular pattern.

Pattern a solid

This button is chosen to pattern the entire solid. You can also select work features to be patterned along with solid by choosing the **Include Work/Surface Features** button.

Figure 6-62 *The expanded **Circular Pattern** dialog box*

Rotation Axis

The **Rotation Axis** button is chosen to select the axis about which the features will be arranged. The entities that can be selected as the rotation axis include a work axis or a linear edge of any face of the model. You can also select a cylindrical feature, whose central axis will be selected as the axis of rotation.

Midplane

This check box is selected to place the items symmetrically on both sides of the original feature. If there are even number of items in the pattern, the additional item is placed on the side in which the direction arrow points.

Creation Method Area

The options under this area will be displayed, when you choose the button with two arrows provided at the lower right corner of this dialog box. These options are discussed next.

Optimized

The **Optimized** radio button is used to create optimized pattern instances for a lesser calculation time. This option is not useful while working on complex patterns such as when the pattern instances are intersected by some other features.

Identical

This radio button is selected, if you want the patterned features to be exactly similar to the original feature, even if they intersect other features.

Adjust to Model

This radio button is selected if any patterned feature terminates at a face of the model. In this case, the patterned features will be modified such that they adjust in the model.

Figure 6-63 shows a model before creating the circular pattern and Figure 6-64 shows the model after creating the circular pattern. In this case, the cylindrical feature is selected for defining the axis of rotation. By doing so, you will select its central axis as the axis of rotation.

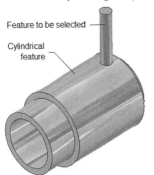

Figure 6-63 Model before creating the pattern   *Figure 6-64* Model after creating the pattern

Positioning Method Area

This area is used to define the spacing between instances of the features. The options in this area works in combination with the **Angle** edit box and they are discussed next.

Incremental

If you select this radio button, the angle that you specify in the **Angle** edit box will be considered as the incremental angle between patterns. Therefore, the circular pattern will be created such that the angle between the two items is equal to the angle specified in the **Angle** edit box. Figure 6-65 shows the pattern created by selecting this radio button and at an incremental angle of 20-degree.

Fitted

If you select this radio button, the circular pattern will be created such that all items are fitted within the angle specified in the **Angle** edit box. This radio button is selected by default in the **Circular Pattern** dialog box. Figure 6-66 shows the pattern created by selecting this radio button and within an angle of 20-degree.

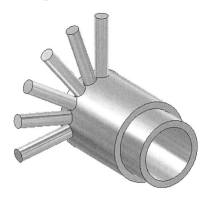

Figure 6-65 Model created using the *Incremental* radio button

Figure 6-66 Model created using the *Fitted* radio button

Creating Rib Features

Ribbon:	Model > Create > Rib
Toolbar:	Part Features > Rib

Ribs are defined as thin wall-like structures used to bind joints together so that they do not fail under an increased load. In Autodesk Inventor, ribs are created using an open profile, see Figures 6-67 and 6-68.

Remember that before invoking the **Rib** tool, you must have an unconsumed sketch. When you invoke the **Rib** tool, the **Rib** dialog box will be displayed, see Figure 6-69. The options in this dialog box are discussed next.

Figure 6-67 *Sketch for the rib feature*

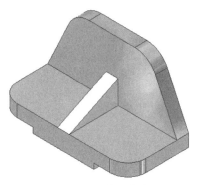

Figure 6-68 *The rib feature*

Shape Area

The options under this area are used to select the profile of the rib or the web feature and the direction of the feature creation. These options are discussed next.

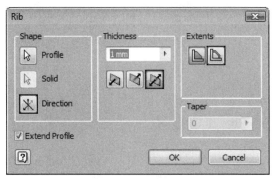

Profile

The **Profile** button is chosen to select the sketch of the rib or the web feature. If there is a single unconsumed sketch, it will be automatically chosen when you invoke the **Rib** tool.

Figure 6-69 *The **Rib** dialog box*

Solid

This button will be active only when there are multiple solid bodies in the graphics window. Choose this button to select the required body from the graphics window for creating the rib or web feature.

Direction

The **Direction** button is chosen to define the direction, in which the rib or the web feature will be created. The feature can be created in a direction normal to the selected sketch or parallel to it. After selecting the sketch for the rib feature, choose the **Direction** button and then move the cursor close to the selected sketch; the directions will be displayed using green arrows. A dynamic preview of the resulting feature can also be seen along with the direction. Note that the rib feature will be successful only if it is created in the direction, in which it intersects the existing model faces.

Thickness Area

The options under this area are used to define the thickness of the rib or the web feature. The thickness is specified in the **Thickness** edit box. This area also has three buttons that are used to define the direction, in which the thickness will be applied. You can apply the thickness on either side of the sketch or equally on both sides.

Extents Area

The buttons in this area are used to specify whether the feature will be extended to the next face or to a specified distance. The two buttons in this area are discussed next.

To Next

If this button is chosen, the rib or web feature will be created such that it merges with the next face, see Figure 6-70.

Finite

Choose the **Finite** button to create the rib or web feature to a specified distance, see Figure 6-71. The distance is specified in the **Extent** edit box that will be displayed in this area when you choose the **Finite** button. The direction is controlled using the **Direction** button in the **Shape** area.

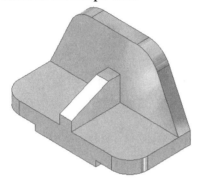 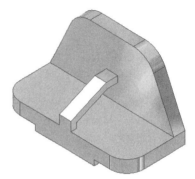

Figure 6-70 Rib created by extending the sketch to the next face

Figure 6-71 Rib created by extending the sketch to a specified distance

Extend Profile

The **Extend Profile** check box will be activated when you select the direction to apply the thickness parallel to the sketch or choose the **Finite** button from the **Extents** area. If the sketch of the rib feature does not intersect with a face of the model, and this check box is selected, the rib feature will be extended such that it intersects the face of the model.

Taper

The edit box in this area is used to specify the taper angle for the rib. Note that you can specify the taper angle only if the rib is being created normal to the plane on which the profile of the rib is sketched.

Thickening or Offsetting the Faces of Features

| **Ribbon:** | Model > Surface > Thicken/Offset |
| **Toolbar:** | Part Features > Thicken/Offset |

You can thicken a specified face or offset it using the **Thicken/Offset** tool. You can achieve the resulting output as a solid face or a surface. You can also use this tool to offset or thicken a surface. The resulting feature can be a surface or a solid face of the specified thickness. On invoking this tool, the **Thicken/Offset** dialog box will be displayed. The options provided in various tabs of this dialog box are discussed next.

Thicken/Offset Tab

The options in the **Thicken/Offset** tab, shown in Figure 6-72, are discussed next.

Select

The **Select** button is chosen to select the face or the surface to thicken or offset. When you invoke the **Thicken/Offset** dialog box, this button is chosen by default and you are prompted to select faces.

Solids

Choose this button to select the required body from the graphics window for offsetting the selected face or surface.

Filter Area

This area is available on upper right side of the **Thicken/Offset** dialog box and it provides two radio buttons. The **Face** radio button is selected to restrict the selection to the faces of the solid models. The **Quilt** radio button is

*Figure 6-72 The **Thicken/Offset** tab of the **Thicken/Offset** dialog box*

selected to restrict the selection to the surfaces only. Note that if you select the **Face** radio button, you can also select a surface. This is because a surface is also considered as a face.

Distance

The **Distance** edit box is used to specify the offset distance or the thickness value of the resulting feature. Note that you are also allowed to offset a selected face or a surface with a zero distance, making a copy at the same location. However, in this case, the output can only be a surface.

Output Area

The two buttons in the **Output** area are used to specify the output of using the **Thicken/Offset** tool. If you choose the **Solid** button, the resulting feature will be a solid face. If you choose the **Surface** button, the resulting feature will be a surface. Figure 6-73 shows a surface and Figure 6-74 shows a solid face created by offsetting the surface by a distance of 4 mm.

Figure 6-73 Original surface

Figure 6-74 Solid face created by offsetting the surface by a distance of 4 mm

Figure 6-75 shows the output of this tool in the form of an offset surface. In this case, the offset distance is also 4 mm.

Operation Area

The **Operation** area is on the right of the **Output** area and has four buttons. These four buttons **Join**, **Cut**, **Intersect** and **New solid** are used to specify the resulting operation to be performed using the **Thicken/Offset** tool. Note that these buttons will not be available if the output of this tool is a surface. The functions of these buttons are the same as those discussed in the **Extrude** dialog box. The

Figure 6-75 *Output in the form of an offset surface*

Join button is chosen for creating a join feature, the **Cut** button for a cut feature; and the **Intersect** button for an intersect feature. The **New solid** button is used to create a new solid that is independent of other solid bodies in the graphics window. Figure 6-76 shows a feature created by offsetting the top face of the base feature by using the **Join** operation. Figure 6-77 shows the feature created by offsetting the same face by using the **Cut** operation.

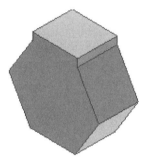

Figure 6-76 *Offsetting the top face by using the **Join** operation*

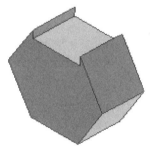

Figure 6-77 *Offsetting the top face by using the **Cut** operation*

Note

As evident from Figures 6-76 and 6-77 that the resulting feature is always created normal to the selected face or surface.

Direction Area

This area with three buttons is located below the **Distance** edit box. The buttons in this area are used to specify the direction, in which the resulting feature will be created.

More Tab

The options in the **More** tab, shown in Figure 6-78, are discussed next.

Automatic Face Chain

This check box is used to automatically select all tangent faces that form a chain with a selected face. To use this option, invoke the **Thicken/Offset** dialog box and then choose the **More** tab. Select this check box and then select the face by using the **Select** button in the **Thicken/Offset** tab. You will notice that all tangent faces that form a chain with the selected face are automatically selected.

Create Vertical Surfaces

This check box is used to create the vertical sides of internal surfaces. Remember that this option is available only if the output of this tool is a surface. Also, it works only if the original face

*Figure 6-78 The **More** tab of the **Thicken/Offset** dialog box*

selected to be offset is a surface. Figure 6-79 shows a surface selected to be offset and Figure 6-80 shows the resulting offset surface with the side faces created by selecting the **Create Vertical Surfaces** check box. Note that the original surface selected to be offset in this case is removed.

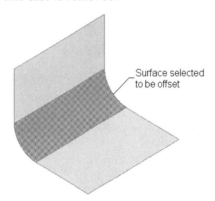

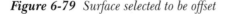

Figure 6-79 Surface selected to be offset   *Figure 6-80 Resulting surface with side faces*

Allow Approximation

This check box is selected to allow Autodesk Inventor to make some assumptions if the exact thicken or offset solution of the model cannot be determined. When you select this check box, the options in this area will be enabled. The drop-down list in this area is used to specify the type of approximation to be made. You can select the **Mean**, **Never too thin**, or **Never too thick** option from this drop-down list. The **Optimized** radio button is selected to make an optimized approximation such that the minimum time is lost.

Selecting the **Specify Tolerance** radio button allows you to specify the tolerance that will be used to make the approximation. If the tolerance is more, the time required to compute the feature will be increased.

Creating the Embossed and Engraved Features

Ribbon:	Model > Create > Emboss
Toolbar:	Part Features > Emboss

 The **Emboss** tool allows you to create an embossed or engraved feature. Generally, this tool is used to emboss or engrave text on an existing feature. This tool can be invoked only when a sketch or a text is available in the graphics window. When you invoke this tool, the **Emboss** dialog box will be displayed, as shown in Figure 6-81. The options in this dialog box are discussed next.

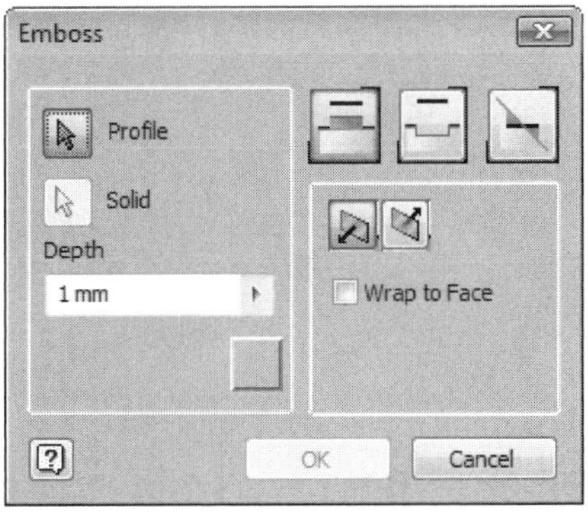

Profile

The **Profile** button is chosen to select the profile or the text to be engraved or embossed. When you invoke this dialog box, this button is chosen automatically and you are prompted to select the profile.

*Figure 6-81 The **Emboss** dialog box*

Solid

This button is used to select the required body from the graphics window for offsetting the selected face or surface.

Depth

The **Depth** edit box is used to enter the depth of the embossed or engraved feature.

Top Face Color

The **Top Face Color** button, present below the **Depth** edit box, is chosen to assign a different color to the top face of the embossed or engraved feature. When you choose this button, the **Color** dialog box will be displayed. This dialog box has a drop-down list that can be used to select a color to assign to the top face of the new feature.

Emboss from Face

The **Emboss from Face** button is used to create an embossed feature. The selected profile or text is projected on a face and then a join feature is created. The shape of the join feature is defined using the profile or text selected to be embossed. Note that the depth you define is calculated from the plane on which the feature is created and not from the sketching plane. Figure 6-82 shows a model with an embossed text.

Engrave from Face

The **Engrave from Face** button is used to create an engraved feature. The selected profile or text is projected on a face and then a cut feature is created. A material equivalent to the shape of the profile or text is removed from the feature on which it is projected. Figure 6-83 shows a model with text engraved in it.

Figure 6-82 *Embossed text*   *Figure 6-83* *Engraved text*

Emboss/Engrave from Plane

The **Emboss/Engrave from Plane** button is used to create a feature that is embossed and engraved feature. The profile or the text is extruded in both the directions of the sketch plane. When you select this option, the **Taper** edit box appears in the **Emboss** dialog box. You can enter the taper value for the emboss/engrave feature in it. Note that when you choose this button, the **Depth** edit box is not displayed. Figure 6-84 shows a model with the embossed/engraved text.

Direction

The direction buttons are used to reverse the direction of the embossed or engraved features.

Wrap to Face

The **Wrap to Face** check box is selected to wrap the embossed or engraved feature such as the face of a revolved feature around a curved face. When you select this check box, the **Face** button will becomes available. This button allows you to select the face on which the feature will be embossed or engraved. Figure 6-85 shows a bottle with an embossed text wrapped on the outer face.

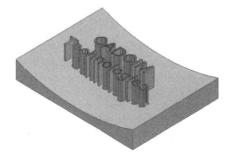

Figure 6-84 *Model with embossed/engraved text*   *Figure 6-85* *Bottle with an embossed text wrapped on the outer face*

Applying Images on a Feature

Ribbon:	Model > Create > Decal
Toolbar:	Part Features > Decal

While designing a product, you may need to apply an image to the product. The image can be the label of a company, a bar code, an instruction for handling the component, and so on. These images can be applied on the feature using the **Decal** tool. When you invoke this tool, the **Decal** dialog box will be displayed, as shown in Figure 6-86. The options in this dialog box are discussed next.

*Figure 6-86 The **Decal** dialog box*

Image

The **Image** button is chosen by default and is used to select the image to be applied to the feature. Note that before invoking the **Decal** tool, you need to insert an image in the sketch by using the **Insert Image** tool from the **Insert** panel of the **Sketch** tab.

Face

The **Face** button is chosen to select the face on which the image will be applied.

Wrap to Face

The **Wrap to Face** check box is selected to wrap an image about a circular face. This check box will not be active if you select a non-circular face. Figure 6-87 shows a bottle after wrapping an image on it. In this figure, the circular face of the bottle was selected as the face to transfer the image.

Figure 6-87 Image wrapped on a bottle

Chain Faces

The **Chain Faces** button is chosen to select all tangentially connected chain faces to transfer an image. Figure 6-88 shows a model with the side edges filleted and an image. The top face of this model is selected to transfer the image. Notice that the image appears on the filleted chain faces automatically, as shown in Figure 6-89.

Figure 6-88 Model and image   *Figure 6-89 Model after applying the image*

ASSIGNING DIFFERENT COLORS/STYLES TO A MODEL

Autodesk Inventor allows you to change the color/style of a model
to improve its appearance. You can apply a different color/style
to a model by selecting an appropriate option from the **Color
Override** drop-down list available on the extreme right of the
Quick Access Toolbar. Note that this drop-down list will be
activated only when a model is available in the graphics window.
By default, the **As Material** style will be applied to the model. To
change the color/style of the model, click on the **Color Override**
drop-down list; the list of all available styles and colors will be
displayed, as shown in Figure 6-90. Select the required style/
color from the list displayed; the selected style or color will
automatically be applied to the model.

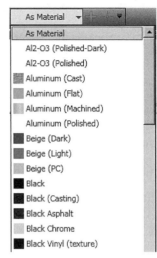

*Figure 6-90 The **Color
Override** drop-down list*

If you want to change the style/color of a particular feature in a
model, select the required feature from the **Browser Bar** or from
the drawing window and then choose the required style or color
from the **Color Override** drop-down list.

You can also assign a different color/style to feature by right-clicking
on it in the **Browser Bar**. On doing so, a shortcut menu will be
displayed. Choose the **Properties** option from the shortcut menu; the **Feature Properties**
dialog box will be displayed. Select the required color/style from the **Feature Color Style**
drop-down list of this dialog box.

To change the style/color of a particular
face, select the required face and right-click;
a shortcut menu will be displayed. Choose
Properties from the shortcut menu; the **Face
Properties** dialog box will be displayed, as
shown in Figure 6-91. Select the required
style/color from the **Face Color Style** drop-down
list and choose the **OK** button.

*Figure 6-91 The **Face Properties** dialog box*

TUTORIALS

Tutorial 1

In this tutorial, you will create a model of the Fixture Base shown in Figure 6-92a. Its dimensions
are given in Figures 6-92b through 6-92d. After creating the solid model, you will change its
color to yellow.   **(Expected time: 45 min)**

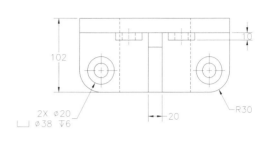

Figure 6-92a Model for Tutorial 1   *Figure 6-92b* Top view of the model

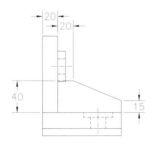

Figure 6-92c Left view of the model   *Figure 6-92d* Front view of the model

The following steps are required to complete this tutorial:

a. Start a new part file and exit the sketching environment. Create the sketch for the base feature on the XZ plane and extrude it to a distance of 102 mm, refer to Figure 6-94.
b. Define a new sketch plane on the back face of the base feature and create the join feature, refer to Figure 6-96.
c. Create two cylindrical features with holes on the front face of the second feature, refer to Figure 6-98.
d. Create the fillet on the base feature, refer to Figure 6-99.
e. Create two counterbore holes taking the reference of the cylindrical faces of fillets by using the **Hole** tool, refer to Figure 6-100.
f. Finally, draw an open sketch and convert it into a rib using the **Rib** tool to complete the model, refer to Figure 6-102.
g. Change the color/style of the model by using the **Color Override** drop-down list in the **Quick Access Toolbar**.

Creating the Base Feature

You need to create the base feature on the XZ plane. By default, the first feature is created on the XY plane when you start a new part file.

1. Start a new metric standard part file and then choose the **Finish Sketch** button from the **Exit** panel of the **Sketch** tab to exit the sketching environment without creating anything.

2. Choose the **Create 2D Sketch** tool from **Model > Sketch > Sketch** drop-down and then select **XZ Plane** from the **Browser Bar** to invoke the sketching environment with XZ as the sketching plane.

3. Create the sketch for the base feature. Add the required constraints and dimensions to it. The sketch after adding constraints and dimensions is shown in Figure 6-93.

4. Exit the sketching environment and extrude the sketch to a distance of 102 mm using the **Extrude** tool to create the base feature. The base feature is shown in Figure 6-94.

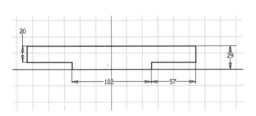

Figure 6-93 *Sketch for the base feature*   ***Figure 6-94*** *Base feature*

Creating a Join Feature on the Back Face of the Base Feature

1. Define a new sketch plane on the back face of the base feature. Draw the sketch for the join feature and then add the required constraints and dimensions to it. The sketch after adding constraints and dimensions is shown in Figure 6-95.

2. Exit the sketching environment and then extrude the sketch to a distance of 20 mm toward the front of the base feature, as is shown in Figure 6-96.

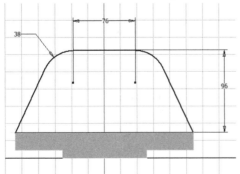

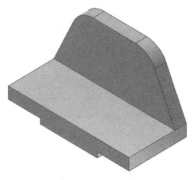

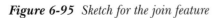

Figure 6-95 *Sketch for the join feature*   ***Figure 6-96*** *Model after creating the join feature*

Creating Cylindrical Features on the Front Face of the Second Feature

To create two cylindrical features, you need to draw a sketch consisting of two concentric circles. The reason for drawing the sketch for both the features together is that both the cylindrical features are to be extruded to the same distance.

1. Define a new sketch plane on the front face of the second feature and draw the sketches for both the cylindrical features, as shown in Figure 6-97.

2. Invoke the **Extrude** tool and extrude the sketches to a distance of 10 mm.

    While selecting profiles for extrusion, make sure that you select a point outside the inner circles but inside the outer circles. As a result, the inner circles are subtracted from the outer circles when you extrude the sketch, thus creating holes. The model after creating the cylindrical features is shown in Figure 6-98.

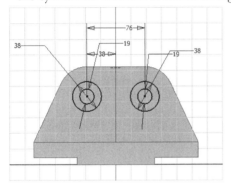

Figure 6-97 Sketches for the cylindrical features

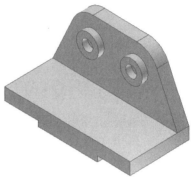

Figure 6-98 Model after creating the cylindrical features

Creating Fillets

The vertical edges of the front face of the base feature need to be filleted so that you can use the cylindrical faces of fillets to define the counterbore holes.

1. Choose the **Fillet** tool from the **Modify** panel of the **Model** tab; the **Fillet** dialog box is displayed and you are prompted to select the edges to be blended. By default, the **Constant** tab is chosen in this dialog box. Fillet

2. Select the outer left and outer right vertical edges on the front face of the base feature.

    As soon as you select the edges, the **Edges** column displays **2 selected** and the preview of the fillet is displayed on the model with the default radius value, which is 2 mm.

3. Click on the default radius value in the **Radius** column and enter **30** in the edit box displayed. Alternatively, enter **30** in the edit box of the mini toolbar. You will notice that the fillet in the preview of the model has also increased accordingly. Choose the **OK** button to exit the **Fillet** dialog box; the fillets are created, as shown in Figure 6-99.

Creating Counterbore Holes

As mentioned earlier, in Autodesk Inventor, you can create holes concentric to cylindrical faces. To create two counterbore holes, you need to use the cylindrical faces of the fillet.

1. Choose the **Hole** tool from the **Modify** panel of the **Model** tab to invoke the **Hole** dialog box.

2. Select the **Counterbore** radio button from the area located on the right of the **Placement** area.

3. Select the **Concentric** option from the drop-down list in the **Placement** area; the **Plane** button is chosen in the **Placement** area and you are prompted select a planar face or a work plane for the placement plane.

4. Select the top planar face of the base feature as the face to place the hole; the preview of the counterbore hole with the current values is displayed. Also, the **Concentric Reference** button is chosen automatically and you are prompted to select a circular edge or a cylindrical face to reference the hole center.

5. Select the cylindrical face of the fillet on the right; the preview of the hole is relocated.

6. Select the **Through All** option from the drop-down list in the **Termination** area. Modify the value of the counterbore diameter in the preview window to **38**. Similarly, modify the value of the bore diameter to **20** and the counterbore depth to **6**.

7. Choose the **Apply** button to create the hole without exiting the **Hole** dialog box.

8. Similarly, using the options already set in the **Hole** dialog box, create another hole concentric to the fillet on the left.

9. Choose **Done** to exit the **Hole** dialog box. The model after creating the counterbore holes is shown in Figure 6-100.

Figure 6-99 *Model after creating fillets*

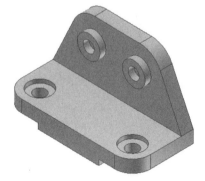

Figure 6-100 *Model after creating counterbore holes*

Creating the Rib Feature

The rib feature is created at the center of the model. Therefore, you need to define an offset work plane at the center on which the rib feature will be created.

1. Choose the **Plane** tool from **Model > Work Features > Plane** drop-down and select the right face of the base feature; the preview of the work plane along with the mini toolbar is displayed in the graphics window.

2. Enter **-108** in the edit box available in the mini toolbar and then choose **OK** from it. The negative value ensures that the work plane will be created inside the model. Select this work plane as the sketching plane.

3. Draw an open sketch for the rib feature and then add the required constraints and dimensions to it, as shown in Figure 6-101.

   When you apply the **Coincident** constraint between the lines in the sketch and the edges of the model, the lines defining the edges are drawn. Make sure these lines are not selected when you select the sketch for the rib feature.

4. Exit the sketching environment. Next, choose the **Rib** tool from the **Create** panel of the **Model** tab; the **Rib** dialog box is displayed and you are prompted to select the rib profile.

5. Select the open profile. Next, choose the **Direction** button and move the cursor below the sketch. Click when the green arrow points downward or toward right.

6. Set the value in the edit box in the **Thickness** area to **20**. Choose **OK** to exit the **Rib** dialog box. The final model after creating all features is shown in Figure 6-102.

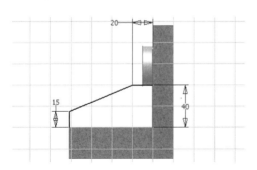

Figure 6-101 *Sketch for the rib feature*   *Figure 6-102* *Final model for Tutorial 1*

Tip. *If the sketch plane is defined inside the model, the sketched entities will be hidden within the faces of the model, and will not be visible to the user. Therefore, sometimes it is difficult to dimension such sketches. To avoid this confusing situation, Autodesk Inventor provides you with an option to slice temporarily the portion of the model that is between the user and the sketch so that the sketch becomes visible. To slice the model, right-click in the drawing window, and then choose* **Slice Graphics** *from the shortcut menu. The model will be restored to the original condition as soon as you exit the sketching environment. You can also invoke the* **Slice Graphics** *tool by pressing F7.*

Changing the Color of the Model

When a model is created, the default material is applied to it. However, in Autodesk Inventor, you can change the default color/style of the model.

1. Select the **Yellow** option from the **Color Override** drop-down list on the right of the **Quick Access Toolbar**; the color of the model changes to the color that you have selected. Note that you do not need to select the model to apply color to it.

2. Save the model with the name *Tutorial1* at the location *C:\Inventor_2011\c06* and then close the file.

Tutorial 2

In this tutorial, you will create a model of the Pivot Base shown in Figure 6-103a. Its dimensions are given in Figures 6-103b through 6-103d. Change the color/style of the model to Zinc Chromate.   **(Expected time: 45 min)**

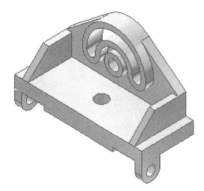

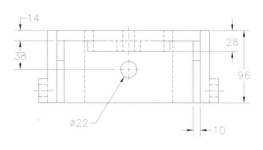

Figure 6-103a *Model for Tutorial 2*   **Figure 6-103b** *Top view of the model*

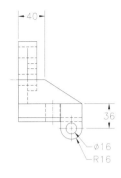

Figure 6-103c *Left view of the model*

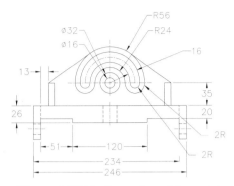

Figure 6-103d *Front view of the model*

The following steps are required to complete this tutorial:

a.   Create the base feature on the XZ plane, refer to Figure 6-105.
b.   Create the join feature on the back face of the base feature, refer to Figure 6-107.
c.   Create another join feature on the front face of the second feature, refer to Figure 6-109.
d.   Create the cut feature on the third feature, refer to Figure 6-111.
e.   Create the rib and the join feature on the right of the model, refer to Figure 6-115.
f.   Mirror the rib and the join feature on the left of the model, refer to Figure 6-117.
g.   Create a hole on the top face of the base feature, refer to Figure 6-118.
h.   Change the style of the model by using the **Color Override** drop-down list in the **Quick Access Toolbar**.

Creating the Base Feature

1.   Start a new metric part file and then change the sketching plane to the XZ plane.

2.   Draw the sketch of the base feature on the XZ plane, as shown in Figure 6-104.

3.   Exit the sketching environment and switch the view to the isometric (home) view.

4.   Click on the sketch in the graphics window; the mini toolbar with the **Create Extrude**, **Create Revolve**, and **Edit Sketch** tools is displayed.

5.   Choose the **Create Extrude** tool; the **Extrude** dialog box is displayed. Also, the preview of the extrude feature along with the mini toolbar is displayed.

6.   Enter **96** in the edit box of the mini toolbar and choose **OK** to create the base feature of the model, as shown in Figure 6-105.

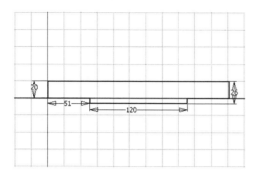

Figure 6-104 Sketch of the base feature

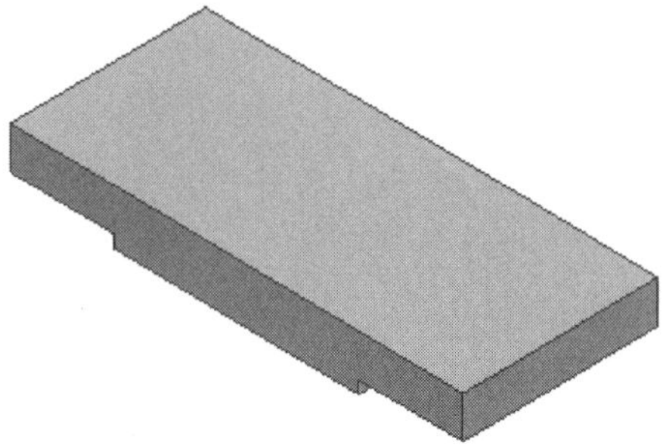

Figure 6-105 Base feature

Creating a Join Feature on the Back Face of the Base Feature

1. Rotate the model by using the ViewCube such that its back face is visible.

2. Select the back face; the mini toolbar along with the **Edit Extrude**, **Edit Sketch**, and **Create Sketch** tools is displayed in the graphics window.

3. Choose the **Create Sketch** tool and draw the sketch for the next feature on it, as shown in Figure 6-106.

4. Extrude the sketch to a distance of 14 mm toward the front of the base feature by using the **Extrude** tool, see Figure 6-107.

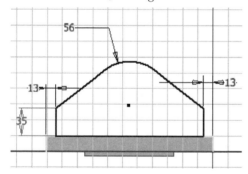

Figure 6-106 Sketch of the join feature

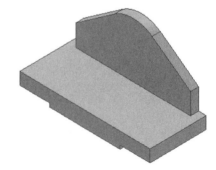

Figure 6-107 Model after creating the join feature

Creating the Join Feature on the Front Face of the Second Feature

1. Define a new sketch plane on the front face of the second feature.

2. Draw two disjoint sketches of the join feature, as shown in Figure 6-108.

3. Extrude both sketches to a distance of 14 mm using the **Extrude** tool. The model after creating the join feature is shown in Figure 6-109. Note that the two sketches are displayed as a single feature in the **Browser Bar** because both the sketches are extruded together.

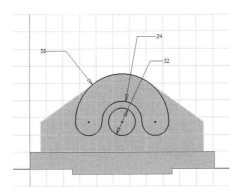

Figure 6-108 *Sketches of the join feature on the front face*

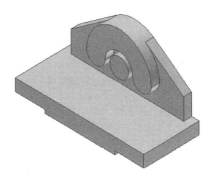

Figure 6-109 *Join feature on the front face of the second feature*

Creating the Cut Feature

Next, you need to create a cut feature that will remove material from the previous feature. You need to draw two disjoint sketches for the cut feature at the same time and extrude them using the **Cut** operation. As the sketches are to be extruded through the model, you need to select both of them together while selecting the profile for creating the cut feature.

1. Define a new sketch plane on the front face of the semicircular feature.

   When you define the sketch plane on the semicircular feature, a sketch defining the semicircular feature is drawn. Offset this sketch inside, as shown in Figure 6-110. Note that after invoking the **Offset** tool, you need to right-click, and then choose the **Loop Select** option from the shortcut menu. This ensures that the entire loop is offset. Since you have used a reference entity to draw the inner sketch, you need to specify just one dimension value, that is, the radius of any of the arcs.

2. Draw the sketch for the cut feature and the circle for the hole, refer to Figure 6-110.

3. Extrude the sketch and the circle by using the **Through All** option of the **Cut** operation in the mini toolbar to create the cut feature, see Figure 6-111.

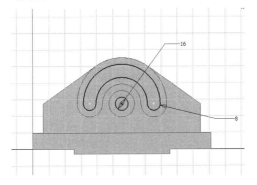

Figure 6-110 *Offset sketch for the cut feature*

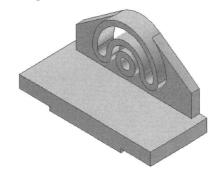

Figure 6-111 *Model after creating the cut feature*

Creating the Rib Feature

The sketch for the rib will be created on the sketch plane defined on the right face of the second feature. The sketch will be extruded toward the left to create the feature.

1. Define a new sketch plane on the right face of the second feature and then draw the sketch of the rib feature. Add the required dimensions and constraints to the sketch, as shown in Figure 6-112.

2. Exit the sketching environment and choose the **Rib** tool from the **Create** panel of the **Model** tab; the **Rib** dialog box is displayed and you are prompted to select the profile for the rib feature.

3. Select the open sketch; all options in this dialog box are enabled. Enter **10** in the edit box in the **Thickness** area. Choose the **Direction** button and move the cursor below the sketch. Click when the green arrow points downward.

4. Choose the second button in the **Thickness** area to extrude the feature toward left; the preview of the rib feature is displayed, showing the sketch extruded toward the left of the sketch.

5. Choose **OK** to exit the **Rib** dialog box; the rib is created, as shown in Figure 6-113.

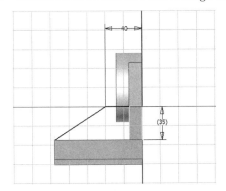

Figure 6-112 Sketch of the rib

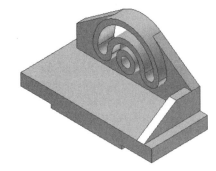

Figure 6-113 Model after creating the rib

Creating the Join Feature on the Right Face of the Base Feature

1. Define a new sketch plane on the right face of the base feature.

2. Draw the sketch of the join feature. Draw a circle inside the sketch such that when extruded, a hole is created automatically. Add the required constraints and dimensions to it, as shown in Figure 6-114, and then exit the sketching environment.

3. Extrude the sketch to a distance of 12 mm to create the feature. Make sure that you select the profile by using a point inside the outer loop but outside the circle. The model after creating the feature is shown in Figure 6-115.

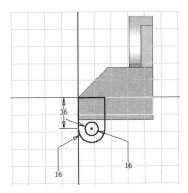

Figure 6-114 *Sketch of the join feature*

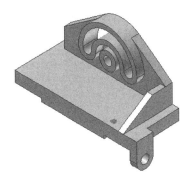

Figure 6-115 *Model after creating the join feature*

Mirroring Features on the other Side of the Model

The second set of rib and join features will be created by mirroring the first set of these features on the other side of the model. The features will be mirrored about the offset work plane created at the center of the model.

1. Choose the **Plane** tool from **Model > Work Features > Plane** drop-down; you are prompted to select a planar surface.

2. Select the right face of the base feature; the preview of the plane along with the mini toolbar is displayed.

3. Enter **-111** in the edit box of the mini toolbar and then choose **OK** from it; the plane is created.

4. Choose the **Mirror** tool from the **Pattern** panel of the **Model** tab; the **Mirror** dialog box is displayed and you are prompted to select the features to be patterned. Select the rib feature and the feature created on the right face of the base feature.

5. Choose the **Mirror Plane** button and select the offset work plane as the mirror plane. The preview of the mirrored features is displayed. Choose **OK** to exit this dialog box.

6. Right-click on the work plane in the **Browser Bar** to display the shortcut menu. Choose the **Visibility** option from the shortcut menu to turn off the visibility of the work plane. The model after mirroring the features is shown in Figure 6-116.

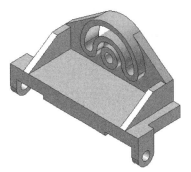

Figure 6-116 *Model after mirroring the features*

Creating the Hole on the Top Face of the Base Feature

Hole

1. Choose the **Hole** tool from the **Modify** panel of the **Model** tab to invoke the **Hole** dialog box.

2. Select the **Linear** option from the drop-down list in the **Placement** area; the **Face** button is chosen and you are prompted to select a planar face or a work plane.

3. Select the top planar face of the base feature. Next, select the edge labeled 1 on the top face of the base feature, refer to Figure 6-117; the mini toolbar is displayed.

4. Modify the value in the edit box of the mini toolbar to **88**.

5. Similarly, select the edge labeled 2 on the top face of the base feature and modify the value to **41**, refer to Figure 6-117.

6. Select the **Through All** option from the drop-down list in the **Termination** area.

7. Set the value of the diameter of the hole in the preview window to **22**; the diameter of the hole in the preview also increases automatically. Choose the **OK** button. The final model for Tutorial 2 is shown in Figure 6-118.

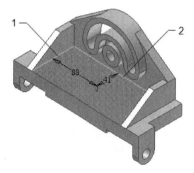   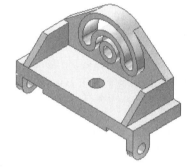

Figure 6-117 *The preview of the hole feature*   *Figure 6-118* *Final model for Tutorial 2*

Changing the Style and Saving the Model

As mentioned earlier, the style of the feature is changed using the **Color Override** drop-down list in the **Quick Access Toolbar**.

1. Select the **Zinc Chromate** option from the **Color Override** drop-down list available on the extreme right of the **Quick Access Toolbar**; the material of the model is changed to Zinc Chromate.

2. Save the model with the name *Tutorial2* at the location *C:\Inventor_2011\c06* and then close the file.

Tutorial 3

In this tutorial, you will create the model shown in Figure 6-119a. Its dimensions are given in Figure 6-119b and Figure 6-119c. After creating a solid model, you will change the color of the front face of base feature to green color.   **(Expected time: 30 min)**

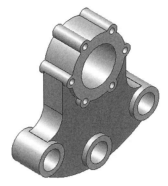

Figure 6-119a Model for Tutorial 3

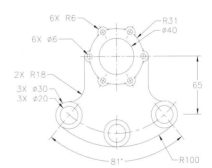

Figure 6-119b Left view of the model   *Figure 6-119c Front view of the model*

The following steps are required to complete this tutorial:

a. Create the sketch of the base feature on the YZ plane and extrude it using the **Symmetric** option, refer to Figure 6-121.
b. Create the second feature on the YZ plane and extrude it using the **Symmetric** option, refer to Figure 6-123.
c. Create one of the holes on the front face of the second feature and then create a circular pattern of this hole, refer to Figures 6-124 and 6-125.
d. Create the cylindrical join feature and then create a hole in it, refer to Figure 6-128.
e. Create the circular patterns of the last join feature and the hole, refer to Figure 6-129.
f. Finally, create the central hole, refer to Figure 6-130.
g. Change the color of the front face of the base feature by using the shortcut menu.

The base feature of this model will be created on the YZ plane. Also, all features in this model will be extruded using the **Symmetric** option because they extend equally from the front face and the back face of the base feature.

Creating the Base Feature

The base feature of this model will be created on the YZ plane. Therefore, you need to exit the sketching environment of the new file and then define a new sketch plane on the YZ plane.

1. Start a new metric standard part file and then change the sketching plane to the YZ plane. Draw the sketch of the base feature, as shown in Figure 6-120.

2. Add the required constraints and dimensions to the sketch, refer to Figure 6-120. Exit the sketching environment and then extrude the sketch to a distance of 22 mm using the **Symmetric** option. The base feature of the model is shown in Figure 6-121.

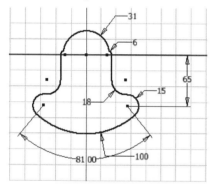

Figure 6-120 *Sketch of the base feature*   ***Figure 6-121*** *Base feature of the model*

Creating the Next Join Feature

As the last feature was created on the YZ plane and extruded using the **Symmetric** option, you can also create other features on the same plane and extrude them using the **Symmetric** option.

1. Choose the **Create 2D Sketch** tool from **Model > Sketch > Sketch** drop-down; you are prompted to select a plane or a planar face to create the sketch.

2. Select **YZ Plane** from the **Browser Bar**; the sketching environment is activated. As the sketch is drawn inside the model, it is hidden by the faces that lie between the sketch and the user. Therefore, you need to slice the model.

3. Right-click in the drawing window to display a shortcut menu and choose **Slice Graphics** from it.

4. Draw the sketch on the join feature, as shown in Figure 6-122. For dimensions, refer to Figure 6-119c.

5. Exit the sketching environment and then extrude the sketch to a distance of 32 mm using the **Symmetric** option. The model after creating the join feature is shown in Figure 6-123.

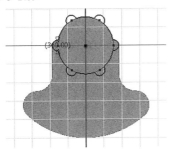

Figure 6-122 *Sketch of the join feature*

Figure 6-123 *Model after creating the join feature*

 Note
It is recommended that you create six small circles individually and one big circle on the periphery of the top portion of the base feature. If you create one small circle and pattern it, you cannot trim the unwanted portions of the sketch.

Creating the Hole and its Pattern

Next, you need to create six holes through the previous feature. Instead of creating all holes, create one hole and then create a circular pattern of this hole. To create the pattern, you need to create one hole by defining the sketch plane on the front face of the previous feature.

1. Choose the **Hole** tool from the **Modify** panel of the **Model** tab; the **Hole** dialog box is displayed. Select the **Concentric** option from the drop-down list in the **Placement** area.

2. Select the front planar face of the second feature as the plane to place the hole and then select one of the six semicircular features.

3. Select the **Through All** option from the drop-down list in the **Termination** area.

4. Modify the value of the diameter of the hole in the preview window to **6**. Choose **OK** to exit the dialog box. The model after creating one of the holes is shown in Figure 6-124.

5. Choose the **Circular Pattern** tool from the **Pattern** panel of the **Model** tab; the **Circular Pattern** dialog box is displayed and you are prompted to select the feature to be patterned.

6. Select the hole from the graphics window. Next, choose the **Rotation Axis** button from the dialog box and then select the outer cylindrical face of the second join feature.

As you select the cylindrical face to specify the rotation axis, an axis passing through its center is displayed and the preview of the hole pattern is displayed on the model. A copy of the hole is displayed on each of the semicircular features.

7. In the **Circular Pattern** dialog box, accept the default values and choose **OK** to exit this dialog box. The model after creating the hole pattern is shown in Figure 6-125.

Figure 6-124 *Model after creating the hole*

Figure 6-125 *Model after creating the hole pattern*

Creating the Cylindrical Join Feature

The cylindrical join feature is also created on the YZ plane and is extruded using the **Symmetric** option.

1. Define a new sketch plane on the YZ plane and then slice the graphics. Draw a circle as the sketch of the cylindrical join feature, as shown in Figure 6-126. Add the required constraints and dimensions to the sketch.

2. Exit the sketching environment and then extrude the circle to a distance of 32 mm using the **Symmetric** option, see Figure 6-127.

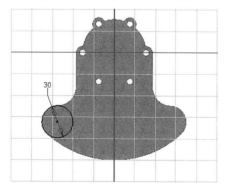 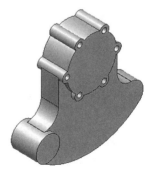

Figure 6-126 *Sketch of the cylindrical join feature*

Figure 6-127 *The cylindrical join feature*

Creating the Hole in the Join Feature

1. Choose the **Hole** tool from the **Modify** panel of the **Model** tab; the **Hole** dialog box is displayed.

2. Select the **Concentric** option from the drop-down list in the **Placement** area, if it has not already been selected.

3. Select the front face of the previous feature and then the cylindrical face of the same feature to place the hole.

4. Select the **Through All** option from the drop-down list in the **Termination** area, if it has not already been selected.

5. Modify the value of the diameter of the hole in the preview window to **20**. Choose **OK** to exit the dialog box; the hole is created. The model after creating the hole on the join feature is shown in Figure 6-128.

Creating Circular Patterns

1. Choose the **Circular Pattern** tool from the **Pattern** panel of the **Model** tab; the **Circular Pattern** dialog box is displayed and you are prompted to select the feature to be patterned.

2. Select the cylindrical join feature and the hole from the graphics window or the **Browser Bar** to pattern; both the features are displayed with a blue outline.

3. Choose the **Rotation Axis** button and select the bottom cylindrical face of the base feature to define the axis of rotation for the pattern.

   The preview of the pattern with six items arranged through an angle of 360-degree is displayed on the model. As the pattern shown in the preview is not the required pattern, you need to modify values in the **Circular Pattern** dialog box.

4. Enter **3** and **81** in the **Occurrence Count** and **Occurrence Angle** edit boxes, respectively in the **Placement** area.

   Note
   *Sometimes the orientation of the pattern features in the preview does not match with the required orientation. In such a case, you need to choose the **Flip** button that is on the right of the **Rotation Axis** button in the **Circular Pattern** dialog box.*

5. Accept the other default values and choose **OK** to create the circular pattern. The model after creating the pattern is shown in Figure 6-129.

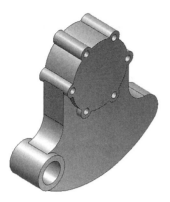

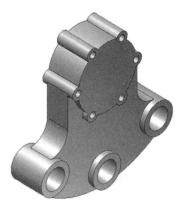

Figure 6-128 *Model after creating the hole on the join feature*

Figure 6-129 *Model after creating the circular pattern of the join feature and the hole*

Creating the Hole on the Second Feature (Join Feature)

1. Choose the **Hole** tool from the **Modify** panel of the **Model** tab; the **Hole** dialog box is displayed. Select the **Concentric** option from the drop-down list in the **Placement** area.

2. Select the front face of the second feature and then the cylindrical face of the same feature to place the hole.

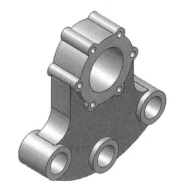

3. Select the **Through All** option from the drop-down list in the **Termination** area, if it has not already been selected.

4. Modify the value of the diameter of the hole in the preview window to **40**.

5. Choose **OK** to create the hole and exit the dialog box. The isometric view of the final model for Tutorial 3 is shown in Figure 6-130.

Figure 6-130 *Final model for Tutorial 3*

Changing the Color of the Front Face of the Base Feature

As mentioned earlier, you need to change the color of the face by using the **Properties** option.

1. Select the front face of the base feature and right-click; a shortcut menu is displayed.

2. Choose the **Properties** option from the shortcut menu; the **Face Properties** dialog box is displayed.

3. Click on the **Face Color Style** drop-down list and select the **Green** option from it. Next, choose the **OK** button; the color of the front face of the base feature turns green.

4. Save the model with the name *Tutorial3* at the location *C:\Inventor_2011\c06* and then close the file.

Tutorial 4

In this tutorial, you will create a bottle and then write text on the upper circular face of the bottle, as shown in Figure 6-131. The wall thickness of the bottle is 1 mm. Next, you will apply an external image on the bottle shown in the same figure. You can select any image from your computer for applying to the bottle. The dimensions of the bottle are shown in Figure 6-132. **(Expected time: 30 min)**

Figure 6-131 Bottle with an image and text wrapped on it

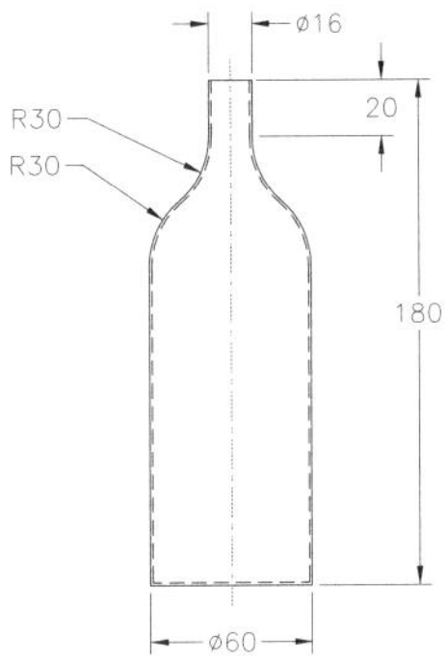

Figure 6-132 Dimensions of the bottle

The following steps are required to complete this tutorial:

a. Create the bottle by revolving a sketch drawn on the XZ plane, refer to Figure 6-133.
b. Write the text such that it can be wrapped on the upper circular face of the bottle, refer to Figure 6-135.
c. Emboss the text on the bottle such that it is wrapped on it, refer to Figure 6-138.
d. Insert an image into the sketching environment and then apply it to the bottle such that it is wrapped around it, refer to Figure 6-138.

Creating the Bottle

First, you need to create the sketch of the bottle on the XZ plane. When you invoke the sketching environment, by default, the XY plane is taken as the sketching plane. You need to exit the sketching environment and then define a new sketching (XZ) plane.

1. Start a new metric template file and then exit the sketching environment by choosing the **Finish Sketch** button from the **Exit** panel of the **Sketch** tab.

2. Choose the **Create 2D Sketch** tool from the
    Sketch panel of the **Model** tab and then select the
    XZ Plane from the **Browser Bar**; the sketching
    environment is invoked.

3. Draw the sketch of the bottle and then offset it
    outward to a distance of 1 mm to create a hollow
    bottle. Join the endpoints of the sketch using the
    Line tool to create a closed sketch, as shown in
    Figure 6-133.

4. Add the required constraints and specify the
    dimensions, refer to Figure 6-133.

Note
*In Figure 6-133, the display of grids has been
turned off for clarity of the sketch.*

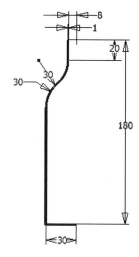

Figure 6-133 Sketch for the bottle

5. Exit the sketching environment and then invoke the **Revolve** tool.

6. Select the sketch from the graphics window and then select **Z Axis** as the axis of revolution
    from the **Browser Bar**; the preview of the revolved feature is displayed in the graphics
    window. Choose **OK** to create the revolved feature and exit the dialog box.

7. Next, click on the down arrow in the **Color Override** drop-down list and select the
    Metal-AL-6061 (Machined) option from the drop-down list. The material of the bottle is
    changed to the selected material, as shown in Figure 6-134.

Embossing the Text on the Bottle

Next, you need to write the text and emboss it on the bottle. The text is written on a work
plane created tangent to the outer face of the bottle and parallel to the YZ plane.

1. Choose the **Tangent to Surface and Parallel to Plane** tool from **Model > Work Features >
    Plane** drop-down; you are prompted to select the curved face or a planar face.

2. Select **YZ Plane** from the **Browser Bar** and then select the lower cylindrical part of the
    bottle; a work plane tangent to the bottle and parallel to the YZ plane is created. Note
    that the plane needs to be created in front of the bottle.

3. Select the new work plane as the sketching plane and then invoke the **Create 2D Sketch** tool.

4. Make the sketching plane normal to the screen by using the ViewCube.

5. Choose the **Text** tool from **Sketch > Draw > Text** drop-down and then drag the cursor
    or click in the drawing window; the **Format Text** dialog box is displayed.

6. Select **3.50 mm** from the **Size** drop-down list and enter **CADCIM Technologies** in the **Text Window** of the **Format Text** dialog box. Choose **OK** to exit the dialog box; the text is displayed in the drawing window, as shown in Figure 6-135. If the text created is not at the position shown in Figure 6-135, you can select it and drag it to the required position.

Figure 6-134 Bottle with the selected material

Figure 6-135 Partial view of the bottle displaying the position of the text

 Tip. *If the text is written in the reverse direction, you need to flip the normal of the work plane. Exit all tools and then select the work plane. Right-click on the selected work plane, and then choose* **Flip Normal** *from the shortcut menu.*

7. Exit the sketching environment and then choose the **Emboss** tool from the **Create** panel of the **Model** tab in the **Ribbon**; the **Emboss** dialog box is displayed and you are prompted to select the profile.

8. Select the text and then choose the **Top Face Color** button below the **Depth** edit box; the **Color** dialog box is displayed. Select the **Gold Metallic** option from the drop-down list in the **Color** dialog box. Choose **OK** to exit this dialog box.

9. Select the **Wrap to Face** check box. Next, choose the **Face** button, if it has not already been chosen, and select the neck of the bottle on which you need to wrap the text. Choose **OK** to exit the dialog box. A partial view of the bottle after wrapping the text on it is shown in Figure 6-136.

Figure 6-136 Partial view of the bottle after wrapping the text

 Note
If the embossed feature is created on the backside of the neck, you need to reverse its direction by choosing the corresponding direction button from the **Emboss** *dialog box. The direction buttons are available above the* **Wrap to Face** *check box.*

Wrapping the Image on the Bottle

Next, you need to insert an image into the sketching environment and then wrap it on the bottle. It is recommended that you copy the image to the current folder and then insert in the sketching environment.

1. Copy any external image to the current folder and then choose the **Create 2D Sketch** tool from the **Sketch** panel of the **Model** tab; you are prompted to select the plane.

2. Select the tangent work plane created earlier as the sketching plane to invoke the sketching environment.

3. Choose the **Image** tool from the **Insert** panel of the **Sketch** tab; the **Open** dialog box is displayed.

4. In the **Open** dialog box, select the image that you have copied and then choose the **Open** button; the preview of the image attached to cursor is displayed in the graphics window and you are prompted to select the sketch point.

5. Click in the graphics window to place the image. Right-click, and then choose **Done** from the shortcut menu. You may need to resize and relocate the image such that its size and location is close to that shown in Figure 6-137.

6. Exit the sketching environment and then choose the **Decal** tool from the **Create** panel of the **Model** tab; the **Decal** dialog box is displayed and you are prompted to select the image.

7. Select the image inserted in the sketching environment. Next, select the face of the bottle to transfer the image.

8. Select the **Wrap to Face** check box and then choose **OK** to exit the **Decal** dialog box; the image is wrapped on the bottle. The final model of the bottle, after wrapping the text and the image on it, is shown in Figure 6-138.

Figure 6-137 Image inserted in the sketching environment

Figure 6-138 Final model of the bottle

9. Save the model with the name *Tutorial4* at the location *C:\Inventor_2011\c06* and then close the file.

Self-Evaluation Test

Answer the following questions and then compare them to those given at the end of this chapter:

1. A hole created by using the **Hole** tool is parametric in nature. (T/F)

2. You can remove any entity from the current selection set by pressing the SHIFT key and then selecting the entity once again. (T/F)

3. You can create both fillets and rounds by using the **Fillet** dialog box. (T/F)

4. You can mirror the entire model or the selected features. (T/F)

5. The diameter of a hole is defined in the _____ of the **Hole** dialog box.

6. _____ is a process of beveling the sharp edges of a model in order to reduce stress concentration.

7. A rib feature is created by using an _____ sketch.

8. The _____ radio button is selected in the **Mirror** dialog box to create a mirrored feature similar to the original feature, even if they intersect other features.

9. _____ are defined as the thin wall-like structures used to bind joints together so that they do not fail under an increased load.

10. A _____ hole is a stepped hole with a bigger diameter and a smaller diameter.

Review Questions

Answer the following questions:

1. In Autodesk Inventor, you can create holes only on the points/hole centers. (T/F)

2. In the Part module, you can use the **Circular Pattern** tool to arrange the selected features around the circumference of an imaginary circle. (T/F)

3. By using the **Distance** button, you can create a chamfer at an angle of 45-degree. (T/F)

4. The options in the **Variable** tab of the **Fillet** dialog box are used to fillet selected edges by applying different radius values along the length of the edge. (T/F)

5. You can use the options in the **Hole** dialog box to create a tapped hole. (T/F)

6.   Which of the following is not a type of hole?

   (a) Counterbore   (b) Countersink
   (c) Countercut   (d) Drilled

7.   Which of the following tabs provides you with an option to create a flat base hole?

   (a) **Type**   (b) **Options**
   (c) **Size**   (d) **Thread**

8.   How many edges are used to define the setback for a vertex?

   (a) 2   (b) 3
   (c) 4   (d) None of these

9.   Which of the following check boxes is displayed in the **Rib** dialog box when you select the direction of applying a thickness parallel to the sketch or choose the **Finite** button from the **Extents** area?

   (a) **Extend Profile**   (b) **Clear Profile**
   (c) **Trim Profile**   (d) None of these

10. How many methods are provided for creating a chamfer?

   (a) 2   (b) 3
   (c) 4   (d) None of these

Exercises

Exercise 1

Create the model shown in Figure 6-139a. Its dimensions are given in Figures 6-139b and 6-139c.   **(Expected time: 45 min)**

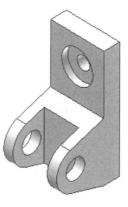

Figure 6-139a Model for Exercise 1

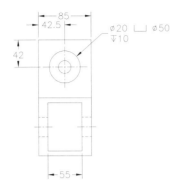

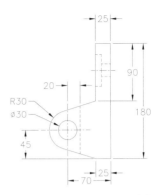

Figure 6-139b *Left view of the model*

Figure 6-139c *Front view of the model*

Exercise 2

Create the model shown in Figure 6-1408a. Its dimensions are given in Figures 6-140b through 6-140d. **(Expected time: 45 min)**

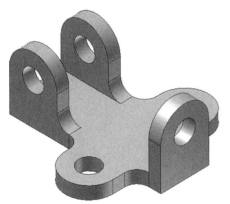

Figure 6-140a *Model for Exercise 2*

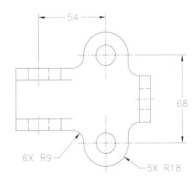

Figure 6-140b *Top view of the model*

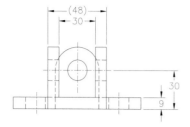

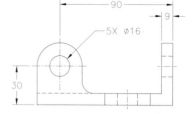

Figure 6-140c *Left view of the model*   ***Figure 6-140d*** *Front view of the model*

Answers to Self-Evaluation Test

1. T, **2.** T, **3.** T, **4.** T, **5.** preview window, **6.** Chamfering, **7.** open, **8. Identical**, **9.** Ribs, **10.** counterbore

Chapter 7

Editing Features and Adding Automatic Dimensions to Sketches

Learning Objectives

After completing this chapter, you will be able to:
- *Edit features in a model.*
- *Update a model after editing.*
- *Edit the sketches of sketched features.*
- *Redefine the sketching plane of a feature.*
- *Suppress features.*
- *Unsuppress features.*
- *Delete features.*
- *Copy features.*
- *Add automatic dimensions to sketches.*

CONCEPT OF EDITING FEATURES

Editing is one of the most important parts of designing. Most of the designs require editing, either during or after their creation. As mentioned earlier, Autodesk Inventor is a feature-based solid modeling tool. As a result, the model created in Autodesk Inventor is a combination of various features. All these features are individual components and can be edited separately. This property gives this solid modeling software an edge over the other non-feature-based solid modeling tools. For example, Figure 7-1 shows a cylindrical part with six countersink holes created at some pitch circle diameter (PCD).

Now, in case you have to edit the features such that the number of holes is to be increased to eight and the countersink holes are to be changed into counterbore holes, you just need to perform two editing operations. The first editing operation will open the **Holes** dialog box, where you can modify the countersink holes to counterbore holes. You can specify various parameters for the counterbore hole in this dialog box. When you exit this dialog box, all the six countersink holes will be modified into counterbore holes. The second editing operation will open the **Circular Pattern** dialog box. In this dialog box, you can change the number of instances to eight, see Figure 7-2.

Figure 7-1 *Part with six countersink holes*   *Figure 7-2* *Modified part with counterbore holes*

Similarly, you can also edit work features or sketches of the sketched features. The features created using the work features will be modified automatically when you edit the work features. For example, if you have created a feature on a work plane that is at an offset of 100 mm, the feature will be automatically repositioned if you change the offset value of the work plane. In Autodesk Inventor, all the editing operations are performed using the **Browser Bar**.

Editing Features of a Model

As mentioned earlier, all editing operations are performed using the **Browser Bar**. To edit a feature, select it in the **Browser Bar**; the selected feature will be highlighted in the model. Right-click on the selected feature in the **Browser Bar** to display a shortcut menu. Next, choose **Edit Feature** from it, see Figure 7-3. Depending on the feature selected for editing, the corresponding dialog box will be displayed. For example, if you right-click on an extruded feature, the **Extrude** dialog box will be displayed. Also, the feature selected to edit will be highlighted in bold in the **Browser Bar**. The dialog box will also have the sequence number of the feature. This means if you right-click on the first extruded feature in a model to display a shortcut menu and then choose **Edit Feature**, the **Extrude : Extrusion1** dialog box will be displayed, see Figure 7-4.

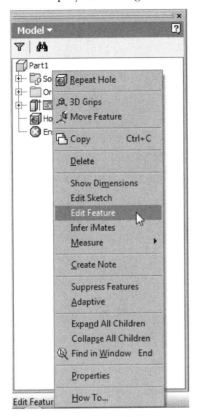

Figure 7-3 *Choosing the* **Edit Feature** *option from the* **Browser Bar** *shortcut menu*

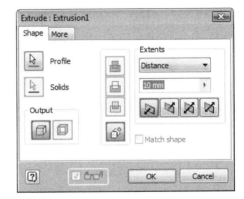

Figure 7-4 *The* **Extrude : Extrusion1** *dialog box for editing an extruded feature*

You can perform the required editing operations using this dialog box. These operations include reselecting the sketch to be extruded, modifying the taper angle, changing the type of operation, and so on. Similarly, if you right-click on a hole feature and then choose **Edit Feature** from the shortcut menu, the **Hole : Hole1** dialog box will be displayed, as shown in Figure 7-5. You can also edit a hole feature by right-clicking on the hole feature in the **Browser Bar** and then choosing the **Show Dimensions** option from the shortcut menu; the hole with all its dimensions will be displayed in blue in the drawing window. Double-click on the diameter dimension; the **Hole Dimensions** dialog box will be displayed, as shown in Figure 7-6. The options in this dialog box will be available depending on whether the hole type is drill, countersink, counterbore, or spotface. Figure 7-6 shows the **Hole Dimensions** dialog box for a counterbore hole.

You can also edit the features (extrusion, revolve feature, hole, fillet, chamfer, and work features) using the mini toolbar. To do so, select the required feature in the graphics window or from the **Browser Bar**; the corresponding mini toolbar will be displayed. Choose the required editing option from the mini toolbar to edit the feature.

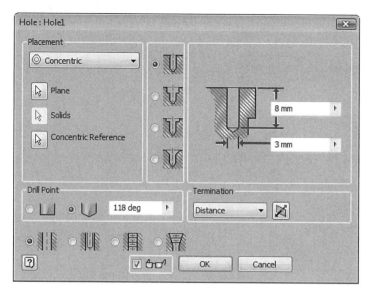

Figure 7-5 The **Hole : Hole1** *dialog box for editing the hole feature*

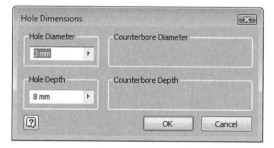

Figure 7-6 The **Hole Dimensions** *dialog box*

Tip. *When you choose the option for displaying the dimensions of the feature for editing, the dimensions will be retained on the screen even after the editing operation is over. To clear these dimensions from the screen, choose* **Update** *from the* **Update** *panel of the* **Manage** *tab or select another feature from the* **Browser Bar**.

Updating Edited Features

If you edit a feature using the **Browser Bar**, you do not have to update the feature to view the effect of the editing operation. This is because as soon as you exit the editing operation, the feature will be automatically updated. However, if you modify the feature using dimensions, you will have to update the feature manually. Until the feature is updated after editing, it will not display the modified values. To update the feature with the modified values, choose the **Local Update** button in the **Quick Access Toolbar** or the **Part Standard** toolbar. This button will be activated when you modify the dimensions of any features.

Editing Features Dynamically by Using 3D Grips

Dynamic editing is a new concept introduced in Autodesk Inventor. Using dynamic editing, you can edit extruded, revolved, or swept features dynamically. To invoke this editing tool, right-click on the feature in the **Browser Bar** or in the drawing window and then choose **3D Grips** from the shortcut menu; the original sketch of the feature will be displayed. The feature will be displayed in wireframe, and all its dependable features will become transparent. You will notice that small circles are displayed on all faces of the model, except the face that lies on the sketching plane. These small circles will also be displayed on all edges that are along the normal direction of the sketching plane, see Figure 7-7. This Figure shows a rectangular block after invoking 3D grips.

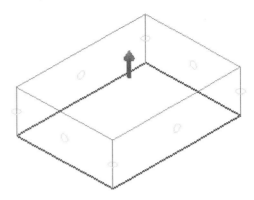

Figure 7-7 Editing of a block using 3D grips

To edit the feature, move the cursor over the circle on any face or edge. If you move the cursor over the circle on a face, an arrow normal to the face will be displayed on the circle. Press and hold the left mouse button at that point and then drag the cursor; the feature will be resized along the normal of that face. Figure 7-8 shows the model, shown in Figure 7-7, being resized normal to the front face. The value by which the feature will be resized is displayed on the right of the cursor.

If you move the cursor on the circles displayed on the edges of the feature and drag, the feature will be simultaneously modified along the X and Y directions of the sketch, as shown in Figure 7-9.

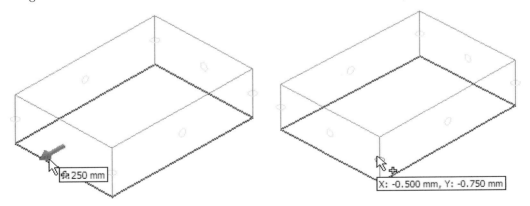

Figure 7-8 Resizing the feature normal to a plane   *Figure 7-9 Resizing the feature using an edge*

The values by which the feature will be resized along the X and Y axes are displayed on the right of the cursor.

After dynamically editing the feature using 3D grips, right-click in the graphics window and choose **Done** from the shortcut menu. Note that the model will be updated only after you choose the **Done** option.

Editing the Sketches of Features

Autodesk Inventor also provides you with the flexibility of editing sketches of the sketched feature. You can add additional entities to the sketch or remove some of the entities from the sketch. Once you have made the necessary changes, you just have to update the sketched feature using the **Local Update** button in the **Quick Access Toolbar**. However, you have to make sure that the sketch after editing remains a closed loop. In case the sketch is not a closed loop, the **Autodesk Inventor 2011 - Exit Sketch Mode** message box will be displayed. It will give an error message that the loop could not be repaired after editing.

To edit the sketch of a sketched feature, right-click on the sketch in the **Browser Bar** to display a shortcut menu. In this shortcut menu, choose **Edit Sketch**; the sketching environment will be activated. Once you have made the necessary changes, choose the **Local Update** button from the **Quick Access Toolbar**.

Dynamically Moving and Rotating the Features

This tool helps you move and rotate the extruded, revolved, or swept features dynamically. To do so, right-click on an extruded, revolved, or swept feature in the **Browser Bar** and then choose **Move Feature** from the shortcut menu. If you select the base feature, the **3D Move / Rotate** dialog box will be displayed, as shown in Figure 7-10 and a triad will be displayed on the model, as shown in Figure 7-11. Depending on where you click on the triad, you can move or rotate the model. The details of using this triad to move or rotate the model are discussed next.

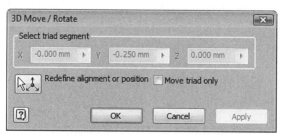

Figure 7-10 The 3D Move / Rotate dialog box

Moving a Selected Feature

The triad allows you to move the feature along the direction of a specified axis in a specified plane, or in 3D. The methods of moving a feature are discussed next.

Moving the Feature along the Direction of a Selected Axis

To move the feature along the direction of a specified axis, move the cursor over the arrowhead of that axis of the triad; it will be highlighted in light red, as shown in Figure 7-12. Make sure you do not drag the cursor over the axis because that will rotate the model. Select the arrowhead when it is highlighted; the edit box of the selected direction will be enabled in the **3D Move / Rotate** dialog box. You can enter the exact value in it and choose **OK**. You can also drag the mouse to move the feature in the selected direction and then right-click in the drawing window. Next, choose **Done** from the shortcut menu.

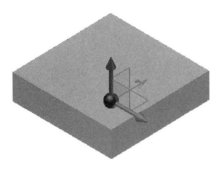

Figure 7-11 *Triad displayed on the model*

Figure 7-12 *Selecting the Y axis to move the feature*

Tip. *You can modify the default snap value while dynamically moving or rotating the feature or while editing the feature using 3D grips. To do so, choose **Tools > Document Settings** from the **Options** panel of the **Ribbon**; the **Document Settings** dialog box will be displayed. Choose the **Modeling** tab and modify the values in the **Distance Snap** and **Angle Snap** edit boxes.*

Moving the Feature in a Selected Plane

To move the feature in a specified plane, select one of the planes displayed in the triad, as shown in Figure 7-13; the related edit boxes will be enabled in the **3D Move / Rotate** dialog box. To move the feature dynamically in the selected plane, you can enter the exact values in the edit boxes or drag the mouse. Next, choose **OK** from the dialog box to execute the editing operation.

Moving the Feature Freely in 3D Space

To move the feature in 3D space, select the sphere of the triad, as shown in Figure 7-14; the edit boxes of all the three axes will be enabled in the **3D Move / Rotate** dialog box. To move the feature dynamically in 3D Space, you can enter the exact values in the edit boxes or drag the mouse. Next, choose **OK** to exit the **3D Move / Rotate** dialog box.

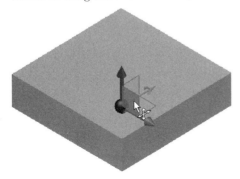

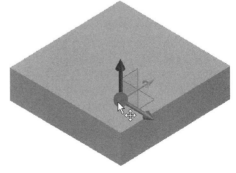

Figure 7-13 *Selecting a plane to move the feature*

Figure 7-14 *Selecting the sphere to move the feature freely in 3D space*

Rotating a Selected Feature

You can rotate the selected feature about any of the three axes of the triad. To rotate the feature, move the cursor over any one of the triad axes; the axis will be highlighted in light red, as shown in Figure 7-15. Select the axis at this stage; the edit box corresponding to the selected axis will be enabled in the **3D Move / Rotate** dialog box. You can enter the exact value of rotation in the edit box or drag the mouse to rotate the feature dynamically. Choose **OK** from the dialog box to complete the editing operation. Figure 7-16 shows a model with the top cut feature at its default orientation and Figure 7-17 shows the same model after rotating the feature.

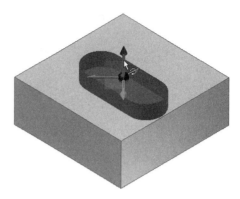

Figure 7-15   *Selecting an axis to rotate the feature*

Figure 7-16   *Original orientation of the feature*

Figure 7-17   *Feature after rotation*

Redefining the Sketching Plane of a Sketched Feature

Sometimes, you may need to relocate a feature drawn on one of the planes to another plane. For example, you may need to relocate a cylinder drawn on the XY plane to the YZ plane. Autodesk Inventor allows you to relocate the features on the other planes by redefining the sketching plane. After redefining it, the necessary changes are automatically made in the orientation of the model. For example, a cylinder drawn on the XY plane stands vertically. However, the same cylinder drawn on the YZ plane lies horizontally.

To redefine the sketching plane of a sketched feature, click on the plus sign (+) located on the left of the sketched feature in the **Browser Bar**; the name of the sketch of the corresponding feature will appear below it in the **Browser Bar**. Right-click on the sketch and choose **Redefine** from the shortcut menu; you will be prompted to select a work plane or planar face to redefine the sketch. Select the new work plane or planar face for the sketched feature; the sketch of the feature will be relocated on the new plane and the model will reorient, based on the new parameters. Also, all the features created with reference to the current features will be updated automatically.

Figure 7-18 shows a model with the base feature created on the XY plane. Figure 7-19 shows the model after redefining the sketching plane of the base feature to the YZ plane. Notice that the base feature and all other features in the model are reoriented based on the new sketching plane.

Figure 7-18 Base feature created on the XY plane   *Figure 7-19* Model after redefining the sketching plane of the base feature to the YZ plane

Note

If one or more features of a model are not relocated after you redefine the sketching plane, a message box will be displayed, informing about the features that are not resolved.

SUPPRESSING FEATURES

Sometimes, there may be a situation where you want that some of the features should not show up in the drawing views of the model or in the printout of the model. In any of the non-feature based solid modeling tools, you will have to either delete the feature or create it after taking the printout. However, in Autodesk Inventor, you can simply suppress the feature that is not needed. Once the feature is suppressed, it will neither be displayed in the drawing views nor in the printout of the model. Remember that in such cases the features are not deleted, they are temporarily turned off. Note that all the features that are dependent on the feature that you select are also suppressed. To suppress a feature, right-click on it in the **Browser Bar** and then choose **Suppress Features** from the shortcut menu.

Note

*All features that are suppressed will be displayed in light gray color in the **Browser Bar**. Also, they will have a line that will strike through the name of the feature in the **Browser Bar**.*

UNSUPPRESSING THE SUPPRESSED FEATURES

The suppressed features can be resumed in the model. To do so, right-click on the suppressed feature in the **Browser Bar** to display the shortcut menu. In this shortcut menu, choose **Unsuppress Features**; the selected feature will be displayed in the model again.

Tip. *After generating the drawing views of the current model, if you suppress any feature in the model, it will not be displayed in the drawing views. However, as soon as you unsuppress the feature, it will be displayed in the drawing views.*

MOVING THE FACES OF A SOLID

Ribbon:	Model > Modify > Move Face
Toolbar:	Part Features > Move Face

 One of the unique features of Autodesk Inventor is its ability to let you move the selected faces of a model. This option is extensively used when you edit a model imported

in Autodesk Inventor. This is because an imported model is displayed as a base feature. To move the faces, choose the **Move Face** button from the **Modify** panel in the **Model** tab; the **Move Face** dialog box will be displayed, as shown in Figure 7-20.

In this dialog box, the **Faces** button will be chosen by default; as a result, you will be prompted to select the faces to be moved. You can select the face(s) and move them using the **Free Move**, **Direction and Distance**, or **Points and Plane** method. These methods are discussed next.

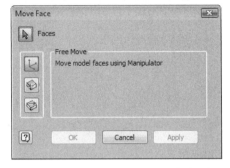

*Figure 7-20 The **Move Face** dialog box*

Free Move Method

Using this method, you can freely move the selected face of a feature. To apply this method, you need to use the **Free Move** button. By default, this button is chosen in the **Move Face** dialog box. As a result, you will be prompted to select the faces to move. Select the required face; a triad will be displayed, as shown in Figure 7-21. Drag the required axis of the triad to move the selected face in the direction of the axis. Alternatively, specify the settings for the movement of the selected face in the mini toolbar. You can also move the selected face at an angle. To do so, drag

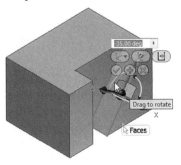

Figure 7-21 Triad displayed on face

the required rotational manipulator from the triad at the required angle. Figure 7-22 shows the selected face moved along the Z-axis by dragging it. Figure 7-23 shows the selected face rotated about the X-axis by dragging the rotational manipulator.

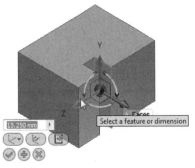

Figure 7-22 Selected face moved along the Z-axis

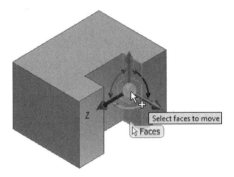

Figure 7-23 Selected face rotated about the X-axis

Direction and Distance Method

The **Direction and Distance** button is available below the **Free Move** button. Therefore, if you select a planar face to be moved, by default, it will move in the direction normal to it. If you want to change the direction, choose the **Direction** button from the **Direction and Distance** area and select an edge to define the direction. You can also choose the **Flip** button to reverse the direction of movement. Figure 7-24 shows the face of the rectangular cut feature being moved in the direction of the normal of that face.

Points and Plane Method

This method allows you to move the selected faces in a specified plane. The distance of the movement is defined using two points. To invoke this method, choose the **Points and Plane** button available below the **Direction and Distance** button and then select the faces to be moved. Choose the **Plane** button; you will be prompted to select a planar face. Select the plane in which you want to move the selected face and then choose the **Points** button; you will be prompted to select the first point. Select a point to specify the start point of the movement. Next, you will be prompted to select the second point. On specifying the second point, the preview of the resulting movement will be displayed, as shown in Figure 7-25.

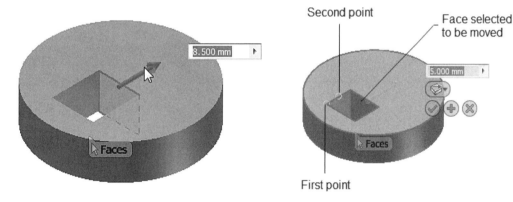

Figure 7-24 *Preview of a face being moved using the* ***Direction and Distance*** *method*

Figure 7-25 *Preview of a face being moved using the* ***Points and Plane*** *method*

If you try to move the faces that have a partial circular cut feature in-between them, as shown in Figure 7-26, the faces move only to the distance at which the partial circle becomes a full circle. If the specified movement value is more than this distance, an error message will be displayed and the faces will not move. Figure 7-27 shows the cut feature that has now become almost a full circle.

DELETING FEATURES

You can delete all unwanted feature from a model. To do so, right-click on the feature to be deleted in the **Browser Bar**; a shortcut menu is displayed. Choose the **Delete** option in the shortcut menu; the **Delete Features** dialog box will be displayed. This dialog box will prompt you to specify whether or not you want to delete the dependent features and sketches. The options that you can select for deleting include the sketch of the feature, the dependent sketches and features, and the dependent work features. The options that are not applicable

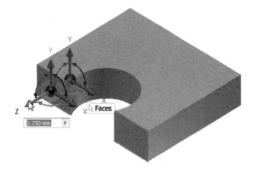 

Figure 7-26 Faces selected to be moved   *Figure 7-27 Partial circular cut feature changed to a circular cut feature by moving the faces*

to the selected feature will be disabled in this dialog box. For example, if you delete a feature that does not have any work feature created with reference to it, the last option in the **Delete Features** dialog box will be disabled.

COPYING AND PASTING FEATURES

Autodesk Inventor allows you to copy and paste a sketch-based feature from the current file to any file or at some other place in the same file. However, the method of copying a feature in Autodesk Inventor is different from that in the other solid modeling tools. To copy a feature, right-click on its name in the **Browser Bar** and then choose **Copy** from the shortcut menu. Note that this option will be available only for the sketch-based features. Now, to paste the feature in another file, open it. Else, open any other existing file. Right-click in the drawing window to display the shortcut menu and then choose **Paste** from it. The **Paste Features** dialog box will be displayed, as shown in Figure 7-28, and the dynamic preview of the feature will be displayed in the drawing window.

*Figure 7-28 The **Paste Features** dialog box*

By default, the feature will be attached to any planar face in the model. However, you can attach the feature to the desired face using the options in the **Paste Features** dialog box. The options in this dialog box are discussed next.

Paste Features

This drop-down list is used to select the option for pasting the features. By default, the **Selected** option is selected in this drop-down list. As a result, only the selected feature will be pasted and the features that are dependent on the selected features will not be pasted. However, if you want to paste all the dependent features, select **Dependent** from this drop-down list.

Parameters

This drop-down list is used to select whether the parameters of the feature should be independent or dependent. You can select the required option from this drop-down list.

Name

This column displays the plane on which the feature will be pasted. When you invoke this dialog box, by default, the feature will be temporarily pasted on any plane. As you move the mouse on any plane, the feature will be temporarily snapped to that plane. You can view all this in the dynamic preview of the feature on the model. Once you select the plane on which the feature should be pasted, the dynamic preview will fix to that plane. Until you select the plane to paste the feature, an icon will be displayed on the left of the profile plane in this column. This icon will display an arrow on the face of a box. This suggests that you have not selected the plane for placing the feature. When you select any plane, this icon is replaced by a box that has a check mark, suggesting that the plane for placing the feature has been selected. In case you want to change the plane for the feature placement, click on **Profile Plane** in this column and then select the required plane.

Angle

This column is used to rotate the pasted feature through an angle by specifying the angle in it. The preview of the feature will be dynamically rotated through the specified angle.

Refresh

The **Refresh** button will be active only after you have selected a plane for pasting the feature. This button is chosen to refresh the feature such that it adjusts to the selected plane. For example, if a feature has a dependent feature that is cut using the **All** option, the preview of the model will display the cut feature extending beyond the plane on which the feature is pasted, see Figure 7-29. However, when you choose the **Refresh** button, the cut feature will be adjusted such that it is not extended beyond the selected plane, see Figure 7-30.

Finish

The **Finish** button is used to paste the required feature on the selected face. The paste operation completes only after you have chosen this button. Figure 7-31 shows a model with the original cut feature and the dependent cut feature and Figure 7-32 shows the model after copying the original cut feature and the dependent cut feature on two different planes.

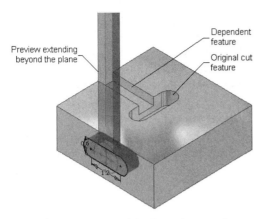

Figure 7-29 Preview of the dependent cut feature extending beyond the selected plane

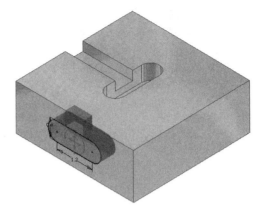

Figure 7-30 Preview of the dependent cut feature adjusted to fit the plane

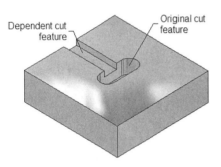

Figure 7-31 Model with the original cut feature and the dependent cut feature

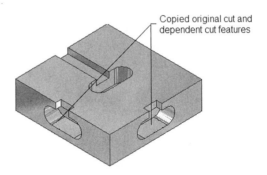

Figure 7-32 Cut features copied on two different planes of the model

Note

You can also shift or reorient the position of the feature on the selected face using the symbols provided on the pasted feature. To do so, move the cursor over the plus symbol; it will turn red, as shown in Figure 7-33. Drag the mouse to the new location and place the feature by releasing the mouse button. You can also dynamically rotate the pasted feature. To do so, move the cursor over the circular symbol; it will turn red, as shown in Figure 7-34. Drag the mouse; the feature will rotate accordingly. To place the feature, release the mouse button.

Figure 7-33 Active Plus symbol

Figure 7-34 Active Circular symbol

ADDING AUTOMATIC DIMENSIONS TO SKETCHES

Ribbon:	Sketch > Constrain > Automatic Dimensions and Constraints
Toolbar:	2D Sketch Panel > Auto Dimensions

 Autodesk Inventor allows you to add dimensions and constraints automatically. Note that you cannot apply all dimensions and constraints required in a sketch. The dimensions are used in association with the general dimensions to fully constrain the sketch. In Autodesk Inventor, automatic dimensions are added using the **Automatic Dimensions and Constraints** tool. When you invoke this tool, the **Auto Dimension** dialog box will be displayed, as shown in Figure 7-35. The options in this dialog box are discussed next.

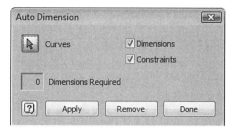

*Figure 7-35 The **Auto Dimension** dialog box*

Curves

The **Curves** button is chosen to select the sketch for applying automatic dimensions. By default, the complete sketch is selected to be dimensioned. As a result, all the entities in the sketch are dimensioned. However, if you want to add automatic dimensions to some of the selected entities, choose this button and then select the required entities from the graphics screen. The selected entities will be highlighted in blue. Choose the **Apply** button to apply the automatic dimensions to the selected entities of the sketch.

Dimensions Required

The **Dimensions Required** display box will display the number of dimensions that are required to fully constrain the sketch. You cannot modify the value in this box.

Dimensions

The **Dimensions** check box is selected to add automatic dimensions to the sketch. If this check box is cleared, the dimensions will not be added to the sketch.

Constraints

The **Constraints** check box is also selected to add constraints to the sketch while applying the automatic dimensions. If this check box is cleared, the constraints will not be added.

 Tip. *You can use the **Automatic Dimensions and Constraints** tool to verify if the sketch you have drawn is fully constrained or not. After adding all required dimensions and constraints, invoke this tool. If the dialog box shows 0 dimensions required, the sketch is fully constrained.*

Apply

The **Apply** button is chosen to apply the automatic dimensions to the selected sketch. Invoke the **Auto Dimension** dialog box and then choose this button to add the dimensions. Note that until this button is chosen, the automatic dimensions will not be applied to the sketch.

Remove

The **Remove** button is chosen to remove the automatic dimensions from the sketch.

Done

The **Done** button is chosen to exit the **Auto Dimension** dialog box.

PROJECTING ENTITIES IN THE SKETCHING ENVIRONMENT

Autodesk Inventor allows you to project the edges of an existing feature to a sketching plane while drawing the sketches. The projected edges are converted into sketched entities and can be used as a part of the sketch. You can project the selected edge or face of a feature, or project the part of the model that is cut by the sketching plane. Note that since the projected entities are reference entities, you cannot dimension them. Both these options of projecting the entities are discussed next.

Projecting Edges or Faces

Ribbon:	Sketch > Draw > Project Geometry
Toolbar:	2D Sketch Panel > ProjectGeometry

Project Geometry

You can project the selected edges or faces of a feature to a sketching plane by choosing the **Project Geometry** tool from the **Draw** panel of the **Sketch** tab (see Figure 7-36). On invoking this tool, you will be prompted to select an edge, vertex, work geometry, or sketch geometry to be projected. If you move the cursor over a face, it will be highlighted with a red outline. Similarly, if you move the cursor over an edge, it will be highlighted in red. Select the geometry to be projected; the selected geometry it will be projected on the current sketching plane as a sketched entity. Figure 7-37 shows a model in which a sketch plane is defined at the center of the model. Figure 7-38 shows the model after projecting the spline edge.

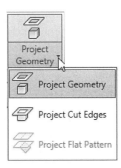

*Figure 7-36 Tools in the **Project Geometry** drop-down*

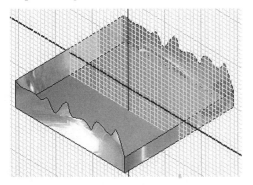

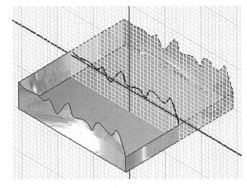

Figure 7-37 *Sketch plane at the center of the model*

Figure 7-38 *Model after projecting the spline edge*

Projecting Cutting Edges

Ribbon:	Sketch > Draw > Project Geometry > Project Cut Edges
Toolbar:	2D Sketch Panel > ProjectGeometry > ProjectCut Edges

Project
Cut Edges

The cutting edges are meant to define the contour of the model that is created when you define a sketching plane on the face of a model or inside the model. When you define a sketching plane inside the model, it cuts the model, thus forming cutting edges. You can project these cutting edges by choosing the **Project Cut Edges** tool from the **Draw** panel of the **Sketch** tab (see Figure 7-36). As soon as you choose this tool, the edges that are cut by the sketching plane will be projected. Figure 7-39 shows a model and the sketching plane cutting through it and Figure 7-40 shows the sketch after projecting the cutting edges.

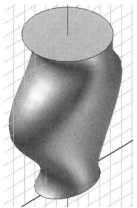

Figure 7-39 Sketch plane at the center of the model

Figure 7-40 Sketch after projecting the cutting edges

Note
*The models shown in Figures 7-38 and 7-39 are created using the **Loft** tool. This tool is discussed in the next chapter.*

TUTORIALS

Tutorial 1

In this tutorial, you will create the model of the Gear-shifter link shown in Figure 7-41a. Its dimensions are shown in Figures 7-41b through 7-41d. **(Expected time: 45 min)**

The following steps are required to complete this tutorial:

a. Create the base feature, which is a reverse C-like feature. Its sketch will be created on the XZ plane and extruded using the **Symmetric** option, see Figure 7-43.
b. Define a new sketch plane on the XZ plane and add the first join feature to the circular face of the base feature, refer to Figure 7-45.
c. Again, define a new sketch plane on the XZ plane and draw the sketch for the second join feature. Extrude this feature using the **Symmetric** option, refer to Figure 7-47.

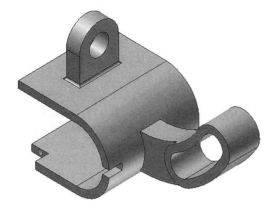

Figure 7-41a Model for Tutorial 1

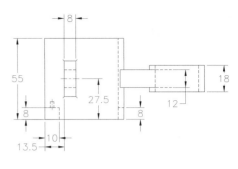

Figure 7-41b Top view of the model

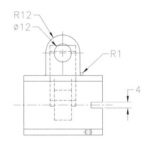

Figure 7-41c Left view of the model

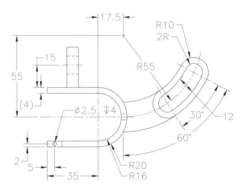

Figure 7-41d Front view of the model

d. Define a new sketch plane on the front face of the second join feature and draw the sketch for the cut feature. Extrude this sketch using the **Cut** operation, refer to Figure 7-49.
e. Suppress all features, except the base feature, and then define a work plane at an offset of 17.5 mm from the left face of the base feature. Draw the sketch for the third join feature and extrude it using the **Symmetric** option, refer to Figure 7-51.
f. Add fillet to the third join feature, refer to Figure 7-53.
g. Suppress the last two features and create the slots and hole on the front face of the base feature, refer to Figure 7-55.
h. Finally, unsuppress all features to complete the model, refer to Figure 7-57.

Creating the Base Feature

1. Start a new metric standard part file and then draw the sketch of the base feature on the XZ plane, as shown in Figure 7-42.

2. Exit the sketching environment and then extrude the sketch to a distance of 55 mm using the **Symmetric** option. The base feature of the model is shown in Figure 7-43.

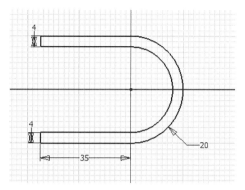

Figure 7-42 Sketch of the base feature

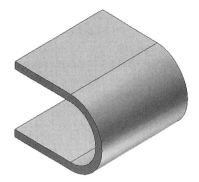

Figure 7-43 Base feature of the model

Creating the Curved Features

As the base feature was created on the XZ plane and was extruded using the **Symmetric** option, you can create the sketches for the curved features on the same plane and then extrude them as required using the **Symmetric** option.

1. Draw the sketch of the curved feature on the XZ plane. Add the required constraints and dimensions to it. The sketch of the first join feature after applying all dimensions and constraints is shown in Figure 7-44.

2. Exit the sketching environment and then extrude the sketch of the first join feature to a distance of 12 mm using the **Join** operation. Use the **Symmetric** option for creating the feature. The isometric view of the model is shown in Figure 7-45.

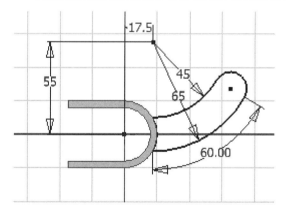

Figure 7-44 Sketch of the first join feature

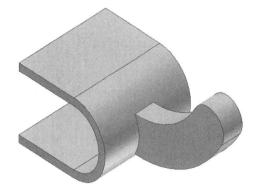

Figure 7-45 First join feature created after extruding the sketch

3. Draw the sketch of the second join feature on the XZ plane, as shown in Figure 7-46. After drawing the sketch, apply the **Concentric** and **Equal** constraints to it and to the existing feature.

Note
*You can use the **Splice Graphics** option for creating the sketch of the second join feature. This option can be invoked from the shortcut menu that is displayed when you right-click in the graphics window in the sketching environment. Alternatively, press the F7 key to slice graphics.*

4. Exit the sketching environment and then extrude the sketch to a distance of 18 mm using the **Join** operation and the **Symmetric** option, see Figure 7-47.

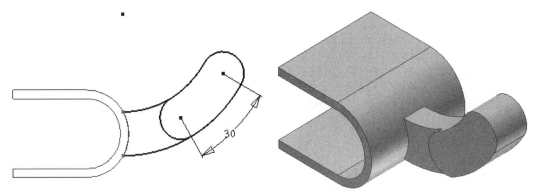

Figure 7-46 *Sketch of the second join feature in the wireframe display*

Figure 7-47 *Model after creating the second join feature*

5. Specify a new sketch plane on the front face of the second join feature and then create the sketch of the cut feature on this plane. You can offset and dimension the reference entities to create the sketch of the cut feature, as shown in Figure 7-48.

6. Exit the sketching environment and then click on the sketch; a mini toolbar is displayed.

7. Choose the **Create Extrude** button from the mini toolbar; the **Extrude** dialog box along with the modified mini toolbar is displayed.

8. Click inside the sketch created for the cut feature and then choose the **Cut** option from the **Operation** area of the mini toolbar.

9. Select the **Through All** option from the **Extents** area and then choose **OK** from the mini toolbar; the cut feature is created, as shown in Figure 7-49.

Suppressing Features

As mentioned earlier, in a complex model, it is better to suppress these features that are not required while creating a particular feature. After creating all features, you can unsuppress the suppressed features. In Autodesk Inventor, the features are suppressed using the **Browser Bar**.

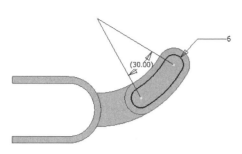

Figure 7-48 *Sketch of the cut feature*

Figure 7-49 *Model after creating the cut feature*

1. Right-click on **Extrusion2** (first join feature) in the **Browser Bar** to display a shortcut menu.

2. Choose **Suppress Features** from the shortcut menu; the **Autodesk Inventor 2011 - Suppress Feature** dialog box is displayed. Also, the first join feature is no more visible. However, the second join feature and the cut feature remain visible on the model.

3. Choose **Accept** from the **Autodesk Inventor 2011 - Suppress Feature** dialog box. Now, right-click on **Extrusion3** (second join feature) in the **Browser Bar** and then choose **Suppress Features** to suppress the second join feature and the cut feature.

   The only feature that is visible now is the base feature of the model.

Creating the Third Join Feature

The third join feature is created on an offset work plane. This work plane will be at an offset distance of -17.5 mm from the left face of the base feature. The negative value will make sure that the work plane is offset inside the model.

1. Choose the **Offset from Plane** tool from **Model > Work Features > Plane** drop-down and define a new work plane at an offset of -17.5 mm from the left face of the base feature. Create the sketch for the third join feature on the new plane.

2. Create a circle inside the sketch so that when you extrude the sketch, a hole is also created, see Figure 7-50.

3. Extrude the sketch to a distance of 8 mm using the **Join** operation and the **Symmetric** option. If the **Autodesk Inventor** warning window is displayed, choose **Accept** from it. The model after creating the third join feature is displayed, as shown in Figure 7-51.

Creating the Fillet Feature on the Third Join Feature

1. Choose the **Fillet** button from the **Modify** panel of the **Model** tab; the **Fillet** dialog box is displayed.

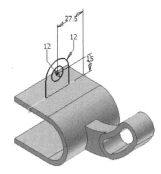

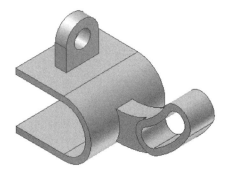

Figure 7-50 *Sketch for the third join feature*   *Figure 7-51* *Model after creating the third join feature*

2.   Select the **Loop** radio button from the **Select mode** area and enter **1** in the **Radius** edit box; you are prompted to select the loop on the model.

3.   Select the loop on the third join feature of the model, as shown in Figure 7-52. Next, choose **OK** from the **Fillet** dialog box; the fillet feature is created, as shown in Figure 7-53.

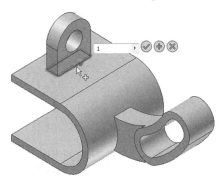

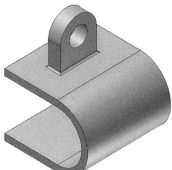

Figure 7-52 *Loop selected for creating the fillet*   *Figure 7-53* *Model after creating the fillet on the third join feature*

Suppressing the Third Join Feature

1.   Right-click on **Extrusion5** (third join feature) in the **Browser Bar** to display a shortcut menu. Choose **Suppress Features** from the shortcut menu; the fillet feature is suppressed because it is dependent on the third join feature. Now, the only visible feature is the base feature.

Creating the Slots and the Hole

Next, slots will be created on the front face of the base feature. As both the slots will be cut to the same distance, you can draw the sketch for both the slots together and then extrude them using the **Cut** operation.

1.   Define a new sketch plane on the front face of the base feature.

2. Draw the sketch for both slots, as shown in Figure 7-54.

3. Invoke the **Extrude** tool and then create the slots of depth 8 mm using the **Cut** operation, as shown in Figure 7-55.

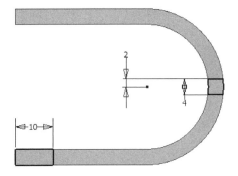

Figure 7-54 *Sketch for slots*

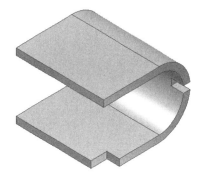

Figure 7-55 *Model after creating slots*

4. Create a drilled hole of 2.5 mm diameter on the left face of the slot, as shown in Figure 7-56. For the location of the hole, refer to Figure 7-41d. The depth of the hole is 4 mm. The model after creating the hole is shown in Figure 7-56.

Note
The orientation of the model in Figures 7-55 and 7-56 has been changed by using the ViewCube for clarity and better understanding.

Unsuppressing the Features

Once all features of the model have been created, you can unsuppress the suppressed features and save the model. As you know, all suppressed features will be displayed in light gray color and will have a line striking through their names in the **Browser Bar**.

1. Right-click on **Extrusion2** (first join feature) in the **Browser Bar** and then choose **Unsuppress Features** from the shortcut menu displayed.

   If Autodesk Inventor encounters any error while updating the features, the **Autodesk Inventor 2011 - Unsuppress Feature** dialog box is displayed. Choose **Accept**, if this dialog box is displayed. The second join feature is unsuppressed.

2. Similarly, unsuppress the remaining suppressed features. Choose **Accept** in the **Autodesk Inventor 2011 - Unsuppress Feature** dialog box whenever it is displayed. The final solid model of the Gear-shifter link after unsuppressing all suppressed features is shown in Figure 7-57.

Saving the Model

1. Save the model with the name *Tutorial1* at the location *C:\Inventor_2011\c07* and then close the file.

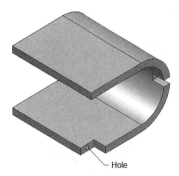

Figure 7-56 *Model after creating the hole*

Figure 7-57 *Final solid model of the Gear-shifter link*

Tutorial 2

In this tutorial, you will create the model shown in Figure 7-58a. Its dimensions are shown in Figures 7-58b through 7-58d.   **(Expected time: 45 min)**

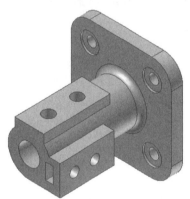

Figure 7-58a *Model for Tutorial 2*

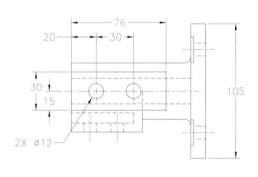

Figure 7-58b *Top view of the model*

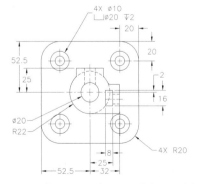

Figure 7-58c *Left view of the model*

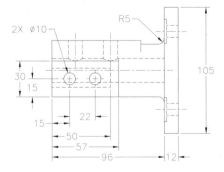

Figure 7-58d *Front view of the model*

Before you start creating the model, it is recommended that you outline the procedure for creating it. The steps required to complete this tutorial are listed next.

a. Create the base feature on the XZ plane, refer to Figure 7-59. The sketch for the base feature consists of a square with fillets on all four corners.
b. On the front face of the base feature, create counterbore holes by using the center points of fillets as the center of holes, refer to Figure 7-60.
c. Suppress the holes and create the cylindrical join feature on the front face of the base feature.
d. Add two rectangular join features to the cylindrical feature and create the rectangular cut feature on one of the rectangular join features, refer to Figure 7-68.
e. Create drilled holes by defining the sketch plane on the required planes. Once all features are created, unsuppress the holes on the base feature, refer to Figure 7-70.
f. Finally, create the fillet of radius 5 mm, refer to Figure 7-70.

Creating the Base Feature

1. Start a new metric part file and then draw the sketch of the base feature on the XZ plane.

   The sketch of the base feature will be a square of side 105 mm and with all four corners filleted with a radius of 20 mm.

2. Exit the sketching environment and extrude the sketch to a distance of 12 mm. The base feature of the model is shown in Figure 7-59.

Creating the Holes

The base feature has four counterbore holes. You can create these holes concentric with the cylindrical faces of the fillets at the corners. Alternatively, you can create one of the holes and then create a rectangular pattern for creating the remaining three holes.

1. Invoke the **Hole** tool and then create four counterbore holes using the **Concentric** placement option. Refer to Figure 7-58c for dimensions.

   The model after creating the counterbore holes is shown in Figure 7-60.

 Note
*You need to use the **Through All** option from the drop-down list given under the **Termination** area to create through holes.*

Figure 7-59 *Base feature of the model*

Figure 7-60 *Model after creating the counterbore holes*

Suppressing the Holes

As you have created four holes, the **Browser Bar** will display these holes with names **Hole1**, **Hole2**, **Hole3**, and **Hole4**. You need to select all four holes and suppress them.

1. Press and hold the SHIFT or the CTRL key and select all four holes from the **Browser Bar**.

2. Right-click on the selected holes in the **Browser Bar** to display a shortcut menu. In the shortcut menu, choose **Suppress Features**; all four holes are suppressed. The only feature that is visible is the base feature.

Creating the Cylindrical and Rectangular Join Features

1. Define a new sketch plane on the front face of the base feature and then draw a circle of 44 mm diameter, as shown in Figure 7-61. Exit the sketching environment.

2. Invoke the **Extrude** tool and then extrude the circle to a distance of 96 mm, as shown in Figure 7-62.

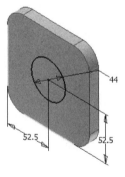

Figure 7-61 *Sketch for the cylindrical feature*

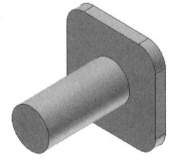

Figure 7-62 *Cylindrical feature created*

3. Define a new sketch plane on the front face of the cylindrical feature and create the sketch of the first rectangular feature, as shown in Figure 7-63. Exit the sketching environment.

4. Invoke the **Extrude** tool and then extrude the sketch to a distance of 76 mm, as shown in Figure 7-64.

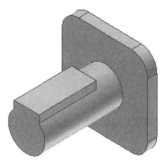

Figure 7-63 Sketch of the first rectangular feature

Figure 7-64 Model after creating the first rectangular feature

5. Similarly, create the sketch of the second rectangular feature and extrude it to a distance of 57 mm, refer to Figures 7-65 and 7-66.

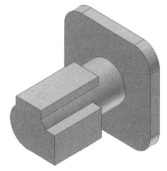

Figure 7-65 Sketch of the second rectangular feature

Figure 7-66 Model after creating the second rectangular feature

Creating the Cut Feature and Holes

1. Define a new sketch plane on the front face of the cylindrical feature and then create the rectangular cut feature of depth 50 mm, refer to Figures 7-67 and 7-68.

2. Create a hole of 20 mm diameter and 96 mm depth on the front face of the cylindrical feature. The model after creating the hole and the cut feature is shown in Figure 7-69.

3. Similarly, create holes one by one on the faces of the rectangular join features, see Figure 7-69. For the dimensions and location of holes, refer to Figures 7-58b and 7-58d.

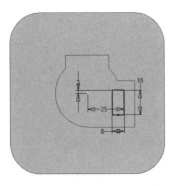

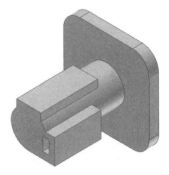

Figure 7-67 *Sketch of the rectangular cut feature*

Figure 7-68 *Model after creating the rectangular cut feature*

Unsuppressing the Counterbore Holes

1. From the **Browser Bar**, select all holes created on the base feature. Right-click on the selected holes and choose **Unsuppress Features** from the shortcut menu; all counterbore holes will again be displayed on the base feature.

Creating Fillet and Saving the File

1. Invoke the **Fillet** tool and create a fillet of radius 5 mm on the circular edge created between base feature and the cylindrical join feature. The final model for Tutorial 2 after unsuppressing the counterbore holes and creating the fillet is shown in Figure 7-70.

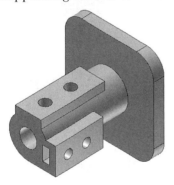

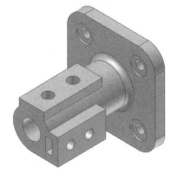

Figure 7-69 *Model after creating holes and cut feature*

Figure 7-70 *Final model for Tutorial 2*

2. Save the model with the name *Tutorial2* at the location *C:\Inventor_2011\c07* and close the file.

Tutorial 3

In this tutorial, you will create the model of the Body of the Butterfly Valve assembly shown in Figure 7-71a. Its dimensions are shown in Figures 7-71b through 7-71d. After creating the model, modify the location of the curved feature on the top face by changing the dimension 175 to 200. The dimensions of the remaining five instances should also change automatically.

(Expected time: 45 min)

Figure 7-71a Model for Tutorial 3

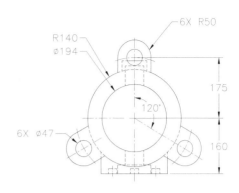

Figure 7-71b Top view of the model

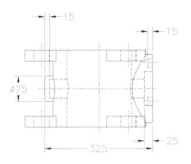

Figure 7-71c Left view of the model

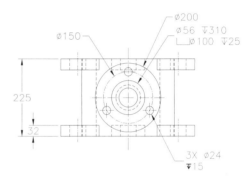

Figure 7-71d Front view of the model

The following steps are required to complete this tutorial:

a. Create the base feature on the XY plane, refer to Figure 7-72. The sketch of the base feature consists of two circles. These circles will be extruded using the **Symmetric** option.
b. Define two new offset work planes to create two cylindrical join features on the cylindrical face of the base feature, refer to Figure 7-76.
c. Add the counterbore hole and three smaller holes on the front face of the second feature, refer to Figure 7-77.
d. Suppress the second and third features and then create the curved sketch feature with a hole on the top face of the model, refer to Figure 7-78.
e. Pattern the last feature using the **Circular Pattern** tool. Finally, mirror all three instances of the circular pattern on the bottom face of the model, see Figure 7-80.
f. After creating the features, edit them as mentioned in the tutorial description, refer to Figure 7-81.

Creating the Base Feature

1. Open a new metric part file and then create the base feature on the XY plane. Take the origin as the center of the two circles in the sketch of the base feature. For the dimensions of circles, refer to Figure 7-71b.

> **Tip**. *While creating the sketch for the base feature, it is recommended that you project the origin and then use it to locate the centers of both the circles. The origin is the point at which the X and Y axes meet in the drawing window or the point at which all three planes meet in the **Part** mode. Now, if the origin is selected as the center of the base feature, you can use the default XZ plane to create the offset planes. If the origin is not selected as the center of the base feature, you will have to first create a work plane tangent to the cylindrical face of the base feature and then use it to define the offset work plane.*

2. Extrude the sketch to a distance of 225 mm using the **Symmetric** option.

The reason of extruding the sketch using the **Symmetric** option is that you can use the XY plane as the plane for mirroring the features on the top face of the model to the bottom face of the model. If the base feature is not extruded using the **Symmetric** option, you will have to create a new work plane for mirroring the features. The base feature of the model is shown in Figure 7-72.

Figure 7-72   *Base feature of the model*

Creating the Join Features on the Cylindrical Faces of the Base Feature

Since the base feature was created taking the origin as the center of the circles, you can use the XZ plane to create the offset work plane.

1. Create a new work plane at an offset of -160 mm from the XZ plane. The negative value ensures that the work plane is created toward the front side of the base feature and not toward the back side.

2. Define a new sketch plane on **Work Plane1** and draw the sketch of the first join feature using the origin of the new sketch plane as the center, as shown in Figure 7-73. Refer to Figure 7-71d for the placement of the first join feature.

3. Invoke the **Extrude** tool and then extrude the sketch using the **To Next** option from the **Extents** area. The model after creating the join feature is shown in Figure 7-74.

4. Similarly, define a new work plane at an offset of 325 mm from **Work Plane1**. Next, define a new sketch plane on **Work Plane2** and create the sketch of the second join feature, as shown in Figure 7-75. Refer to Figures 7-71c and 7-71d for the placement of the second join feature.

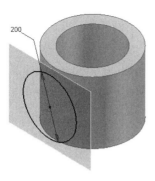

Figure 7-73 Sketch for the first join feature

Figure 7-74 Model after creating the first join feature

5. Invoke the **Extrude** tool and then extrude the sketch using the **To Next** option from the **Extents** area. The model after creating the second join feature is shown in Figure 7-76.

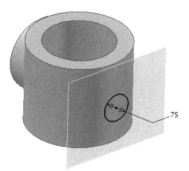

Figure 7-75 Sketch of the second join feature

Figure 7-76 Model after creating the second join feature

Creating the Counterbore Hole and the Drilled Holes on the Front Face of the First Join Feature

1. Using the **Concentric** option, create the flat-ended counterbore hole on the front face of the first join feature, refer to Figure 7-71d for the dimensions and placement of the hole.

2. Create a sketch point on the front face of the first join feature to locate the hole. Refer to Figure 7-71d for the location of the hole. Invoke the **Hole** tool and create one of the drilled holes. For the dimensions of the hole, refer to Figure 7-71d.

3. Create a circular pattern containing three instances of the drilled holes. The model after creating the counterbore hole and the three smaller drilled holes is shown in Figure 7-77.

Figure 7-77 Model after creating the holes

Suppressing the Features

As the features, other than the base feature, are not required for creating the remaining features in the model, you can suppress them. This will reduce the complicacy of the model and make it easier for you to create the remaining features.

1. Right-click on **Extrusion2** (first join feature) in the **Browser Bar** and choose **Suppress Features**; the first join feature gets suppressed.

   In this step, you will see that the counterbore hole and the three drilled holes are also suppressed. This is because the holes are created on the first join feature and so are dependent on it.

2. Similarly, right-click on **Extrusion3** (second join feature) in the **Browser Bar** and choose **Suppress Features**; the second join feature gets suppressed.

Creating the Third Join Feature on the Top Face of the Base Feature

1. Define a new sketch plane on the top face of the base feature and draw the sketch of the third join feature, refer to Figure 7-71b for dimensions. Include the circle in the sketch so that the hole is created automatically.

2. Extrude the sketch to a distance of 32 mm. The model after creating the third join feature on the top face of the base feature is shown in Figure 7-78.

Creating the Circular Pattern of the Third Join Feature

1. Create a circular pattern of the third join feature on the top face of the base feature. The model after creating the circular pattern is shown in Figure 7-79.

Figure 7-78 *Third join feature created*   *Figure 7-79* *Model after creating the circular pattern*

Mirroring the Features on the Bottom Face of the Base Feature

As the base feature was extruded using the **Symmetric** option, you can use the XY plane for mirroring the feature on the bottom face of the base feature.

1. Choose the **Mirror Feature** tool and then select the third join feature created on the top face of the base feature and the circular pattern as the features to be mirrored.

2. Mirror the features using the XY plane as the mirror plane and choose **OK**.

Unsuppressing the Features

1. Right-click on **Extrusion2** (first join feature) in the **Browser Bar** and then choose **Unsuppress Features** from the shortcut menu. The first join feature and the holes are unsuppressed.

2. Right-click on **Extrusion3** (second join feature) and then choose the **Unsuppress Features** option from the shortcut menu to unsuppress the second join feature also. The model after creating all features is shown in Figure 7-80.

Figure 7-80 Model after creating all features

Modifying the Dimensions of Feature on the Top Face of the Model

Out of the three instances of the third join feature on the top face of the model and the three instances on the bottom face, only one was actually sketched. The rest were created either using the **Circular Pattern** tool or using the **Mirror** tool. Therefore, if you modify the original feature, the rest of the features will be automatically modified.

1. Right-click on **Extrusion4** (third join feature) in the **Browser Bar** to display a shortcut menu. In this menu, choose **Show Dimensions**; the basic sketch of the third join feature is displayed along with its dimensions. You can double-click on any dimension to display the **Edit Dimension** toolbar. This toolbar can be used to edit the selected dimension value.

2. Double-click on the dimension 175 mm to display the **Edit Dimension** toolbar and then enter **200** as the dimension value.

   On changing the dimension value the temporary sketch of the third join feature, which is displayed in the drawing window gets modified. However, the features will not be modified because the model is not yet updated.

3. Choose the **Update** button from the **Update** panel of the **Manage** tab; all six instances of the third join feature are automatically modified. The model after editing the feature is shown in Figure 7-81.

Note

*While drawing the sketch for the feature that you modified in the last step, if you do not apply the **Coincident Constraint** between the lower endpoint of the lines of the sketch and the outer circle of the base feature, the feature will be separated from the base feature when you modify it. You can also apply the **Coincident Constraint** between the arc of the sketch and the outer circle of the base feature to avoid separation.*

Figure 7-81 Final model after editing the features

4. Save the model with the name *Tutorial3* at the location *C:\Inventor_2011\c07* and then close the file.

Self-Evaluation Test

Answer the following questions and then compare them to those given at the end of this chapter:

1. Most of the designs require editing, either during or after their creation. (T/F)

2. In Autodesk Inventor, all editing operations are performed using toolbars. (T/F)

3. You can also edit a hole feature by right-clicking on it in the **Browser Bar** and then choosing **Show Dimensions**. (T/F)

4. You can also display the dimensions of a feature on the model by double-clicking on the feature in the **Browser Bar**. (T/F)

5. If you right-click on the third extruded feature in a model and then choose **Edit Feature** from the shortcut menu, the _____ dialog box will be displayed.

6. The features edited using the dimensions can be updated by choosing the _____ button from the _____.

7. The features in the model can be suppressed by first right-clicking on the feature and then choosing _____ from the shortcut menu displayed.

8. The _____ dialog box is used to paste the copied features in a new file.

9. The _____ button in the **Paste Features** dialog box is used to adjust the preview of the pasted feature on the selected plane.

10. While suppressing a feature, its _____ features are also suppressed.

Review Questions

Answer the following questions:

1. In Autodesk Inventor, you can copy features from one file to the other. (T/F)

2. In Autodesk Inventor, you can edit the sketches of the sketched features. (T/F)

3. When you choose the option of displaying the dimensions of the feature for editing, the dimensions will be retained on the screen even after the editing operation is over. (T/F)

4. The feature to be copied can be rotated at any angle. (T/F)

5. After editing the sketch of a feature, you have to make sure that the sketch is still a closed loop. (T/F)

6. You can redefine the sketching plane of a sketched feature. (T/F)

7. You can specify whether or not to delete the dependent sketches and features. (T/F)

8. In the **Paste Features** dialog box, you can specify whether to paste only the selected feature or both the selected feature and the dependent features. (T/F)

9. All suppressed features are displayed in light gray color in the **Browser Bar**. (T/F)

10. If you edit a feature using the **Browser Bar**, you do not need to update it to view the effect of the editing operation. (T/F)

Exercises

Exercise 1

Create the model of the Slide Bracket shown in Figure 7-82a. Its dimensions are shown in Figures 7-82b through 7-82d.   **(Expected time: 45 min)**

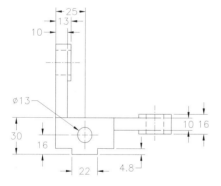

Figure 7-82a *Model for Exercise 1*

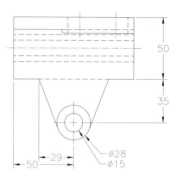

Figure 7-82b *Top view of the model*

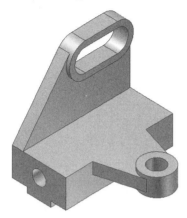

Figure 7-82c *Left view of the model*

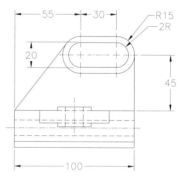

Figure 7-82d *Front view of the model*

Exercise 2

Create the model shown in Figure 7-83a. Its dimensions are shown in Figures 7-83b through 7-83d. **(Expected time: 45 min)**

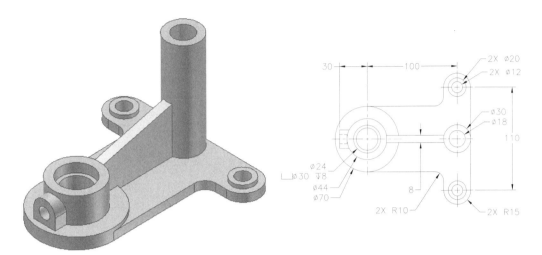

Figure 7-83a *Model for Exercise 2*   **Figure 7-83b** *Top view of the model*

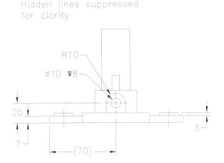

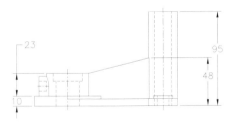

Figure 7-83c *Left view of the model*   **Figure 7-83d** *Front view of the model*

Exercise 3

Create the model shown in Figure 7-84a. Its dimensions are shown in Figures 7-84b through 7-84d.   **(Expected time: 45 min)**

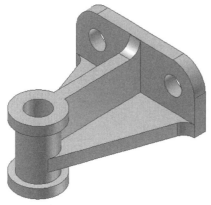

Figure 7-84a *Model for Exercise 3*

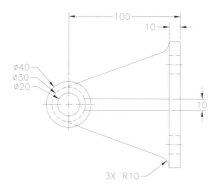

Figure 7-84b *Top view of the model*

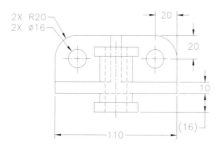

Figure 7-84c *Left view of the model*

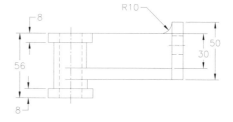

Figure 7-84d *Front view of the model*

Exercise 4

Create the model shown in Figure 7-85a. Its dimensions are shown in Figures 7-85b through 7-85d.   **(Expected time: 45 min)**

Figure 7-85a *Model for Exercise 4*

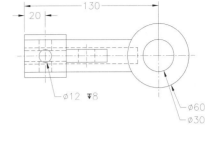

Figure 7-85b *Top view of the model*

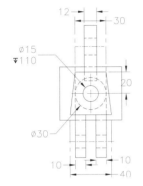

Figure 7-85c *Left view of the model*

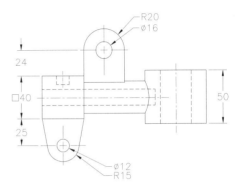

Figure 7-85d *Front view of the model*

Exercise 5

In this exercise, you will create the model of the Bottom Seat shown in Figure 7-86a. After creating this model, you will perform the modifications given below. The model after performing the modification is shown in Figure 7-86b. The views and dimensions of the original model are shown in Figure 7-86c.

1. Change the two holes on the front face of the model to countersunk holes.
2. Change the hole on the right face of the model to counterbore hole.
3. Change the curved pocket feature on the upper face of the model to a rectangular slot.

(Expected time: 45 min)

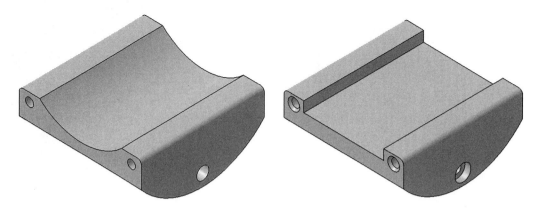

Figure 7-86a *Model of the Bottom Seat*

Figure 7-86b *Model after performing the modifications*

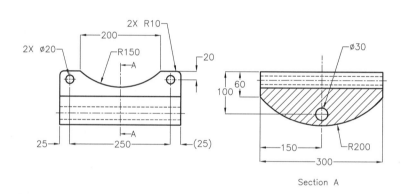

Figure 7-86c *Views and dimensions of the original model*

Answers to Self-Evaluation Test
1. T, **2.** F, **3.** T, **4.** T, **5. Extrude: Extrusion3**, **6. Local Update**, **Quick Access Toolbar**, **7. Suppress Features**, **8. Paste Features**, **9. Refresh**, **10.** dependent

Chapter 8

Advanced Modeling Tools-II

Learning Objectives

After completing this chapter, you will be able to:
- *Create sweep features.*
- *Create lofted features.*
- *Create coil features.*
- *Create internal or external threads.*
- *Create shell features.*
- *Apply drafts on the faces of a model.*
- *Split the faces of a model or a complete model.*
- *Delete the selected faces of a model.*
- *Replace the selected faces of a model with surfaces.*
- *Add surface patches.*
- *Stitch multiple surfaces to a single surface.*
- *Create sculpt features.*
- *Understand the use of sketch doctor and design doctor.*

ADVANCED MODELING TOOLS

The first few advanced modeling tools are discussed in Chapter 6, Advanced Modeling Tools-I. In this chapter, you will learn about the remaining tools.

Creating Sweep Features

Ribbon:	Model > Create > Sweep
Toolbar:	Part Features > Sweep

The next advanced modeling tool is the **Sweep** tool and is used to create sweep features. A sweep feature is created when a closed sketch is swept along an open or a closed path. Therefore, to create a sweep feature, you need two unconsumed sketches: a closed sketch (called profile) and a path. It is recommended that you create the path in such a way that the profile should not make self intersecting sections when it is swept along the path. When a profile curve makes self intersecting sections, then the sweep feature cannot be created, and a message box is displayed informing about the failure of feature creation.

The path for the sweep feature is created by using the usual method of creating sketches. It can be a combination of sketcher entities such as lines, arcs, circles, splines, and ellipses. It is recommended that the profile should be normal to the path. Therefore, after you have finished drawing the path, create a work plane normal to the path and at its start point. To create a work plane normal to the path through a point, exit the sketching environment and choose the **Normal to Curve at Point** tool from the **Work Features** panel. Next, select the curve and a point on it; a work plane normal to the curve at the specified point will be created. Create the profile on the work plane. Figure 8-1 shows a profile and a 2D path and Figure 8-2 shows the resulting sweep feature.

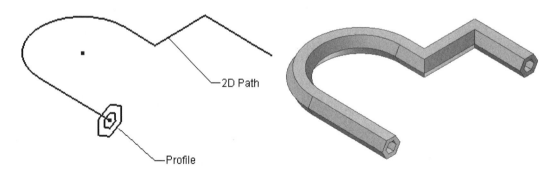

Figure 8-1 *Path and profile for the sweep feature*   **Figure 8-2** *Resulting sweep feature*

To create the sweep feature, choose the **Sweep** tool from the **Create** panel of the **Model** tab; the **Sweep** dialog box will be displayed, as shown in Figure 8-3. The options in this dialog box are discussed next.

Shape Area

This area is available on the top left corner of the dialog box and provides the following three buttons:

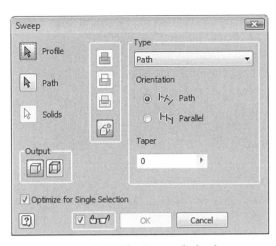

Profile

The **Profile** button is chosen to select the profile for the sweep feature. Remember that the profile has to be a closed loop for creating the solid sweep feature. When you invoke the **Sweep** dialog box, the **Profile** button will be chosen by default and you will be prompted to select the profile for the sweep feature.

Path

The **Path** button is chosen to select the path for the sweep feature.

Figure 8-3 The Sweep dialog box

Solids

The **Solids** button is chosen to select participating solid bodies from multiple bodies. This button will be activated only when there are multiple solid bodies in the graphics window.

Output Area

The buttons in the **Output** area are chosen to specify the type of output of the **Sweep** tool. If the profile selected is closed, the **Solid** button is chosen by default. As a result, a solid sweep feature will be created. If you choose the **Surface** button, the resulting sweep will be a surface feature. The **Surface** button is chosen automatically, if you select an open profile.

Operation Area

This area contains the following buttons:

Join

The **Join** button is the first button provided in the area that is on the right side of the **Shape** area. This button is chosen to create a sweep feature by adding material to the model.

Cut

The **Cut** button is provided below the **Join** button and is chosen to create a sweep feature by removing material from the model. If the sweep feature is the first feature, this button will not be activated.

Figure 8-4 shows the profile and path curves and Figure 8-5 shows the sweep features created using the **Join** and **Cut** operations.

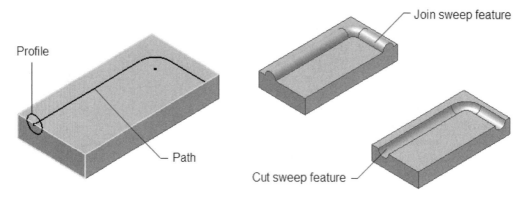

Figure 8-4 *Profile and path curves created for the sweep feature*

Figure 8-5 *Join and cut sweep features*

Intersect

The **Intersect** button is provided below the **Cut** button and is used only when you have an existing feature. This means that this button will not be available if the sweep feature is the first feature in the model. This operation is used to create a sweep feature such that the material common to the profile and the existing feature is retained. The remaining material is removed from the model.

New solid

This button is chosen by default and is used to create a new solid body. The new solid body is independent of other solid bodies, if present in the part file.

Optimize for Single Selection

If this check box is selected, the next selection step is activated automatically after you complete the first selection. For example, the **Path** button is automatically chosen as soon as you select any one sketch as the profile. If you clear this check box, you can select nested sketches as the profile.

Type Area

The options available in this area allow you to create three types of sweeps: using only the path, using a path and a guide curve, and using a path and a guide surface. Creating all these three types of sweeps is discussed next.

Creating Sweep Features by Using a Path Curve

By default, the **Path** option is selected from the drop-down list in the **Type** area. As a result, the option to create the sweep feature with the path curve is active. This option allows you to create a sweep feature that follows the specified path. You can specify whether the orientation of the profile will be constant to the path or parallel to the sketching plane. The options that are available when you select the **Path** option from the **Type** drop-down list are discussed next.

Path

This radio button is selected by default. It forces the profile to remain constantly oriented to the path at all points.

Parallel

This radio button forces the sketch to remain parallel to the sketching plane throughout the sweep feature.

Figure 8-6 shows the profile and the path to create the sweep feature. Figure 8-7 shows the sweep feature created with the **Path** radio button selected. As evident from this figure, the profile remains oriented to the path throughout the sweep feature. Figure 8-8 shows the sweep feature with the **Parallel** radio button selected. As evident from this figure, the profile is oriented parallel to the sketching plane throughout the sweep feature.

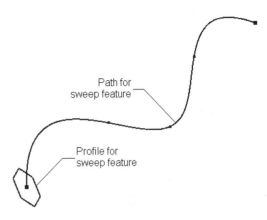

Figure 8-6 Profile and path for the sweep feature

Figure 8-7 Sweep feature created using the ***Path*** *radio button*

Figure 8-8 Sweep feature created using the ***Parallel*** *radio button*

Taper

This edit box is used to define the taper angle for the sweep feature. A positive taper angle tapers the sweep feature outward and a negative taper angle tapers it inward. Figure 8-9 shows a sweep feature with a positive taper angle and Figure 8-10 shows a sweep feature with a negative taper angle.

Figure 8-9 Sweep feature created with a positive taper angle

Figure 8-10 Sweep feature created with a negative taper angle

Creating Sweep Features by Using Path and Guide Curves

To create a sweep feature with the path and guide curves, select the **Path & Guide Rail** option from the drop-down list in the **Type** area; the options in this area will be modified, as shown in Figure 8-11. These options are discussed next.

Guide Rail

This button is chosen to select the guide curve for creating the sweep feature.

Profile Scaling

The radio buttons available in this area are used to specify the scaling method for the profile that is swept using a path and a guide curve. Selecting the **X & Y** radio button ensures that the sweep feature is scaled in both X and Y directions. Figure 8-12 shows the profile, path, and guide curve to create the sweep feature and Figure 8-13 shows the preview of the sweep feature scaled in the X and Y directions.

Figure 8-11 The **Type** area with modified options

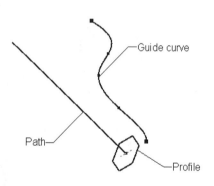

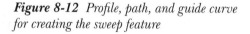

Figure 8-12 Profile, path, and guide curve for creating the sweep feature

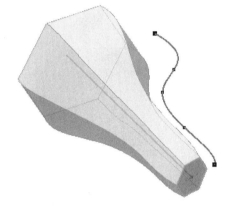

Figure 8-13 Sweep feature scaled in both X and Y directions

Selecting the **X** radio button ensures that the sweep feature is scaled only along the X direction, as shown in Figure 8-14. Selecting the **None** radio button ensures that there is no scaling in the sweep feature. However, if there is any rotation in the guide curve, it will reflect in the sweep feature also. Figure 8-15 shows the preview of the feature with no scaling.

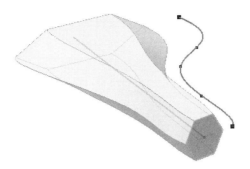

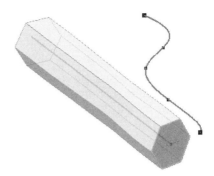

Figure 8-14 *Sweep feature scaled only along the X direction*

Figure 8-15 *Sweep feature with no scaling*

Creating Sweep Features by Using a Path and a Guide Surface

To invoke this option, select the **Path & Guide Surface** option from the drop-down list in the **Type** area; the **Guide Surface** button will be displayed in this area and you will be prompted to select the surface to control the profile twist. Figure 8-16 shows the path and the profile for the sweep feature. Figure 8-17 shows a sweep feature created using the **Path** option and Figure 8-18 shows the sweep feature with the same profile and path, but created using the **Path & Guide Surface** option with the top face of the base feature taken as the guide surface. As evident from Figure 8-18, the shape and twist of the sweep feature is controlled by the guide surface.

Figure 8-16 *Profile and path for creating the sweep feature*

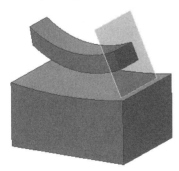

Figure 8-17 *Sweep feature created using the* **Path** *option*

Figure 8-18 *Sweep feature created using the* **Path** & **Guide Surface** *option*

Creating Lofted Features

Ribbon:	Model > Create > Loft
Toolbar:	Part Features > Loft

Lofted features are created by blending more than one dissimilar geometry together. The dissimilar geometries may or may not be parallel to each other. The sketches for the solid loft features should be closed profiles or points. However, for a surface model, the sketches can be open profiles. Figure 8-19 shows a circle, a triangle, and a point drawn on planes parallel to each other, but at some offset. Figure 8-20 shows the resulting lofted feature.

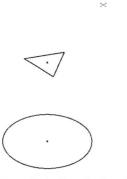

Figure 8-19 *Three dissimilar sketches drawn on parallel planes*

Figure 8-20 *Lofted feature created after blending the sketches*

In Autodesk Inventor, lofted features are created using the **Loft** tool. When you invoke this tool, the **Loft** dialog box will be displayed. The options in various tabs of this dialog box are discussed next.

Curves Tab

The options in the **Curves** tab, as shown in Figure 8-21, are used to select sketches, rails, and centerlines for creating loft features. These options are discussed next.

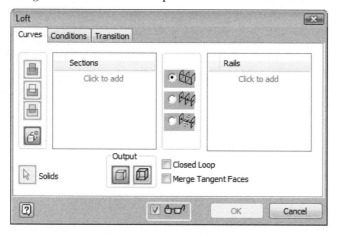

Figure 8-21 *The **Curves** tab of the **Loft** dialog box*

Operation Area

The options in the Operation area are used to specify the type of operation performed using the **Loft** tool. If this is the first feature, only the **Join** button will be available in this area. The buttons in this area are discussed next.

Join: The **Join** button is the first button in the **Operation** area and is used to create a loft feature by adding material to the model.

Cut: The **Cut** button is chosen to create a loft feature by removing material common to the loft and the model. This button will not be available if the loft feature is the first feature.

Intersect: The **Intersect** button is provided below the **Cut** button and is chosen to create a loft feature by retaining material common to the loft and the model. The remaining material will be removed from the model. This button will also not be available if the loft feature is the first feature.

New solid: This button is chosen by default and is used to create a new solid body. The new solid body is independent of other solid bodies, if present in the part file.

Sections Area

When you invoke the **Loft** dialog box, you will be prompted to select a sketch for creating the loft feature. The **Sections** area prompts you to select the sketched and displays them in the list box. When you select the sketches, a green arrow will appear on the graphics screen showing the path for the loft feature. For example, if you select three sketches: Sketch1, Sketch2, and Sketch3 in the same sequence, two arrows will appear on the graphics screen. The first arrow will point from Sketch1 to Sketch2 and the second arrow will point from Sketch2 to Sketch3. This suggests that the resulting loft feature is a blend of Sketch1-Sketch2 and Sketch2-Sketch3.

Tip. *You can also modify the sequence in which the sketches are selected using the* **Sections** *area. To modify the sequence, select the sketch in this area and drag it above or below the other sketch. The arrow direction will also change automatically in the preview of the model.*

Output Area

The options in the **Output** area are used to specify the output of the **Loft** tool. If you select closed loops to blend, the **Solid** button is chosen in this area. As a result, a solid loft feature is created. If you choose the **Surface** button, the resulting loft will be a surface.

Rails

 This is the first radio button available on the right of the **Sections** area. If this radio button is selected, the **Rails** area will be displayed in the **Loft** dialog box. You can use the options in this area to select rails for the loft feature. Rails are used to control the shape of the entire body of the loft. You can use open sketches as rails for controlling the shape of the loft. Note that rails should intersect all sections selected to loft and they must be tangent continuous. To add rails, click on **Click to add** in the

Rails area and then select rails; the names of the selected rails will be displayed in this area. Figure 8-22 shows the sections and rails used to create the loft feature. Figure 8-23 shows the loft feature without selecting rails and Figure 8-24 shows the loft feature with rails.

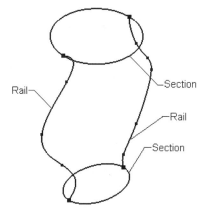

Figure 8-22 Sections and rails for the loft feature

Figure 8-23 Loft feature without selecting rails   *Figure 8-24 Loft feature with rails*

 Tip. *The rails used to guide the shape of the loft should intersect all sections of the loft. If rail does not intersect the sections, an error message will be displayed. You can make sure that the sketch of the rail intersects the sections by projecting the sections on the sketching plane of rails and then adding the **Coincident** constraint between the rail and the projected sections. Make sure you convert projected entities into construction elements before exiting the sketching environment.*

Closed Loop

The **Closed Loop** check box is selected to close the loft feature by joining the end section with the start section. This check box will function only when you select the **Rails** radio button from the **Loft** dialog box. Figure 8-25 shows an open-ended loft feature and Figure 8-26 shows a closed-ended loft feature.

Figure 8-25 *Open-ended loft feature*   *Figure 8-26* *Closed-ended loft feature*

Merge Tangent Faces

If this check box is selected, the tangent faces are merged together and no edge is created between the tangent faces of the loft feature.

Center Line

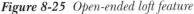 This radio button is available below the **Rails** radio button. If this radio button is selected, the **Center Line** area to select the center line for the loft feature will be displayed in the **Loft** dialog box. A center line is a curve to which the resulting loft feature is normal at every point. A center line may or may not intersect the sections. Figure 8-27 shows the two sections that are drawn on parallel planes and the curve to be used as the center line. Figure 8-28 shows the loft feature without selecting the center line and Figure 8-29 shows the loft feature with the center line.

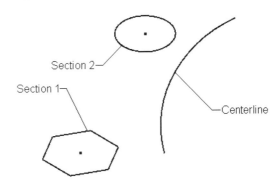

Figure 8-27 *Sections and center line for the loft feature*

Area Loft

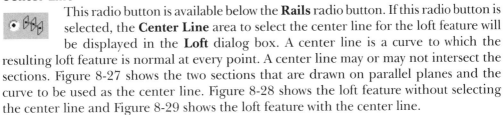 This radio button is available below the **Center Line** radio button and is used to create a loft feature with varying cross-sections at required points on a center line. After specifying cross-sections for the loft feature, select the **Area Loft** radio button; you will be prompted to select a sketch to define the center line. Click once in the **Center Line** list box in the **Loft** dialog box and then select the center line from the graphics window; the preview of the loft feature will be displayed along with the

Figure 8-28 *Loft without selecting the center line*   **Figure 8-29** *Loft with center line*

callouts displaying the position and area of the sections defined at the start and the end of the center line. Also, you will be prompted to select a point. Figure 8-30 shows the preview of the loft feature created with the **Area Loft** radio button selected. This figure also shows the sections and the center line for the loft feature along with the default callouts displayed at the start point and the endpoint of the center line.

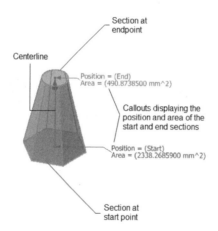

Figure 8-30 *Sections and center line for the loft feature with default callouts*

Notice that as you move the cursor toward the center line, the cursor will be attached to a yellow dot. Click at the desired location on the center line; a new cross-section will be created at that location and a callout displaying the position and area of the cross-sections will be displayed, as shown in Figure 8-31. Also, the corresponding **Section Dimensions** dialog box will be displayed, as shown in Figure 8-32. You can edit the dimensions and position of the new cross-section by using this dialog box. On doing so, the name of the newly added sections will be displayed in the **Placed Sections** list box. After modifying the parameters, choose the **OK** button from the **Section Dimensions** dialog box.

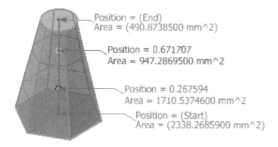

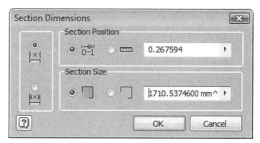

Figure 8-31 *The new sections of the loft feature and their callouts*

Figure 8-32 *The **Section Dimensions** dialog box*

Figure 8-33 shows a loft feature created between a hexagonal section and a circular section. This feature is created by selecting the **Rails** radio button from the **Loft** dialog box. Figure 8-34 shows a loft feature created between a hexagonal section and a circular section by selecting the **Area Loft** radio button from the **Loft** dialog box.

Figure 8-33 *Loft feature created by selecting the **Rails** radio button*

Figure 8-34 *Loft feature created by selecting the **Area Loft** radio button*

Conditions Tab

The options in the **Conditions** tab, as shown in Figure 8-35, are used to control the shape of a lofted feature by applying end conditions to the sections at the two ends. The two end sections or edges selected to create the loft feature are displayed in the list box of this tab.

You can apply the different types of end conditions using the drop-down list that is available when you click on the field on the left of the **Angle** column.

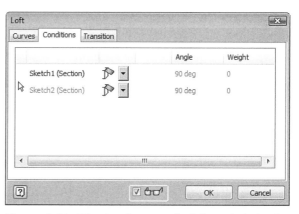

Figure 8-35 *The **Conditions** tab of the **Loft** dialog box*

Free Condition

If this option is selected, no end condition is applied to the end sections of the loft feature. In this type of end condition, the **Angle** and **Weight** columns will not be enabled.

Tangent Condition

The **Tangent Condition** option will be available only if the start section or the end section is a planar face of an existing feature. If this option is selected, the resulting loft feature will be tangent to the adjacent faces of the planar face selected as one of the end sections. Figure 8-36 shows the preview of the loft feature in which the upper section is a hexagon and the lower section is a cylindrical edge of the top face of a cylinder. In this preview, no end condition is applied by selecting the **Free Condition** option. Figure 8-37 shows the preview using the same conditions. But in this figure, the tangent condition is applied. As evident from Figure 8-37, the loft feature is tangent to the base cylinder at the start section because of the tangent condition.

Figure 8-36 Loft feature with no end condition

Figure 8-37 Loft feature with tangent end condition

 Tip. *An angle value greater than 90-degree will create an obtuse section in the loft feature. Similarly, an angle value less than 90-degree will create an acute section in the loft feature.*

Smooth (G2) Condition

This option is available below the **Tangent Condition** option. If this option is selected, the resulting loft feature will have curvature continuity (G2 continuity) with the adjacent faces of the planar face, as shown in Figure 8-38. You can visualize the curvature continuity by using the **Zebra** tool in the **Analysis** panel of the **Inspect** tab.

Figure 8-38 Loft with smooth end condition

Direction Condition

The **Direction Condition** option is selected to define the end conditions using the **Angle** and **Weight** edit boxes. This type of end condition is available only when the profiles or sections for the loft feature are 2D sections.

Angle

The **Angle** edit box will be available only when the value in the **Weight** edit box is more than zero (default value). This edit box is used to define the angle at the start and end sections of the loft. This angle specifies the transition between the section or rail plane and the face of the loft feature created. Remember that you cannot define an angle for the intermediate sketches. To specify the value of the angle at the start section, select the first sketch from the **Conditions** area and then set the value in this edit box. Similarly, to specify the value of the angle at the end section, select the last sketch from the **Conditions** area and then set the value in this edit box. Figure 8-39 shows angles at the start and end sections of the loft.

Weight

The **Weight** edit box is used to specify the distance to which the resulting feature will maintain the angle value or tangency at the start or the end sections before going for the next transition. Greater the value of weight, more will be the distance to which the angle value or tangency will be maintained. To define the weight value, select the first or the last sketch from the **Conditions** area and then specify the value in this edit box. Figure 8-39 shows various weight values at the start and end sections of the loft.

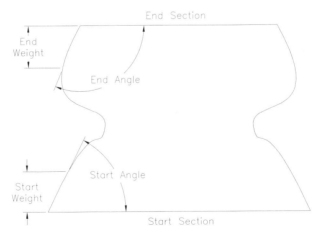

Figure 8-39 Parameters associated with a loft feature

Figure 8-40 shows a loft with weight 0.75 at the tangent end and weight 4 at the other end. Figure 8-41 shows the same loft with weight at the tangent end as 1.5 and at the other end as 8.

Transition Tab

The options in the **Transition** tab are used to set the mapping options for the segments of the various sections while blending.

Figure 8-40 *Start weight=0.75, end weight=4*   **Figure 8-41** *Start weight=1.5, end weight=8*

Automatic Mapping

This check box is selected by default when you invoke the **Loft** dialog box. As a result, all segments of various sections map to each other using the default options and there is minimum or no twisting in the loft feature. If this check box is cleared, the remaining areas in the **Transition** tab will be active, as shown in Figure 8-42. Figure 8-43 shows the preview of the loft feature. The lines at the vertices in this figure show how various segments and points map to each other while blending. Figure 8-44 shows the loft feature created by using automatic mapping.

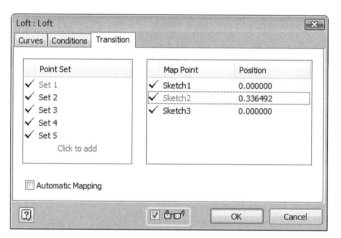

Figure 8-42 *The **Transition** tab of the **Loft** dialog box*

Point Set

The **Point Set** area will be enabled only when the **Automatic Mapping** check box is cleared. This area displays all sets of points used to map the segments and points of various sections in the loft feature. The number of sets of points in this area is equal to the number of green lines in the preview of the loft feature. The first set of points will be displayed in red in the preview. Similarly, the set of points you click on in this area will be displayed in red in the preview. To introduce twist in the loft feature, delete all sets of points in this area by clicking on them and then pressing the DELETE key. Next, click on **Click to add**; you will be prompted to select a point. Select one point each on all sketches.

Figure 8-43 *Preview of the default mapping*   ***Figure 8-44*** *Resulting loft feature*

Similarly, to create the second set of points, click on **Click to add** and then select the set of points on all sections. Follow this procedure to create the required number of sets and then choose **OK** from the **Loft** dialog box. The loft feature will follow the path created by the mapping points. Figure 8-45 shows the path created by defining the mapping points and Figure 8-46 shows the resulting twisted loft feature.

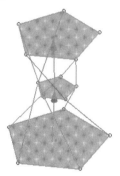

Figure 8-45 *Path created by defining the mapping points*   ***Figure 8-46*** *Resulting twisted loft feature*

Map Point Area

The **Map Point** area displays the section points corresponding to the point set selected in the **Point Set** area. For example, **Sketch1** in this area represents the mapping point of the first section corresponding to the point set selected in the **Point Set** area. The number of items in this area depends on the number of sections in the loft.

Position Area

The **Position** area displays the position of the mapping point in terms of the length of the edge on which it lies. The total length of the edge on which the point lies is considered as 1. As a result, if the mapping point lies on the start point of the edge, its position is taken as 0 and so it is displayed as 0 in this area. Similarly, if the mapping point lies on the endpoint of the edge, its position is displayed as 1 in this area. You can select any intermediate point on the edge to define the location of the mapping point.

Creating Coil Features

Ribbon:	Model > Create > Coil
Toolbar:	Part Features > Coil

A coil feature is created by sweeping a profile about a helical path. The examples of coil feature are springs, filaments of light bulbs, and so on.

To create a coil feature, you need a profile and an axis, refer to Figure 8-47. You can also select the standard X, Y, Z axes, or a new work axis to create the coil feature. Coil features are created using various tabs from the **Coil** dialog box. This dialog box is invoked by choosing the **Coil** tool from the **Create** panel of the **Model** tab. Depending on the parameters specified in the **Coil** dialog box, an imaginary helical path is created and the profile is swept along that path. Therefore, to create a coil feature, you need only one unconsumed sketch, which defines the profile of the coil section. The options in the **Coil** dialog box are discussed next.

Coil Shape Tab

The options in the **Coil Shape** tab, as shown in Figure 8-48, are used to select the profile of the coil feature and the axis about which the imaginary helical path is created. You can also specify whether the coil will be created in the clockwise or counterclockwise direction by using the options in this tab. All options in this tab are discussed next.

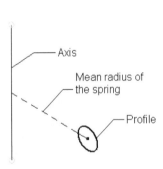

Figure 8-47 Profile and axis for creating a coil feature

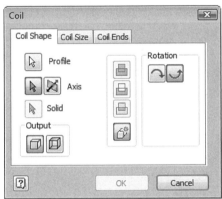

*Figure 8-48 The **Coil Shape** tab of the **Coil** dialog box*

Shape Area

The options in this area are used to select the profile and the axis of the coil.

Profile: The **Profile** button is chosen to select the profile of the coil. If the drawing consists of a single unconsumed sketch, it will be automatically selected as the profile of the coil feature.

Axis: The **Axis** button is chosen to select the axis for creating the coil feature. When you select the axis, an imaginary helical path will be displayed around the selected axis in the graphics window. The entities that can be selected as the axis for creating the coil feature are work axes, linear edges of a model, line segments, and so on. You can reverse the direction of the path by choosing the **Flip** button provided on the right of the **Axis** button.

Join

The **Join** button is the first button in the area between the **Shape** area and the **Rotation** area. This operation is used to create a coil feature by adding material to a model, see Figure 8-49.

Cut

The **Cut** button is provided below the **Join** button and is chosen to create a coil feature by removing material from a model, see Figure 8-50.

Figure 8-49 *Coil feature created on a cylinder using the **Join** operation*

Figure 8-50 *Coil feature created on a cylinder using the **Cut** operation*

Note
*The **Cut** operation of the **Coil** tool can be used to create internal or external threads in the model. However, it is recommended that you use the **Thread** tool for creating the threads directly. The use of this tool will be discussed later in this chapter.*

Intersect

The **Intersect** button is provided below the **Cut** button. This operation is used to create a coil feature by retaining material common to the model and the coil. The remaining material will be removed.

Note
*The area with the **Join**, **Cut**, and the **Intersect** buttons will not be available, if the coil is the first feature.*

New solid

This button is located below the **Intersect** button and is chosen by default. As a result, the resulting coil will be a new solid body.

Output Area

This area is used to specify whether the resulting coil will be a solid feature or a surface.

Coil Size Tab

The options in this tab are used to define the method and the other parameters that will be used for creating the coil, see Figure 8-51.

Type

The **Type** drop-down list is used to select the method for creating the coil feature. The methods that are available in this drop-down list for creating the coil are discussed next.

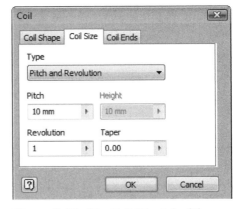

*Figure 8-51 The **Coil Size** tab of the **Coil** dialog box*

Pitch and Revolution: The **Pitch and Revolution** method is used to create coil by defining the pitch and the number of revolutions in the coil. The pitch value can be specified in the **Pitch** edit box and the number of revolutions can be specified in the **Revolution** edit box. You can also define a taper angle for the coil feature in the **Taper** edit box. A positive taper angle tapers the coil outward and a negative taper angle tapers the coil inward. Figure 8-52 shows a coil created with a positive taper and Figure 8-53 shows a coil created with a negative taper.

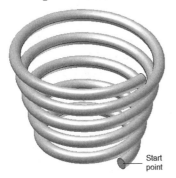

Figure 8-52 Coil feature created with a positive taper angle

Figure 8-53 Coil feature created with a negative taper angle

Revolution and Height: The **Revolution and Height** method is used to create the coil by defining the number of revolutions in it and its total height. The number of revolutions can be defined in the **Revolution** edit box and the height can be defined in the **Height** edit box.

Pitch and Height: The **Pitch and Height** method is used to create the coil by defining the pitch of the coil and the total height of the coil. The value of the pitch can be defined in the **Pitch** edit box and the height can be defined in the **Height** edit box.

Spiral: The **Spiral** method is used to create a spiral coil in a single plane. The spiral coil can be created using the pitch of the coil and the number of revolutions in the coil. As the spiral coil is created in a single plane, the **Height** edit box will not be available when you use this method. Also, you cannot define the taper angle for a spiral coil and so the **Taper** edit box will not be available. Figure 8-54 shows a spiral coil.

Coil Ends Tab

The options in this tab are used to specify the type of ends of the imaginary helical path to be used to create the coil, see Figure 8-55. These options are discussed next.

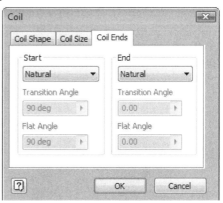

Figure 8-54 Spiral coil

*Figure 8-55 The **Coil Ends** tab of the **Coil** dialog box*

Start Area

The options in the **Start** area are used to specify the end type at the start section of the imaginary helical path. The type of start section can be selected from the drop-down list in this area. These options are discussed next.

Natural: The **Natural** option is selected by default. As a result, no other option in the **Start** area is available.

Flat: If the **Flat** option is selected, you can specify a different start section of the helical path. The other options in the **Start** area will be available only if this option is selected.

Transition Angle: The **Transition Angle** edit box is used to specify the angle of transition of the coil at the start section of the coil. This option works in association with the number of revolutions in the coil and is generally used in coils with less than one revolution. The value of the transition angle can vary from 0-degree to 360-degree.

Flat Angle: The **Flat Angle** edit box is used to specify the angle through which the coil will extend beyond the transition at the start section of the coil. The value of the transition angle can vary from 0-degree to 360-degree.

End Area

The options in the **End** area are similar to those discussed in the **Start** area. The only difference is that these options are used to specify the end type at the end section of the imaginary helical path.

Creating Threads

Ribbon:	Model > Modify > Thread
Toolbar:	Part Features > Thread

Thread   Autodesk Inventor allows you to create internal or external threads directly in a model. Internal threads are created on the inner surface of a feature. For example, the threads created on the hole inside a cylinder are called internal threads, see Figure 8-56. External threads are created on the outer surface of a feature or a model. For example, threads created on a bolt, see Figure 8-57. You can create threads using the **Thread** tool. When you invoke this tool, the **Thread** dialog box will be displayed. The options in the **Thread** dialog box are discussed next.

Figure 8-56 Internal threads in a cylinder

Figure 8-57 External threads on a bolt

Location Tab

The options in the **Location** tab are used to define the location, length, and offset of threads, see Figure 8-58. These options are discussed next.

Face

The **Face** button is chosen to select the face on which the threads will be created. When you invoke the **Thread** dialog box, this button will be automatically chosen and you will be prompted to select the face on which the threads will be created.

Display in Model

The **Display in Model** check box is selected

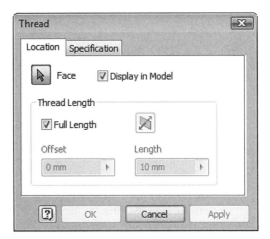

*Figure 8-58 The **Location** tab of the **Thread** dialog box*

to display the threads in the model. If this check box is cleared, the threads will be created, but will not be displayed in the model. They will be displayed only in the **Browser Bar**.

Thread Length Area
The options in the **Thread Length** area are used to specify the length of the threads. These options are discussed next.

Full Length: The **Full Length** check box is used to create threads through the length of the selected face. By default, this check box is selected. As a result, no other option in the **Thread Length** area will be available. Figure 8-59 shows a bolt with threads created through its length. If you clear this check box, the remaining options in this area will be activated.

Figure 8-59 Full length threads on a bolt

Flip: The **Flip** button is used to reverse the direction of thread creation.

Offset: The **Offset** edit box is used to define distance by which threads will be offset from the starting edge of the face selected for creating threads. By default, the value of the offset distance is zero. If you specify any offset value, the start point of threads will move away from the start of the face selected for threading. Figure 8-60 shows the threads created at an offset distance of 0 mm from the top face and Figure 8-61 shows the threads created at an offset distance of 20 mm from the top face.

Figure 8-60 Threads at an offset of 0 mm

Figure 8-61 Threads at an offset of 20 mm from the top face

Length: The **Length** edit box is used to specify the length up to which the threads will be created on the selected face.

Note
You cannot define a negative value for the length of the threads or the offset of the threads. If you want to create the threads in the opposite direction, choose the Flip button. The direction will reverse automatically.

Specification Tab

The options in this tab are used to define the type of threads to be created and the other parameters related to these threads, see Figure 8-62.

Thread Type

The **Thread Type** drop-down list is used to select the predefined thread types. These predefined thread types are saved in Microsoft Excel spreadsheet. This spreadsheet is stored in the directory *C:\Autodesk\AutoCAD_Inventor_ Suite_2011_Win_64bit\x64\en-us\Inventor\ Application Data\Autodesk\Inventor 2011\Design Data\Thread.xls*. You can also add custom thread types in this spreadsheet and use them in the model.

Figure 8-62 The Specification tab of the Thread dialog box

Size

The **Size** drop-down list is used to select the nominal diameter of the threads. Depending on the type of thread selected from the **Thread Type** drop-down list, the values in this drop-down list will change. You can select the required value of the diameter of the threads from this drop-down list.

Designation

The **Designation** drop-down list is used to select the designation of the required threads. The designation depends on the type and size of threads.

Class

The **Class** drop-down list is used to select the predefined class of threads, which will depend on the face on which the threads will be created.

Right hand/Left hand

These radio buttons are selected to specify whether the resulting threads will be the right hand threads or the left hand threads. The right hand threads are those that allow the screw to be tightened when rotated in the clockwise direction. The left hand threads are those that allow the screw to be tightened when rotated in the counterclockwise direction.

Note
For some of the thread types, the Designation and the Class drop-down lists will not be available.

Creating Shell Features

Ribbon: Model > Modify > Shell
Toolbar: Part Features > Shell

Shelling is a process of scooping out material from a model to make it hollow. The resulting model will be a structure of walls with cavity. You can also remove some of the faces of the model or apply different wall thicknesses to some of the faces. Figure 8-63 shows a model with constant shelling and with the front face removed.

In Autodesk Inventor, the shell feature is created using the **Shell** tool. When you invoke this tool, the **Shell** dialog box will be displayed, see Figure 8-64. The options in the **Shell** tab are discussed next. Note that the options in the **More** tab are similar to those discussed in the **Thicken/Offset** tool. Therefore, these options are not discussed here.

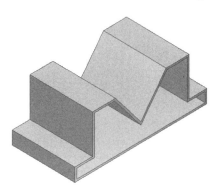

Figure 8-63 *Model after creating the shell feature*

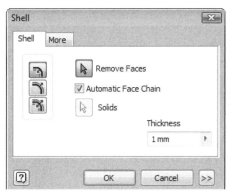

Figure 8-64 *The **Shell** tab of the **Shell** dialog box*

Remove Faces

The **Remove Faces** button is used to select the faces that you want to remove from a model. On invoking the **Shell** dialog box, this button will be chosen by default and you will be prompted to select the faces to be removed. The selected faces will be displayed in blue. Figure 8-65 shows the face selected to be removed and Figure 8-66 shows the resulting shelled model.

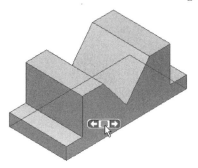

Figure 8-65 *Face selected to be removed*

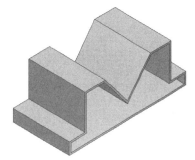

Figure 8-66 *Resulting shelled model*

Tip. *If you have selected a wrong face by mistake, press and hold the SHIFT key and select the face again; the face will be removed from the current selection set.*

Automatic Face Chain

If you select a face with the **Automatic Face Chain** check box selected, then all faces that are tangentially connected to the selected face will be selected automatically.

Solids

The **Solids** button is used to select a body from multiple part bodies from the graphics window.

Thickness

The **Thickness** edit box is used to specify the wall thickness of the resulting shelled model.

Inside

The **Inside** button is the first button in the area provided on the left of the **Shell** tab of the **Shell** dialog box. This button is chosen to define the wall thickness inside, with respect to the outer faces of the model. In this case, the outer faces of the model will be considered as the outer walls of the resulting shell feature.

Outside

The **Outside** button is provided below the **Inside** button and is chosen to define the wall thickness outside the model with respect to its outer faces. In this case, the outer faces of the model will be considered as the inner walls of the resulting shell feature.

Both

The **Both** button is provided below the **Outside** button and is chosen to calculate the wall thickness equally in both the directions of the outer faces of the model.

> >

The button with two arrows, is at the lower right corner of the **Shell** dialog box. On choosing this button, the **Shell** dialog box will expand and display the **Unique face thickness** area, see Figure 8-67. Using the options in this area, you can select faces and apply different wall thicknesses to them.

To select faces, click on **Click to add**; you will be prompted to select surfaces to apply different wall thicknesses. The thicknesses of the selected surfaces can be specified in the **Thickness** column of the **Unique face thickness** area. Similarly, you can select another set of faces by clicking on **Click to add** and specifying different wall thicknesses to them. Figure 8-68 shows a model with different wall thicknesses applied to various faces.

Figure 8-67 The **Unique face thickness** area

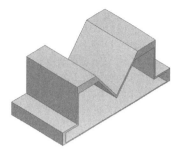

Figure 8-68 Shell feature with different wall thicknesses

Applying Drafts

Ribbon:	Model > Modify > Draft
Toolbar:	Part Features > Draft

Face draft is a process of tapering the outer faces of a model for its easy removal from casting during manufacturing. You can add a face draft using the **Draft** tool. On invoking this tool, the **Face Draft** dialog box will be displayed, see Figure 8-69. The options in this dialog box are discussed next.

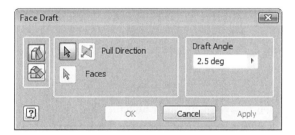

Figure 8-69 The **Face Draft** dialog box

Fixed Edge

This is the first button in the area on the left side of the **Face Draft** dialog box. The **Fixed Edge** button is chosen when you want to draft a face using an edge. Note that all edges tangent to the edge that you select to create the face draft are automatically selected.

Fixed Plane

The **Fixed Plane** button is available below the **Fixed Edge** button. This button is used to create a face draft by using a fixed plane. Figure 8-70 shows the top planar face of the model selected as the fixed plane to create the face draft as well as shows various parameters associated with the face draft.

Pull Direction/Fixed Plane

This is the first button available in the area in the center of the **Face Draft** dialog box. Depending on whether you choose the **Fixed Edge** or **Fixed Plane** button, the name of this button will be **Pull Direction** or **Fixed Plane**. This button is used to define the pull direction in case of a fixed edge and draft plane in case of a fixed plane. The pull direction is the direction defined by a plane that will be used to apply the face draft. The draft angle for the selected faces will be calculated using the plane selected to define the pull direction. Once you have selected the plane or the edge to define the pull direction, an arrow will be displayed. This arrow will define the pull direction for applying the draft angles, see Figure 8-71. You can reverse the pull direction by choosing the **Flip pull direction** button provided on the right of the **Pull Direction** button.

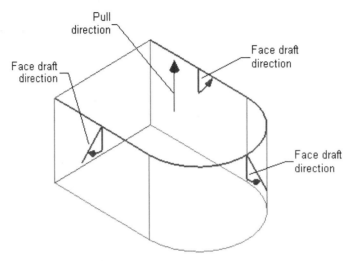

Figure 8-70 Various parameters associated with face draft

Faces

The **Faces** button is chosen to select the faces on which the draft angle will be applied. If the selected face has some tangent faces, they will also be selected for applying the face draft. After you have selected the pull direction, this button will be automatically chosen and you will be prompted to select the faces and the fixed edges to apply the face draft. If you move the cursor close to a face, it will be highlighted and an arrow will be displayed on that face. This arrow will define the direction in which the draft angle will be applied. Depending upon the point that is used to select the face, the nearest edge parallel to the pull direction will be selected. This edge is defined as the fixed edge. The direction of the draft angle will be calculated using this fixed edge.

Draft Angle

The **Draft Angle** edit box is used to specify a draft angle for the selected faces. Remember that the value of the draft angle should be less than 90-degree.

Figure 8-71 shows the model to which the face draft has been applied using the tangent edge of the top face as the fixed edge and with the pull direction upward. Figure 8-72 shows a model after applying the face draft using the same fixed edge, but after reversing the pull direction by using the **Flip pull direction** button. In both these figures, the value of the draft angle is 15-degree.

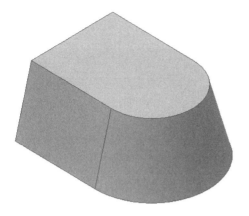

Figure 8-71 *Face draft with the pull direction upward*

Figure 8-72 *Face draft with the pull direction downward*

Creating Split Features

Ribbon:	Model > Modify > Split
Toolbar:	Part Features > Split

 In Autodesk Inventor, the **Split** tool can be used for splitting the entire part or the faces of the part. The three uses of the **Split** tool are discussed next.

Splitting Faces

The **Split** tool allows you to split all or selected faces of a model. Generally, faces are split in order to apply different draft angles to both sides of a model. When you invoke the **Split** tool, the **Split** dialog box will be displayed, as shown in Figure 8-73. By default, the **Split Face** button will be chosen from the **Method** area, see Figure 8-73, and is used to split the faces of a model. As the **Split Face** button is chosen in the **Split** dialog box, the options for splitting faces will be available in this dialog box. These options are discussed next.

Figure 8-73 *The **Split** dialog box*

Split Tool

The **Split Tool** button is chosen to select the tool that will be used to split the faces of the model. The tools that can be used to split the faces are the sketched lines, existing faces of the model, surfaces, or work planes.

Tip. *If you want to use a sketched line to split the faces of the model, make sure the sketched line intersects the faces to be split in its current form or when it is projected normal to the plane on which it is sketched.*

Faces

This button is chosen to select the faces to be split.

Faces Area

The options in this area are used to select all faces of a model to split, or to specify the faces to split. These options are discussed next.

All: If the **All** button is chosen, all faces that the splitting tool intersects in its current form or when projected will be selected for splitting.

Select: The **Select** button is chosen to select faces to split. Faces can be selected by choosing the **Faces** button. On choosing the **Faces** button, you will be prompted to select the faces to be split. Select the faces; the selected faces will be split and the rest of the faces will remain unchanged even if they intersect the split tool. Figure 8-74 shows the sketched lines to be used for splitting the faces of the model and Figure 8-75 shows the split faces.

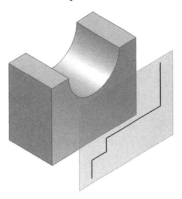

Figure 8-74 *Sketched lines for splitting the faces of the model*

Figure 8-75 *Model after splitting the faces and making the work plane invisible*

Trimming the Model

In addition to splitting the faces, you can trim a solid by using the **Split** dialog box. To do so, choose the **Trim Solid** button from the **Split** dialog box and then select the part to be trimmed. Next, select the required sketch, plane, or surface as a split tool and choose **OK**; the solid will be trimmed. The options displayed in the **Split** dialog box when you choose the **Trim Solid** button, as shown in Figure 8-76, are discussed next.

Figure 8-76 *Various options displayed in the **Split** dialog box on choosing the **Trim Solid** button*

Split Tool

The **Split Tool** button is chosen to select the entity that will be used as the trimming tool.

Solid

This button is chosen to select the body participating in feature creation from multiple bodies in the graphics window.

Figure 8-77 shows the solid part to be trimmed and the sketched line to be used as the split tool. Figure 8-78 shows the solid part after trimming.

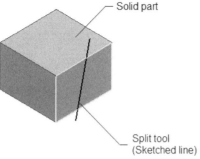

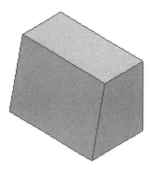

Figure 8-77 *Solid part and split tool*

Figure 8-78 *Solid part after trimming*

Remove Area

The buttons in this area are used to select the portion of the model to be removed while splitting. When you select the splitting tool, an arrow will appear on the model. This arrow points toward the portion of the model to be removed after splitting. To remove the other portion from the model, choose the other button in the **Remove** area.

Splitting the Model

The **Split** tool can also be used to split a model. This is done by choosing the **Split Solid** button from the **Split** dialog box. On choosing this button, the options related to splitting a part are displayed, see Figure 8-79. These options have been discussed earlier. Figure 8-80 shows the solid part of Figure 8-77 after splitting.

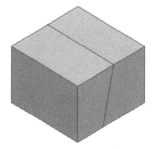

Figure 8-79 *Various options displayed in the Split dialog box on choosing the Split Solid button*

Figure 8-80 *Model after splitting*

Trimming Surfaces

| **Ribbon:** | Model > Surface > Trim Surface |
| **Toolbar:** | Part Features > Trim Surface |

 This tool is used to trim surfaces by using another surface, a non-intersecting sketch, a work plane, or a face of an existing model. On invoking this tool, the **Trim Surface** dialog box will be displayed, as shown in Figure 8-81, and you will be prompted to select surfaces, work planes, or sketches as the cutting tool. As soon as you select the cutting tool, the **Remove** button is chosen and you are prompted to select faces to remove. If you move the cursor on the face to be removed, it will be highlighted in red. Click on the face to select it, the selected surface portion is highlighted in green. You can choose the **Invert Selection** button to select the part of the surface that lies on the other side of the cutting tool. The **Invert Selection** button is on the right of the **Remove** button and is activated after you select a face to be removed.

*Figure 8-81 The **Trim Surface** dialog box*

Figure 8-82 shows two intersecting surfaces. In this figure, the horizontal surface has been used as the cutting tool. You can trim the upper part or the lower part of this surface. Figure 8-83 shows the surfaces after trimming the top part of the vertical surface.

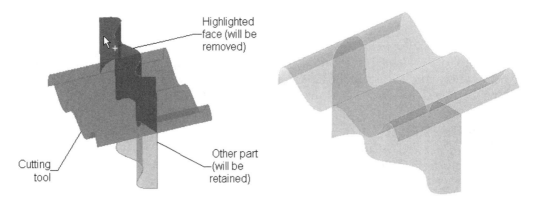

Figure 8-82 Cutting tool and surface to trim   *Figure 8-83 Surfaces after trimming*

Figure 8-84 shows a sketch selected as the cutting tool and the part of the surface to be trimmed. Note that in this figure, the sketch is drawn on a plane that is at some offset from the surface. Figure 8-85 shows the surface after trimming.

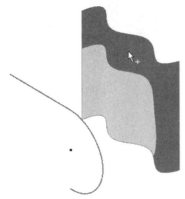

Figure 8-84 Sketch to be used as the cutting tool and the surface to be trimmed   *Figure 8-85 Surface after trimming*

Extending Surfaces

Ribbon: Model > Surface > Extend
Toolbar: Part Features > Extend

Extend

This tool allows you to extend or stretch the edges of a surface. On invoking this tool, the **Extend Surface** dialog box will be displayed, as shown in Figure 8-86. The options available in this dialog box are discussed next.

Edges

This button is chosen by default when you invoke the **Extend Surface** dialog box. It is used to select the edges to extend or stretch. On selecting an edge, the preview of the extension along with an arrow is displayed. Drag the arrow to specify the extension. Alternatively, specify the extension in the edit box below the **Extents** drop-down list.

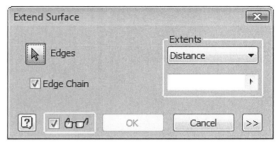

*Figure 8-86 The **Extend Surface** dialog box*

Edge Chain

If this check box is selected, all edges that are tangentially connected to the selected edge will also be selected.

Extents

This area provides the options to specify the values of the extended or stretched surfaces. You can select the **Distance** or **To** options from the drop-down list in this area. These options are similar to those discussed in the **Extrude** dialog box.

>> (More)

This button is available at the lower right corner of the dialog box. On choosing this button, the **Extend Surface** dialog box will expand and display the **Edge Extension** area, as shown in Figure 8-87. The options in this area are discussed next.

*Figure 8-87 More options of the **Extend Surface** dialog box*

Extend

This radio button is selected by default. As a result, the surface is extended along the direction of the edges adjacent to the selected edges. Figure 8-88 shows the surface in which the top edge is being extended using this option. As evident from this figure, the edge is being extended along the direction of the vertical edges adjacent to the top edge of the surface.

Stretch

This radio button is selected to extend a surface by stretching it in 3D space. Figure 8-89 shows a surface in which the top edge is being extended using this option. As evident from this figure, the edge is being extended proportionately in the 3D space.

Figure 8-88 *Surface being extended along the direction of the adjacent edges*

Figure 8-89 *Surface being extended in the 3D space*

Deleting Faces

| **Ribbon:** | Model > Surface > Delete Face |
| **Toolbar:** | Part Features > Delete Face |

 Autodesk Inventor allows you to delete one or more planar faces or nonplanar lumps in a model or in a surface. Depending on the face selected to be deleted, the resulting model is converted into a surface. You can also force the adjacent faces to extend and intersect such that they heal the surface. This tool can also be used to fill the hollow model created using the **Shell** tool without removing any face. On invoking the **Delete Face** tool, the **Delete Face** dialog box will be displayed, as shown in Figure 8-90. The options in this dialog box are discussed next.

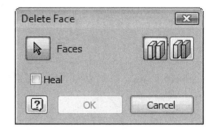

Figure 8-90 *The **Delete Face** dialog box*

Faces

The **Faces** button is used to select the faces to be deleted. When you invoke the **Delete Face** dialog box, this button is chosen automatically and you are prompted to select the faces to be deleted.

Select individual face

The **Select individual face** button is chosen to select the individual faces to be deleted. Figure 8-91 shows a model with the top face selected to be removed and Figure 8-92 shows the resulting surface model created by deleting the top face.

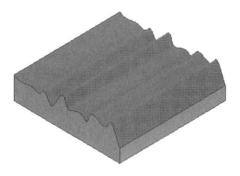

Figure 8-91 *Top face selected to be deleted*

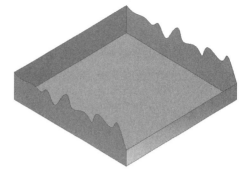

Figure 8-92 *Resulting surface model*

Select lump or void

The **Select lump or void** button is chosen to select a lump or a void. This button is generally used to select the void created using shelling without removing a face. Because no face of the model is removed, the shelling is not visible until you change the display type to wireframe. To remove such a shelling, choose this button and move the cursor over the model. The cycle tool will be displayed. Cycle through the various entities and then select the void. When you exit this tool, the shelling will be removed.

Heal

The **Heal** check box is selected to force the adjacent faces to extend and meet so that the deleted face is healed. For example, if you delete a filleted or chamfered face and select this check box, the adjacent faces forming the fillet or chamfer will be extended to recover the lost face. Note that when you heal the face, the model is not converted into a surface model. Figure 8-93 shows a model with all fillets and rounds applied. In this model, all fillets and rounds are applied with a different color. Figure 8-94 shows the model after deleting some of the fillets and rounds and healing the faces.

Figure 8-93 *Model with fillets and rounds applied*

Figure 8-94 *Model after healing some faces*

Tip. *You can also delete split surfaces by using the **Delete Face** tool.*

Replacing Faces with Surfaces

Ribbon:	Model > Surface > Replace Face
Toolbar:	Part Features > Replace Face

🔼 Replace Face   Autodesk Inventor allows you to replace the selected faces of a model with one or more selected surfaces or work planes. Note that the surface must intersect the complete face that you want to replace. Figure 8-95 shows a model and a surface. The top face of the model is replaced by the surface. The surface in this model has been created by sweeping a spline about another spline. Figure 8-96 shows the model after replacing the top face with the surface and making the surface invisible.

Figure 8-95 Surface and model before replacing the face

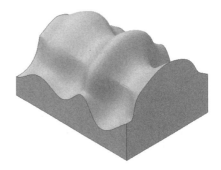

Figure 8-96 Model after replacing the top face with the feature

As evident from Figure 8-96, this tool is used not only to remove material from the model, but also to add material to the model to match the profile of the surface. This is the basic difference between splitting a part by using the surface and by replacing the face. While splitting a part, Autodesk Inventor only removes material and does not add material to a model.

You can select one or more than one surface to replace a face. To replace a face, invoke the **Replace Face** tool; the **Replace Face** dialog box will be displayed, as shown in Figure 8-97. The options in this dialog box are discussed next.

*Figure 8-97 The **Replace Face** dialog box*

Existing Faces

The **Existing Faces** button is chosen to select the faces of the model to be replaced. When you invoke the **Replace Face** dialog box, this button is chosen by default.

New Faces

The **New Faces** button is chosen to select the surfaces that will replace the selected faces. Note that the surfaces should completely intersect the selected faces or should extend beyond them. If the surfaces do not intersect the faces, the feature will not be created and an error message will be displayed.

Automatic Face Chain

The **Automatic Face Chain** check box is selected to automatically select all tangent faces that form a continuous chain with a selected face.

Figure 8-98 shows a model with two surfaces to be used for replacing the top face of the model and Figure 8-99 shows the model after replacing the face and making the surfaces invisible using the **Browser Bar**.

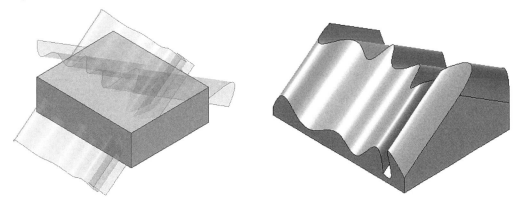

Figure 8-98 *Surfaces to replace the top face*   *Figure 8-99* *Model after replacing the face*

Creating Planar Boundary Patches

Ribbon:	Model > Surface > Boundary Patch
Toolbar:	Part Features > Boundary Patch

Autodesk Inventor allows you to create planar boundary patches on one or more closed loops or edges using the **Boundary Patch** tool. On invoking this tool, the **Boundary Patch** dialog box will be displayed, as shown in Figure 8-100, and you will be prompted to select a profile that defines the boundary of the planar patch. This dialog box has two areas: **Boundary** and **Condition**. These areas are discussed next.

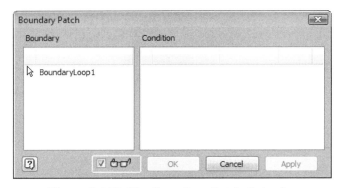

Figure 8-100 *The **Boundary Patch** dialog box*

Boundary Area

The **Boundary** area displays the number of closed loops you select to create the boundary patch.

Condition Area

The **Condition** area displays the entity selected to create the boundary patch. If you select the edges, it will list all edges that you selected to create the boundary. Similarly, if you select a sketch, it displays the name of the sketch in this area. The third column in this area displays a drop-down list that can be used to specify the edge condition for the boundary patch. You can specify the free or the tangent condition, depending on the edge selected.

Figure 8-101 shows a surface model before creating the boundary patch and Figure 8-102 shows the surfaces after creating contact boundary patches on the top and bottom faces. Note that both these surfaces are created separately one by one.

Figure 8-101 *Surfaces before creating the boundary patch*

Figure 8-102 *Surfaces after creating the contact boundary patches*

Figure 8-103 shows the tangent boundary patch created at the ends of the faces of the model.

Figure 8-103 *Tangent boundary patch on one of the ends*

Stitching Surfaces

Ribbon:	Model > Surface > Stitch Surface
Toolbar:	Part Features > Stitch

 Sometimes, while splitting parts, you may need to use more than one surface as the splitting tool. The **Split** tool allows you to select only one surface to split parts or faces. In such cases, you can join more than one surface together so that they form a single surface. You can stitch surfaces using the **Stitch** tool. On invoking this tool, the **Stitch** dialog box will be displayed, as shown in Figure 8-104. The tabs in this dialog box are discussed next.

*Figure 8-104 The **Stitch** dialog box*

Stitch Tab

The options in this tab are used to select the surfaces to be stitched and specify tolerances for stitching. By default, the **Surfaces** button is chosen and you are prompted to select the bodies to be stitched. Note that if there is a small gap between the selected surfaces, the gap will be filled with a new surface and the stitched surface will be displayed as **Stitch Surface** in the **Browser Bar**. You can specify tolerance between free edges by entering a value in the **Maximum Tolerance** edit box. You can view the remaining free edges and their tolerance values in the **Find Remaining Free Edges** area.

By default, the **Maintain as surface** check box is cleared. As a result, if you stitch the surfaces that form a closed volume, the resultant feature will be a solid feature. However, if you select this check box, the resultant feature after stitching the surfaces that form a closed volume, will be a surface.

Note

*Tutorial 5 in Chapter 14 uses the concept of hybrid surface-solid modeling. You will use the **Stitch Surface** tool in that tutorial to stitch surfaces.*

Analyze Tab

The options in the **Analyze** tab, as shown in Figure 8-105, are used to analyze the edges of the stitched surfaces, end conditions of edges, and errors associated with the edges. If you select the **Show Edge Conditions** check box, the stitched edges will be displayed in black, whereas the edges that fail to stitch will be displayed in red. You can view the edges that are nearly tangent to each other by selecting the **Show Near Tangent** check box. On doing so, the nearly tangent edges will be highlighted in magenta.

*Figure 8-105 The **Analyze** tab of the **Stitch** dialog box*

Working with the Sculpt Tool

Ribbon:	Model > Surface > Sculpt
Toolbar:	Part Features > Sculpt

This tool allows you to add or remove material from an existing model by using a surface or a datum plane. The existing model can be a solid model or a surface model, refer to Figure 8-106. This figure shows an existing solid base plate and a revolved surface. Figure 8-107 shows the material added to the base plate using the **Sculpt** tool. As evident from this figure, the shape and size of the material added is defined by the surface.

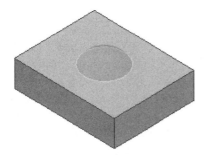

Figure 8-106 *The base plate and the surface to create the sculpt feature*

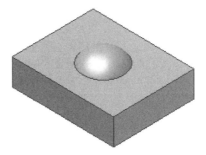

Figure 8-107 *The base plate after adding the material using the **Sculpt** tool*

To create a sculpt feature, invoke the **Sculpt** tool; the **Sculpt** dialog box will be displayed, as shown in Figure 8-108. The options in this dialog box are discussed next.

Add

This button is used to add material to an existing model, refer to Figure 8-107. Remember that the shape and size of the material added is determined by the shape and size of the surface selected.

Figure 8-108 *The **Sculpt** dialog box*

Remove

This button is chosen to remove material from an existing model.

Note
*Sometimes, while removing material from the model using the **Sculpt** tool, you may get an error message. In that case, you need to change the side of material removal by using the **More** button of the **Sculpt** dialog box. The use of the **More** button will be discussed later in this topic.*

New solid

If you choose this button, the resultant sculpt feature will be a new solid body.

Surfaces

This button is chosen to select the surface to create the sculpt feature.

Enable/Disable feature preview

This check box is selected to enable or disable the dynamic preview of the sculpt feature in the drawing window.

More

When you choose this button, the **Sculpt** dialog box expands and displays the **Side Selection** area. The surfaces that you select to create the sculpt feature are displayed in the **Surfaces** column of this area. Also, an icon corresponding to the selected surface appears on the right of surface name. When you click on this icon, a drop-down list appears. You can use this drop-down list to specify the side along which the sculpt feature will be created.

 Note
*While removing the material using the **Remove** option of the **Sculpt** tool, the side of the model that turns pink will be removed.*

Working with the Bend Part Tool

Ribbon:	Model > Modify > Bend Part
Toolbar:	Part Features > Bend Part

Bend Part   This tool allows you to bend components or portions of components by using different options. To bend a component, first you need to sketch a line about which the component will be bent. This line is called the Bend Line. It can also be defined as the tangency line at which the component transforms into a bend. After specifying the tangency conditions between the bend line and the component, you can define the side of the component to be bent, the direction and angle of the bend, and other parameters. To bend components, choose the **Bend Part** tool from the **Modify** panel of the **Model** tab, the **Bend Part** dialog box will be displayed, as shown in Figure 8-109, and you will be prompted to select a bend line. Note that the bend line has to be sketched tangential to a cylindrical component or to the surface intended to be bent. The options in the **Bend Part** dialog box are discussed next.

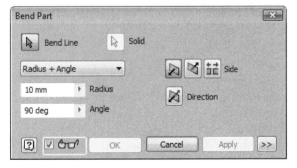

*Figure 8-109 The **Bend Part** dialog box*

Bend Line

This button is chosen by default when you invoke the **Bend Part** dialog box and allows you to specify the bend line for component. The bend line can also be defined as the line about which a component hinges or folds.

The drop-down list below the **Bend Line** button is used to bend components by three methods namely, **Radius + Angle**, **Radius + Arc Length**, and **Arc Length + Angle**. These three methods are discussed next.

Radius + Angle

This option is selected by default and is used to bend components by specifying the bend radius and angle. Figure 8-110 shows the preview of a component bent with a radius value 2 mm and angle 180-degree.

Radius + Arc Length

This option is used to bend components by specifying the bend radius and arc length. Figure 8-111 shows the preview of a component bent with a radius value 5 mm and arc length 10 mm.

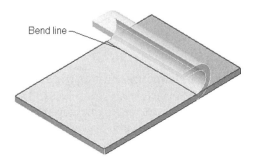

Figure 8-110 *Preview of a component bent with the radius 2 mm and angle 180-degree*

Arc Length + Angle

This option is used to bend components by specifying the arc length and angle. Figure 8-112 shows the preview of a component bent with arc length 10 mm and angle 150-degree.

 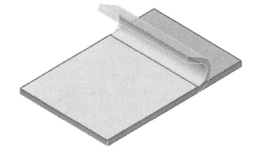

Figure 8-111 *Preview of a component bent with the radius 5 mm and arc length 10 mm*   *Figure 8-112* *Preview of a component bent with the arc length 10 mm and angle 150-degree*

Solid

This button is chosen to select the participating body from the graphics window.

Side

The **Side** buttons allow you to specify the direction of the bend by using three buttons. These three buttons are discussed next.

Bend left

This button is chosen by default and is used to bend the portion that is on the left of the bend line. Figure 8-113 shows the preview of the component bent by choosing the **Bend left** button.

Bend right

This button is used to bend the portion that is on the right of the bend line. Figure 8-114 shows the preview of the component bent by using the **Bend right** button.

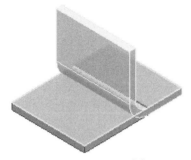 

Figure 8-113 Preview of the component bent by using the **Bend left** button

Figure 8-114 Preview of the component bent by using the **Bend right** button

Bend Both

When this button is chosen, the portions on the right and left of the bend line is bent.

Direction

This button is used to flip the direction of the bend to the left or right of the neutral plane. The plane used to create the bend line acts as a neutral plane while creating the bend.

Figure 8-115 shows a cylindrical component with the bend line and the neutral plane. Figure 8-116 shows the component bent by choosing the **Bend Both** button and selecting the **Radius + Angle** option from the drop-down list.

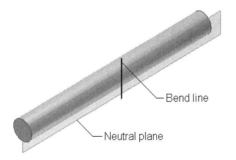 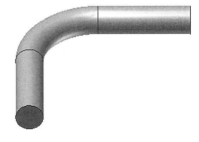

Figure 8-115 Component before bending

Figure 8-116 Component after bending

More

When you choose this button, the **Bend Part** dialog box expands and displays the **Bend Minimum** check box. This check box is selected by default. If the bend line intersects a component at multiple points, select the **Bend Minimum** check box to specify the portion of the component to be bent.

REORDERING THE FEATURES

Autodesk Inventor allows you to change the order of the feature creation in a model. You can move a feature before or after another feature. However, note that reordering is possible only between the features that are independent of each other. For example, if the fourth feature of a model is dependent on the third feature, you cannot reorder the fourth feature before the third.

In Autodesk Inventor, features are reordered using the **Browser Bar**. To reorder a feature, select it in the **Browser Bar** and drag it above or below other features. If a black circle with a line appears while dragging a feature, you cannot reorder the feature because the selected feature is dependent on the feature before which you want to place it in some way or the other. However, if the feature is not dependent, a black line appears while dragging the feature. Figure 8-117 shows a model that has a base feature, a cut feature on the base feature, rectangular pattern of the cut feature, a shell feature, and finally a split feature.

Note that in this model, the shell feature is created after the rectangular pattern of the cut feature on the base feature. As a result, the same wall thickness is retained around all instances of the rectangular cut features.

Now, if you reorder the features such that the shell feature is placed before the extruded cut feature and the pattern of the cut feature, all walls around the rectangular cuts will be removed. Figure 8-118 shows the reordering of the features in the **Browser Bar**.

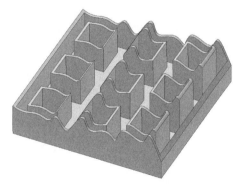

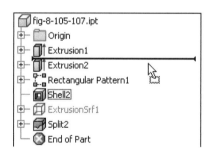

Figure 8-117 *Model with the shell feature created after the cut feature and its pattern*

Figure 8-118 *Reordering the shell feature*

Figure 8-119 shows the model after reordering the shell feature. Notice that because the shell feature is now created before the rectangular pattern, the resulting model has simple cuts without any walls around them.

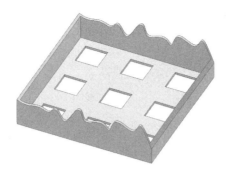

Figure 8-119 *Model after reordering the shell feature before the cut feature and its pattern*

Tip. *Similar to reordering the features, you can also rollback the model using the* **Browser Bar**. *To rollback the model, select the text* **End of Part** *that appears at the end of the list of features in the* **Browser Bar**. *Next, drag and drop this text before the features in the* **Browser Bar**. *All features that are placed after this text are automatically suppressed in the model. To resume the features, drag this text to the end of the features in the* **Browser Bar**.

USING THE SKETCH DOCTOR

Sketch doctor is a diagnostic tool. It provides information about the problems that occur while sketching. For example, if you try to extrude an open loop by choosing the **Solid** button from the **Output** area in the **Extrude** dialog box, refer to Figure 8-120, the **Examine Profile Problems** (with red plus sign) button will be displayed in the dialog box. Choose this button; the **Sketch Doctor** dialog box with the description of the problem in the **Examine** page will be displayed, as shown in Figure 8-121. Also, the endpoints of the open loop will be highlighted in the drawing area. Choose the **Next** button; the **Select a treatment** area will be displayed in the **Treat** page. Choose the

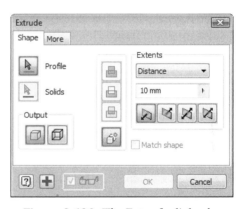

Figure 8-120 *The* **Extrude** *dialog box*

Edit Sketch option and then choose the **Finish** button to invoke the sketching environment for editing the sketch.

If you need more information about the sketch, choose the **Diagnose Sketch** option from the **Select a treatment** area and choose the **Finish** button; the possible error in the sketch will be displayed in the **Diagnose Sketch** dialog box. Choose the **OK** button from this dialog box; the problem to be rectified will be listed in the **Sketch Doctor** dialog box. In this case, it indicates that the sketch is an open loop. Choose the **Next** button again; the description of the problem will be displayed. Choose the **Next** button once again to view the diagnostics and select a suitable treatment from the **Select a treatment** area. After selecting a treatment, choose the **Finish** button; the sketching environment will be displayed, where you can edit the sketch.

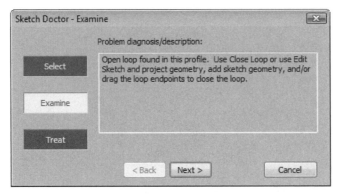

Figure 8-121 *The **Sketch Doctor** dialog box*

USING THE DESIGN DOCTOR

Design doctor is a diagnostic tool, which is very similar to the sketch doctor. It provides information about the problems that occur while designing, modifying previous sketches or features, and so on. For example, if you convert the closed loop of a sketch that is already extruded to an open loop and exit the sketching environment, the **Autodesk Inventor 2011 - Exit Sketch Mode** dialog box will be displayed, as shown in Figure 8-122. Choose the red plus sign icon from this dialog box; the **Autodesk Inventor Professional 2011** message box will be displayed. Choose the **Yes** button from this message box; the problem to be solved will be listed in the **Design Doctor** dialog box, as shown in Figure 8-123. In this case, it indicates the broken loop in Extrusion1. Also, the endpoint of the open loop will be highlighted in the graphics area. Choose the **Next** button; the **Problem diagnosis/description** area will be displayed in the **Design Doctor** dialog box. Again, choose the **Next** button to view the diagnostics and to select a suitable treatment from the **Select a treatment** area. This area will have the options to edit and diagnose the sketch. If you need more information about the problem, choose the **Diagnose Sketch** option from the **Select a treatment** area and then choose the **Finish** button; the possible error in the sketch will be displayed in the **Diagnose Sketch** dialog box. Choose the **OK** button from this dialog box; the problem to be solved will be listed in the **Sketch Doctor** dialog box. Rectify the problem as discussed in the earlier section. If you need to edit the sketch, choose the **Edit Sketch** option from the **Select a treatment** area and then choose the **Finish** button; the sketching environment will be invoked. Rectify the sketch and return to the **Part** module.

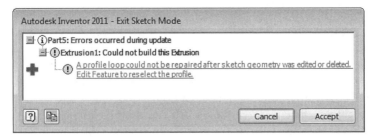

Figure 8-122 *The **Autodesk Inventor 2011 - Exit Sketch Mode** dialog box*

Figure 8-123 The **Design Doctor** *dialog box*

TUTORIALS

Tutorial 1

In this tutorial, you will create the model shown in Figure 8-124a. Its dimensions are given in Figures 8-124b through 8-124d. **(Expected time: 45 min)**

Figure 8-124a Model for Tutorial 1

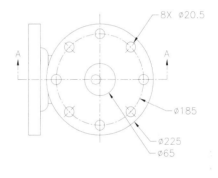

Figure 8-124b Top view of the model with the hidden lines suppressed for clarity

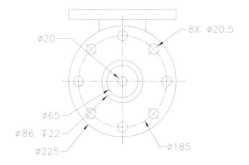

Figure 8-124c Left side view of the model with the hidden lines suppressed for clarity

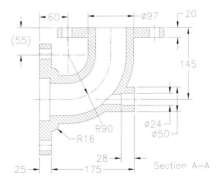

Figure 8-124d Sectioned front view of the model

The following steps are required to complete this tutorial:

a. The base feature of the model is a sweep feature. Create the path of the sweep feature on the XZ plane, refer to Figure 8-125. Next, define a work plane normal to the path and position it at its start point of the path, refer to Figure 8-126. Create the profile of the sweep feature on this work plane, refer to Figure 8-127. Use the **Sweep** tool to create the sweep feature, refer to Figure 8-128.

b. Create the inner cavity using the **Shell** tool, refer to Figure 8-129.

c. Add the remaining features (join features, drilled holes and their patterns, counterbore hole) on both ends of the sweep feature.

Creating the Path for the Sweep Feature

As mentioned earlier, the base feature of the model is a sweep feature. To create the sweep feature, first you need to create its path on the XZ plane. The path is a combination of two lines and an arc.

1. Start a new metric standard template file and create the path of the sweep feature on the XZ plane. Add the required dimensions. Exit the sketching environment, and if required, change the view to the isometric view, as shown in Figure 8-125.

Creating the Work Plane Normal to the Start Section of the Path

After creating the path, you need to create a work plane normal to the start section of the path and position at its start point. A work plane is used to draw profile for a sweep feature. The start section of the path can be either the horizontal line or the vertical line of 35 mm length. In this tutorial, the horizontal line is taken as the start section of the path.

1. Choose the **Normal to Axis through Point** tool from **Model > Work Feature > Plane** drop-down; you are prompted to select an edge/axis or a point.

2. Select the line that is at the bottom-left of the sketch and then click at its endpoint.

   As soon as you select the start point of the line, a work plane normal to the line is created and is positioned at its start point. The work plane at the start point of the path is shown in Figure 8-126.

Drawing the Profile of the Sweep Feature

The profile of the sweep feature is created on the new work plane. Therefore, you need to define a sketch plane on the new work plane.

1. Choose the **Create 2D Sketch** tool from **Model > Sketch > Sketch** drop-down and then select the new work plane as the plane for sketching.

As soon as you select the new work plane as the plane for sketching, the sketching environment is activated. Notice that the origin of the sketching environment coincides with the start point of the start section of the path. This helps you position the profile of the sweep feature.

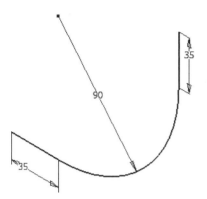

Figure 8-125 *Path for the sweep feature in the isometric view*

Figure 8-126 *Work plane normal to the path*

2. Draw a circle of 97 mm diameter as the profile of the sweep feature. Take the center of the circle as the origin of the sketching environment. Exit the sketching environment and change the view to the isometric view, if required. The profile of the sweep feature is shown in Figure 8-127.

Sweeping the Profile

1. Choose the **Sweep** tool from the **Create** panel of the **Model** tab; the profile of the sweep feature is selected automatically in the graphics window. Also, the **Path** button is chosen in the **Sweep** dialog box and you are prompted to select the path.

2. Select the path and then choose **OK** from the **Sweep** dialog box. The sweep feature after changing the viewing direction is shown in Figure 8-128.

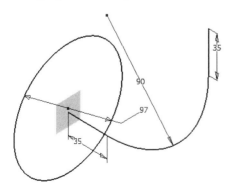

Figure 8-127 *Profile of the sweep feature*

Figure 8-128 *The sweep feature*

Creating the Shell Feature

The shell feature scoops out material from the sweep feature and leaves behind a model with some wall thickness. You need to remove the front and top faces of the sweep feature to view the cavity inside.

1. Choose the **Shell** tool from the **Modify** panel of the **Model** tab; the **Shell** dialog box is displayed and you are prompted to select the surfaces to be removed.

2. Select the front and top faces of the sweep feature; the selected faces are highlighted in blue.

    The diameter of the inner cavity is 65 mm and the diameter of the sweep feature is 97 mm. As a result, the wall thickness comes out to be 16 mm.

3. Enter **16** in the **Thickness** edit box and choose the **OK** button. The model after creating the shell feature is shown in Figure 8-129.

Tip. *An alternate way of creating the shell feature is by using the **Sweep** tool. In case of the **Sweep** tool, you need to create two concentric circles of required size and a path curve. When you sweep both circles along the path curve, the inner circle is subtracted from the outer one. This way the inner cavity can be created automatically. In this tutorial, you will use the **Shell** tool to create the inner cavity.*

Creating the Remaining Features

1. Create the remaining features by defining new sketch planes at the required faces. To create a join feature with a fillet on the front face of the base feature, draw a circle of 129 mm [Ø97+2*radius (16) of fillet] diameter and extrude it to a distance of 16 mm. Then, create a fillet of 16 mm on the outer edge of this feature.

    The join feature at the cylindrical tangent surface can be created by defining an offset work plane. You can create a hole on the join feature by using the **Hole** tool. Similarly, create a hole on the top and bottom features of the model and then create the pattern of these holes. The final model for Tutorial 1 is shown in Figure 8-130.

Figure 8-129 Model after creating the shell feature

Figure 8-130 Final model for Tutorial 1

2. Save the model with the name *Tutorial1.ipt* at the location *C:\Inventor_2011\c08* and close the file.

Tutorial 2

In this tutorial, you will create the model of the Joint shown in Figure 8-131a. Its dimensions are shown in Figures 8-131b and 8-131c. The threads to be created are ANSI Metric M Profile of size 14 and designation M14x2. The class of the threads is 6g. Make sure that the threads are right-handed. **(Expected time: 30 min)**

Figure 8-131a *Solid model of the Joint*

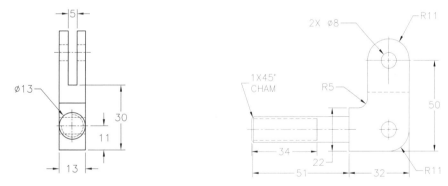

Figure 8-131b *Left side view of the model*   *Figure 8-131c* *Front view of the model*

The following steps are required to complete this tutorial:

a. Create the base feature of the model on the YZ plane, refer to Figure 8-132.
b. Create the cut feature, refer to Figure 8-133.
c. Create the cylindrical join feature on the left face and then create the chamfer feature.
d. Finally, create threads on the cylindrical join feature using the **Thread** tool.

Creating the Base Feature

1. Create the base feature of the model on the YZ plane, as shown in Figure 8-132. For dimensions of the base feature, refer to Figure 8-131b and 8-131c.

Creating the Cut Feature in the Base Feature

1. Create the cut feature by defining a sketch plane on the right face of the base feature, as shown in Figure 8-133. For dimensions of the cut feature, refer to Figure 8-131b.

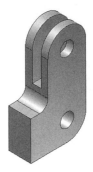

Figure 8-132 Base feature for the model   *Figure 8-133* Model after creating the cut feature

Creating the Join and Chamfer Features

1. Create the cylindrical join feature, as shown in Figure 8-134. For dimensions, refer to Figures 8-131b and 8-131c.

2. Create the chamfer feature on the end face of the cylindrical feature using the **Distance and Angle** button of the **Chamfer** dialog box, see Figure 8-135. For dimensions, refer to Figure 8-131c.

Figure 8-134 Model after creating the join feature   *Figure 8-135* Model after chamfering

Creating Threads

1. Choose the **Thread** tool from the **Modify** panel of the **Model** tab to invoke the **Thread** dialog box. Select the cylindrical join feature; the preview of threads is displayed on the model.

2. In the **Thread Length** area of the **Location** tab, clear the **Full Length** check box. Next, enter **34** in the **Length** edit box.

3. Choose the **Specification** tab to display the options related to the specifications of the threads. Select **ANSI Metric M Profile** from the **Thread Type** drop-down list and **14** from the **Size** drop-down list.

4. Select **M14x2** from the **Designation** drop-down list and **6g** from the **Class** drop-down list. Make sure that the **Right hand** radio button is selected. Choose **OK** from the dialog box to create the threads. The model after creating threads is shown in Figure 8-136.

5. Save the model with the name *Tutorial2.ipt* at the location *C:\Inventor_2011\c08* and then close the file.

Figure 8-136 *Final model for Tutorial 2*

Tutorial 3

In this tutorial, you will create the model of the Nut shown in Figure 8-137a. Its dimensions are shown in Figure 8-137b. The threads to be created are ANSI Metric M Profile with the designation M10x1.5. The class of threads is 6H and it is a right-handed thread.

(Expected time: 30 min)

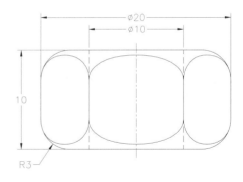

Figure 8-137a *Model of the Nut with threads*   **Figure 8-137b** *Dimensions of the Nut*

The following steps are required to complete this tutorial:

a. Create the base feature, refer to Figure 8-138.
b. Create a hole concentric with the base feature, refer to Figure 8-139.
c. Fillet the top and bottom faces of the cylindrical feature, refer to Figure 8-140.
d. Define a new sketch plane on the top face of the base feature. Draw a hexagon on this plane and extrude it using the **Intersect** operation, refer to Figure 8-141.
e. Finally, create internal threads using the **Thread** tool, refer to Figure 8-142.

Creating the Base Feature

1. Create the base feature (cylinder) of the Nut on the XY plane, as shown in Figure 8-138. The diameter of the cylinder is 20 mm.

Creating the Hole Feature Concentric with the Base Feature

1. Invoke the **Hole** tool and create a through hole of diameter 10 mm on the base feature. Figure 8-139 shows the hole feature created on the base feature.

Figure 8-138 *Base feature of the Nut*

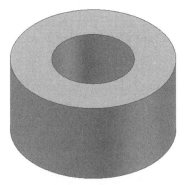

Figure 8-139 *Model after creating the hole feature*

Filleting the Top and Bottom Edges

1. Fillet the top and bottom edges of the model using the **Fillet** tool. The radius of the fillet is 3 mm. The model after creating the fillets is shown in Figure 8-140.

Creating the Intersect Feature

The next feature is the intersect feature. You need to create this feature by defining a new sketch plane on the top or bottom face of the model. After defining the sketch plane, you will draw an inscribed hexagon.

1. Define a new sketch plane on the top face of the base feature. Draw an inscribed hexagon on the new sketch plane.

Figure 8-140 *Model after creating the fillets at the top and bottom edges*

The diameter of the circle in which the hexagon is inscribed should be equal to the diameter of the base feature. You can use the **Inventor Precise Input** toolbar to specify the value of the diameter of the circle in which the hexagon is inscribed.

2. Exit the sketching environment and extrude the sketch using the **Intersect** operation and the **All** extents. The model after creating the intersect feature is shown in Figure 8-141.

Creating Threads

1. Choose the **Thread** tool from the **Modify** panel of the **Model** tab to invoke the **Thread** dialog box.

2. Select the hole as the face for creating threads.

3. Choose the **Specification** tab and select **ANSI Metric M Profile** from the **Thread Type** drop-down list.

4. Select **10** from the **Size** drop-down list and **M10x1.5** from the **Designation** drop-down list.

5. Select **6H** from the **Class** drop-down list and select the **Right hand** radio button, if it is not selected.

6. Choose **OK** to exit the **Thread** dialog box and create threads. The final model after creating threads is shown in Figure 8-142.

Figure 8-141 *Model after creating the intersect feature*

Figure 8-142 *Final model of Nut*

7. Save the model with the name *Tutorial3.ipt* at the location *C:\Inventor_2011\c08* and then close the file.

Tutorial 4

In this tutorial, you will create the model shown in Figure 8-143a. Its dimensions are shown in Figures 8-143b and 8-143c. After creating the model, apply a face draft of 1-degree on its left and right faces. The angle for the face draft should be 1-degree.

(Expected time: 45 min)

Figure 8-143a *Model for Tutorial 4*

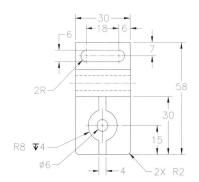

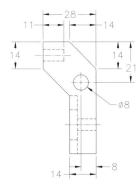

Figure 8-143b *Front view of the model*   *Figure 8-143c* *Right-side view of the model*

The following steps are required to complete this tutorial:

a.   Create the base feature with a hole on the YZ plane, refer to Figure 8-144.
b.   Add cut features and holes to the base feature, refer to Figure 8-145.
c.   Create the face draft by selecting the top face of the model as the pull direction.
d.   Finally, create the fillet of radius 2 mm.

Creating the Base Feature
1.   Create the base feature of the model on the YZ plane, as shown in Figure 8-144. For dimensions of the base feature, refer to Figures 8-143b and 8-143c.

Creating the Cut Features
1.   Create the cut features on the model. Figure 8-145 shows the model after creating the cut features. For dimensions of the cut features, refer to Figures 8-143b and 8-143c.

Adding the Face Draft
1.   Choose the **Draft** tool from the **Modify** panel of the **Model** tab to invoke the
     Face Draft dialog box.

Figure 8-144 *Base feature of the model*

Figure 8-145 *Model after creating the cut features*

2. Choose the **Fixed Plane** button; you are prompted to select the planar face or the work plane.

3. Select the top face of the model as the pull direction, and make sure that the arrow points downward. If the arrow points upward, choose the **Flip pull direction** button provided on the right of the **Draft Plane** button to reverse the direction.

   As soon as you specify the pull direction, the **Faces** button is chosen and you are prompted to select the faces to draft.

4. Select both the side faces one by one, see Figure 8-146.

5. Change the value of the draft angle in the **Draft Angle** edit box to **1** and then choose **OK**; the **Face Draft** dialog box is closed and the face draft is applied to the model.

6. Add a fillet of radius 2 mm to the edges on the bottom face of the model. The final model for Tutorial 4 is shown in Figure 8-147.

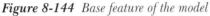

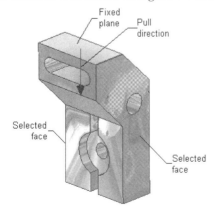

Figure 8-146 *Selecting the options for the face draft*

Figure 8-147 *Final model for Tutorial 4*

7. Save the model with the name *Tutorial4.ipt* at the location *C:\Inventor_2011\c08* and then close the file.

Tutorial 5

In this tutorial, you will create the solid model of the receiver of a phone shown in Figure 8-148a. The dimensions of Section 1 and Section 2 of the receiver are shown in Figures 8-148b and 8-148c. Section 3 is a mirror image of Section 1, but you need to create it separately as an individual sketch.   **(Expected time: 45 min)**

Figure 8-148a Solid model of the receiver

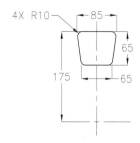

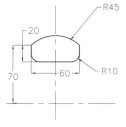

Figure 8-148b Dimensions of Section 1   *Figure 8-148c Dimensions of Section 2*

The model consists of three sections blended together using the **Loft** tool. Section 1 is created on the XZ plane; Section 2 on the XY plane; and Section 3 on the XZ plane. However, you will create Section 3 below the origin. To maintain accuracy while creating these sections, you need to dimension them with reference to the origin point. You can place a sketch point at the origin and add the **Fix** constraint to it. Next, you need to dimension the section with respect to the sketch point.

The following steps are required to complete this tutorial:

a. Start a new metric template file and draw the sketch for Section 2 on the XY plane. As sketches can be created in any sequence while creating a loft feature, you do not need to create Section 1 first.

b. Draw the sketch for Section 1 on the XZ plane. Exit the sketching environment.

c. Again, define the sketch plane on the XZ plane and draw the sketch for Section 3.

d. Exit the sketching environment and invoke the **Loft** tool. Select three sections to create the loft feature.

Drawing the Sketch for Section 2

1. Start a new metric part file.

2. Draw the sketch for Section 2 on the XY plane. Dimension it with respect to the origin (0,0,0). Refer to Figure 8-148c for the dimensions of Section 2.

3. Exit the sketching environment.

Drawing the Sketch for Section 1

1. Define a new sketch plane on the XZ plane.

2. Draw the sketch for Section 1 and dimension it with respect to the origin. Refer to Figure 8-148b for the dimensions of Section 1.

3. Exit the sketching environment.

Drawing the Sketch for Section 3

The sketch for Section 3 is the mirror image of the sketch of Section 1.

1. Define a new sketch plane on the XZ plane.

2. Draw the sketch for Section 3 and dimension it with respect to the origin.

3. Exit the sketching environment. The three sketches are shown in Figure 8-149.

Blending Sections Using the Loft Tool

You need to blend the sections using the **Loft** tool.

1. Choose the **Loft** tool from the **Create** panel of the **Model** tab; the **Loft** dialog box is invoked and you are prompted to select a sketch.

   In this dialog box, the **Curves** tab is active by default.

2. Select Section 1 as the first sketch; the sketch is highlighted in blue and you are prompted again to select a sketch.

3. Select Section 2 and then Section 3; the preview of the feature is displayed in the drawing window. However, this is not the kind of feature you require. You need to add some weight at the start and end sections.

4. Choose the **Conditions** tab; an arrow appears on the left of Sketch3 in the **Conditions** area of this tab. This indicates that the settings that you configure will be for this sketch.

5. Choose the **Direction Condition** option from the drop-down list (end condition) in this tab. This option allows you to add direction conditions at the start and end sections.

6. Enter **50** in the **Weight** edit box. This value is for the end section.

7. Next, select Sketch2 from the **Conditions** area and then choose the **Direction Condition** option.

8. Enter **50** in the **Weight** edit box. This value is for the start section. Choose **OK** to create the loft feature.

9. Apply the **Blue Pastel** color to the model. Change the viewing direction of the model. The model of the receiver is shown in Figure 8-150.

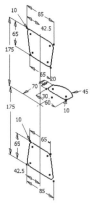
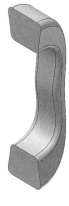

Figure 8-149 *Sketches of three sections*   **Figure 8-150** *Solid model of the receiver*

10. Save the model with the name *Tutorial5.ipt* at the location *C:\Inventor_2011\c08* and then close the file.

Self-Evaluation Test

Answer the following questions and then compare them to those given at the end of this chapter:

1. To create a solid sweep feature, the profile should be a closed sketch. (T/F)

2. The lofted features are created by blending more than one dissimilar geometry. (T/F)

3. You can apply different wall thicknesses to various faces of a shell feature. (T/F)

4. You need to select the **Area Loft** radio button to create a lofted feature with varying cross-sections at required points on a centerline. (T/F)

5. The _____ method is used to create a spiral coil in a single plane.

6. You can trim a solid by using the _____ button from the **Split** dialog box.

7. In Autodesk Inventor, features are reordered using the _____.

8. _____ is applied to the faces of a model so that it can be removed easily from casting.

9. You can create face drafts by using a fixed _____ or _____.

10. If the faces on which you want to apply the face draft have some _____, they will be selected automatically for applying the face draft.

Review Questions

Answer the following questions:

1. The _____ operation of the **Coil** tool can also be used to create internal or external threads in a model.

2. In Autodesk Inventor, the _____ tool is used to split the faces of models or a complete model.

3. The _____ dialog box is used to create external or internal threads directly.

4. The _____ tool is used to combine more than one surface into a single surface.

5. _____ is defined as a process of scooping out material from a model and making it hollow from inside.

6. Which of the following options is used to create a coil in a single plane?

    (a) **Revolution and Height**   (b) **Pitch and Revolution**
    (c) **Spiral**   (d) **Pitch and Height**

7. Which of the following check boxes in the **Delete Face** dialog box is used to recover faces by extending adjacent faces?

    (a) **Heal**   (b) **Delete**
    (c) **Remove**   (d) None of these

8. Which of the following check boxes in the **Thread** dialog box is selected to create threads through the length of the selected face?

    (a) **Length**   (b) **Full Length**
    (c) **Full**   (d) None of these

9. Which of the following check boxes needs to be cleared in the **Thread** dialog box to turn off the display of threads in a solid model?

    (a) **Display in Model**   (b) **Display**
    (c) **Off**   (d) None of these

10. Which of the following check boxes needs to be cleared to enable the **Point Set** area?

    (a) **Display in Model**   (b) **Automatic Mapping**
    (c) **Merge Tangent Faces**   (d) None of these

Exercises

Exercise 1

Create a solid model for Exercise 1, as shown in Figure 8-151a. The dimensions to be used for creating the model are given in Figures 8-151b through 8-151d.   (**Expected time: 45 min**)

Figure 8-151a Solid model for Exercise 1

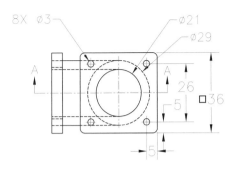

Figure 8-151b Top view of the model

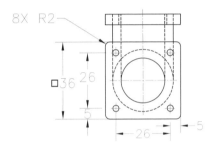

Figure 8-151c Left side view of the model

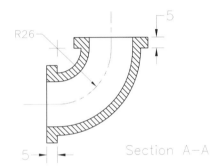

Figure 8-151d Sectioned front view of the model

Exercise 2

Create a solid model of the hexagonal Cap Screw shown in Figure 8-152a. Its dimensions are shown in Figure 8-152b. The threads to be created are ANSI Metric M Profile of size 10 and designation M10x1.5. The class of threads is 6g. Make sure that the threads are right-handed.

(Expected time: 30 min)

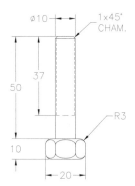

Figure 8-152a Solid model of the Cap Screw   *Figure 8-152b* Dimensions of the Cap Screw

Chapter 9

Assembly Modeling-I

Learning Objectives

After completing this chapter, you will be able to:
- *Understand the concept of the bottom-up and top-down assemblies.*
- *Create components of the top-down assemblies in the assembly file.*
- *Insert components of the bottom-up assemblies in the assembly file.*
- *Understand various assembly constraints and use them to assemble components.*
- *Move and rotate individual components in the assembly file.*
- *Use constraint limits to assemble components.*

ASSEMBLY MODELING

An assembly design consists of two or more components assembled at their respective working positions. In Autodesk Inventor, the components of the assembly can be bound using the parametric assembly constraints. As the assembly constraints are parametric in nature, you can modify or delete them whenever you want. In Autodesk Inventor, the assemblies are created in the **Assembly** module. To proceed to the **Assembly** module, invoke the **New File** dialog box and open the **Standard (mm).iam** file, as shown in Figure 9-1.

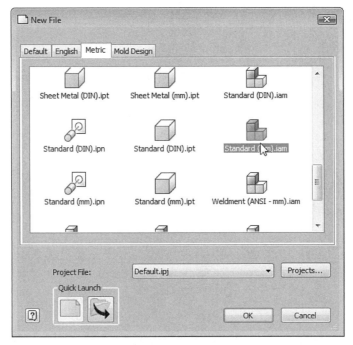

*Figure 9-1 Opening a new assembly file from the **Metric** tab of the **New File** dialog box*

When you select the assembly file, the assembly environment will be activated. The screen display of Autodesk Inventor in the **Assembly** module is shown in Figure 9-2. This figure displays the **Browser Bar** and various tools in the **Assemble** tab.

Note
*When you enter the **Assembly** module, you will notice that only some tools are active in the **Assemble** tab. Other tools in this tab will become active only when you insert or create a component.*

TYPES OF ASSEMBLIES

In Autodesk Inventor, you can create two types of assemblies: top-down assemblies and bottom-up assemblies. Both these assemblies are discussed next.

Top-down Assemblies

A top-down assembly is an assembly whose components are created within the assembly file. In this type of assembly, first the components are created in the assembly file and then assembled using the assembly constraints. The process of creating the components in the **Assembly** module of Autodesk Inventor is designed in such a way that the components you create in the **Assembly** module are also saved as individual parts or assembly files. This eliminates the risk of losing the individual components, in case there is an error in the assembly file. Also, the assembly file contains the information related to only the assembly, which helps in keeping the size of the assembly file to the minimum.

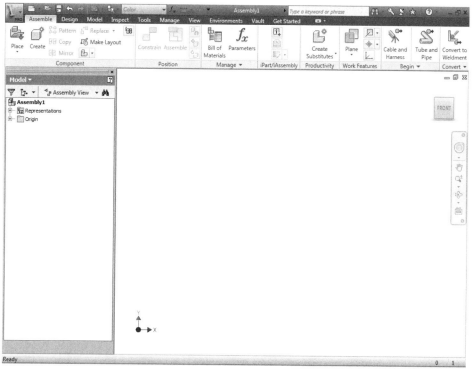

*Figure 9-2 Screen display in the **Assembly** module*

Bottom-up Assemblies

A bottom-up assembly is an assembly whose components are created as separate part files and are referenced in the assembly file as external components. In this type of assembly, the components are created in the **Part** module as part files *(.ipt)*. Once all components of the assembly are created, you will open an assembly file *(.iam)* and then insert all the component files using the tools in the **Assembly** module. After inserting the components, they are assembled using the assembly constraints. Because the assembly file has information related only to the assembling of components, this file size is not large and requires less storage space.

Note
*An assembly that uses a combination of bottom-up and top-down approaches is called a middle-out assembly. Also, if a component referenced in the assembly is moved from its original location, it will not show up when you open the assembly next time. Autodesk Inventor will look for the component only in the folder in which it was originally stored. If the component is not found at its original location, then the **Resolve Link** dialog box will be displayed. In this dialog box, you need to specify the new location of the component.*

CREATING TOP-DOWN ASSEMBLIES

As mentioned earlier, in top-down assemblies, all components are created within the assembly file. To create the components, you require the environment where you can draw the sketches of the sketched features and also the environment where you can convert the sketches into features. In other words, to create the components in the assembly file, you require the Sketching environment and the part modeling environment. Autodesk Inventor provides you the liberty of invoking both these environments in the **Assembly** module by using the **Create** tool. The use of this tool is discussed next.

Creating Components in the Assembly Module

Ribbon: Assemble > Component > Create
Toolbar: Assembly Panel > Create Component

 In Autodesk Inventor, you can create components in the **Assembly** module. One of the advantages of creating the components in the **Assembly** module is that these components can also be saved as a separate part file (*.ipt*) or an assembly file (*.iam*).
Create Therefore, if you again need any of the components created in the **Assembly** module, you can use the individual part or assembly file. The components in the **Assembly** module are created using the **Create** tool. When you invoke this tool, the **Create In-Place Component** dialog box will be displayed, as shown in Figure 9-3. The options in this dialog box are discussed next.

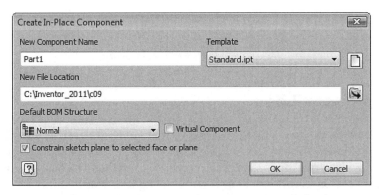

*Figure 9-3 The **Create In-Place Component** dialog box*

New Component Name

The **New Component Name** text box is used to specify the name of the component to be created.

Template

The **Template** drop-down list is used to select the template for the new file. There are four default templates in this drop-down list: **Sheet Metal.ipt**, **Standard.iam**, **Standard.ipt**, and **Weldment.iam**. You can also select the template by choosing the **Browse Templates** button on right of the **Template** drop-down list. On choosing this button, the **Open Template** dialog box will be displayed, as shown in Figure 9-4. Select the **Standard.iam** template and then choose **OK** to start a new assembly file. Alternatively, double-click on the **Standard.iam** template to start a new assembly file.

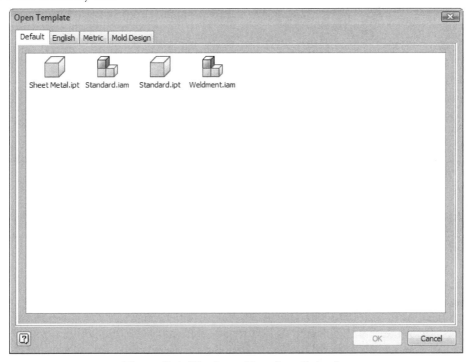

Figure 9-4 The **Open Template** dialog box

Tip. *The assembly template is used to create smaller assemblies that consist of a few components. These smaller assemblies can be assembled later in a separate assembly file to form the main assembly.*

New File Location

The **New File Location** edit box is used to specify the location for saving the new file. You can either specify the location in this edit box or choose the **Browse to New File Location** button provided on the right of the edit box to specify the location. When you choose this button, the **Save As** dialog box will be displayed, as shown in Figure 9-5. Using this dialog box, you can select the folder in which you want to save the new file.

Default BOM Structure

This drop-down list is used to specify the type of Bill of Material (BOM) structure for the new component. You will learn more about BOM structure in the next chapter.

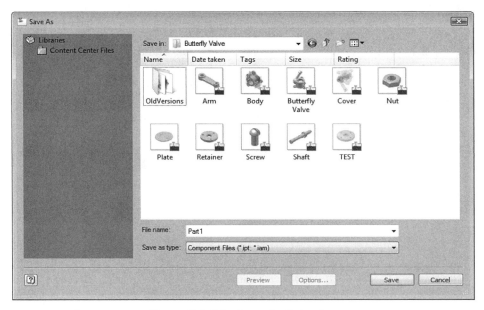

*Figure 9-5 The **Save As** dialog box*

Virtual Component

This check box is used to create a virtual component only for the purpose of adding a row in the BOM.

Constrain sketch plane to selected face or plane

The **Constrain sketch plane to selected face or plane** check box is used to constrain the plane, on which the base feature of the model will be created, to the selected face of an existing model or work plane. Note that, if the component that you create is the first component, it will be grounded and this check box will not be available in the **Create In-Place Component** dialog box. A grounded component is the first component of the assembly using which the remaining components will be assembled. All the degrees of freedom of the grounded component will be eliminated so that it is not able to move from its original location. Even if you are placing external components, by default, the first component will be grounded.

 Tip. *In the **Browser Bar**, you can easily distinguish between a grounded and an ungrounded component. A grounded component will have a push pin icon on the left of its name in the **Browser Bar**. To make a grounded component ungrounded, right-click on a grounded component in the **Browser Bar**, you will notice a tick mark in front of the **Grounded** option in the shortcut menu. To unground the component, choose this option again; the push pin icon will be replaced with the original part icon, suggesting that the component is now ungrounded.*

After setting all options in the **Create In-Place Component** dialog box, choose **OK**; you will be prompted to select a sketch plane for the base feature. Select a plane; the sketching environment will be activated and you can draw the sketch for the base feature of the model. After creating the sketch, choose the **Finish Sketch** button from the **Exit** panel of the **Sketch** tab; the part modeling environment will be activated with all part modeling tools. Once you have created a part using the sketching environment and the part modeling environment, you can switch back to the **Assembly** module by choosing the down arrow below the **Return** tool in the **Return** panel of the **Model** tab. On doing so, a flyout will be displayed. Choose the **Return to Top** option from the flyout; the **Model** tab will be replaced by the **Assemble** tab and all tools in this tab will be activated.

The alternative method of switching from the **Part** module to the **Assembly** module is by using the **Quick Access Toolbar**. In this method, first you need to create a sketch and then click on the down arrow on the right of the **Return** tool in the **Quick Access Toolbar**. On doing so, a flyout will be displayed. Choose the **Return to Parent** option from the flyout; the part modeling environment will be activated. Create the component and then click on the down arrow on the right of the **Return** tool again; a flyout will be displayed. Choose the **Return to Top** option from the flyout to switch back to the **Assembly** module.

In this way, you can create as many components as you want in the assembly. Once all the components are created, you can start assembling them using the assembly constraints.

CREATING BOTTOM-UP ASSEMBLIES

As mentioned earlier, in the bottom-up assemblies, the components are created as separate part files. All the individual part files are then inserted in an assembly file and are assembled using the assembly constraint. The first component inserted in the assembly will be grounded and its origin will coincide with that of the assembly file. Also, the three default planes of the part file will be placed in the same orientation as that of the default planes of the assembly file. The individual components are inserted in the assembly file using the **Place** tool. This tool is discussed next.

Placing Components in the Assembly File

Ribbon:	Assemble > Component > Place
Toolbar:	Assembly Panel > Place Component

Place

The **Place** tool is used to insert an inventor file in the current assembly file. On invoking this tool, the **Place Component** dialog box is displayed, as shown in Figure 9-6. This dialog box is similar to the **Open** dialog box used for opening the files. In this dialog box, you can also preview the component before inserting it in the current assembly file. The file type you want to insert can be selected from the **Files of type** drop-down list.

Select the file to be inserted from this dialog box and then choose the **Open** button. If it is the first component in the assembly file, one instance of the selected component will be placed automatically in the current file and you will be prompted to place another instance of the selected component. You can place as many copies of the selected component as you want by specifying the points on the screen. Once you have placed the required number of instances of the component, right-click and choose **Done** from the shortcut menu. As mentioned earlier, the first component will be a grounded component. Therefore, the origin of the first component will coincide automatically with the origin of the assembly file. Similarly, you can place the other components using the **Place** tool. However, remember that

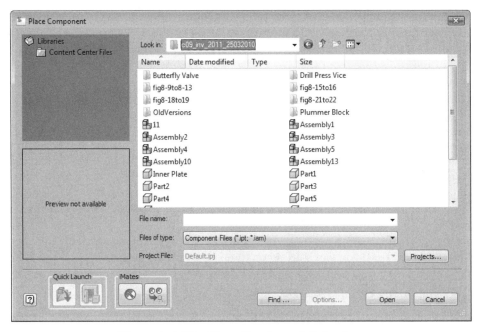

*Figure 9-6 The **Place Component** dialog box*

if one or more components are already placed in the current assembly file, then no instance of the selected component will be placed automatically and therefore you will have to manually specify the location of the first instance of the component.

Tip. *There are two more methods to place a component in an existing assembly file. In the first method, you need to open a part file and then choose the **Tile All tool from View > Windows > Tile** drop-down. On doing so, both the assembly and part files will be displayed on the screen. Alternatively, choose the **Arrange** button available below the graphics window. This button will be available only when you open multiple files that may include part files or assembly files. Now, click on the name of a part in the **Browser Bar** and drag and drop the part file in the assembly window. In the second method, you can drag and drop the part file from the Windows explorer to the current assembly.*

ASSEMBLING COMPONENTS BY USING THE CONSTRAIN TOOL

Ribbon:	Assemble > Position > Constrain
Toolbar:	Assembly Panel > Constrain

In Autodesk Inventor, the components are assembled using four types of assembly constraints, two types of motion constraints, and a transitional constraint. All these constraints are available in different tabs of the **Place Constraint** dialog box that is invoked by choosing the **Constrain** tool. These constraints are discussed next.

Mate Constraint

The **Mate** constraint is invoked using the **Mate** button provided in the **Type** area of the **Assembly** tab, see Figure 9-7. This constraint is used to make the selected planar face, axis, or point of a component coincident with that of another component. Depending on the solution selected from the **Solution** area, the components will be assembled with the normal of the faces pointing in the same direction or in the opposite direction. When you choose the **Mate** button, various options will be displayed in the **Assembly** tab of the **Place Constraint** dialog box. These options are discussed next.

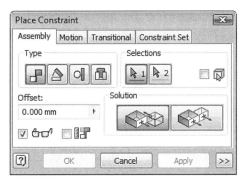

*Figure 9-7 The **Mate** constraint options in the **Assembly** tab of the **Place Constraint** dialog box*

Selections Area

The options in this area are used to select the faces, axes, edges, or points of the selected model for applying the **Mate** constraint. These options are discussed next.

> **Tip**. *You can press and hold the F4 key to rotate the view of the model for selection purpose. Later in this chapter you will learn that you can also rotate the view of an individual component.*

1 (First Selection)

This button is automatically chosen when you invoke the **Mate** constraint. This button is used to select a face, axis, edge, or point on the first component to apply the **Mate** constraint. Move the cursor close to the component that you want to select. If the cursor is close to a face, it will be highlighted and an arrow will be displayed along with a cross. This arrow will point in the direction of the normal of the selected face. The components are assembled in the direction of the normal of the faces. Similarly, if you move the cursor close to an edge, axis, or a point, it will be highlighted.

2 (Second Selection)

This button is automatically chosen after you select the first component and is used to select a face, axis, edge, or point on the second component to apply the **Mate** constraint. Figure 9-8 shows the **Mate** constraint being applied on the faces of two components. In Figure 9-8, notice the arrows displayed on the selected faces of both the components. These arrows point in the direction of the normals of the selected faces. The selected components will be assembled in the direction of these faces.

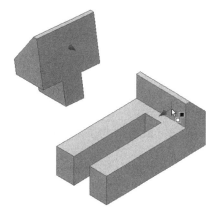

*Figure 9-8 Applying the **Mate** constraint on the faces of two components*

Pick part first

The **Pick part first** check box is provided on the right side in the **Selections** area. This check box is used for the assembly that has a large number of components and it is difficult to select the axis, edge, face, or point of one of the components due to the complicacy. If this check box is selected, you will first have to select the component and then select the element in that component to apply the constraint.

Note

*You can preview the assembly of the components on the screen after you have selected both the components to apply the constraint. However, remember that until you choose the **Apply** button from the **Place Constraint** dialog box, the constraint will not be actually applied.*

Offset

The **Offset** edit box is used to specify the offset distance between the mating components. If the offset distance is zero, the mating entities will be in contact with each other. If there is an offset distance between the mating components, they will be placed at a distance from each other. Figure 9-9 shows the components assembled with an offset distance of 0 mm and Figure 9-10 shows the components assembled with an offset distance of 10 mm between the faces.

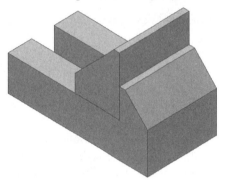

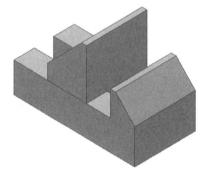

Figure 9-9 *Components assembled with an offset distance of 0 mm*

Figure 9-10 *Components assembled with an offset distance of 10 mm*

Tip. *Generally, components are not assembled using a single constraint. Depending on the components, you may require two to three constraints. The same constraint can be applied several times.*

Show Preview

The **Show Preview** check box is selected to display the preview of the assembled components. When you select two components to apply the constraint, a preview of the assembly will be displayed in the graphics window even if you have not chosen the **Apply** button. This is because the **Show Preview** check box is selected. If this check box is cleared, the preview of the assembly will not be displayed.

Predict Offset and Orientation

The **Predict Offset and Orientation** check box is selected to allow Autodesk Inventor to predict the offset and the orientation of the selected components. The predicted offset value is automatically specified in the **Offset** edit box.

Solution Area

The buttons in the **Solution** area are used to specify whether the components being assembled should be placed in a mating position or in a flushing position. A mating position is the one in which the normal of the faces are facing in the opposite directions, see Figure 9-11. A flushing position is the one, in which the normal of the faces are facing in the same direction, see Figure 9-12.

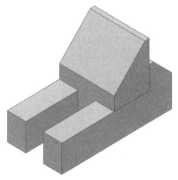

Figure 9-11 *A mating position*

Figure 9-12 *A flushing position*

Angle Constraint

 The **Angle** constraint is invoked by using the **Angle** button in the **Type** area of the **Assembly** tab. This constraint is used to specify the angular position of the selected planar faces or edges of two components. Figure 9-13 shows the options that will be displayed when you choose the **Angle** button. Some of the options in this constraint are the same as those in the **Mate** constraint. The remaining options are discussed next.

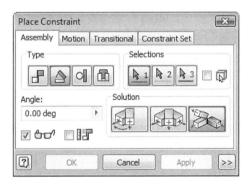

Figure 9-13 *The **Angle** constraint options in the **Assembly** tab of the **Place Constraint** dialog box*

Selections Area
3 (Third Selection)

 This button will be enabled only when you choose the **Explicit Reference Vector** button from the **Solution** area. This button is used to select a face, an edge, an axis, or a work plane to apply the **Angle** constraint.

Angle

This edit box is used to specify the angle between the selected planar faces or edges of two components. The components will be separated by an angle value specified in this edit box. You can specify a positive or a negative value in this edit box.

Solution Area

This area provides three buttons. The first button is the **Directed Angle** button and is used to apply the **Angle** constraint based on the right hand thumb rule. The second button is the **Undirected Angle** button and is used to apply the constraint based on the default orientation of the components. The third button is the **Explicit Reference Vector** button and is used to define the direction of the Z axis vector.

Figure 9-14 shows the components selected to apply the **Angle** constraint and Figure 9-15 shows the components after applying the **Angle** constraint of 90-degree. Figure 9-16 shows the vertical component selected using the **Explicit Reference Vector** button to apply the **Angle** constraint and Figure 9-17 shows the components at an angle of 90-degree after applying the **Angle** constraint by using the **Explicit Reference Vector** button.

Figure 9-14 *Selecting the faces to apply the* **Angle** *constraint*

Figure 9-15 *Components after applying the* **Angle** *constraint of 90-degree*

Figure 9-16 *Selecting the third face to apply the* **Angle** *constraint*

Figure 9-17 *Components after applying the* **Angle** *constraint by using the* **Explicit Reference Vector** *button*

Note
*The remaining options in the **Angle** constraint are the same as those discussed in the **Mate** constraint.*

Tangent Constraint

The **Tangent** constraint is invoked by choosing the **Tangent** button in the **Type** area of the **Assembly** tab. This constraint forces the selected circular face of the component to become tangent to the circular or planar face of the other component. The options that are displayed when you choose the **Tangent** button are shown in Figure 9-18. Some of the options are similar to those discussed earlier. The remaining options are discussed next.

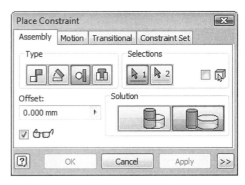

*Figure 9-18 The **Tangent** constraint options in the **Assembly** tab of the **Place Constraint** dialog box*

Solution Area

The **Solution** area provides the **Inside** and **Outside** buttons for the **Tangent** constraint. On choosing the **Inside** button, the **Tangent** constraint is applied between the outside of the first selected face and the inside of the second selected face. As a result, the first component will move inside the second component. On choosing the **Outside** button, the constraint is applied between the outside of both the selected faces.

Figure 9-19 shows the **Tangent** constraint with the **Inside** button chosen and Figure 9-20 shows the **Tangent** constraint with the **Outside** button chosen.

*Figure 9-19 The **Tangent** constraint with the **Inside** button chosen*

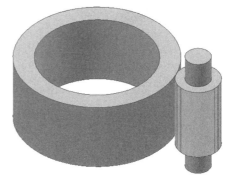

*Figure 9-20 The **Tangent** constraint with the **Outside** button chosen*

Insert Constraint

The **Insert** constraint is applied using the **Insert** button in the **Type** area of the **Assembly** tab of the **Place Constraint** dialog box. This constraint is used to force two different cylindrical or conical components or features of components to share the same location and orientation of the central axis. This constraint also makes the selected face of the first coaxial coplanar with the selected face of the other component. The options displayed on choosing the **Insert** button in the **Assembly** tab are shown in Figure 9-21. These options are discussed next.

Solution Area

The options provided in the **Solution** area are used to specify whether the normal of the mating faces will point in the same directions or in the opposite directions. If you choose the **Opposed** button, the normal of the mating faces will point in the opposite directions. If you choose the

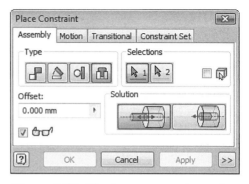

Figure 9-21   *The **Insert** constraint options in the **Assembly** tab of the **Place Constraint** dialog box*

Aligned button, the mating faces will point in the same direction. However, the central axes of both the components will share the same orientation. Figure 9-22 shows the components selected to apply the **Insert** constraint and Figure 9-23 shows the components after applying the **Insert** constraint.

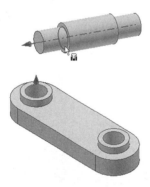

Figure 9-22   *Selecting the components for applying the **Insert** constraint*

Figure 9-23   *Components after applying the **Insert** constraint*

Note
*The remaining options in the **Tangent** and **Insert** constraints are the same as those discussed in the **Mate** constraint.*

Rotation Constraint

The **Rotation** constraint is invoked by choosing the **Rotation** button in the **Type** area of the **Motion** tab. This constraint is used to rotate one of the components in relation with the other component at the specified ratio. The components rotate about the specified central axis. The options that are displayed when you choose the **Rotation** button from the **Type** area of the **Motion** tab in the **Place Constraint** dialog box are shown in Figure 9-24. These options are discussed next.

Ratio

The **Ratio** edit box is used to specify the ratio by which the second component will rotate with respect to one complete rotation of the first component. For example, if you enter **2** in this edit box, the second component will rotate twice if the first component is rotated once. Similarly, if you enter **10**, the second component will rotate ten times if the first component is rotated once.

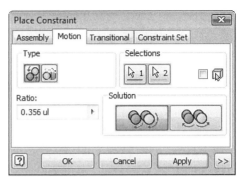

Solution Area

The options in the **Solution** area are used to specify the direction of rotation of the components. Choose the **Forward** button to rotate the components in the same direction. Choose the **Reverse** button to rotate the components in the reverse direction.

Figure 9-24 *The* ***Rotation*** *constraint options in the* ***Motion*** *tab of the* ***Place Constraint*** *dialog box*

Note

To view the results after applying the ***Rotation*** *constraint, you need to move the first component by dragging it. The constraints in the* ***Motion*** *tab of the* ***Place Constraint*** *dialog box work only with the degree of freedom that is not restricted. These constraints do not interfere with the other assembly constraints.*

The remaining options in the ***Rotation*** *constraint are the same as those discussed in the* ***Mate*** *constraint.*

Rotation-Translation Constraint

 The **Rotation-Translation** constraint is invoked by choosing the **Rotation-Translation** button in the **Type** area of the **Motion** tab. This constraint is used to rotate the first component in relation with the translation of the second component. The options in the **Motion** tab of the **Place Constraint** dialog box are shown in Figure 9-25. These options are discussed next.

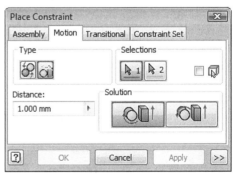

Distance

The **Distance** edit box is used to specify the distance by which the second component will move in relation with one complete rotation of the first component. For example, if you enter **2** in this edit box, the second component will move a distance of 2 mm for one complete rotation of the first component.

Figure 9-25 *The* ***Rotation-Translation*** *constraint options in the* ***Motion*** *tab of the* ***Place Constraint*** *dialog box*

Solution Area

The buttons in the **Solution** area are used to specify whether the second component will move in the forward direction or the reverse direction for every forward rotation of the first component. Choose the **Forward** button to move the component in the forward direction and the **Reverse** button to move the component in the reverse direction.

Transitional Constraint

The **Transitional** constraint is invoked by choosing the **Transitional** button from the **Type** area of the **Transitional** tab, see Figure 9-26. This constraint ensures that the selected face of the cylindrical component maintains contact with the other selected face when you slide the cylindrical component about the degree of freedom. The options in this tab are similar to those discussed in the previous constraints.

*Figure 9-26 The **Transitional** constraint options in the **Transitional** tab of the **Place Constraint** dialog box*

SPECIFYING THE LIMITS FOR CONSTRAINING

With this release of Autodesk Inventor, you can specify the limits (maximum and minimum) for constraining the components. Specifying the limits enable you to define an allowable range for the movement of components which can translate or rotate. You can specify these limits by using the options in the expanded **Place Constraint** dialog box. To expand the **Place Constraint** dialog box, choose the **>>** button given on the lower right corner of this dialog box; different options will be displayed in this dialog box, refer to Figure 9-27. These options are discussed next.

Name

This edit box is used to specify a unique name for a constraint. If you leave this edit box blank, the default name will be assigned to the constraint.

Use Offset As Resting Position

Select this check box to use the offset value as the resting position of a constraint with the specified limits. On selecting this check box, the offset value will be used to specify the maximum limit of the constraint.

*Figure 9-27 The expanded **Place Constraint** dialog box*

Maximum

Select this check box to specify the maximum limit of the constraint movement. On selecting this check box, the edit box below this check box will be enabled. You can enter the maximum limit of constraint movement in this edit box. To deactivate this edit box, clear the **Maximum** check box.

Minimum

Select this check box to specify the minimum limit of the constraint movement. On selecting this check box, the edit box below this check box will be enabled. You can enter the minimum limit of constraint movement in this edit box. To deactivate this edit box, clear the **Minimum** check box.

The constraint with the specified limits will be displayed with a unique specified name along with **+/-** symbols on its left in the **Browser Bar**. Drag the components to view the affect of the specified maximum and minimum limits. On dragging the component, the movement or rotation of the component will be restricted within these specified limits.

ASSEMBLING PARTS BY USING THE ASSEMBLE TOOL

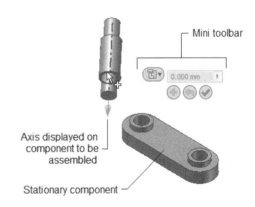

Figure 9-28 *Fixed component, component to be assembled, and the mini toolbar*

With this release of Autodesk Inventor, you can constrain the parts by using the **Assemble** tool. The available constraint types that can be applied using this tool change depending upon the type of geometry or feature selected. To define the constraint using this tool, choose the **Assemble** tool from the **Position** panel; a mini toolbar will be displayed, refer to Figure 9-28. Also, you will be prompted to select the first geometry to constrain. Select the geometry on the part that can move, refer to Figure 9-28. In other words, select the geometry on the part that is not grounded; the selected component will become translucent and will get attached to the cursor. If you move the cursor toward the matching geometry on the fixed part, the selected component will be snapped to the fixed component, refer to Figure 9-29. Also, you will be prompted to select the secondary geometry to constrain. Select the geometry on the fixed/grounded part from the drawing area; the constraints will be defined for both parts. You can change the type of constraint from the drop-down list available in the mini toolbar. You can also specify the offset value, angle value, or the solution by using the mini toolbar. After specifying the required options, choose **Apply** and then **OK** from the mini toolbar to assemble the parts using the specified constraints, refer to Figure 9-30.

Figure 9-29 *Selected component snapped to the fixed component*

Figure 9-30 *Assembled components*

Note that at a time, you can constrain only one component with another component by using the **Assemble** tool. Also, if conflicting constraints are found in the parts to be assembled, the **Assemble Constraint Management** dialog box will be displayed, as shown in Figure 9-31. If conflicts exist, then this dialog box will show you the option suggesting either to suppress or to delete the constraints for resolving the conflicts.

USING ALT+DRAG TO APPLY ASSEMBLY CONSTRAINTS

Autodesk Inventor allows you to apply the assembly constraints without invoking the **Place Constraint** dialog box. This is done by pressing the ALT key and then dragging the component. The following steps explain the procedure to apply assembly constraints using the ALT+Drag method.

Figure 9-31 *The Assemble Constraint Management dialog box*

1. Press and hold the ALT key and then drag the required component toward the component to be assembled with; the symbol of the **Mate** constraint will be displayed below the cursor. This is because when you use the ALT+Drag method, by default, the **Mate** constraint is applied.

2. Release the ALT key but make sure you do not release the left mouse button. If you release the left mouse button, the constraints cannot be applied. Press the SPACEBAR key to change the mate position to the flush position. Drag the selected component to the component that you want to select as the second component and then release the left mouse button; the assembly constraint will be applied.

If you do not want to apply the **Mate** constraint, you can use the keyboard keys after releasing the ALT key to apply the other relations. The table given next provides the details of various keys that you can use to apply the assembly constraints:

Key	Description	Function of SPACEBAR
M or 1	Applies the **Mate** constraint	Changes the mate position to the flush position
A or 2	Applies the **Angle** constraint	Reverses the direction of applying the **Angle** constraint
T or 3	Applies the **Tangent** constraint	Reverses to inside or outside face for applying the **Tangent** constraint
I or 4	Applies the **Insert** constraint	Reverses the direction of insertion
R or 5	Applies the **Rotation** constraint	Reverses the direction of rotation
S or 6	Applies the **Rotation-Translation** constraint	Reverses the direction of translation
X or 8	Applies the **Transitional** constraint	No use of SPACEBAR

MOVING INDIVIDUAL COMPONENTS

Ribbon: Assemble > Position > Move
Toolbar: Assembly Panel > Move

Autodesk Inventor allows you to move the individual components in the assembly file without disturbing the position and location of the other components in the assembly file. This is done using the **Move Component** tool. On invoking this tool, you will be prompted to drag the component to a new location. As you move the cursor close to any component, it will be highlighted. Select the component and then drag it to the desired location. The component will be relocated and the other components in the assembly file will not be disturbed.

ROTATING INDIVIDUAL COMPONENTS IN 3D SPACE

Ribbon: Assemble > Position > Rotate
Toolbar: Assembly Panel > Rotate

You can also rotate individual components in the current assembly file without changing the orientation of the other components. This is done using the **Rotate Component** tool. When you invoke this tool, you will be prompted to drag the component to a new location. Select the component that you want to rotate, but note that you cannot drag the grounded component. As soon as you select an ungrounded component, the rim along with the handles will be displayed around the model. Also, the cursor will be changed to rotation mode cursor.

You can use the same tool to rotate other individual components also. After you have finished rotating a component, right-click to invoke the shortcut menu. Choose **Done** from this shortcut menu. Similarly, you can select any individual component to rotate in 3D space.

TUTORIALS

Tutorial 1

In this tutorial, you will create the components of a Butterfly Valve assembly and then assemble them, refer to Figure 9-32. The Body and the Shaft will be created in the assembly file and the remaining components will be created as individual parts in separate part files. As a result, you will use a combination of top-down and bottom-up assemblies. The views and dimensions of the components are given in Figures 9-33 through 9-38. Assume the missing dimensions for the components and the parameters for the threads. **(Expected time: 3 hrs 30 min)**

Figure 9-32 Butterfly Valve assembly

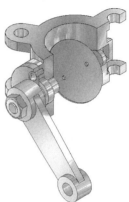

Figure 9-33 Inside view of the Butterfly Valve assembly

Figure 9-34a Solid model of the Body

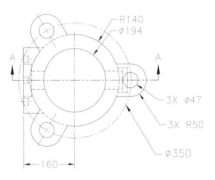

Figure 9-34b Top view of the Body

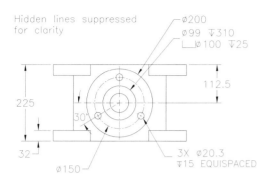

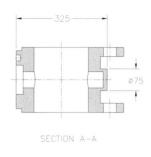

Figure 9-34c *Left view of the Body*

Figure 9-34d *Sectioned front view of the Body*

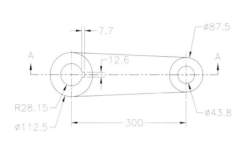

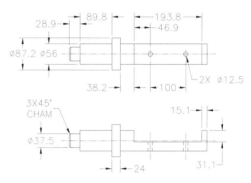

Figure 9-35a *Top view of the Arm*

Figure 9-35b *Dimensions of the Shaft*

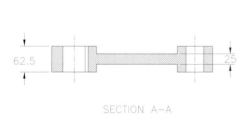

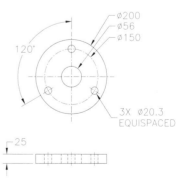

Figure 9-36 *Sectioned front view of the Arm*

Figure 9-37 *Dimensions of the Retainer*

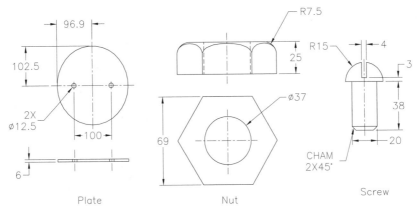

Figure 9-38 Dimensions of the Plate, Nut, and Screw

The following steps are required to complete this tutorial:

a. Create the Body and the Shaft in the assembly file and then assemble these two components using the **Place Constraint** dialog box. Save and close the assembly file.
b. Start new metric standard part files and, one by one, create the other individual components.
c. Open the assembly file and insert the individual components in the assembly file using the **Place** tool.
d. Assemble the components using the **Place Constraint** dialog box to complete the Butterfly Valve assembly.

Creating a New Project for the Assembly

Before creating the new project file for the assembly, create a folder with the name *Butterfly Valve* at the location *C:\Inventor_2011/c09*.

1. Close all Autodesk Inventor 2011 files and then choose the **Projects** tool from the **Launch** panel of the **Get Started** tab; the **Projects** dialog box is displayed.

2. Choose the **New** button from the **Projects** dialog box; the **Inventor project wizard** dialog box is displayed.

3. Select the **New Single User Project** radio button and then choose the **Next** button from the **Inventor project wizard** dialog box.

4. Enter **Butterfly Valve** as the name of the new project in the **Name** edit box.

5. Choose the **Browse for project location** button available on the right of the **Project (Workspace) Folder** edit box; the **Browse for Folder** dialog box is displayed.

6. Browse to the location *C:\Inventor_2011\c09* and select the folder *Butterfly Valve*. Next, choose the **OK** button from the **Browse for Folder** dialog box.

7. Choose the **Next** button and then the **Finish** button from the **Inventor project wizard** dialog box to exit.

8. Double-click on the newly added project in the **Project** name area to make it current and then choose the **Done** button to exit the **Projects** dialog box.

Creating the Body

You need to create the Body and the Shaft in the assembly file by using the top-down approach of assembly modeling. To create these two components, you first need to start a new metric assembly file.

1. Choose the **New** tool from the **Quick Access Toolbar** to invoke the **New File** dialog box. Choose the **Metric** tab and double-click on **Standard (mm).iam** to start a metric assembly file; the assembly environment is activated.

   You will notice that only a few tools are enabled in the **Assemble** tab. This is because no component is present in the assembly file. Once a component is placed or created, all other tools will be available for use.

2. Choose the **Create** tool from the **Component** panel of the **Assemble** tab or choose the **Create Component** tool from the **Assembly Panel** toolbar to invoke the **Create In-Place Component** dialog box.

Create

3. Enter **Body** as the name of the new part file in the **New Component Name** edit box.

4. Choose the **Browse Templates** button; the **Open Template** dialog box is displayed. Select **Standard (mm).ipt** from the **Metric** tab of this dialog box. Choose the **OK** button from the **Open Template** dialog box to exit.

5. Specify the location of the new part file in the **New File Location** edit box as *C:\Inventor_2011\c09\Butterfly Valve*.

> **Tip**. *It is recommended that you create separate folders for saving individual component files of assemblies because a number of assemblies have components with similar names. For example, the name Body is commonly used for a number of assemblies. Therefore, if you create a part, name it as Body and then store it in the folder of a particular assembly, so that there is no confusion in placing the components. Also, when you open the assembly next time, there will be no confusion in referring to the required component.*

6. Next, choose the **OK** button from the **Create In-Place Component** dialog box; you will be prompted to specify a sketch plane for the base feature. You can now create the Body of the Butterfly Valve assembly.

Note
*Remember that if you save the file when the part modeling environment is active, then only the part file will be saved, and not the assembly file. This means while creating the Body, if you choose the **Save** tool from the **Quick Access Toolbar**, the Body.ipt file will be saved, and not the current assembly file. To save the current assembly file, you need to exit the part modeling environment and then choose the **Save** tool in the assembly modeling environment.*

7. Create the Body of the Butterfly Valve using the dimensions given in Figures 9-34b through 9-34d. The screen display of the assembly file after creating the Body is shown in Figure 9-39.

Figure 9-39 *Assembly file in the part modeling environment after creating the Body*

You will notice that the part modeling environment is still active in the assembly file. To proceed further, you need to save the part file and then exit the part modeling environment.

8. Choose the **Save** tool to save the part file and then choose the **Return** tool from the **Return** panel of the **Model** tab to exit the part modeling environment.

When you choose the **Return** tool, you will notice that the **Assemble** tab is activated in place of the **Model** tab.

As mentioned earlier, until you exit the part modeling environment, only the part file will be saved when you choose the **Save** tool. The assembly file will be saved only after you exit the part modeling environment.

9. Choose the **Save** tool from the **Quick Access Toolbar** and save the assembly with the name *Butterfly Valve.iam* in the *Butterfly Valve* folder.

Creating the Shaft

The second component that has to be created in the assembly file is the Shaft. Therefore, you need to again activate the sketching environment and the part modeling environment to create the Shaft. But, as the Body is already present in the assembly file, it might restrict the view of the part that you will be creating next. Considering this, the part modeling environment is designed in such a way that when you start creating the components in the assembly file, all the existing components become transparent and the view of the newly created parts is not restricted.

1. Choose the **Create** tool from the **Component** panel of the **Assemble** tab or choose the **Create Component** tool from the **Assembly Panel** toolbar to invoke the **Create In-Place Component** dialog box.

2. Choose the **Browse Templates** button on right of the **Template** drop-down list to invoke the **Open Template** dialog box. Choose the **Metric** tab and then open the **Standard (mm).iam** template from the **Open Template** dialog box.

3. Enter the name of the new part file as **Shaft.ipt** in the **New Component Name** edit box of the **Create In-Place Component** dialog box.

4. Specify the location of the new part file in the **New File Location** edit box as *C:\Inventor_2011\c09\Butterfly Valve*.

5. Clear the **Constrain sketch plane to selected face or plane** check box and then choose **OK**; you are prompted to select the plane for the base feature.

6. Select **XY Plane** from the **Browser Bar**.

As soon as you select the XY plane, the sketching environment is activated and the Body becomes transparent. You can now proceed with creating the Shaft.

7. After creating the Shaft, save it with the name *Shaft.ipt*. Next, exit the part modeling environment by choosing the **Return** tool from the **Return** panel of the **Model** tab. Save the assembly file by choosing the **Save** tool from the **Quick Access Toolbar**.

When you exit the part modeling environment, you will notice that the Body is no more transparent. Also, both the components in the assembly file interfere with each other. Therefore, before proceeding with assembling these components, you need to move one of the components such that it does not interfere with the other. You can move the individual component using the **Move Component** tool.

8. Choose the **Move Component** tool from the **Position** panel of the **Assemble** tab and then move the cursor over the Body; you are prompted to drag the component to a new location. Select the Body and drag it to a new location where it does not interfere with the Shaft. Choose the **Zoom All** tool to increase the display area. The screen display of the assembly file with both the components is shown in Figure 9-40.

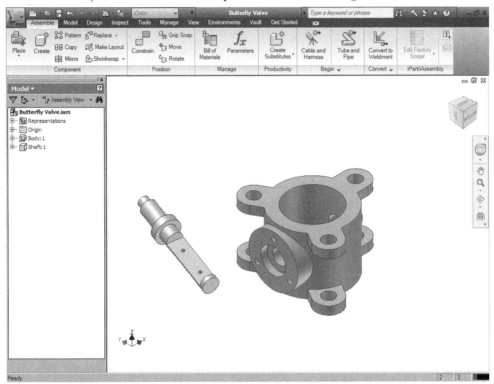

Figure 9-40 *The assembly file after creating the Body and the Shaft*

Note

*If the orientation of the Shaft and the Body is different from the one shown in Figure 9-40, you can reorient them using the **Rotate Component** tool of the **Position** panel in the **Assemble** tab.*

Assembling the Components

The Shaft has to be inserted in the counterbore hole of the Body. Therefore, you can use the **Insert** constraint to assemble these components. As mentioned earlier, the **Insert** constraint forces the selected components or features to share the same location and orientation of the central axis. It also makes the selected faces coplanar. Therefore, the Shaft will be assembled with the Body using the **Insert** constraint. Next, the flat part of the Shaft has to be at an angle to the top face of the Body. To assemble it at an angle with the top face, you will have to use the **Angle** constraint.

1. Choose the **Constrain** tool from the **Position** panel of the **Assemble** tab or choose **Constraint** from the **Assembly Panel** toolbar to invoke the **Place Constraint** dialog box.

   By default, the **Mate** constraint is selected. For assembling the Shaft with the Body, you require the **Insert** constraint.

2. Choose the **Insert** button from the **Type** area of the **Assembly** tab in the **Place Constraint** dialog box; you will notice that the **Insert** constraint symbol is attached to the cursor. This symbol is displayed along with the cursor when you move the cursor in the drawing window.

3. Select the first edge on the Shaft, as shown in Figure 9-41.

   You will notice that the selected edge is highlighted and an arrow is displayed along the direction of the central axis of the Shaft. This arrow will also point in the direction in which the Shaft will be assembled. Also, the **2** button in the **Selections** area of the **Place Constraint** dialog box is automatically chosen.

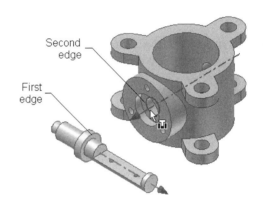

4. Select the inner edge of the counterbore hole, refer to Figure 9-41. As soon as you select the second edge for applying the constraint, the preview of the Shaft assembled with the Body is displayed. This is because the **Show Preview** check box is selected by default in the **Place Constraint** dialog box.

*Figure 9-41 Selecting the edges to apply the **Insert** constraint*

5. Choose the **Apply** button to assemble the Shaft with the Body and then choose **Cancel** from the dialog box to exit.

6. Rotate the assembly using the ViewCube such that the flat face of the Shaft is visible, refer to Figure 9-42.

7. Next, invoke the **Constrain** tool to display the **Place Constraint** dialog box again.

8. Choose the **Angle** button from the **Type** area in this dialog box; the symbol of the **Angle** constraint is attached to the cursor, suggesting that the assembling of components is resumed.

9. Select the flat face of the Shaft as the first face to apply the **Angle** constraint, see Figure 9-42.

10. Select the top face of the Body as the second face to apply the **Angle** constraint, see Figure 9-42.

11. Enter **45** in the **Angle** edit box; the flat face rotates toward the right side. If the flat face rotates toward the left, enter **-45** in the **Angle** edit box and choose the **Directed Angle** button from the **Solution** area to make sure the face rotates toward the right. Choose the **Apply** button to apply the constraint. Exit the dialog box by choosing the **Cancel** button. Change the view back to the previous view by pressing the F5 key.

*Figure 9-42 Selecting faces to apply the **Angle** constraint*

Creating Other Components

1. Save the current assembly file and then close it by choosing **Close > Close** from the **Application Menu**.

2. Create the other components as individual part files and save them with their names in the *Butterfly Valve* folder.

3. Exit the part files and then again open the *Butterfly Valve.iam* file.

Note
*It is recommended to create the holes in the Retainer using the **Circular Pattern** tool. This is because, in Chapter 10, you need to assemble the Screws with the Retainer using the **Pattern** tool.*

Assembling the Retainer

The next component to be assembled is the Retainer. The Retainer is also a circular part and so it can be assembled using the **Insert** constraint. The three holes of the Retainer have to match those on the front planar face of the Body. Also, the central hole of the Retainer has to match with the central hole of the front planar face of the Body. Therefore, you need to apply the **Insert** constraint twice - the first time to align one of the smaller holes on the Retainer with one of the smaller holes on the left flat face of the Body, and the second time to align the central holes. But first, you need to place the Retainer in the assembly using the **Place Component** tool.

1. Choose the **Place** tool from the **Component** panel of the **Assembly** tab to invoke the **Place Component** dialog box.

2. Select **Retainer** and then choose the **Open** button; the **Open** dialog box is closed and the Retainer is attached to the cursor. Also, you are prompted to place the component.

3. Place the Retainer at a location where it does not interfere with the existing components.

After you have placed an instance of the Retainer, you are again prompted to place the component. Because you need to place only one instance of the Retainer, you can exit the component placement option.

4. Right-click in the drawing window to display the shortcut menu and choose **Done** to exit the component placement option.

5. Choose the **Constrain** tool from the **Position** panel of the **Assemble** tab; the **Place Constraint** dialog box is displayed. If the **Place Constraint** dialog box is restricting the viewing of the components in the drawing window, you can move it by selecting its title bar and dragging it.

6. Choose the **Insert** button from the **Type** area. Select the circular edge of one of the smaller holes on the top face of the Retainer as the first edge, see Figure 9-43.

7. Select the circular edge of one of the smaller holes on the front planar face of the circular feature on the Body to apply the constraint, see Figure 9-43. Next, choose the **Apply** button.

As soon as you select the second face, the Retainer moves from its location and is assembled with the Body such that both the selected holes are concentric and the top face of the Retainer is coplanar with the front planar face of the circular feature on the Body. However, you will notice that the central hole of the Retainer is not concentric with the central hole of the left circular feature of the Body and the Shaft. Therefore, you need to apply the **Insert** constraint once again to align them.

8. Select the inner edge of the Retainer that is coplanar with the Body as the first edge to apply the constraint, see Figure 9-44. You may have to rotate the model to select this edge.

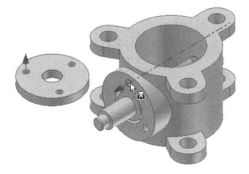
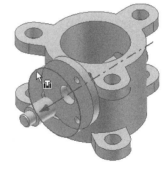

Figure 9-43 *Selecting the edges to apply the* ***Insert*** *constraint*

Figure 9-44 *Selecting the edges to apply the* ***Insert*** *constraint again*

9. Select the outer circular edge on the flat face of the front circular feature on the Body as the second face to apply the constraint, see Figure 9-44. Choose **Apply** to assemble the components and then choose **Cancel** to exit the dialog box.

Assembling the Arm

The next component to be assembled is the Arm. You need to use two constraints to assemble it. The first constraint is the **Insert** constraint and the second constraint is the **Angle** constraint, which will be used to apply an angle between the XZ plane of the Arm and the top face of the Body. You will place the Arm using the **Place Component** tool.

1. Choose the **Place** tool from the **Component** panel of the **Assemble** tab to invoke the **Place Component** dialog box.

2. Double-click on the Arm; the Arm gets attached to the cursor.

3. Place the Arm at a location where it does not interfere with the existing components.

4. Right-click in the drawing window to display the shortcut menu and choose **Done** to exit the component placement option.

5. Choose the **Constrain** tool from the **Position** panel of the **Assemble** tab; the **Place Constraint** dialog box is displayed.

6. Choose the **Insert** button and then select the top circular edge of the hole with the keyway in the Arm as the first face, see Figure 9-45.

7. Select the outer circular edge on the front planar face of the Retainer as the second face to apply the **Insert** constraint, see Figure 9-45. Next, choose the **Apply** button.

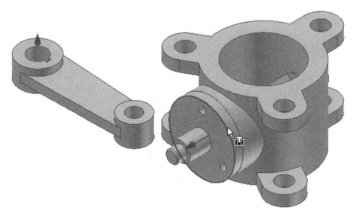

Figure 9-45 *Selecting the faces to apply the **Insert** constraint*

After performing the above steps, the Arm will be assembled with the Retainer and the Shaft will be inserted in the bigger hole of the Arm. The second constraint will be used to reorient the Arm such that it is assembled at an angle to the top face of the Body. This angle is the same as the angle between the top face of the Body and the flat face of the Shaft.

Note

*In this case, it is presumed that the cylindrical features of the Arm are created on the XY plane. Also, the bigger and smaller cylindrical features are created from left to right along the X axis direction when placed on the XY plane. Therefore, the XZ plane will pass through the center of the two cylindrical features. This XZ plane will be used to apply the **Angle** constraint.*

8. Choose the **Angle** button from the **Type** area and then select the top face of the Body as the first face to apply the constraint.

The second face to be selected to apply the constraint is the XZ plane of the Arm. The XZ plane of the Arm will not be displayed in the **Browser Bar**. You need to display this plane using the **Origin** folder in the **Browser Bar**.

9. Click on the + sign located on the left of the Arm in the **Browser Bar** to display the **Origin** folder. Next, click again on the + sign located on the left of the **Origin** folder to display all the work planes of the Arm. Now, select the XZ plane.

10. Enter **-135** as angle in the **Angle** edit box. Choose **Apply** to apply the constraint and then **Cancel** to close the dialog box. Click on the - sign on the left of the Arm in the **Browser Bar** to collapse the folders. The assembly after assembling the Arm is shown in Figure 9-46.

Figure 9-46 Assembly after assembling the Arm

Assembling the Plate

The next component to be assembled is the Plate. You first need to place it in the assembly file and then assemble it on the flat face of the Shaft. In this process, you need to apply the **Insert** constraint twice to assemble the Plate with the Shaft. The first constraint will align one of the holes on the Plate with one of the holes on the Shaft. The second constraint will align the second hole on the Plate with a hole on the Shaft.

Since the Shaft is assembled inside the Body, the Body will cause a restriction in viewing the components being assembled. To avoid this, Autodesk Inventor allows you to turn off the display of the components that you do not require for assembling the other components. Therefore, before proceeding with the assembling of the Plate, you can turn off the display of the Body. This is done using the **Browser Bar**.

1. Right-click on the Body in the **Browser Bar** to display the shortcut menu. You will notice that in the shortcut menu, there is a tick mark in front of the **Visibility** option. This suggests that the display of this component is turned on. Choose the **Visibility** option again to turn off the display of the Body.

   The component whose visibility is turned off will be displayed in gray color in the **Browser Bar**.

   Tip. *If you clear the **Enabled** check box instead of the **Visibility** check box in the shortcut menu, then the selected part in the **Browser Bar** will turn green in color and the component will become transparent.*

2. Choose the **Place** tool from the **Component** panel of the **Assemble** tab to invoke the **Place Component** dialog box.

3. Double-click on the **Plate**; the Plate gets attached to the cursor.

4. Place the Plate at a location where it does not interfere with the existing components.

5. Right-click in the drawing window to display the shortcut menu and choose **Done** to exit the component placement option.

6. Choose the **Constrain** tool from the **Position** panel of the **Assemble** tab; the **Place Constraint** dialog box is displayed.

7. Choose the **Insert** button and then select the circular edge of one of the holes on the top face of the Plate as the first face to apply the constraint, see Figure 9-47.

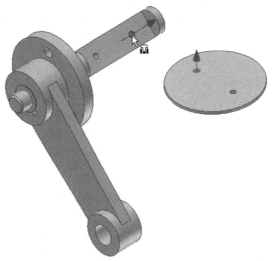

Figure 9-47 Selecting the faces to apply the constraint

8. Select the circular edge of the right hole on the flat face of the Shaft as the second face to apply the constraint, see Figure 9-47. Then, choose **Apply** to apply the constraint.

    As soon as you select the second face to apply the constraint, the Plate will move from its location and will be assembled with the Shaft. Now, the second constraint has to be applied on the other hole of the Plate. But the hole has to be selected on the face that is made coplanar with the flat face of the Shaft. Therefore, you need to reorient the model such that the back face of the Plate is visible and you can select the hole on that face to apply the constraint.

9. Rotate the assembly using the ViewCube such that the back face of the Plate is visible.

10. Select the circular edge on one of the holes on the back face of the Plate as the first face to apply the constraint.

    Since you have you rotated the model such that the back face of the Plate is visible, the flat face of the Shaft is not visible in the current view. Therefore, you need to switch back to the previous view. Sometimes when you use the **Place** tool, you cannot use the F5 key to invoke the previous view. In such cases, you need to invoke the **Rotate Component** tool and then right-click to display a shortcut menu. Then, you need to choose **Previous View** from this menu to switch back.

11. Press the F5 key or choose the **Rotate Component** tool from the **Position** panel, and then right-click in the drawing window to display a shortcut menu. Choose the **Previous View** option to switch back to the previous view. Again, right-click and choose **Done** to exit the **Rotate Component** tool.

12. Select the other hole on the flat face of the Shaft to apply the constraint. Choose the **Apply** button to apply the constraint and then choose the **Cancel** button to exit the dialog box. The assembly after assembling the Plate is shown in Figure 9-48.

Figure 9-48 Assembly after assembling the Plate

Assembling the Screws

There are three instances of the Screw that need to be assembled such that they are inserted in the three holes on the Retainer. But before assembling the Screws, you need to turn off the display of the Arm so that it does not interfere in the display while assembling the other components.

1. Right-click on the Arm in the **Browser Bar** and choose the **Visibility** option to turn off the display of the Arm in the assembly.

2. Choose the **Place** tool from the **Component** panel to invoke the **Place Component** dialog box.

3. Double-click on the Screw; the Screw gets attached to the cursor.

4. Place three instances of the Screw at a location where they do not interfere with the existing components.

5. Choose the **Constrain** tool from the **Position** panel of the **Assemble** tab; the **Place Constraint** dialog box is displayed.

6. Choose the **Insert** button, and then select the circular edge on the flat face of the head of the Screw as the first face to apply the constraint.

7. Select the circular edge of one of the smaller holes on the front face of the Retainer as the second face to apply the constraint. Next, choose **Apply** to apply the constraint.

8. Similarly, assemble the other two Screws with the other two smaller holes on the Retainer.

Assembling the Nut

Next, you need to assemble the Nut with the Shaft. Since the threaded portion of the Shaft has to be inserted inside the hole of the Nut, you need to use the **Insert** constraint to assemble these components.

1. Choose the **Place** tool from the **Component** panel to invoke the **Place Component** dialog box.

2. Double-click on the Nut; the Nut gets attached to the cursor.

3. Place the Nut at a location where it does not interfere with the existing components. Rotate the Nut using the **Rotate Component** tool such that the flat face of the Nut is visible in the current view.

4. Choose the **Constrain** tool from the **Position** panel of the **Assemble** tab; the **Place Constraint** dialog box is displayed.

5. Choose the **Insert** button and then select the circular edge of the hole on the flat face of the Nut as the first face to apply the constraint.

6. Select the end face (not on the side of the chamfered edge) of the threaded feature of the Shaft. Choose **Apply** to apply the constraint and then choose **Cancel** to exit the dialog box.

Turning on the Display of the Body and the Arm

1. Right-click on the Body in the **Browser Bar** and choose **Visibility** from the shortcut menu to turn on the display of the Body in the assembly.

2. Similarly, right-click on the Arm in the **Browser Bar** and choose **Visibility**; the display of the Arm will be turned on in the assembly. Next, choose the **Zoom All** tool from the **Navigate** panel of the **View** tab to zoom in the view. The final Butterfly Valve assembly is shown in Figure 9-49.

Figure 9-49 *Final Butterfly Valve assembly*

3. Save the assembly and close the file.

Tutorial 2

In this tutorial, you will create the components of a Plummer Block assembly. All components should be created as separate part files. After creating the components, place them in the assembly file and then assemble them. The dimensions of the components are shown in Figures 9-50 through 9-55. Assume the missing dimensions and the parameters for the threads. **(Expected time: 3 hrs)**

Note
The orientation of the Casting that you will draw should match the orientation of the Casting shown in the assembly in Figure 9-50. This is because when you place the first component in the assembly file, it is placed on the same plane on which it was originally created in the part file. Since the Casting will be the first component that you will place in the assembly file, its base should be created on the XY plane. Therefore, when you place it in the assembly file, it is placed on the XY plane. The orientation of the other components also depends on the first component that you place in the assembly file.

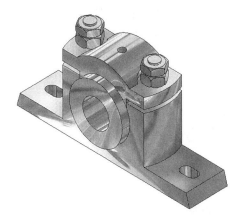

Figure 9-50 *Plummer Block assembly*

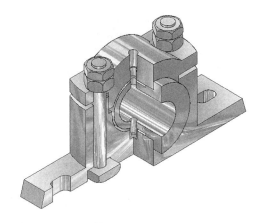

Figure 9-51 *Half-sectioned isometric view of the Plummer Block assembly*

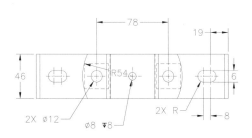

Figure 9-52a *Top view of the Casting*

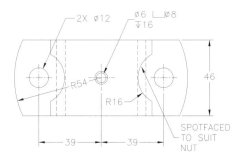

Figure 9-52b *Top view of the Cap*

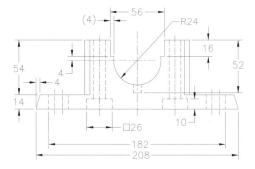

Figure 9-53a *Front view of the Casting*

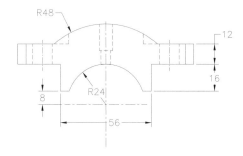

Figure 9-53b *Front view of the Cap*

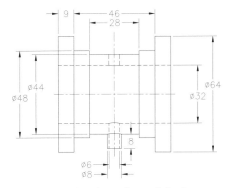

Figure 9-54 *Dimensions of the Brasses*

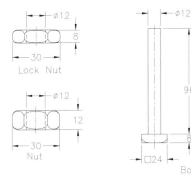

Figure 9-55 *Dimensions of the Lock Nut, Nut, and Bolt*

The following steps are required to complete this tutorial:

a. Create all the components of the assembly as separate part files and save them in the *Plummer Block* folder at the location *Inventor_2011\c09*.
b. Start a new metric assembly file and then place the Casting and the Cap by using the **Place** tool.
c. Assemble the two components using the assembly constraints.
d. Next, turn off the display of the Cap and then place the Brasses in the assembly. Assemble the Brasses with the Casting and then turn off the display of the Brasses too.
e. Place two instances of the Bolt in the assembly file and then assemble them with the Casting.
f. Turn on the display of the Cap and place two instances of the Nut and the Lock Nut. Assemble both the instances of the Nut with the Cap and then assemble the Lock Nut with the Nut.
g. Finally, turn on the display of the Brasses to complete the Plummer Block assembly.

Creating a New Project for the Assembly

1. Create a new folder with the name *Plummer Block* in the *c09* folder and set it as the current project folder using the procedure described in Tutorial 1.

Creating the Components

1. Create all components of the Plummer Block assembly as separate part files. Then, save the files with corresponding names, refer to Figures 9-52a through 9-55. The files should be saved at the location *C:\Inventor_2011\c09\Plummer Block*.

Assembling the Casting and the Cap

The Casting and the Cap will be assembled using two assembly constraints. The first constraint is the **Insert** constraint that will align one of the holes on the top face of the Cap with the corresponding hole on one of the horizontal face of the Casting. You will also apply an offset of **4** units between the mating faces in this constraint. The other constraint is the **Mate** constraint that will align the front face of the Cap with the front face of the Casting.

1. Start a new assembly file and save it with the name *Plummer Block.iam* in the *Plummer Block* folder at the location *C:\Inventor_2011\c09*. The *Plummer Block* is the folder in which all the individual part files are saved.

2. Choose the **Place** tool from the **Component** panel of the **Assemble** tab to invoke the **Place Component** dialog box.

3. Double-click on the Casting; the Casting gets attached to the cursor.

   Notice that one instance of the Casting is automatically placed in the assembly file. This instance is grounded and has a push pin icon in front of it in the **Browser Bar**. Also, you are again prompted to place the component.

4. As you need to place only one instance of casting, right-click and choose **Done** from the shortcut menu. Similarly, place one instance of the Cap in the current assembly file. The location of the Cap should be such that it does not interfere with the Casting.

5. Choose the **Rotate Component** tool from the **Position** panel of the **Assemble** tab and rotate the Cap such that its bottom face is visible in the current view.

6. Choose the **Constrain** tool from the **Position** panel of the **Assemble** tab; the **Place Constraint** dialog box is displayed.

7. Choose the **Insert** button and then select the circular edge of the right hole on the bottom face of the Cap as the first face to apply the constraint.

8. Select the circular edge of the right hole on the top face of the Casting as the second face to apply the constraint. Next, enter **4** in the **Offset** edit box and then choose **Apply**.

   The Cap is assembled with the Casting. However, the alignment of the front face of the Cap does not match the alignment of the front face of the Casting. Therefore, you need to apply the **Mate** constraint.

9. Choose the **Mate** button from the **Type** area and then select the front face of the Cap as the first face to apply the constraint. Rotate the assembly, if required.

10. Select the front face of the Casting as the second face to apply the constraint and then choose the **Flush** button from the **Solution** area. Next, choose **Apply** to apply the constraint and then choose **Cancel** to exit the dialog box. The assembly after assembling the Cap and the Casting is shown in Figure 9-56.

Assembling the Brasses

The Brasses is a circular part and so it can be assembled using the **Insert** constraint. Notice that in the Brasses, there is a circular join feature (snug) created on the cylindrical face. The snug on the cylindrical face should match the hole on the circular face of the Casting. To proceed with assembling the Brasses, you first need to turn off the display of the Cap because it is not required for assembling the Brasses.

1.   Right-click on the Cap in the **Browser Bar** and choose **Visibility** from the shortcut menu to turn off the display of the cap.

2.   Place the Brasses in the graphics window by using the **Place** tool. Next, invoke the **Place Constraint** dialog box by using the **Constrain** tool.

3.   Choose the **Insert** button from the **Type** area of this dialog box and select the semicircular edge of the Casting as the first edge to apply the constraint, as shown in Figure 9-57.

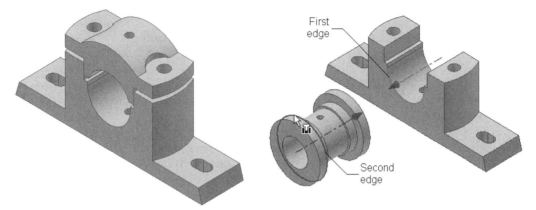

Figure 9-56 *Assembly after assembling the Cap with the Casting*   *Figure 9-57* *Selecting the edges to apply the Insert constraint*

4.   Select the circular edge of the Brasses, refer to Figure 9-57, as the second edge to apply the constraint. Make sure the arrow points in the backward direction and then choose the **Apply** button.

     The next constraint is used to align the central axis of the snug created on the cylindrical face of the Brasses with that of the hole on the cylindrical face of the Casting. Note that the hole in the casting will not be visible even if you change the orientation of the assembly, therefore you need to change the display mode from shaded to wireframe. In the wireframe display, the inside holes and features will also be displayed.

5.   Change the display mode to wireframe by choosing the **Wireframe** tool from **View > Appearance > Visual Style** drop-down. Choose the **Mate** button from the **Type** area of the **Place Constraint** dialog box and move the cursor close to the snug on the cylindrical face of the Brasses. When you move the cursor close to the snug, the central axis of the snug will be displayed. If not, you can use the **Cycle Through** tool to select the central axis of the circular join feature as the first element to apply the constraint.

6.   Select the central axis of the hole in the cylindrical face of the Casting as the second selection set. Now, choose the **Apply** button to apply the constraint and then choose the **Cancel** button to exit the dialog box.

7. Turn on the visibility of the Cap again using the **Browser Bar** and change the display from wireframe to shaded. The assembly after assembling the Brasses is shown in Figure 9-58.

Assembling the Bolts

There are two instances of the Bolts that have to be assembled in the current assembly. Since the Brasses are not required for assembling the Bolts or the Nuts, you can turn off their display. After turning off the display of the Brasses, you need to assemble the Bolts.

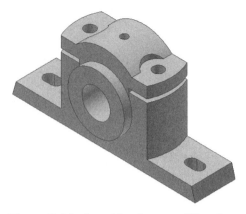

1. Turn off the display of the Brasses using the **Browser Bar**. Next, place two instances of the Bolt using the **Place** tool.

Figure 9-58 *Assembly after assembling the Brasses*

2. Change the display mode to wireframe, as discussed earlier. Invoke the **Place Constraint** dialog box and then choose the **Insert** button from the **Type** area.

3. Select the circular edge on the top face of the base square feature of the Bolt as the first face to apply the constraint, refer to Figure 9-59.

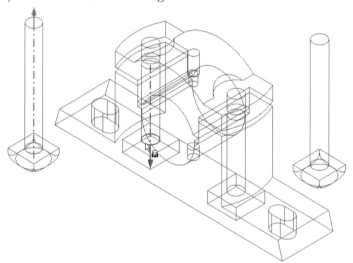

Figure 9-59 *Selecting the faces to apply the constraint*

4. Change the display type to wireframe and then select the circular edge on the top face of the square cut on the bottom face of the Casting, see Figure 9-59. Next, choose the **Apply** button to apply the constraint.

5. Similarly, assemble the other Bolt and then change the display mode to shaded.

Assembling the Nuts and the Lock Nuts

1. Place two instances each of the Nut and the Lock Nut using the **Place** tool.

2. Invoke the **Place Constraint** dialog box and choose the **Insert** button. Select the circular edge of the hole on the top face of one of the Nuts as the first face to apply the constraint.

3. Select the circular edge of the left hole on the top face of the Cap as the second face to apply the constraint. On doing so, the Nut will be assembled with the Cap. Next, choose the **Apply** button to apply the constraint.

4. Select the circular edge of the hole on the top face of one of the Lock Nuts as the first face to apply the constraint.

5. Now, select the circular edge of the hole on the top face of the Nut that is assembled with the Cap as the second face to apply the constraint. Next, choose the **Apply** button to apply the constraint.

6. Similarly, assemble the other Nut and the Lock Nut. Turn on the display of all the hidden components using the **Browser Bar**. The final Plummer Block assembly is shown in Figure 9-60.

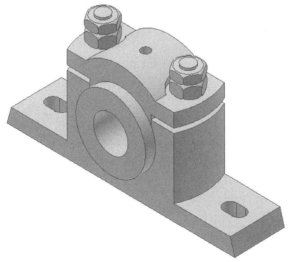

Figure 9-60 *Final Plummer Block assembly*

7. Save the assembly by choosing the **Save** tool from the **Quick Access Toolbar**.

Tutorial 3

In this tutorial, you will create the components of the Anti Vibration Mount and then assemble them, as shown in Figure 9-61. All components should be created as separate part files. The views and dimensions of the components are shown in Figures 9-62a through 9-62e.

(Expected time: 2 hours)

Figure 9-61 *The Anti Vibration Mount assembly for Tutorial 3*

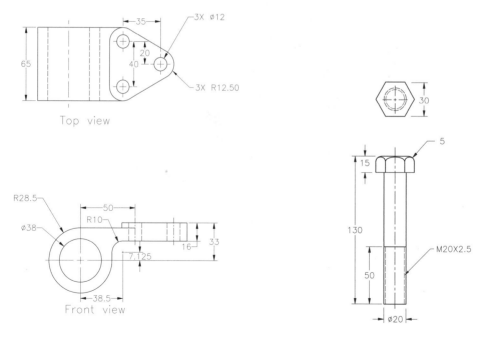

Figure 9-62a *Top and front views of Body*   *Figure 9-62b* *Top and front views of Hex Bolt*

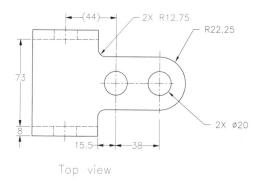

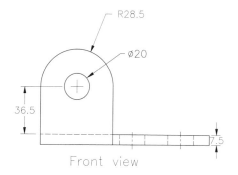

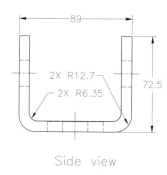

Top view

Front view

Side view

Figure 9-62c *Top, front, and side views of Yoke Plate*

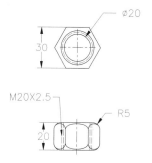

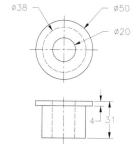

Figure 9-62d *Top and front views of Nut*

Figure 9-62e *Top and front views of Bushing Rubber*

The following steps are required to complete this tutorial:

a) Create all components of the assembly as separate part files and save them at the location *\Inventor_2011\c09\Anti Vibration Mount*.

b) Start a new metric assembly file and place the Body and two instances of Bushing Rubber using the **Place** tool.

c) Assemble the components by using the assembly constraints.

d) Place the Yoke Plate using the **Place** tool and then assemble it using the assembly constraints.

e) Place the Hex Bolt and assemble it by using the assembly constraints.

f) Place the Nut and then assemble it by using the assembly constraints.

Creating the Components

Before creating the assembly, you need to create its components as separate part files. You need to save them at a common location for ease of assembling.

1. Start a new metric part file and then create the sketch on the XY plane, as shown in Figure 9-63. Apply the required dimensions and constraints to the sketch.

2. Exit the sketching environment by choosing the **Finish Sketch** button from the **Exit** panel of the **Sketch** tab.

3. Choose the **Extrude** tool and then extrude the sketch to a depth of 16 mm, as shown in Figure 9-64

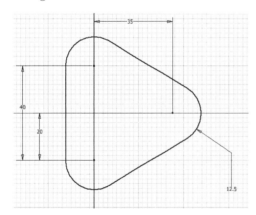
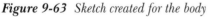

Figure 9-63   *Sketch created for the body*   *Figure 9-64*   *Sketch extruded*

4. Turn on the visibility of the YZ plane by using the **Browser Bar**.

5. Choose the **Tangent to Surface and Parallel to Plane** tool from **Model > Work Features > Plane** drop-down and then select the **YZ Plane** from the graphics window or from the **Browser Bar**.

6. Next, select the rounded face on left of the YZ plane; a plane tangent to the selected face and parallel to the YZ plane is created.

7. Similarly, create the work plane on right of the YZ plane and then turn off the visibility of the YZ plane by using the **Browser Bar**. The extruded feature after creating the work planes is shown in Figure 9-65. The work planes created are named as Work Plane 1 and Work Plane 2. These work planes are displayed in the **Browser Bar**.

8. Choose the **Create 2D Sketch** tool from **Model > Sketch > Sketch** drop-down and select Work Plane 1 as the sketching plane.

9. Create the sketch for extrusion feature, as shown in Figure 9-66 and exit the sketching environment. The model in this figure is displayed in wireframe for clarity of the sketch.

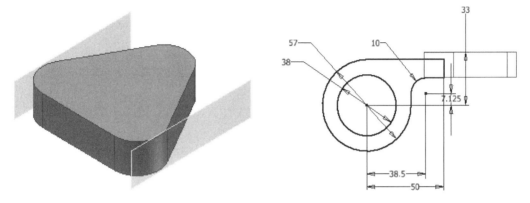

Figure 9-65 Work planes created   *Figure 9-66 Sketch for the extrusion feature*

10. Choose the **Extrude** tool from the **Create** panel of the **Model** tab and extrude the sketch up to Work Plane 2.

11. Hide both work planes by using the **Browser Bar**. Choose the **Home** icon from the ViewCube to display the model in isometric view, as shown in Figure 9-67.

12. Create three holes of 12 mm diameter on the triangular face of the model by using the **Hole** tool. You can use the rounded faces of the triangular feature as the concentric references for the holes. Figure 9-68 shows the model after creating the holes.

Figure 9-67 Model in isometric view   *Figure 9-68 Holes created on the model*

13. Save the file with name *Body* at the location given below:

    \Inventor_2011\c09\Anti Vibration Mount

14. Similarly, create the other components of the assembly and save them at the same location.
    For dimensions of the components, refer to Figures 9-62c through 9-62e.

Placing the Body and Bushing Rubber in the Assembly
You need to start a new assembly file and then place the Body in it. Next, you need place
two instances of Bushing Rubber in the same assembly.

1. Start a new metric assembly file, and then choose the **Place** tool from the **Component**
   panel in the **Assemble** tab; the **Place Component** dialog box is displayed.

2. Browse to the *Anti Vibration Mount* folder and double-click on **Body** in this dialog box; the
   Body is placed in the assembly.

3. Right-click in the drawing area and then choose **Done**.

4. Similarly, place two instances of the Bushing Rubber in the drawing area.

Assembling the Components
After placing the components in the assembly file, you need to assemble them.

1. Choose the **Constrain** tool from the **Position** panel of the **Assemble** tab; the **Place
   Constraint** dialog box is displayed.

2. Choose the **Insert** button from the **Type** area of the **Assembly** tab in this dialog box. Next,
   select the cylindrical edges of the Body and the Bushing Rubber, as shown in Figure 9-69;
   the selected components are aligned axially with each other.

3. Choose **Apply** from the **Place Constraint** dialog box to confirm the constraint applied.
   The assembled components are shown in Figure 9-70.

Figure 9-69 *Edges selected to apply the*
Insert *constraint*

Figure 9-70 *Assembly after assembling the*
body with one instance of Bushing Rubber

4. Similarly, assemble the other instances of the Bushing Rubber with the Body. The assembly after assembling both the instances of the Bushing Rubber is shown in Figure 9-71.

Assembling the Yoke Plate with the Assembly

Next, you need to place the Yoke Plate in the assembly and then assemble it with the other components in the assembly.

1. Place the Yoke Plate in the drawing area using the **Place Component** dialog box, as discussed earlier in the tutorial.

2. Use the **Move Component** tool and the **Rotate Component** tool to place the yoke plate at the position shown in Figure 9-72.

Figure 9-71 *Assembly after assembling the body with both instances of Bushing Rubber*

Figure 9-72 *Yoke Plate moved and placed at different position*

3. Choose the **Constrain** tool from the **Position** panel of the **Assemble** tab; the **Place Constraint** dialog box is displayed.

4. Choose the **Insert** button from the **Type** area of the **Assembly** tab in this dialog box. Next, select the cylindrical edges of the Bushing Rubber and the Yoke Plate, as shown in Figure 9-73; the selected components are aligned axially with each other.

5. Choose **Apply** from the **Place Constraint** dialog box to confirm the constraint applied. The assembly after applying the **Insert** constraint is shown in Figure 9-74.

6. Choose the **Angle** button from the **Type** area of the **Assembly** tab in the **Place Constraint** dialog box.

7. Choose the **>>** button in the **Place Constraint** dialog box to expand it, if the dialog box is collapsed.

8. Select the **Maximum** or **Minimum** check box in the **Limits** tab of the dialog box; the edit boxes below these check boxes are activated.

9. Enter **45** and **0** in the **Maximum** and **Minimum** edit boxes, respectively.

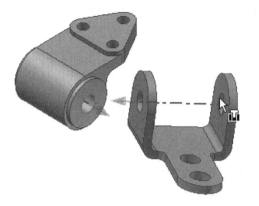

Figure 9-73 *Edges selected to apply the* ***Insert*** *constraint*

Figure 9-74 *Assembly after applying the* ***Insert*** *constraint*

10. Select the faces of the components in the assembly in the order shown in Figure 9-75.

11. Next, choose **OK** from the **Place Constraint** dialog box; the assembly after assembling the Yoke Plate is shown in Figure 9-76.

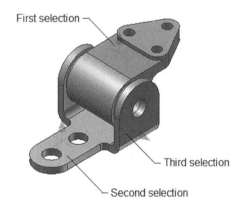

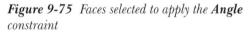

Figure 9-75 *Faces selected to apply the* ***Angle*** *constraint*

Figure 9-76 *Assembly after applying the* ***Angle*** *constraint*

As you have provided the maximum and minimum limits as 45-degree and 0-degree respectively, you can rotate the Yoke Plate around its central axis from 0-degree to 45 degrees by dragging it. This provides some degree of freedom to the Yoke Plate.

Assembling the Hex Bolt with the Assembly

Next, you need to assemble the Hex Bolt with the assembly.

1. Place the Hex Bolt in the assembly by using the **Place** tool.

2. Choose the **Rotate Component** tool from the **Position** panel of the **Assemble** tab and rotate the Hex Bolt to the view shown in Figure 9-77. Note that if you rotate the components, you can easily select the entities for assembling the components.

3. Invoke the **Place Constraint** dialog box as discussed earlier.

4. Choose the **Insert** button from the **Type** area of the **Assembly** tab in this dialog box. Next, select the cylindrical edges of the Yoke Plate and the Hex Bolt, as shown in Figure 9-78; the selected components are aligned axially with each other.

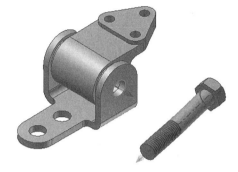

Figure 9-77 *Rotated Hex bolt*   *Figure 9-78* *Edges selected to apply the* ***Insert*** *constraint*

5. Choose **Apply** from the **Place Constraint** dialog box to confirm the constraint applied.

6. Next, choose **Angle** button from the **Type** area of the **Assembly** tab in the **Place Constraint** dialog box.

7. Choose the **Directed Angle** button from the **Solutions** area of the **Assembly** tab in the **Place Constraint** dialog box.

8. Select the planar faces of the Body and the Hex Bolt in the assembly, as shown in Figure 9-79.

9. Next, choose **OK** from the **Place Constraint** dialog box; the assembly after assembling the Hex Bolt is shown in Figure 9-80.

Assembling the Nut

Finally, you need to assemble the Nut with the assembly.

1. Place the Nut in the assembly by using the **Place** tool.

2. Rotate the assembly by using the ViewCube, so that the back face of the Yoke Plate is visible.

3. Invoke the **Place Constraint** dialog box as discussed earlier. By default, the **Mate** button is chosen from the **Type** area of the **Assembly** tab.

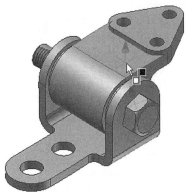

Figure 9-79 *Faces selected for applying the*
Angle *constraint*

Figure 9-80 *Hex bolt assembled in the assembly*

4. Select the planar faces on the Yoke Plate and the Nut, as shown in Figure 9-81; the selected components are mated.

5. Next, select the axes of the Hex Bolt and the Nut, as shown in Figure 9-82; the Hex Bolt and the Nut are aligned axially with each other.

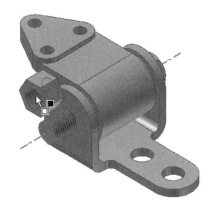

Figure 9-81 *Faces selected on Yoke Plate and Nut for applying the* **Mate** *constraint*

Figure 9-82 *Axes selected for the* **Mate** *constraint*

6. Next, choose **OK** from the **Place Constraint** dialog box to confirm the constraints applied and to exit the dialog box.

7. Choose the **Home** icon from the ViewCube to display the final assembly in the isometric view, as shown in Figure 9-83.

Saving and Closing the Assembly

After assembling all components, you need to save the assembly.

Figure 9-83 *Isometric view of the final assembly*

1. Choose the **Save** tool from the **Quick Access Toolbar**; the **Save As** dialog box is displayed.

2. Enter **Anti Vibration Mount** as the name of the assembly and save it at the location given below:

    \Inventor_2011\c09\Anti Vibration Mount

3. Choose **Close > Close** from the **Application Menu** to close the assembly file.

Self-Evaluation Test

Answer the following questions and then compare them to those given at the end of this chapter:

1. In Autodesk Inventor, you can use the bottom-up approach as well as the top-down approach for creating assemblies. (T/F)

2. An assembly that uses a combination of top-down and bottom-up approaches is called a middle-out assembly. (T/F)

3. You can rotate individual components in the assembly file. (T/F)

4. You cannot invoke the sketching environment in the assembly file. (T/F)

5. The _____ tool is used to place the components in the assembly file.

6. The _____ icon is displayed in front of the grounded component in the **Browser Bar**.

7. When you invoke the **Constrain** tool, the _____ dialog box is displayed.

8. The _____ constraint is used to make the selected planar face, axis, or point of a component coincident with that of another component.

9. By default, the first component placed in the assembly file is _____.

10. The individual components in the assembly file can be moved using the _____ tool.

Review Questions

Answer the following questions:

1. You can change the display type of the components even when you are using a tool to perform a function. (T/F)

2. You can rotate or move a component while assembling it with the base feature. (T/F)

3. The components that are not grounded by default can also be grounded if required. (T/F)

4. The display of the components that is not required for assembling other components can be turned off using the **Browser Bar**. (T/F)

5. If the component files are moved from their original location, they will not show up the next time you open the assembly file. (T/F)

6. The top-down assemblies are those in which all components are created as individual part files and are placed in the assembly file. (T/F)

7. How many types of assembly constraints are available in Autodesk Inventor?

    (a) 4   (b) 5
    (c) 7   (d) 8

8. How many types of motion constraints are available in Autodesk Inventor?

    (a) 2   (b) 3
    (c) 4   (d) 5

9. Which of the following tools is used to rotate the individual components in the assembly file?

    (a) **Rotate**   (b) **Move**
    (c) **Place**   (d) None of these

10. Which of the following constraints is used to rotate one of the components in relation to other component?

(a) **Rotation**   (b) **Rotation-Translation**
(c) **Mate**   (d) **Tangent**

Exercise

Exercise 1

Create the components of the Drill Press Vice assembly and then assemble them, as shown in Figure 9-84. The dimensions of the components are shown in Figures 9-85 through 9-88b. Create a folder with the name *Drill Press Vice* at the location *C:\Inventor_2011\c09* and save all the components and the assembly file at this folder. Assume the missing dimensions. You will use the bottom-up approach for creating this assembly.   **(Expected time: 3 hrs 15 min)**

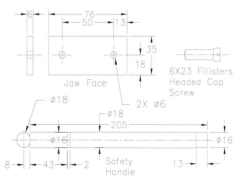

Figure 9-84 *Drill Press Vice assembly*

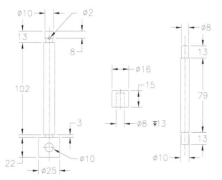

Figure 9-85 *Dimensions of the Clamp Screw, Handle Stop, and Clamp Screw Handle*

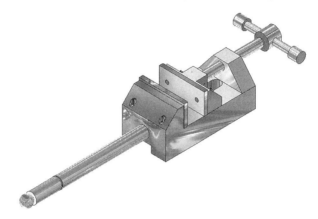

Figure 9-86 *Dimensions of the Jaw Face, Cap Screw, and Safety Handle*

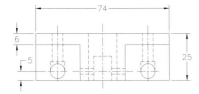

Figure 9-87a *Top view of the Movable Jaw*

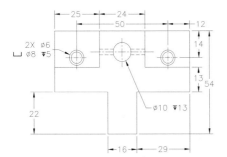

Figure 9-87b *Front view of the Movable Jaw*   ***Figure 9-87c*** *Side view of the Movable Jaw*

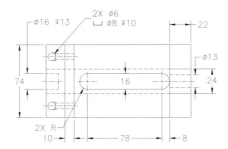

Figure 9-88a *Top view of the Base*

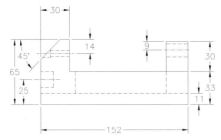

Figure 9-88b *Front view of the Base*

Answers to Self-Evaluation Test

1. T, **2.** T, **3.** T, **4.** F, **5. Place**, **6.** push pin, **7. Place Constraint**, **8. Mate**, **9.** grounded,
10. Move

Chapter 10

Assembly Modeling-II

Learning Objectives

After completing this chapter, you will be able to:
- *Edit assembly constraints.*
- *Create subassemblies.*
- *Create and edit the pattern of components in the assembly file.*
- *Replace components in an assembly file with other components.*
- *Mirror subassemblies or components of an assembly.*
- *Create the section view of assemblies in an assembly file.*
- *Analyze assemblies for interference.*
- *Create design views of assemblies.*
- *Drive assembly constraints.*
- *View the Bill of Material of the current assembly.*
- *Understand and create assembly features.*

EDITING ASSEMBLY CONSTRAINTS

Generally, after creating an assembly or during the process of assembling the components, you have to edit the assembly constraints that were used to assemble the components. The editing operations that can be performed on the assembly constraints include modifying the type of assembly constraint, the offset or angle values, the type of solution, or changing the component to which the constraint was applied. In Autodesk Inventor, the assembly constraints are edited using the **Browser Bar**. By default, the constraints that are applied on the components will not be displayed in the **Browser Bar**. To display the assembly constraint applied on a component, click on the plus (+) sign located on the left of the component in the **Browser Bar**; the **Origin** folder will be displayed along with the list of constraints that are applied to that component. To edit a constraint, right-click on it in the **Browser Bar** and choose **Edit** from the shortcut menu, see Figure 10-1.

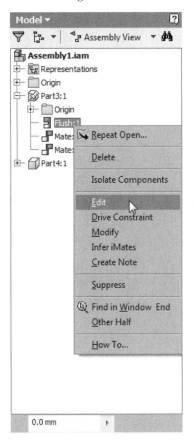

Figure 10-1 Editing assembly constraints
using the **Browser Bar**

 Note
*When you select the assembly constraint in the **Browser Bar**, an edit box is displayed below the **Browser Bar**. This edit box will display the value of the offset or angle for the selected constraint. You can modify the angle or the offset value using this edit box.*

When you choose **Edit** from the shortcut menu, the **Edit Constraint** dialog box will be displayed, see Figure 10-2. This dialog box is similar to the **Place Constraint** dialog box and can be used to edit the assembly constraints. This dialog box is used to change the constraint type, edit the offset or the angle value, modify the solution, or change the components to which the constraints are applied.

EDITING COMPONENTS

Sometimes after assembling the components in an assembly, you need to edit the components. In Autodesk Inventor, you can edit the components by two methods. These methods are discussed next.

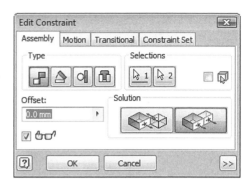

Figure 10-2 *The* ***Edit Constraint*** *dialog box for editing the assembly constraints*

Editing Components in the Assembly File

The first method of editing components is to invoke the part modeling environment and the sketching environment in the assembly file and then edit the component. This method of editing components is similar to the top-down approach of assembly modeling. To edit a component in the assembly file, right-click on the component in the **Browser Bar**; a shortcut menu will be displayed. From this menu, choose the **Edit** option, as shown in Figure 10-3; the part modeling environment will be activated in the assembly file. You will notice that the other components in the assembly file have become transparent. This is because the **Transparency On** tool is chosen by default in the **Appearance** panel of the **View** tab. Also, the name of the feature will be displayed with a gray background in the **Browser Bar** and the component selected for editing will be displayed with a white background. The component that is displayed in white background is called active component. You can edit the active component in the assembly file. Remember that only one component can be active at a time. Note that you can switch off the transparency of the component by choosing the **Transparency Off** tool that will be available on clicking the down arrow on the right of the **Transparency On** tool. Once you have edited the component, choose the **Return** tool from the **Return** panel to switch back to the **Assembly** module.

Tip. *1. If you move the cursor on the assembly constraint in the* ***Browser Bar***, *the components on which that constraint is applied are highlighted in the assembly on the graphics screen.*

2. Autodesk Inventor allows you to locate the other half of the selected constraint in the ***Browser Bar***. *This enables you to locate the other component on which the selected constraint has been applied in large assemblies with a huge number of components. To locate the other half of the constraint, choose* ***Other Half*** *from the shortcut menu, refer to Figure 10-1; the other half of the selected constraint will be highlighted in the* ***Browser Bar***.

Figure 10-3 *Choosing the **Edit** option from the shortcut menu*

After making changes in the component of the assembly file, when you save it, the **Save** dialog box will be displayed, see Figure 10-4. If you want to save the changes made in the part files, choose **Yes to All** and then choose **OK**. Choosing **OK** will save the changes in all parts. If you do not want to save the changes in any part, choose **No to All**.

If you want to save the changes in the selected file, click on **No** in the **Save** column of this dialog box; you will notice that **No** is replaced by **Yes**. As a result, the changes will be saved in the selected file. However, the changes will not be saved in the remaining files that show **No** in the **Save** column.

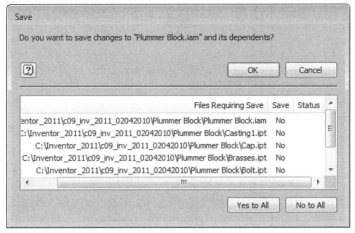

Figure 10-4 *The* **Save** *dialog box*

Editing Components by Opening their Part Files

The second method of editing the components is by opening their part files and making the necessary changes in them. To open the part file for editing, right-click on the component in the **Browser Bar**; a shortcut menu will be displayed. Choose **Open** from this shortcut menu, as shown in Figure 10-5. When you choose the **Open** option, the part file of the selected component will be opened in the **Modeling** environment. Make the necessary changes in the part file and then save the changes by choosing the **Save** tool from the **Quick Access Toolbar**. Now, exit the part file by choosing **Close > Close** from the **Application Menu**. The changes that you made in the part file will be automatically reflected in that component in the assembly file. This is because Autodesk Inventor is bidirectionally associative. This means that the changes made to the components in any of the modules of Autodesk Inventor will be automatically reflected in the other modules.

CREATING SUBASSEMBLIES

Autodesk Inventor allows you to create assemblies with small units. These small units are called as subassemblies. You can assemble parts and subassemblies to create the main assembly. A large assembly can have multiple subassemblies. You can construct very large assemblies efficiently by planning and building subassemblies. Different methods of creating subassemblies in the main assembly are discussed next.

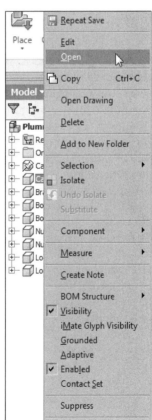

Figure 10-5 *Opening the part file for editing*

Creating a Subassembly Using the Bottom-up Design Approach

In the bottom-up subassembly design approach, the subassemblies are created separately and then saved as individual assembly files. To place a subassembly in the main assembly, open the main assembly and then place the subassembly by using the **Place** tool, as you place the parts. After placing the subassembly, you will observe that an assembly icon is displayed on left of the subassembly in the **Browser Bar**. If you double-click on the subassembly icon, the corresponding subassembly and its children (components) will be activated, and now you can place or create a component in that subassembly. In this way, you can create multilevel subassemblies. To activate the parent assembly, you need to double-click on it.

Creating a Subassembly Using the Top-down Design Approach

To create a subassembly using the top-down approach, open an assembly file and then create a component in it using the **Create** tool. Next, select the component from the **Browser Bar** and right-click on it; a shortcut menu will be displayed. Now, choose **Component > Demote** from the shortcut menu; the **Create In-Place Component** dialog box will be displayed. Using the options in the dialog box, save the component at the required location, as explained in the previous chapter.

CHECKING DEGREES OF FREEDOM OF A COMPONENT

As mentioned earlier, you can restrict the degrees of freedom of a component by applying assembly constraints to it. You can view the degrees of freedom that are not restricted in a component by choosing the **Degrees of Freedom** tool from the **Visibility** panel of the **View** tab.

When you choose this tool, the symbol of the degrees of freedom will be displayed on the screen. In Autodesk Inventor, every component has six degrees of freedom. These are linear movement along X, Y, and Z axes and rotational movement about X, Y, and Z axes. These degrees of freedom are displayed using an icon similar to the 3D indicator at the lower left corner of the drawing window. For a component whose all degrees of freedom are not restricted, the symbol of degrees of freedom will consist of three linear axes pointing in the X, Y, and Z directions and circular arrows on all three axes, as shown in Figure 10-6.

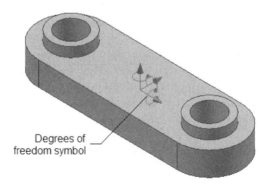

Figure 10-6 Component with all degrees of freedom

When you apply the assembly constraints, these movements are restricted and therefore, the degrees of freedom are removed. When a particular degree of freedom is removed, it will not be displayed in the symbol of the degrees of freedom. For example, if you apply the assembly constraint such that the linear movement of the component is restricted along the Z axis, the linear axis along the Z axis will not be displayed in the symbol of degrees of freedom. However, the circular axis along the Z axis will still be displayed because you have not restricted that movement. Therefore, for a component whose all degrees of freedom are restricted, there will be no symbol of the degrees of freedom.

Tip. *By default, the first component that you place or create in an assembly file is grounded. A grounded component has all its degrees of freedom restricted, and therefore, the symbol of the degrees of freedom is not displayed on it. However, if the first component is ungrounded after assembling other components with it, you will notice that the symbol of the degrees of freedom is displayed on it, indicating that all degrees of freedom of the component are not restricted. You will also notice that a small green color cube is displayed on all other components that were assembled with the grounded component. This cube indicates that all these components are assembled with an under-constrained component. Note that the component became under-constrained when you ungrounded it. To view the under-constrained component, move the cursor on the green color cube on any one of the assembled components. The green color cube will turn red and the under-constrained component will also change to red on the graphics screen. It will also get highlighted in bold text in the **Browser Bar**. The component will change back to its original color when you move the cursor away from the cube.*

CREATING THE PATTERN OF COMPONENTS IN AN ASSEMBLY

Ribbon:	Assemble > Component > Pattern
Toolbar:	Assembly Panel > Pattern Component

While creating the assemblies, you have to sometimes assemble more than one instance of a component about a specified arrangement. For example, in case of a Butterfly Valve assembly, you have to assemble three instances of Screw with the Retainer and the Body (refer to Tutorial 1 of Chapter 9). All these three instances were recalled in the current assembly file and then assembled using the assembly constraint. Also, if you have to increase the number of holes in the Retainer and the Body from three to four, you will have to recall another instance of the Screw and insert it using the assembly constraint. However, this is a very tedious and time-consuming process. Therefore, to reduce the time for assembling the components, Autodesk Inventor has provided a tool for creating the pattern of the components. You can create circular or rectangular patterns. This will reduce the assembling time as well the time taken in recalling the number of instances of the components. Another advantage of creating the pattern is that if you increase the number of instances in the pattern feature on the original part, the number of instances of the components in the pattern will also increase automatically. For example, if you increase the number of holes from three to four in the Retainer of the Butterfly Valve assembly, one more instance of the Screw will be automatically recalled in the assembly file and inserted in the fourth hole of the Retainer.

The pattern of components in the assembly file is created using the **Pattern** tool. On invoking this tool, the **Pattern Component** dialog box will be displayed, as shown in Figure 10-7.

Component

The **Component** button is chosen to select the component that you want to pattern in an assembly file. When you invoke the **Pattern Component** dialog box, this button is chosen automatically and you are prompted to select the component to be patterned. The options in various tabs of this dialog box are discussed next.

Associative Tab

The **Associative** tab (Figure 10-7) will be active by default when you invoke the **Pattern Component** tool. The options in this tab are used to select the pattern of the feature on the base part to which the pattern of components will be associated. This pattern can be selected

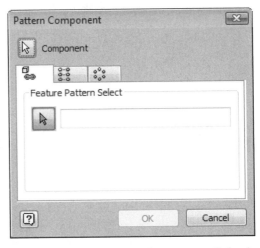

*Figure 10-7 The **Pattern Component** dialog box*

by choosing the **Associated Feature Pattern** button provided in the **Feature Pattern Select** area of this tab. When you choose this button, you will be prompted to select the feature pattern to which the pattern of components will be associated. You can select the pattern of the feature on the base part. Depending on whether the pattern selected is rectangular or circular, it will be displayed in the display box provided on the right of the **Associated Feature Pattern** button. Also, the selected component will be assembled with all the instances of the feature pattern. Remember that the number of instances of components assembled using this tool will be updated upon modification in the number of instances in the pattern of feature only if the pattern of the component is created using the **Associative** tab.

Figure 10-8 shows the selection of the hexagonal bolt after choosing the **Component** button from the **Component Pattern** dialog box. Note that the bolt is assembled with a base plate using the **Insert** constraint. The holes in the plate are created as a pattern feature. Figure 10-9 shows the selection of the hole feature after choosing the **Associated Feature Pattern** button. Figure 10-10 shows the resultant model.

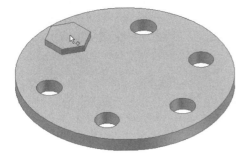

Figure 10-8 Selection of the component to be patterned

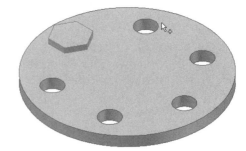

*Figure 10-9 Selection of the hole feature on using the **Associated Feature Pattern** button*

Rectangular Tab

The options in this tab are used to create a rectangular pattern of the selected component in the assembly file, see Figure 10-11. The options in this tab are similar to those discussed in the **Rectangular Pattern** dialog box in Chapter 6.

 Note
*Similar to the **Rectangular Pattern** dialog box, the options in the **Rectangular** tab of the **Pattern Component** dialog box will be available only after you specify the directions for the column and row placement.*

Figure 10-10 Resultant model

Circular Tab

The options in the **Circular** tab of the **Pattern Component** dialog box are used to create a circular pattern of the selected component, see Figure 10-12. The options in this tab are similar to those discussed in the **Circular Pattern** dialog box in Chapter 6.

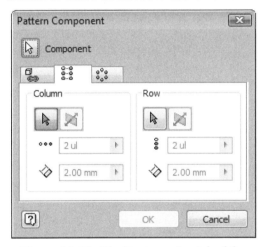

*Figure 10-11 The **Rectangular** tab of the **Pattern Component** dialog box*

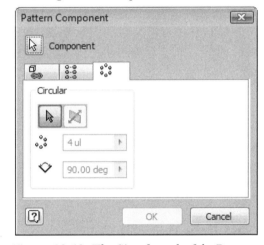

*Figure 10-12 The **Circular** tab of the **Pattern Component** dialog box*

 Note
*The **Angle** edit box in the **Circular** tab is used to specify the incremental angle between the individual instances of the pattern.*

Tip: *While creating an assembly, you may need to place a particular component more than once. In such cases, select the required component from the **Browser Bar** and then drag it to the graphics area. By default, the dragged component will be oriented as it was oriented in the **Part** environment. But if you need to place the dragged component according to the last orientation in the **Assembly** environment, choose the **Applications Options** tool from the **Options** panel of the **Tools** tab. On doing so, the **Application Options** dialog box will be displayed. Choose the **Assembly** tab in this dialog box and then select the **Use last occurrence orientation for component placement** check box. Next, choose the **OK** button to exit the **Application Options** dialog box.*

REPLACING A COMPONENT FROM THE ASSEMBLY FILE WITH ANOTHER COMPONENT

Autodesk Inventor allows you to replace a component in the assembly file with another component that you specify. You can replace the single instance of the component or all the instances of the selected component with another specified component. If the shape of the new component is the same as that of the original component that you replaced, the assembly constraints will be retained. However, if the shape of the new component is not similar to that of the original component, the assembly constraints will be lost and you will have to apply the constraints again. The new component will be placed at the same location as that of the original component. The methods of replacing the components are discussed next.

Replacing a Single Instance of the Selected Component

Ribbon:	Assemble > Component > Replace
Toolbar:	Assembly Panel > Replace Component

⌐⌐Replace   The single instance of a component can be replaced by the **Replace** tool. When you invoke this tool, you will be prompted to select the component to be replaced. When you select the component to be replaced, the **Place Component** dialog box will be displayed, as shown in Figure 10-13.

Note
*You can select the component to be replaced before or after invoking the **Replace** tool. If you select the component from the graphics window or from the **Browser Bar** and then invoke the **Replace** tool, the **Place Component** dialog box will be displayed directly.*

You can use this dialog box to specify the name and location of the new component. You can either double-click on the component or select it and choose the **Open** button. The selected component will be placed at the location of the previous component. Remember that the assembly constraints will be retained only if the shape of the new component is the same as that of the original component.

If there are chances that the assembly constraints that you have applied on the component to be replaced are going to be lost, the **Possible Constraint Loss** message box will be displayed, as shown in Figure 10-14. This dialog box will inform you that the constraints and notes

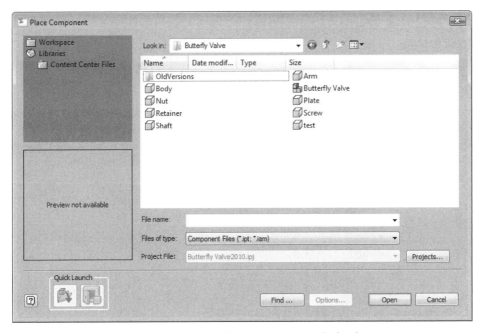

Figure 10-13 The *Place Component* dialog box

associated with the component may be lost. Choose the **OK** button to continue with the process of replacement of the component. To abort the process, choose the **Cancel** button.

Note
Sometimes, when you choose the OK button from the Possible Constraint Loss message box, the Autodesk Inventor 2011 - Replace Component information box is displayed. Choose the Accept button from this dialog box to continue with the part replacement.

Figure 10-14 The *Possible Constraint Loss message box*

Replacing all Instances of the Selected Component

Ribbon:	Assemble > Component > Replace drop-down > Replace All
Toolbar:	Assembly Panel > Replace > Replace All

You can replace all instances of a component by choosing the **Replace All** tool from the **Component** panel. On doing so, you will be prompted to select the component to be replaced. Select it from the screen or the **Browser Bar**. On selecting the component to be replaced, the **Place Component** dialog box will be displayed. You can use this dialog box to select the new component. All the instances of the selected component will be replaced with the component selected in the **Place Component** dialog box.

MIRRORING SUBASSEMBLIES OR COMPONENTS OF AN ASSEMBLY

Ribbon:	Assemble > Component > Mirror
Toolbar:	Assembly Panel > Mirror Component

⊞⊟ Mirror   Autodesk Inventor allows you to mirror assemblies or assembly components using the **Mirror** tool. You can use this tool to specify whether the mirrored components or subassemblies will be inserted in the current file or in a new assembly file. When you invoke this tool, the **Mirror Components: Status** dialog box will be displayed, as shown in Figure 10-15. The options in this dialog box are discussed next.

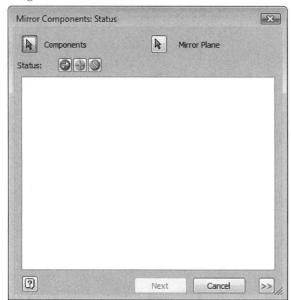

Figure 10-15 The **Mirror Components: Status** dialog box

Components

When you invoke the **Mirror Components: Status** dialog box, the **Components** button is chosen by default and you are prompted to select the components to be mirrored. You can select the components from the drawing window or from the **Browser Bar**. The components or subassemblies that you select are added to the list box in the **Mirror Components: Status** dialog box. Note that the constraints will be copied only if all the components on which the constraints are applied are selected to be mirrored.

Mirror Plane

This button is chosen to select the mirror plane. This is the plane about which the assembly or components will be mirrored.

List Box

The list box in the **Mirror Component: Status** dialog box lists the components and subassemblies selected to be mirrored. You can also use the list box to specify whether the resultant components will be mirrored or reused. By default, the components are mirrored as mirror components. These components have a green circle icon with two arrows facing in the opposite directions on the left of their names in the **Mirror Components: Status** dialog box. They are displayed in transparent green in the mirror preview. The components that are mirrored using this option are saved as separate files when you save the assembly file. You can also mirror the selected component as mirror, reused, or excluded component by choosing the corresponding buttons on the right of the **Status** area. The name of the files can be specified by using the **Mirror Components: File Names** dialog box that is displayed on choosing **Next** from the **Mirror Components: Status** dialog box.

If you click once on the green circle icon, it changes to a yellow circle with a plus sign in between. This suggests that the selected components are mirrored as reused. The reused components are displayed in transparent yellow in the preview.

If you click again on the yellow circle icon, it changes to gray with an inclined line. This suggests that the components are excluded from the current selection set and will not be mirrored.

More

This is the button with two arrows on the lower right side of the **Mirror Components: Status** dialog box. When you choose this button, the **Mirror Components: Status** dialog box expands and provides the options discussed next.

Reuse Standard Content and Factory Parts

The **Reuse Standard Content and Factory Parts** check box is selected to make sure that the content library components and factory parts are reused and not mirrored.

Preview Components Area

The check boxes in this area are used to specify whether the mirrored, reused, or content library components will be shown in the preview.

After selecting the components to mirror and setting the parameters in the **Mirror Components: Status** dialog box, when you choose **Next**, the **Mirror Components: File Names** dialog box will be displayed, as shown in Figure 10-16. This dialog box is used to specify whether the resultant components are placed in the same assembly file or copied in a new assembly file. The options in this dialog box are discussed next.

List Box

The list box in this dialog box lists all subassemblies and components that were selected to be mirrored. This list box has four columns, which are discussed next.

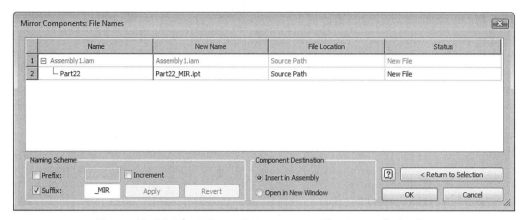

Figure 10-16   *The **Mirror Components: File Names** dialog box*

Name

This column lists the names of the original components or subassemblies selected to be mirrored.

New Name

This column lists the new name by which the selected components will be saved. You can click on the name field to change the name of the new component. The default naming options also depend on the parameters defined in the **Naming Scheme** area of this dialog box.

File Location

This column lists the location of the part file, in which the new component will be saved. By default, it shows **Source Path**. As a result, the new component file will be saved in the same folder, in which the original file is saved. You can right-click on **Source Path** to change the path to a user defined path or the current work place.

Status

This column defines the status of the resultant component. By default, it shows **New File**. As a result, the file will be saved as a new part file. If you specify the name of the new component that already exists in the folder in which the part file will be saved, the status changes to **Reuse Existing**. This suggests that a part file with the same name already exists and that you can reuse the existing file.

Naming Scheme Area

This area is used to set the parameters for the default name of the new part files that are listed in the **New Name** column of the list box in this dialog box. By default, the **Suffix** check box is selected and **_MIR** is entered in the text box on the right of the **Suffix** check box. As a result, the name of the new part file is the name of the original part file selected to be mirrored with **_MIR** as suffix. Similarly, you can also add some prefix to the default name by selecting the **Prefix** check box. The prefix that you want to add can be entered in the text box available on the right of the **Prefix** check box. You can select the **Increment** check box to add an incremental number to the name of the new file. Remember that after setting the parameters in this area, you need to choose the **Apply** button. You can restore the original name settings by choosing the **Revert** button.

Component Destination Area

This area is used to specify whether the new components will be placed in the current assembly file or will be inserted in a new assembly file. Select the **Insert in Assembly** radio button to insert the parts in the current assembly file. If you want to copy the parts in a new assembly file, select the **Open in New Window** radio button. The selected components will be copied in a new assembly file and that assembly file will be opened on the screen. Note that if you select the **Open in New Window** radio button, you can also modify the name of the new assembly in the **New Name** column of the list box.

Return to Selection

You can choose the **Return to Selection** button to return to the **Mirror Components: Status** dialog box.

After setting the parameters in the **Mirror Components: File Names** dialog box, choose the **OK** button. The selected components will be mirrored in the current assembly file or will be copied in a new assembly file, depending on the parameters selected.

COPYING SUBASSEMBLIES OR COMPONENTS OF AN ASSEMBLY

Ribbon:	Assemble > Component > Copy
Toolbar:	Assembly Panel > Copy Component

Similar to mirroring the components, you can also copy a subassembly or components of an assembly using the **Copy** tool. On invoking this tool, the **Copy Components: Status** dialog box will be displayed, as shown in Figure 10-17. This dialog box is similar to the **Mirror Components: Status** dialog box.

After selecting the components to copy, when you choose **Next** from this dialog box, the **Copy Components: File Names** dialog box will be displayed. The options in this dialog box are similar to those discussed in the **Mirror Components: File Names** dialog box.

Figure 10-17 The **Copy Components: Status** *dialog box*

DELETING COMPONENTS

You can delete the unwanted instances or the unwanted components from the assembly using the **Browser Bar**. In the **Browser Bar**, right-click on the unwanted component and choose **Delete** from the shortcut menu; the selected component will be deleted from the assembly.

To delete the components that were assembled using the **Pattern** tool, right-click on **Component Pattern** in the **Browser Bar**. Choose **Delete** from the shortcut menu; all instances of the component assembled using the **Pattern** tool will be deleted. Note that the original component will not be deleted. You can delete the original instance also by right-clicking on it in the **Browser Bar** and choosing **Delete** from the shortcut menu.

EDITING THE PATTERN OF COMPONENTS

Autodesk Inventor allows you to edit the pattern of the components created using the **Pattern** tool. To edit the pattern of components, right-click on **Component Pattern** in the **Browser Bar** and choose **Edit** from the shortcut menu; the **Edit Component Pattern** dialog box will be displayed that can be used to edit the pattern. Note that this dialog box will have only the tab that was used for creating the pattern of the component. For example, if the pattern of the component was created using the **Associative** tab of the **Pattern Component** dialog box, the **Edit Component Pattern** dialog box will have only the **Associative** tab. Similarly, if the pattern of the component was created using the **Circular** tab of the **Pattern Component** dialog box, the **Edit Component Pattern** dialog box will have only the **Circular** tab. Figure 10-18 shows the **Edit Component Pattern** dialog box for editing the pattern created using the **Associative** tab of the **Pattern Component** dialog box.

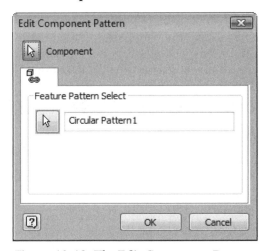

*Figure 10-18 The **Edit Component Pattern** dialog box*

Note
*The options in the **Edit Component Pattern** dialog box are similar to those discussed in the **Pattern Component** dialog box.*

MAKING A PATTERN INSTANCE INDEPENDENT

You can also make a selected instance independent, which will be displayed as a separate component in the **Browser Bar** and will not be deleted when you delete its pattern. To make the selected instance independent, click on the plus (+) sign located on the left of **Component Pattern** in the **Browser Bar**. All instances of the pattern will be displayed as elements in the **Browser Bar**. The first element is the original component and you cannot make this element independent because it is not dependent on the pattern. Right-click on any other element and then choose **Independent** from the shortcut menu. You will notice that a red cross is displayed on the left of the independent element in the **Browser Bar**.

You can again make the independent element dependent. Right-click on the independent element in the list of elements in the **Browser Bar** to display the shortcut menu. You will notice that a check mark is displayed on the left of the **Independent** option. Choose this option again. The red cross on the element will no more be displayed, suggesting that it has again become dependent on the pattern. Note that when you make a component dependent again, the instance of the component that was placed in the assembly as a separate component and displayed in the **Browser Bar**, will not be removed. You will have to manually delete the component.

DELETING ASSEMBLY CONSTRAINTS

You can delete the unwanted assembly constraints using the **Browser Bar**. To delete the assembly constraint, click on the plus (+) sign located on the left of the component in the **Browser Bar**. The **Origin** folder, along with all the constraints that are applied on the component, will be displayed. Right-click on the constraint to be deleted and choose **Delete** from the shortcut menu; the selected constraint will be deleted.

CREATING ASSEMBLY SECTION VIEWS IN THE ASSEMBLY FILE

Ribbon:	View > Appearance > Section View drop-down

Sometimes, while assembling components in an assembly, some of the components are hidden behind the other components of the assembly. To visualize such components, Autodesk Inventor allows you to create the section views of the assembly. However, remember that these section views are for reference only and components are not actually chopped when you create the section views. You can create three types of section views: quarter section view, half section view, and three quarter section view.

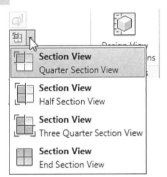

Figure 10-19 Tools in the *Section View* drop-down

To create the quarter section view, choose the **Quarter Section View** tool from the **Appearance** panel, see Figure 10-19. On doing so, you will be prompted to select work planes or planar faces that will be used to section the assembly. Select two planar faces, two work planes, or a planar face and a work plane to section the assembly; the assembly will be sectioned as soon as you select two planes. You can flip the direction of quarter section by first right-clicking and then choosing **Flip Section** from the shortcut menu. Continue choosing this option until the required quarter is displayed. Once the required quarter is displayed, right-click and choose **Done** from the shortcut menu.

To create the three quarter section view, invoke the shortcut menu and choose **Three Quarter Section View** from it. You can also create the three quarter section view by choosing the **Three Quarter Section View** tool from the **Appearance** panel, refer to Figure 10-19. On doing so, you will be prompted to select the work plane or the planar face for creating the section view. If you select the work plane or the planar face, you will be prompted to select the work plane or planar face. Select the second work plane or planar face; the three quarter section view will be created.

To create the half section view, choose the **Half Section View** tool from the **Appearance** panel, refer to Figure 10-19. On doing so, you will be prompted to select the planar face or the work plane for creating the section view. Since for creating a half section, you require only one plane, therefore, as soon as you select the planar face or the work plane, the assembly will be sectioned about it. You can flip the section by right-clicking and choosing **Flip Section** from the shortcut menu. Once the required section is displayed, right-click and choose **Done** from the shortcut menu.

You can exit the section views by choosing the **End Section View** tool from the **Appearance** panel, refer to Figure 10-19. On choosing this tool, the whole assembly is displayed. Figure 10-20 shows the quarter section view of an assembly and Figure 10-21 shows the three quarter section view of the same assembly.

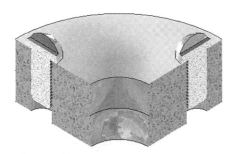

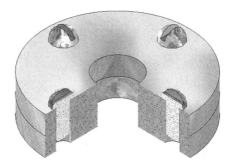

Figure 10-20 *Quarter section view of an assembly*

Figure 10-21 *Three quarter section view of the given assembly*

ANALYZING ASSEMBLIES FOR INTERFERENCE

Ribbon: Inspect > Interference > Analyze Interference

Whenever you assemble the components of an assembly, no component should interfere with the other components of the assembly. If there is an interference between the components, this suggests that the dimensions of the components are incorrect or the components are not assembled properly. You will have to eliminate this interference in the assembly to increase the efficiency of the assembly and also eliminate the material loss. In Autodesk Inventor, you can analyze the assemblies for interference using the **Analyze Interference** tool. This tool can be invoked from the **Interference** panel of the **Inspect** tab. Alternatively, press the A key to invoke this tool. You need to select two sets of components to analyze interference. When you invoke this tool, the **Interference Analysis** dialog box will be displayed, as shown in Figure 10-22. The options in this dialog box are discussed next.

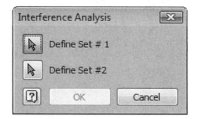

Figure 10-22 *The Interference Analysis dialog box*

Define Set # 1

The **Define Set # 1** button is chosen to select the first set of components. When you invoke the **Interference Analysis** dialog box, this button is chosen by default and you will be prompted to select the component to add to the selection set. The selected components will be highlighted and displayed in a blue outline.

Define Set # 2

The **Define Set # 2** button is chosen to select the second set of components. When you choose this button, the objects selected using the **Define Set # 1** button will be displayed in a green outline. The components that you select now will be displayed in a blue outline.

OK

After selecting the components in the first set and the second set, choose this button to analyze the assembly. If there is no interference between the components, the **Autodesk Inventor Professional 2011** dialog box will be displayed. This dialog box will inform you that there is no interference between the components. However, if there is an interference, the **Interference Detected** dialog box will be displayed and the portion of the interfering components will be displayed in red in the assembly. The **Interference Detected** dialog box will inform you about the number of interferences found and the total volume of interference. This dialog box has a button with two arrows at the lower right corner. If you choose this button, this dialog box will expand and will provide you additional information about the interfering components, see Figure 10-23. You can copy this information on the clipboard and later paste it in a file or print it.

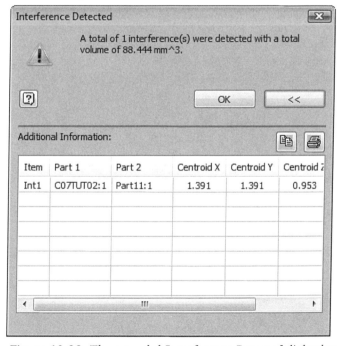

*Figure 10-23 The expanded **Interference Detected** dialog box*

CREATING DESIGN VIEW REPRESENTATIONS

Ribbon: View > Saved Views > Design View Representations

The design view representations are user-defined views that are used to view assemblies or generate presentation views or drawing views of a particular view of an assembly. You can specify any orientation of an assembly by using the combination of drawing display tools and then save the assembly view with that orientation. Once the view is saved, you can open it by its name, whenever required. In addition to the assembly file, you can also use design views for generating views both in the presentation file and in the drawing file.

To create a design view representation, first you need to define the viewing characteristics that you want to save in it. To define the viewing characteristics, use the display control tools such as ViewCube, SteeringWheels, Zoom, and so on. After a representation is created, you need to save it. To do so, right-click on the **Representations** node in the **Browser Bar** and choose the **Expand All Children** option from the shortcut menu; the **View: Default** node along with various representations will be displayed in the **Browser Bar**. Next, right-click on the **View: Default** node and choose the **New** option from the shortcut menu; the new representation with a different name **View1** will be added to the **View: Default** node. You can rename this representation by entering a new name in the edit box that is displayed when you double-click on it. Now, right-click on the **View1** representation and choose the **Lock** option from the shortcut menu; the design view representation will be created. For creating other design view representations, follow the same procedure. You can activate any design view by right-clicking on it and then choosing the **Active** option from the shortcut menu.

You can view different view representations in the **Design View Representations** dialog box. To invoke this dialog box, choose the **Design View Representations** button from the **Saved Views** panel of the **View** tab, see Figure 10-24. The options available in this dialog box are discussed next.

*Figure 10-24 The **Design View Representations** dialog box*

Storage Location Area

This area is used to create two types of design view representations: public and private. A public design view representation is the one that is saved with an assembly and can be invoked only in the same assembly. By default, the **Public** radio button is selected in the **Storage Location** area and is used to store the representation in the current assembly file. A public representation is associative to drawing views and thus, can be used to create drawing views, whereas a private design view representation is the one that is saved as a separate *.idv* file and can be imported to any assembly file. Note that the private views are non-associative and cannot be used to create drawing views. To create a private design view representation, enter a name in the edit box of the **Design View Representation** area and then choose the **New** button. Now, choose the button on the right of the edit box in the **Storage Location** area and specify the storage location of this design view representation. To import a private design view representation in the current assembly, select the **Private File** radio button. Next, choose the **Browse** button to browse and select the *.idv* file that you want to use in the current assembly. When you import this design view representation to another file, the design view with the specified name will be displayed in the list box of the **Design View Representation** area.

Design View Representation Area

This area displays a list of design view representations. The options in this area are used to create a new design view, delete an existing design view, or make a design view current. To create a new design view, set the orientation of the assembly using the **Rotate** tool or other drawing display tools. Next, enter the name of the view in the edit box provided in this area; the **New** button will be available. Choose this button; you will notice that the new design view is added to the list box in the **Design View Representation** area. You can delete the design view by selecting it from the list box and then choosing the **Delete** button. Note that you can also delete the default design view.

An existing design view can be made the current view by selecting it from the list box and then choosing the **Activate** button. You will notice that the assembly on the graphics screen is reoriented such that it is displayed using the selected design view.

SIMULATING THE MOTION OF COMPONENTS OF AN ASSEMBLY BY DRIVING ASSEMBLY CONSTRAINTS

Autodesk Inventor allows you to simulate the motion of the components of an assembly by driving the assembly constraints. Remember that in the **Assembly** module, you can simulate the motion of the component using only one constraint at a time. However, you can create some relation parameters and equations for simulating the motion of the components using more than one constraint at a time. To drive a constraint, right-click on it in the **Browser Bar** and choose **Drive Constraint**, see Figure 10-25. On doing so, the **Drive Constraint** dialog box will be displayed, see Figure 10-26.

The options in this dialog box are discussed next.

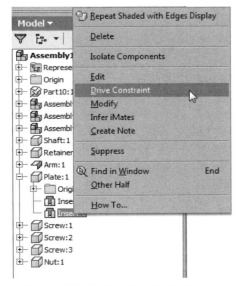

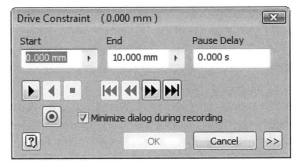

Figure 10-25 *Choosing the* **Drive Constraint** *option*

Figure 10-26 *The* **Drive Constraint** *dialog box*

Start

The **Start** edit box is used to specify the position of the starting point of simulation. The value in this edit box depends on the type of constraint you have selected to drive. For example, if you have selected the **Insert** constraint to drive, the value in this edit box will be entered in millimeter. If you have selected the **Angle** constraint to drive, the value in this edit box will be entered in degrees. The default value of the angle or offset in this edit box will be the value that you have specified for the constraint. For example, if you have applied an angle value of 90 degrees between two components, the default value in the **Start** edit box will be 90.

Note

The value in the **Start** *edit box will also be displayed on the title bar of the* **Drive Constraint** *dialog box. Therefore, if the value of start point of the constraint simulation is -90 degrees, the name of the dialog box will be* **Drive Constraint (-90 deg)**.

End

The **End** edit box is used to specify the position for ending the simulation. Similar to the **Start** edit box, the values in this edit box will be dependent on the type of constraint selected for simulation. The default value in this edit box will be the default value in the **Start** edit box plus 10.

Pause Delay

The **Pause Delay** edit box is used to specify some delay in the simulation of the components. The value in this edit box is entered in terms of seconds. By default, the value in this edit box is zero. Therefore, there will be no delay in the simulation of the components. If you enter **2** in this edit box, there will be a delay of 2 seconds between the steps of the simulation.

Forward

The **Forward** button is used to start the simulation of the component in the forward direction.

Reverse

The **Reverse** button is used to start the simulation of the component in the reverse direction.

Pause

The **Pause** button is used to temporarily stop the simulation of the component. The simulation can be resumed by choosing the **Forward** button or the **Reverse** button again.

Minimum

The **Minimum** button is chosen to reset the simulation such that the component is positioned at the start point of the simulation.

Reverse Step

The **Reverse Step** button is chosen to position the component one step behind the current step in the simulation. This button will not be available if the component is positioned at the start point of the simulation.

Forward Step

The **Forward Step** button is chosen to position the component one step ahead of the current step in the simulation. This button will not be available if the component is positioned at the endpoint of the simulation.

Maximum

The **Maximum** button is chosen to reset the simulation such that the component is positioned at the endpoint of the simulation.

Record

The **Record** button is chosen to record the simulation of the component in the form of *.avi* or *.wmv* file. When you choose this button, the **Save As** dialog box will be displayed. Using this dialog box, you can specify the name of the *.avi* file, in which you want to record the simulation. After specifying the name and location of the *.avi* or *.wmv* file, choose the **Save** button; the **Video Compression** or the **ASF Export Properties** dialog box will be displayed, respectively. These dialog boxes are used to specify the settings of the *.avi* or *.wmv* files, respectively. After specifying the options, close the respective dialog boxes. Next, choose the **Forward** or the **Reverse** button from the **Drive Constraint** dialog box to record the simulation. You can also choose both the buttons one by one to record the complete cycle of simulation. After recording the simulation, choose the **Record** button again to exit recording.

Note
While recording the simulation, whatever is displayed inside the graphics window will be recorded. Remember that if you activate another application while the simulation is being recorded, the work done in that application will also be recorded in the .avi or the .wmv file.

More

The **More** button is the one with two arrows on the lower right corner of the **Drive Constraint** dialog box. When you choose this button, the dialog box expands and displays more options to simulate components, see Figure 10-27. These options are discussed next.

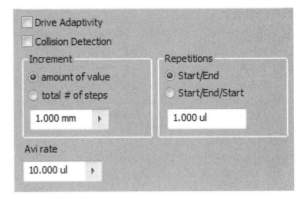

Drive Adaptivity

If the **Drive Adaptivity** check box is selected, the adaptive components will adapt during the process of simulation.

*Figure 10-27 More options in the **Drive Constraint** dialog box*

Collision Detection

If the **Collision Detection** check box is selected, the simulation will stop at the point where the collision is detected. The collision will be displayed in red and the **Autodesk Inventor Professional 2011** information box will also be displayed. This information box will inform you that a collision has been detected.

Increment Area

The options in the **Increment** area are used to specify the method for defining the increment during the simulation of the component. These options are discussed next.

amount of value

The **amount of value** radio button is selected to specify the increment of simulation in terms of value of the steps. The value of the steps can be entered in the edit box available in the **Increment** area.

total # of steps

The **total # of steps** radio button is selected to specify the increment of simulation in terms of the total number of steps in the simulation. The number of steps can be entered in the edit box in the **Increment** area.

Repetitions Area

The options in the **Repetitions** area are used to specify the method for defining the number of repetitions of the cycles in the simulation. These options are discussed next.

Start/End

The **Start/End** radio button is selected to simulate a component from the start position to the end position. If the number of repetitions is more than one, the component will be repositioned at the start position after the first cycle is over. Since the component is repositioned at the start position after the completion of the first cycle, the second cycle begins from the start position and the simulation process gets repeated.

Start/End/Start

The **Start/End/Start** radio button is selected to simulate a component such that the simulation is between the start position and the end position, and then again from the end position to the start position. If the number of repetitions is more than one, the second cycle will begin from the end position and the third cycle will start from the begin position, thus forming a loop. In other words, the start position of one cycle is the end position of the other cycle. So, if you want to simulate an assembly from the start position to the end position and then again from the end position to the start position, you need to enter **2** in the edit box provided in this area.

In addition to these radio buttons, there is an edit box in the **Repetitions** area, which is used to specify the number of cycles in the simulation.

Avi rate

The **Avi rate** edit box is used to specify the number of steps that will be removed before a step of simulation is recorded in the *.avi* file.

CREATING POSITIONAL REPRESENTATIONS

Positional representations are the views of the assembly that represent assemblies in different component positions. For example, you can create a positional representation of an assembly in which the components are driven to a certain distance from their original assembly position. By default, every assembly has a main default positional representation. This positional representation represents the components at their default assembly position. You can create additional positional representations in which you can move the components from their default location by driving their constraints.

To create positional representations, click on the plus (+) sign located on the left of **Representations** in the **Browser Bar**; the tree view expands. Right-click on **Position** and choose **New** from the shortcut menu, as shown in Figure 10-28; the name **Position** is changed to **Position : Position1** in the **Browser Bar** and the plus (+) sign is added to its left. Click on the plus (+) sign; the tree view expands and shows **Master** and **Position1** in the **Browser Bar**. Also, a check mark is displayed on the left of **Position1**, suggesting that this representational view is current by default. Now, drive the constraints of the assembled components to create a positional representation of the assembly.

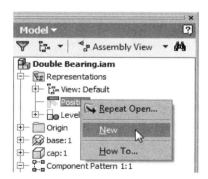

*Figure 10-28 Choosing the **New** option from the shortcut menu*

Before saving and exiting the assembly document, you need to restore the master positional representation. To do so, double-click on **Master** in **Position: Position 1** in the **Browser Bar**.

Note

Whenever you try to save an assembly in a positional representation, an error message will be displayed informing you that the assembly cannot be saved in a positional representation. Further, you will be prompted to specify whether you want to save the master assembly. If you choose **OK** *from this dialog box, the master representation will be invoked and the assembly will be saved. To restore a positional representation, double-click on it in the* **Browser Bar**.*

VIEWING THE BILL OF MATERIAL OF THE CURRENT ASSEMBLY

Ribbon:	Assemble > Manage > Bill of Materials

Autodesk Inventor allows you to view the Bill of Material of the current assembly in the assembly document itself. To view the Bill of Material, choose the **Bill of Materials** tool from the **Manage** panel of the **Assemble** tab; the **Bill of Materials** dialog box, which lists the components of the current assembly in a tabular form will be displayed, as shown in Figure 10-29.

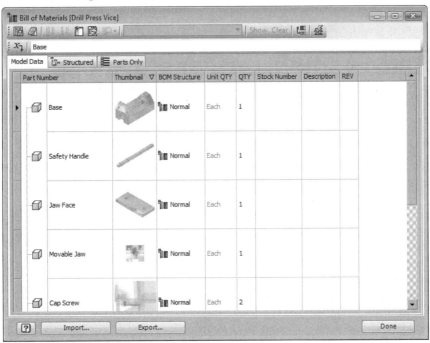

*Figure 10-29 The **Bill of Materials** dialog box*

By default, the **Model Data** tab is chosen in this dialog box. As a result, the BOM data displayed will be similar to the modeling structure of the assembly. However, this data cannot be reported as the actual BOM in the parts list. Choose the **Structured** tab to view the actual

BOM of the assembly. Alternatively, choose the **Parts Only** tab to invoke the **Parts Only** BOM view that shows all components of the subassembly as separate components. If the BOM data is not displayed, choose the down arrow on the right of the **View Options** button that is in the toolbar provided above the tabs in the **Bill of Materials** dialog box. On doing so, a flyout will be displayed. Choose the **Enable BOM View** option from the flyout; all components of assembly and the subassembly will be displayed as separate components in the BOM. The **Bill of Materials** dialog box has two toolbars: **Bill of Materials Toolbar** and **Formula Toolbar**. The **Bill of Materials Toolbar** located on top of this dialog box is used to export bill of materials, sort and renumber items, control the display of BOM data, update the mass properties of items, and so on. The **Formula Toolbar** located below the **Bill of Materials Toolbar** helps you to create or edit an expression for the selected BOM cell in the **Bill of Materials** dialog box. You can import the BOM customization setting into the current assembly by choosing the **Import** button. On doing so, the **Import BOM Customization** dialog box will be displayed. In this dialog box, open the required *.xml* file to import the BOM customization setting. You can also export the BOM customization setting of the current assembly to the required location by choosing the **Export** button from the **Bill of Materials** dialog box. On doing so, the **Export BOM Customization** dialog box will be displayed. Specify the name and location of the *.xml* file to be exported and then save it.

WORKING WITH ASSEMBLY FEATURES

Autodesk Inventor allows you to perform some metal cutting operations such as extrude, revolve, swept cuts, chamfer, and holes in an assembly file. Note that these operations are restricted only to the assembly file and are not performed on individual components. For example, if you create an extruded cut feature on a component in the assembly environment, the cut feature created in the assembly will not be created on the original component. As a result, this cut feature will be displayed only in the assembly environment and not in the original component file. Note that these operations are not restricted to a particular component, but extend to all the components of the assembly. For example, if you create a through-all cut feature in an assembly, the material will be removed not only from the component on which the sketch is created, but also from the components that come across the sketch.

To create assembly cut features such as extruded, revolved, and swept cuts, first you need to select a sketching plane on which the sketches will be drawn. To create a sketch, choose the **Create 2D Sketch** tool from the **Sketch** panel and then select a planar face of any component or a work plane. The sketching environment will be activated and all the sketching tools will become available in the **Sketch** tab.

Note
The basic difference between editing the components in the assembly file and working with the assembly features is that the assembly features are not created on the original component. On the other hand, the editing operations performed on a component while editing them are actually made on the original component.

TUTORIALS

Tutorial 1

In this tutorial, you will open the Butterfly Valve assembly created in Tutorial 1 of Chapter 9 and then analyze the assembly for interference. Next, you will delete the last two instances of the Screw and assemble the remaining instances by creating a pattern of the first instance.

(Expected time: 30 min)

Before you start working on this tutorial, it is important to understand the procedure of completing the tutorial. The following steps are required to complete this tutorial:

a. Copy the *Butterfly Valve* folder from the *c09* folder to the *c10* folder.
b. Open the *Butterfly Valve.iam* file and analyze it for interference using the **Analyze Interference** tool.
c. Delete the two instances of the Screw assembled with the Retainer and then create the two instances using the **Pattern Component** tool.

Copying the Butterfly Valve Folder

In this tutorial, you will open the Butterfly Valve assembly created in *c09* folder. However, it is recommended that before opening the assembly file, you should copy the entire folder of the Butterfly Valve in the *c10* folder. This helps you keep the *c09* folder unaffected when you make changes in the Butterfly Valve Assembly. Therefore, first you will copy the *Butterfly Valve* folder in the *c10* folder and then open the *Butterfly Valve.iam* file from this folder.

1. Start a new session of Autodesk Inventor. Open the folder *c09* from the location *C:\Inventor_2011*.

    You will notice that there is a folder with the name *Butterfly Valve* in *c09* folder. This is the folder, where you have stored all part files and the assembly file of the Butterfly Valve.

2. Right-click on the *Butterfly Valve* folder and choose **Copy** from the shortcut menu.

3. Now, open the folder *C:\Inventor_2011\c10*. If this folder does not exist, you can create it using the **Create New Folder** button in the **Open** dialog box.

4. Right-click in the folder and paste the *Butterfly Valve* folder in the *c10* folder. Open the *Butterfly Valve* folder and then open the *Butterfly Valve.iam* file from it.

    The Butterfly Valve assembly is displayed on the screen.

Analyzing the Assembly for Interference

After displaying the assembly on the screen, you will invoke the **Analyze Interference** tool and analyze the assembly for interference. There should be no interference in the assembly.

1. Choose the **Analyze Interference** tool from the **Interference** panel of the **Inspect** tab to display the **Interference Analysis** dialog box. In this dialog box, the **Define Set # 1** button is chosen by default. As a result, you are prompted to select the components to add to the selection set.

2. Select Body from the graphics screen and then choose the **Define Set # 2** button from the dialog box. On doing so, you are again prompted to select the components to add to the selection set. Select the remaining components using the **Browser Bar**.

3. Choose the **OK** button; the **Analyzing Interference** dialog box is displayed. Also, you will notice that the system is analyzing the assembly for interference. After the analysis is complete, the **Autodesk Inventor Professional 2011** dialog box is displayed, informing you that no interference is detected. Choose **OK** from this dialog box to exit it.

Creating the Pattern of the Screw

While creating the Butterfly Valve assembly in Chapter 9, you assembled three instances of the Screw with the Retainer. You will retain the first instance of the Screw and delete the other two instances from the assembly. The other two instances will be assembled using the **Pattern** tool.

1. Select **Screw:2** from the **Browser Bar** and then press the SHIFT/CTRL key. Next, select **Screw:3** from the **Browser Bar**; you will notice that both the selected components are displayed in blue color in the **Browser Bar**. Also, the components are displayed with a blue outline on the graphics screen.

2. Press the DELETE key to delete the two instances of the Screw.

   Since the holes on the Retainer are not visible in the current view, you need to turn off the visibility of the Arm.

3. Turn off the visibility of the Arm using the **Browser Bar**.

4. Choose the **Pattern** tool from the **Component** panel of the **Assemble** tab; the **Pattern Component** dialog box is invoked. In this dialog box, the **Component** button is chosen and you are prompted to select the component to be patterned.

5. Select Screw as the component to be patterned. Choose the **Associated Feature Pattern** button from the **Feature Pattern Select** area of the **Associative** tab; you are prompted to select the feature pattern to associate to.

6. Select the hole on the lower right side of the Retainer. You will notice that the two instances of the Screw are assembled with the two holes on the Retainer. Also, the display box on the right of the **Associated Feature Pattern** button displays **Circular Pattern1**. This is the name of the pattern of holes on the Retainer.

Note

*If you have created holes on the Retainer as circles while creating its basic sketch, you cannot use them to create associative component patterns because you can only associate the pattern to the feature pattern, and not to the sketch pattern. In this case, you can create a non-associative pattern using the **Circular** tab of the **Pattern Component** dialog box. However, as mentioned earlier, the pattern created using a tab other than the **Associative** tab will not be modified if the number of instances of the feature in the feature pattern is increased.*

7. Choose **OK** to create the pattern of the component and exit the **Pattern Component** dialog box.

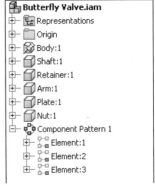

You will notice that the Screw is not displayed in the **Browser Bar**, instead the **Component Pattern 1** node is displayed in it. If you click on the plus (+) sign on the left of this node, the three instances of the Screw with the name **Element:1**, **Element:2**, and **Element:3** are displayed in the **Browser Bar**.

8. Turn on the display of the Arm using the **Browser Bar**. Next, choose the **Save** tool from the **Quick Access Toolbar** to save the changes in the assembly. The display of the **Browser Bar**, after making all changes in the assembly, is shown in Figure 10-30.

Figure 10-30 Display of the **Browser Bar** *for Tutorial 1*

9. Next, close the file.

Tutorial 2

In this tutorial, you will open the Drill Press Vice assembly created in *Exercise 1* of *c09* folder and then check the interference between the Base and the remaining components of the assembly. After checking the interference, you will drive the **Mate** constraint applied between the Clamp Screw and the Movable Jaw.   **(Expected time: 30 min)**

The following steps are required to complete this tutorial:

a. Copy the Drill Press Vice assembly from the *c09* folder to the *c10* folder.
b. Open the *Drill Press Vice.iam* file and analyze it for interference.
c. Drive the **Mate** constraint applied between the vertical faces of the Jaw Face and the Base.

Copying the Drill Press Vice Assembly

As you do not want to modify the assembly created in *c09* folder, you need to copy the entire folder of the Drill Press Vice assembly to the *c10* folder. After copying the folder, you will open the assembly file and check components for interference. Note that there should be no interference between the components.

1. Choose the **Open** tool from the **Launch** panel of the **Get Started** tab; the **Open** dialog box is displayed. Using this dialog box, open the folder *c09* from the location *C:\Inventor_2011*.

2. Right-click on the *Drill Press Vice* folder and then choose **Copy** from the shortcut menu.

3. Open the folder *C:\Inventor_2011\c10*. Right-click and choose **Paste** to paste the *Drill Press Vice* folder in the *c10* folder.

4. Open the *Drill Press Vice.iam* file from the *Drill Press Vice* folder.

Checking the Assembly for Interference

1. Choose the **Analyze Interference** tool from the **Interference** panel of the **Inspect** tab; the **Interference Analysis** dialog box is invoked.

    In this dialog box, the **Define Set # 1** button is chosen by default. As a result, you are prompted to select the components to add to the selection set.

2. Select Base from the graphics screen. Next, choose the **Define Set # 2** button from the dialog box and then select the remaining components in the **Browser Bar**.

3. Choose **OK** from the **Interference Analysis** dialog box; the **Analyzing Interference** dialog box is displayed, informing you that the interference is being analyzed.

4. After the analysis is complete, the **Autodesk Inventor Professional 2011** dialog box is displayed, informing you that no interference was found in the assembly.

Driving the Constraint to Simulate the Motion of the Assembly

The Clamp Screw Handle and the two instances of the Handle Stop were assembled with the Clamp Screw using assembly constraints. Therefore, when you simulate the Clamp Screw by driving its constraint, you will notice that the Clamp Screw Handle and both the instances of the Handle Stop will also move along with the Clamp Screw.

1. Click on the plus (+) sign located on the left of the **Jaw Face** node in the **Browser Bar**; the node is expanded and the **Origin** folder along with various constraints applied to it is displayed.

2. Move the cursor over the **Mate 7** constraint; the Jaw Face and the Base are highlighted on the graphics screen. This is done to ensure that the constraint you selected is the correct one. Next, right-click on the **Mate 7** constraint, and then choose **Drive Constraint** from the shortcut menu; the **Drive Constraint** dialog box is displayed.

3. Enter **10** and **60** in the **Start** and **End** edit boxes as the start and end values of the simulation.

4. Choose the **More** button to expand the dialog box. Select the **Start/End/Start** radio button from the **Repetitions** area and then enter **2** in the edit box provided in the same area.

If you enter 2 in the edit box, two cycles of simulation of the assembly are created. The first cycle will be from the start position to the end position and the second cycle will be from the end position to the start position.

5. Choose the **Forward** button; you will notice that there is horizontal simulation of the Jaw face. Also, the other components assembled to it are moved along with it. As there are two repetitions, first the components will move 30 mm away from the Movable Jaw and then move back to the start position.

6. Exit the **Drive Constraint** dialog box by choosing the **Cancel** button. Save the changes made to the assembly and then close the file.

Tutorial 3

In this tutorial, you will create the components of the Double Bearing assembly and then assemble them, as shown in Figure 10-31. Figure 10-32 shows the required positional representation of the assembly. Use the **Pattern** tool while assembling the Bolts. The dimensions of various components are given in Figures 10-33 through 10-35. After assembling the components, drive the **Insert** constraint of the first Bolt such that the remaining three instances are also simulated. Create a positional representation of the assembly with the Bolts at the new location.

(Expected time: 2 hrs)

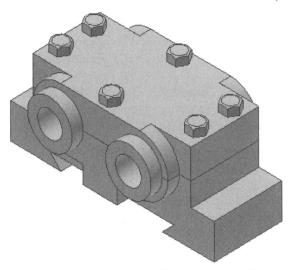

Figure 10-31 *The Double Bearing assembly*

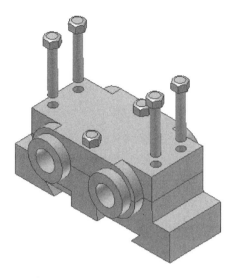

Figure 10-32 *Required positional representation of the Double Bearing assembly*

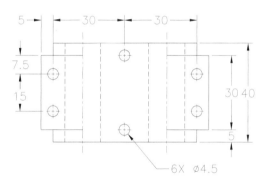

Figure 10-33a *Top view of the Cap*

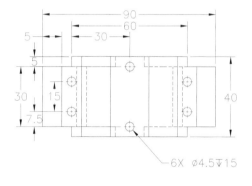

Figure 10-33b *Top view of the Base*

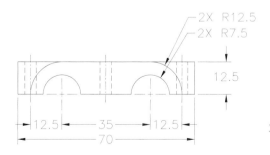

Figure 10-34a *Front view of the Cap*

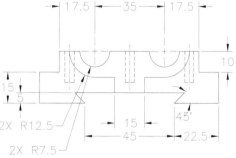

Figure 10-34b *Front view of the Base*

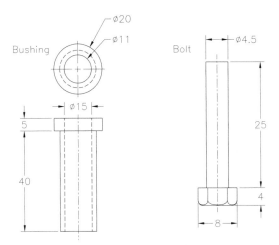

Figure 10-35 *Dimensions of the Bushing and Bolt*

The following steps are required to complete this tutorial:

a. Create a folder with the name *Double Bearing* inside the *c10* folder. Create all components of the Double Bearing assembly and save them in this folder.
b. Open a new assembly file and assemble the components of the Double Bearing assembly. Only two instances of Bolt should be assembled and the rest should be assembled by patterning.
c. Create a new positional representation of the assembly.
d. Drive the **Insert** constraint applied between one of the Bolts and the Cap so that the Bolts are moved to a new location in the current positional representation.

Creating Components

1. Create a folder with the name *Double Bearing* at the location *C:\Inventor_2011\c10* and then create all components in individual part files and save them in this folder.

2. Open a new assembly file and save it with the name *Double Bearing.iam* at the location *C:\Inventor _2011\c10\Double Bearing*.

Assembling Components

The first component that has to be restored is the Base. Next, you need to restore the Cap. Then you need to assemble the base and the cap using the assembly constraints. Next, you need to assemble two instances of the Bushing and then two instances of the Bolt. The remaining instances of the Bolt will be assembled using the **Pattern** tool.

1. Place one instance each of the Base and the Cap in the assembly file using the **Place** tool.

2. Assemble these components using the **Constrain** tool. The assembly after assembling the Base and the Cap is shown in Figure 10-36.

3. Place two instances of the Bushing and then assemble them using the **Constrain** tool, refer to Figure 10-37.

4. Similarly, place two instances of the Bolt and then assemble them using the **Constrain** tool, as shown in Figure 10-37.

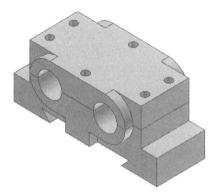
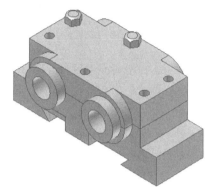

Figure 10-36 *Assembly of the Base and the Cap*   *Figure 10-37* *Assembly after assembling two*
instances each of the Bolt and the Bushing

It is presumed that one of the four holes at the corners of the Cap was created and the other three were patterned. Similarly, one of the holes in the middle of the Cap was created and the other was patterned. Since you have not created all the six holes using the single pattern, you need to use the **Pattern** tool twice. First time the tool will assemble the Bolt on the remaining three holes at the corners and the second time it will assemble the Bolt in the remaining hole in the middle of the Cap.

5. Choose the **Pattern** tool from the **Component** panel of the **Assemble** tab; the **Pattern Component** dialog box is invoked. Also, you are prompted to select the component to be patterned.

6. Select the Bolt at the upper left corner of the Cap.

7. Choose the **Associated Feature Pattern** button from the **Feature Pattern Select** area; you are prompted to select the feature pattern to associate to.

8. Select one of the three holes at the corners of the Cap; the three instances of the Bolt are assembled at three holes.

    As the **Pattern** tool is still active, you are again prompted to select the component to be patterned. Note that to complete the assembling of Bolts using the **Pattern** tool, you need to choose **OK** from the **Pattern Component** dialog box and exit. If you select the Bolt again, the pattern creation will not be the required one.

Note
*The pattern of bolts created depends on the pattern of hole created on the cap and the location of the first hole on the cap. Therefore, you need to be careful while specifying the location of the first instance of the hole on the cap in the **Part** environment.*

9. Choose **OK** to assemble the remaining three instances of the Bolt and exit this dialog box.

10. Invoke the **Pattern Component** dialog box again and select the Bolt assembled with the hole in the middle of the Cap.

11. Choose the **Associated Feature Pattern** button from the **Feature Pattern Select** area; you are prompted to select the feature pattern to associate to.

12. Select the other hole in the middle of the Cap and choose **OK**. The final Double Bearing assembly is shown in Figure 10-38.

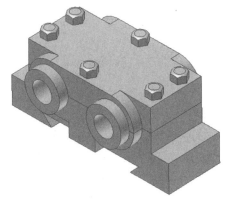

Figure 10-38 Double Bearing assembly

13. Choose the **Save** tool from the **Quick Access Toolbar** to save the assembly.

Creating the Positional Representation of the Assembly

As mentioned in the tutorial description, you need to create the positional representation of the assembly with the Bolts moved to an offset position of 30 mm. To do so, you first need to create a positional representation and then drive the constraints of Bolts such that the Bolts are moved to a new location in the current positional representation. The positional representations are created using the **Browser Bar**.

1. Click on the plus (+) sign located on the left of the **Representations** node in the **Browser Bar** to expand the tree view.

2. Right-click on **Position** in the **Browser Bar** and choose **New** from the shortcut menu; the **Position** changes to **Position : Position 1** node and a plus (+) sign is added on its left.

3. Click on the plus (+) sign located on the left of **Position : Position1** in the **Browser Bar**; the tree view expands. You will notice that a check mark is displayed on the left of **Position1**, suggesting that this is the current representation.

Driving the Constraint of the Bolt

When you drive the constraint of the first Bolt at the upper left corner of the Cap, you will notice that the remaining three instances at the corners of the Cap also simulate along with the first Bolt because the remaining three instances were assembled using the **Pattern** tool. This tool will force the three instances to behave in the same way as original Bolt does.

1. Click on the plus (+) sign located on the left of **Component Pattern 1:1** in the **Browser Bar**. You will notice that four instances of the Bolts are displayed with the name **Element:1**, **Element:2**, **Element:3**, and **Element:4**.

2. Click on the plus (+) sign on the left of **Element:1**; the **Bolt:1** is displayed. Similarly, click on the plus (+) sign on left of **Bolt:1** to display the **Insert** constraint.

3. Right-click on the **Insert** constraint, and then choose **Drive Constraint** from the shortcut menu; the **Drive Constraint** dialog box is displayed.

4. Enter **30** in the **End** edit box and then choose the **More** button to expand the dialog box.

5. Select the **Start/End/Start** radio button from the **Repetitions** area and then enter **2** in the edit box available in this area.

6. Choose the **Forward** button; all four bolts at the corners of cap will be simulated and moved to a distance of 30 mm in the upward direction. All the four bolts are then moved back to their original positions without any pause between the cycles.

    As you need to create a positional representation of the assembly with the bolts at an offset of 30 mm from the original location, you need to stop the movement of the Bolts at the top most position. To do this, you need to modify the value in the edit box in the **Repetitions** area of the **Drive Constraint** dialog box.

7. Enter **1** in the edit box of the **Repetitions** area and then choose the **Forward** button; the Bolts move up to a distance of 30 mm in the upward direction. Figure 10-39 shows the assembly with four bolts at the new position.

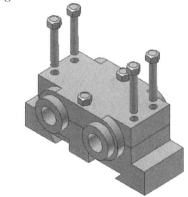

8. Choose the **OK** button to exit the **Drive Constraint** dialog box. Choose **Yes**, if the **Autodesk Inventor 2011** message box is displayed. This message box informs you that the value of the constraint must be overridden in the current positional representation to preserve the value.

Figure 10-39 Position of the Bolts after using the **Drive Constraint** *option*

9. Choose the **Save** tool from the **Quick Access Toolbar**; the **Autodesk Inventor 2011** dialog box is displayed and you are informed that you cannot save the assembly when the assembly is in the positional representation.

10. Choose **OK** from this dialog box to restore the master representation and save the assembly file.

11. Close the assembly document.

Self-Evaluation Test

Answer the following questions and then compare them to those given at the end of this chapter:

1. The components assembled using the **Pattern** tool can be replaced by the other components. (T/F)

2. You can edit components in an assembly file. (T/F)

3. For a grounded component, the symbol of degrees of freedom is not displayed. (T/F)

4. The pattern of a component created using the **Circular** tab of the **Pattern Component** dialog box will be automatically modified, if the pattern of the feature is modified. (T/F)

5. Autodesk Inventor allows you to open the part file of a component for editing. This is done by right-clicking on the component in the **Browser Bar** and choosing _____ from the shortcut menu.

6. If a component is assembled using an under-constrained component, a small green color cube will be displayed on the component after choosing _____ from the **View** tab.

7. The assembly constraints applied on a component can be edited by right-clicking on the constraint in the **Browser Bar** and choosing _____ from the shortcut menu.

8. The three types of assembly section views that can be created in an assembly file are _____, _____, and _____.

9. To analyze an assembly for interference, choose _____ from the **Interference** panel of the **Inspect** tab.

10. The motion of assembly components can be simulated using the _____ dialog box.

Review Questions

Answer the following questions:

1. You can replace all instances of a component in the assembly file. (T/F)

2. Any instance of a component assembled using the **Pattern** tool can be made independent. (T/F)

3. You can flip the section of a section view in an assembly. (T/F)

4. The information of interference between components can be printed. (T/F)

5. The simulation of the components of an assembly can be saved to an *.avi* file. (T/F)

6. Which of the following tools can be used to replace only one instance of a component in an assembly?

    (a) **Create**   (b) **Replace All**
    (c) **Replace**   (d) None of these

7. Which of the following buttons in the **Drive Constraint** dialog box is used to store the information related to the simulation of components in an *avi* file?

    (a) **Record**   (b) **Forward**
    (c) **Reverse**   (d) None of these

8. Which of the following formats is used to save the design view files?

    (a) **.avi*   (b) **.idv*
    (c) **.ipt*   (d) **.iam*

9. Which of the following tools is used to exit section views in an assembly file?

    (a) **Full Section View**   (b) **No Section View**
    (c) **Half Section View**   (d) **End Section View**

10. Which of the following tabs will be available in the **Edit Component Pattern** dialog box if the pattern of a component is created using the **Circular** tab of the **Pattern Component** dialog box?

    (a) **Associative**   (b) **Rectangular**
    (c) **Circular**   (d) None of these

Exercise

Exercise 1

Open the Plummer Block assembly created in Tutorial 2 of Chapter 9 and then create a design view representation with the name Plummer Block, refer to Figure 10-40. After creating the design view, analyze the assembly for interference and then simulate the motion of the two Bolts. Note that the bolts should move in the downward direction.

(Expected time: 30 min)

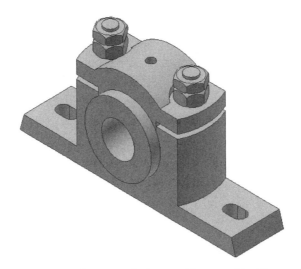

Figure 10-40 *Plummer Block assembly created in Chapter 9*

Answers to Self-Evaluation Test
1. T, **2.** T, **3.** T, **4.** F, **5. Open**, **6. Degrees of Freedom**, **7. Edit**, **8.** quarter section view, half section view, three quarter section view, **9. Analyze Interference**, **10. Drive Constraint**

Chapter *11*

Working with Drawing Views-I

Learning Objectives

After completing this chapter, you will be able to:

- *Understand the use of drawing module.*
- *Understand various types of drawing views in Autodesk Inventor.*
- *Generate, edit, delete, move, copy, and rotate drawing views.*
- *Assign different hatch patterns to different components in assembly section views.*
- *Suppress components in assembly section views.*

THE DRAWING MODULE

After creating a solid model or an assembly, you need to generate their drawing views. Drawing views are the two-dimensional (2D) representations of a solid model or an assembly. Autodesk Inventor provides you with a specialized environment for generating drawing views. This specialized environment is called the **Drawing** module and has only those tools that are related to drawing views. As mentioned earlier, all modules of Autodesk Inventor are bidirectionally associative. This property ensures that any changes made in a part or an assembly are reflected in drawing views. Also, changes in the dimensions of a component or an assembly in the **Drawing** module are reflected in the part or assembly file. You can invoke the **Drawing** module for generating drawing views by selecting any *.idw* format file from the **Metric** tab of the **New File** dialog box, see Figure 11-1. Autodesk Inventor has various .idw files with predefined drafting standards such as the ISO standard, BIN standard, DIN standard, and so on. You can use the required standard file and proceed to the **Drawing** module for generating drawing views. The selected sheet follows its standard in generating and dimensioning the drawing views. However, you can change the standards that will be followed by modifying the standards in the sheet.

Figure 11-1 *Various .idw format files for starting a new file using the **New File** dialog box*

The default screen appearance of a sheet in the **Drawing** module is shown in Figure 11-2. Note that a default sheet with a title block is available when you start this module. This drawing sheet is similar to that on which the drawing views are drawn using the manual methods. This sheet is your working environment and you can generate as many views as you want on it. You can also change the sheet style, title block style, or add more sheets for generating drawing views.

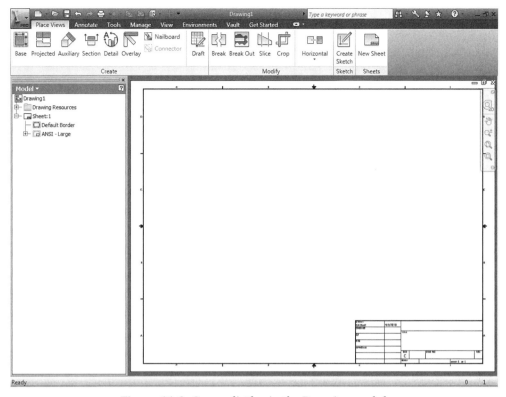

Figure 11-2 *Screen display in the* **Drawing** *module*

TYPES OF VIEWS

In Autodesk Inventor, you can generate nine types of views from a model, assembly, or presentation. Additionally, you can also draft a view using the sketcher entities. The technique of generating drawing views from models, assemblies, and presentations is called generative drafting. This is because you generate the drawing views. The technique of drafting a drawing view using the sketcher entities is called interactive drafting. The types of drawing views that you can generate are discussed next.

Base View

The base view is the first view generated in the drawing sheet. This view is generated using the original model, assembly, or presentation. The base view is an independent view and is not affected by changes in any other view in the drawing sheet. Most of the other views in the sheet will be generated taking this view as the parent view.

Projected View

The projected view is generated taking any of the existing views as the parent view. This view is generated by projecting the lines normal to the parent view or at an angle to the parent view to generate a 3D view. If the lines are projected normal to the parent view, the resulting view will be an orthographic view such as top view, front view, side view, and so on. If the lines are projected at an angle, the resulting view will be a 3D view such as an isometric view. In this view, you can visualize the X, Y, and Z axes of the model. These views are 2D representations of a three-dimensional (3D) model.

Auxiliary View

An auxiliary view is a drawing view that is generated by projecting the lines normal to a specified edge of an existing view.

Section View

A section view is generated by chopping a part of an existing view using a plane and then viewing the parent view from a direction normal to the section plane.

Detail View

A detail view is used to display the details of a portion of an existing view. You can select the portion whose detail view has to be shown in the parent view. The portion that you have selected will be magnified and placed as a separate view. You can control the magnification of the detail view.

Broken View

A broken view is used to display a component by removing a portion of it from the middle and keeping the ends of the drawing view intact. This type of view is used for displaying the components whose length to width ratio is very high. This means that either the length is more as compared to the width or the width is more as compared to the length. The broken view will break the view along the horizontal or vertical direction such that the drawing view fits the area you require. Note that in these views, the dimension of the edge that is broken will still be displayed as the actual value. However, this dimension will have a broken symbol suggesting that the dimension value is for the edge that is broken in the view.

Break Out View

A break out view is used to remove a part of the existing view and display the area of the model or the assembly behind the removed portion. This type of view is generated using a closed sketch that is associated with the parent view.

Overlay View

An overlay view is used to display an alternate position of the components in an assembly. It uses positional representations created in the assembly environment for generating the drawing view.

Slice View

A slice view is used to indicate important portions of a part or an assembly file as a zero depth section. It is generated on a target view by creating a sketch for the material to be removed on the source view.

Note
*To create sketches that are associated with the drawing view, select the drawing view from the drawing sheet and then choose the **Create Sketch** tool from the **Sketch** panel of the **Place Views** tab. On doing so, the sketching environment will be activated. Also, the sketch to be drawn in this environment will be associated with the drawing view.*

GENERATING DRAWING VIEWS
The methods of generating all nine types of views are discussed next.

Generating the Base View

Ribbon:	Place Views > Create > Base
Toolbar:	Drawing Views Panel > Base View

As mentioned earlier, the first view that will be generated in the drawing sheet is the base view. This view is generated using the **Base** tool. To create a base view, choose the **Base** tool from the **Create** panel. Alternatively, right-click on the sheet or in the **Browser Bar** and then choose **Base View** from the shortcut menu. On invoking this tool, the **Drawing View** dialog box will be displayed. The options in this dialog box are discussed next.

Component Tab
The options in the **Component** tab are used to select the component or the assembly whose drawing view you want to generate as well as change the scale orientation, and display style of the drawing view, refer to Figure 11-3. These options are discussed next.

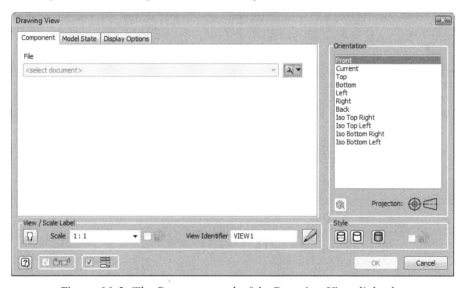

*Figure 11-3 The **Component** tab of the **Drawing View** dialog box*

File
The **File** drop-down list displays the files that are selected for creating the drawing views.

By default, this drop-down list is grayed out. This is because no file is selected. To select a file for generating the drawing views, choose the **Open an existing file** button located on the right of the **File** drop-down list; the **Open** dialog box will be displayed. Using this dialog box, you can select a part, sheet metal, assembly, or presentation file to generate the drawing views. After you have selected the file, you will notice that its name and location is displayed in the **File** drop-down list.

Representation Area
This area will be displayed if the selected file is an assembly file. The options in this area are discussed next.

View: If the selected assembly file has some design view representations associated to it, they will be displayed in the **View** list box. You can select a view representation from the list.

Associative: This check box is selected to make the design view associative to the view to be generated. As a result, if the design view representation is changed in the assembly environment, the drawing view also changes automatically.

Position: This text box is used to select the positional representation of an assembly using which the drawing views will be generated.

Level of Detail: This list box is used to select the level of detail that is required for a drawing view.

Presentation View Area
This area will be displayed if the selected file is a presentation file. The presentation views created in the presentation file will be displayed in the list box. You can make the drawing view associated to the presentation view by selecting the **Associative** check box.

View / Scale Label Area
Toggle Label Visibility: This is a toggle button available on the left side of the **Scale** edit box. This button is used to turn on/off the visibility of the **View Identifier** label of the drawing view.

Scale: The **Scale** edit box is used to specify the scale relative to the part, assembly, or parent view. You can enter the scale value in this edit box or select the predefined standard scale by choosing the down arrow on the right of this edit box.

View Identifier: This text box allows you to specify a label for the view. You can enter the name of the label in this text box for the identification of the view. Note that the label will appear on the drawing sheet only if the **Toggle Label Visibility** button is chosen.

Edit View Label: This button is used for editing the text and format of the **View Identifier** label. Choose this button; the **Format Text** dialog box will be displayed. The options in this dialog box have already been discussed in Chapter 4.

Orientation Area

The options in this area are used to specify the orientation of the drawing view. You can select any predefined view such as top, front, right, left, isometric top-right, isometric top-left, and so on. The resulting view will be based on the option selected from this list box. You can also create a drawing view with a user-defined orientation by choosing the **Change view orientation** button provided below the list box. On choosing this button, the **Custom View** tab of Autodesk Inventor will be activated and the default view of the model will be displayed in the drawing window, as shown in Figure 11-4.

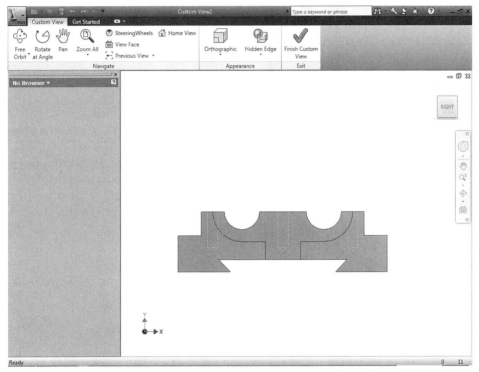

*Figure 11-4 The **Custom View** tab for creating a user-defined view*

The **Custom View** tab has only the drawing display tools that can be used to modify the view orientation. Once you have achieved the required view orientation, choose the **Finish Custom View** button from the **Exit** panel of the **Custom View** tab; the **Custom View** tab will be closed and you will return to the **Drawing** module of the Autodesk Inventor window. The preview of the view created by using the drawing display tools in the **Custom View** tab will be attached to the cursor and you will be prompted to click at a location to place the view.

Style Area

The buttons in the **Style** area are used to specify the display type for drawing views. You can generate a view with hidden lines, without hidden lines, or with shaded display by choosing their respective buttons from this area. Figure 11-5 shows the drawing view with hidden lines and Figure 11-6 shows the drawing view without hidden lines.

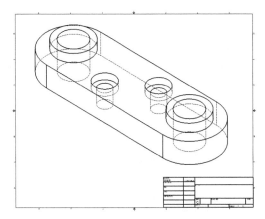

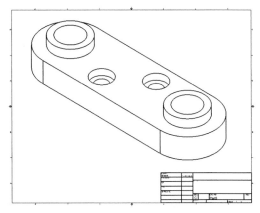

Figure 11-5 *Drawing view with hidden lines*   **Figure 11-6** *Drawing view without hidden lines*

Create projected views immediately after base view creation

This check box, available on the right of the **Enable/Disable feature preview** area of the **Drawing View** dialog box, is selected by default, refer to Figure 11-3. As a result, after placing the base view in the drawing sheet, the **Projected** tool will be invoked automatically. Next, you can place multiple projected views immediately one after the other. Also, the preview of the projected view will be attached to the cursor and you will be prompted to specify the location of the projected view. If you clear this check box, you can create only the base view.

Model State Tab

The options in the **Model State** tab of the **Drawing View** dialog box are discussed next, refer to Figure 11-7.

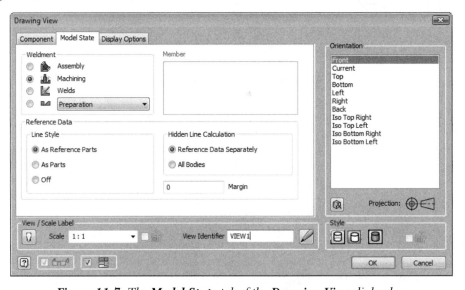

Figure 11-7 *The **Model State** tab of the **Drawing View** dialog box*

Weldment Area

The **Weldment** area will be activated only when you select the weldment file to generate the drawing views. You can specify the weldment state to be displayed in the drawing view by selecting its respective radio button from this area.

Member Area

The list box in this area is available only for the assemblies with positional representations and is used to select in the member that should be selected from an iAssembly file to be displayed in the drawing views.

Reference Data Area

The options in the **Reference Data** area are used to set the line style for the reference data. You can select the desired line style from the **Line Style** area. The **Hidden Line Calculation** area is used to set the option for the calculation of hidden lines. You can set the option to calculate hidden lines separately for reference data. The **Margin** edit box is used to specify the value by which the view boundaries will be extended on all sides to display additional reference data in the drawing view.

Display Options Tab

The options in the **Display Options** tab of the **Drawing View** dialog box are used to specify the parameters that you want to be displayed in the drawing views, refer to Figure 11-8. For example, if you select the **All Model Dimensions** check box, the parametric dimensions that were used to create the model in the **Part** module will be displayed in the drawing view. Similarly, you can also specify whether or not the thread features or tangent edges should be displayed in the drawing view.

*Figure 11-8 The **Display Options** tab of the **Drawing View** dialog box*

The **Section Standard Parts** drop-down list is used to select an option to specify whether or not the standard parts inserted using the Content Library will be sectioned in the assembly section view. By default, the **Obey Browser Settings** option is selected. As a result, the settings that you configure in the **Browser Bar** will be used. Selecting **Always** will always section the standard parts in the assembly section view and selecting **Never** will never section the standard parts.

The **View Justification** drop-down list is used to specify the justification for the drawing view. By default, the justification is **Centered**. You can also select the **Fixed** justification from this drop-down list.

Tip. *By default, the model dimensions are displayed in the drawing view using the default dimensioning standards and dimension style. If the default dimension standard uses dimensions in inches, the dimensions in the drawing views will be displayed in inches even if the dimensions were specified in millimeters in the model. However, you can modify the dimension standards as well as the dimension style. This will be discussed in later chapters.*

Note
*In the **Display Options** tab, only the options that are applicable to the selected view will be enabled. Some of these options also depend on whether you select a part file or an assembly file to generate the drawing view. For example, the option to display model dimensions will not be available while generating the drawing views of an assembly.*

The **Cut Inheritance** area is used to display the sectional views of a component. Each of the check boxes in this area namely **Break Out**, **Broken**, **Slice**, and, **Section**, if selected, display the corresponding sectional view that has been generated from the base view of the component. The options in the **Cut Inheritance** area will be available only while editing the drawing views and not while creating them.

Generating Projected Views

Ribbon:	Place Views > Create > Projected
Toolbar:	Drawing Views Panel > Projected View

As mentioned earlier, the projected views are generated by projecting the lines from an existing view. You can generate the projected views by using the **Base** tool as well as the **Projected** tool. In case of the **Base** tool, you need to select the **Create projected views immediately after base view creation** check box in the **Drawing View** dialog box. After selecting this check box, if you place the base view, the preview of the projected view will be attached to the cursor and you will be prompted to specify the location of the projected view. Specify the location of the projected view and then right-click; a shortcut menu will be displayed. Choose **Create** from the shortcut menu to create the projected view. Another method of creating the projected views is by invoking the **Projected** tool and then selecting the parent view that you want to use to generate the projected view. After selecting the parent view, you will be prompted to specify a location for the projected view. Left-click on the drawing sheet to specify the location. If you move the cursor in the horizontal or vertical direction, an orthographic view will be generated. If you move the cursor at an angle from the parent view, a 3D view will be generated. You can preview the resulting view on the drawing sheet. Once you have specified the location for the projected view, a rectangle will be displayed at that location and you will be prompted again to specify the location of the projected view. To generate the view, right-click on the drawing sheet and then choose **Create** from the shortcut menu.

Note
The display type of the projected views will be the same as that of the parent view. However, you can later modify the display type of the projected view.

Figure 11-9 shows the drawing sheet with the base view and the projected views. The base view is the top view placed on the top of the drawing sheet. The front and isometric views are generated as projected views using the top view as the parent view.

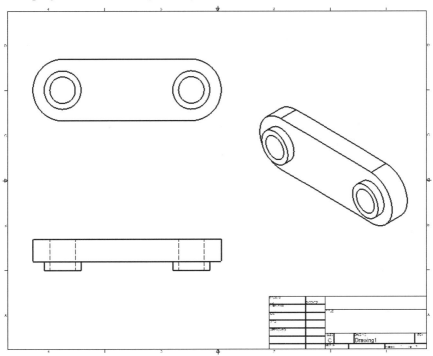

Figure 11-9 Drawing sheet with the base view and the projected views

Tip. *While generating the projected view, if you move the cursor in the horizontal or vertical direction from the parent view, a centerline will be displayed from the center of the parent view to the center of the projected view. This centerline will indicates that the view being projected is normal to the parent view. Therefore, the resulting view will be an orthographic view.*

Generating Auxiliary Views

Ribbon:	Place Views > Create > Auxiliary
Toolbar:	Drawing Views Panel > Auxiliary View

Auxiliary

As mentioned earlier, auxiliary views are generated by projecting the lines normal to a specified edge in the parent view. To generate an auxiliary view, invoke the **Auxiliary** tool and then select the parent view. On selecting the parent view, the **Auxiliary View** dialog box will be displayed, as shown in Figure 11-10. The options in the **View / Scale Label** and **Style** areas are similar to those discussed earlier in the **Drawing View** dialog box. The other option in this dialog box is discussed next.

*Figure 11-10 The **Auxiliary View** dialog box*

Definition in Base View

Select this check box to create a definition line parallel to the edge selected for generating the auxiliary view.

After specifying the required parameters, select the parent view; you will notice that the parent view is enclosed in a red rectangle and an inclined line is attached to the cursor. Select an edge in the parent view that will be used for generating the auxiliary view; the preview of the auxiliary view will be generated and displayed on the sheet in the shaded mode. You will notice that the view being generated is parallel to the selected edge. Also, a center line will be displayed, which is normal to the edge as well as to the auxiliary view, see Figure 11-11. This centerline and the **Auxiliary View** dialog box will automatically disappear once you place the view.

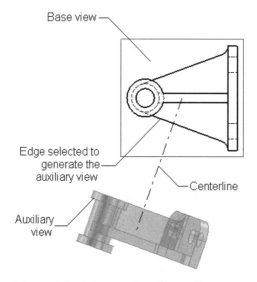

Figure 11-11 Generating the auxiliary view

Generating Section Views

Ribbon:	Place Views > Create > Section
Toolbar:	Drawing Views Panel > Section View

Section

As mentioned earlier, section views are generated by chopping a portion of an existing view using a cutting plane (defined by sketched lines) and then viewing the parent view from the direction normal to the cutting plane. To create a section view, invoke the **Section** tool and then select the parent view. The cursor, which was originally an arrow, will be replaced by a plus (+) cursor. The plus (+) cursor is used to specify a cutting plane. In Autodesk Inventor, a cutting plane is defined by sketching one or more than one line. You can use the temporary tracking option for drawing the lines that will define the section plane. After you have drawn the lines, right-click on the drawing sheet and then choose **Continue** from the shortcut menu; the **Section View** dialog box will be displayed, as shown in Figure 11-12, and you will be prompted to specify the location for the section view. You will notice that the line that you have drawn is converted into a section plane and the preview of the section view is displayed on the drawing sheet. The preview will move as you move the cursor on the drawing sheet. However, it always remains parallel to the section plane. Click on the drawing window to specify the location of the view, refer to Figure 11-13.

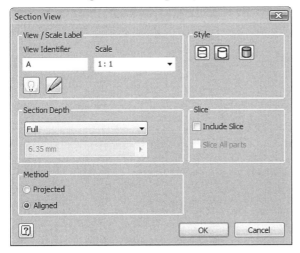

*Figure 11-12 The **Section View** dialog box*

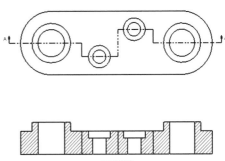

Figure 11-13 Base view and section view

While creating the section view, you can use the options in the **Section Depth** area to specify the offset distance of another section plane behind the original section plane. By default, the **Full** option is selected. To define the depth of sectioning, select the **Distance** option and then set the distance value in the edit box in the **Section Depth** area. Another section plane will be defined parallel to the original section plane at the distance you define and will chop the model. To see the use of this option, generate the isometric view of the section view.

The **Slice** area allows you to display the sliced section view that was created for the base view. Select the **Include Slice** check box to display the sliced section view along with the section view. The **Slice All parts** check box will be available only if the selected base view is an assembly. If you select this check box, the sliced section view of all parts of the assembly passing through the specified section plane will be displayed. You will learn about slicing the views later in this chapter.

The **Method** area is used to specify the method of projection while sectioning a component with multiple line segments. By default, the **Projected** radio button is selected in this area. As a result, the section view defined by the section line normal to the plane is generated. Select the **Aligned** radio button to create an aligned section view. In an aligned section view, the sectioned portion revolves around an axis normal to the viewing plane such that it is straightened, refer to Figure 11-14. This figure shows the aligned section view of a model. Notice that the inclined feature that is sectioned in this view is straightened. Therefore, the section view is longer than the parent view.

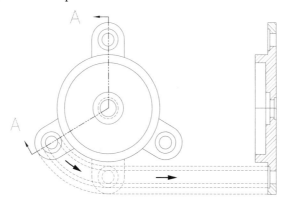

Figure 11-14 *The base view and the aligned section view*

 Tip. *You can also create a sketch associated with a drawing view and then use it to generate section views. To create an associated sketch, select the drawing view and then choose the **Create Sketch** tool from the **Sketch** panel of the **Place Views** tab; the sketching environment will be activated. Draw the sketch to be used to generate the section view and exit the sketching environment. Now, right-click on the sketch that you have created; a shortcut menu will be displayed. Choose the **Create Section View** option from it to generate the section view using the associated sketch.*

Generating Detail Views

| **Ribbon:** | Place Views > Create > Detail |
| **Toolbar:** | Drawing Views Panel > Detail View |

 Detail views are used to display the details of a portion of an existing view by magnifying that portion and displaying it as a separate view. To create a detail view, invoke the **Detail View** tool and then select a view; the selected view will be the parent view for the detailed view. On selecting the parent view, the **Detail View** dialog box will be displayed, as shown in Figure 11-15. The options in this dialog box are similar to those discussed in the **Auxiliary View** dialog box.

When you invoke the **Detail View** dialog box and select the parent view, a circle with a cross mark at its center will get attached to the cursor and you will be prompted to specify the center point of the fence. The fence is the boundary that encloses the portion of the parent view to be magnified and displayed as the detail view. You can select the option to draw a rectangular or a circular boundary by choosing the respective button from the **Fence Shape** area. The **Cutout Shape** area allows you to define the boundary of the detail view and has two buttons, **Jagged** and **Smooth**. The **Jagged** button is chosen by default and displays the boundary of the detailed view as an irregular toothed pattern. The **Smooth**

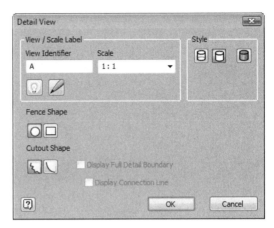

*Figure 11-15 The **Detail View** dialog box*

button, if chosen, displays the boundary of the detail view as a smooth continuous curve. The **Display Full Detail Boundary** check box will be available only when the **Smooth** button is chosen from the **Cutout Shape** area and displays a circular or rectangular boundary around the detail view. The **Display Connection Line** check box will be available only when you select the **Display Full Detail Boundary** check box. This check box generates a centerline between the fence specified on the parent view and the full boundary of the detail view.

After specifying the options in the **Detail View** dialog box, select a point on the parent view that will act as the center point of the fence. This point should lie on the area that you want to magnify. The specified point will be taken as the center of the circular or rectangular boundary. After specifying a point, you will be prompted to specify the endpoint of the fence. Click to specify the endpoint; the portion that is enclosed within the boundary will be magnified by the value defined in the **Scale** drop-down list and the view will be attached to the cursor. Also, you will be prompted to specify the location for the view. Specify the placement point for the drawing view; the detail view will be placed at the point that you specify. Figure 11-16 shows the parent view and the detail view of a component with a circular fence after choosing the **Jagged** button. Figure 11-17 shows the parent view and the detail view of a component with the circular fence after choosing the **Smooth** button.

Figure 11-18 shows the parent view and the detail view of a component with the **Smooth** button chosen and the **Display Full Detail Boundary** check box selected. Figure 11-19 shows the parent view and the detail view of a component with the **Smooth** button chosen and the **Display Full Detail Boundary** and **Display Connection Line** check boxes selected.

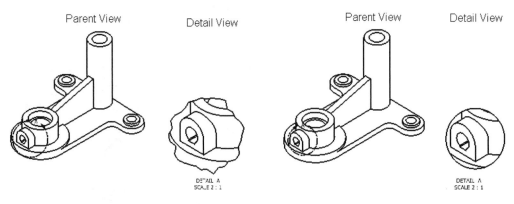

Figure 11-16 *The parent and detail views displayed with a circular fence after choosing the **Jagged** button*

Figure 11-17 *The parent and detail views displayed with a circular fence after choosing the **Smooth** button*

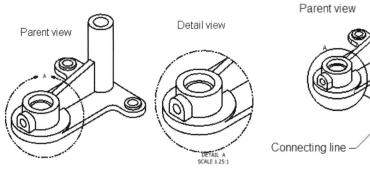

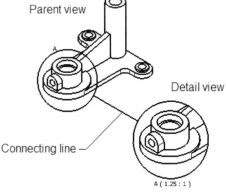

Figure 11-18 *The parent and detail views displayed on selecting the **Display Full Detail Boundary** check box*

Figure 11-19 *The parent and detail views displayed on selecting the **Display Connection Line** and **Display Full Detail Boundary** check boxes*

Generating Broken Views

Ribbon:	Place Views > Modify > Break
Toolbar:	Drawing Views Panel > Break

Break

The broken view is the one in which a user-defined portion of the drawing view is removed, keeping the ends of the drawing view intact. The broken view is generally used to display the drawing view of the models that have a high length to width ratio. Note that this tool will not create a separate view. It will break an existing view such that a specified portion of the view is removed and the remaining portion is displayed along with the ends of the views. The views will be broken with the help of two planes defined by lines. You do not have to draw the lines for defining the cutting planes. You just have to specify the location of the first and the second cutting plane. The portion of the view that lies inside the two cutting planes will be removed and the remaining view will be displayed. To break a view, invoke the **Break** tool and then select the view to be broken; the **Break** dialog box will be displayed, as shown in Figure 11-20, and you will be prompted to select the start point of the material to be removed. The options in this dialog box and the methods to define break lines are discussed next.

Style Area

The buttons in the **Style** area are used to specify the style for displaying the break symbol. The style options provided in this area are discussed next.

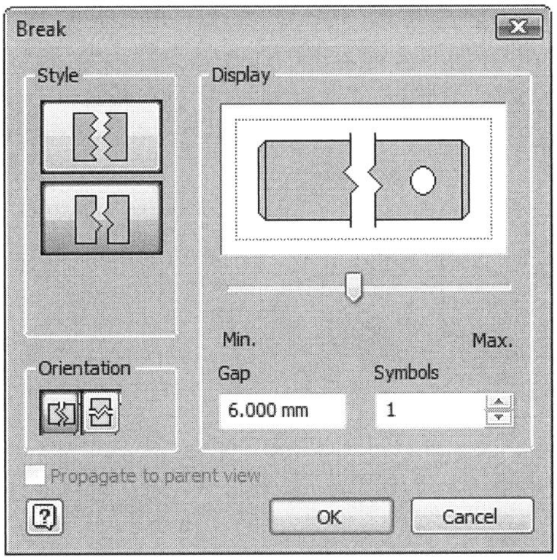

Rectangular Style

The **Rectangular Style** button is used to break the views of a non cylindrical component.

Structural Style

The **Structural Style** button is used to break the views of a cylindrical component.

Orientation Area

The buttons in the **Orientation** area are used to

Figure 11-20 The **Break** dialog box

specify the break in the horizontal or the vertical direction. Depending on whether the view is vertical or horizontal, you can choose the required button from this area.

Display Area

The options in the **Display** area are used to control the display of break lines in the broken view. The preview window in this area will display the break lines that will be displayed on the broken view. As you modify the options in the **Break** dialog box, the preview in the preview window will also change. The scale of break lines can be modified using the slider bar in this area. The preview of the change in scale will be displayed in the preview window and on the drawing sheet when you move the cursor on the drawing sheet.

Gap

The **Gap** edit box is used to specify the value of the break gap in the broken view.

Symbols

The **Symbols** spinner is used to specify the number of break spinners in the break line when the **Structural Style** button is selected from the **Style** area. The maximum number of symbols that are allowed is three. This spinner will not be available if you choose the **Rectangular Style** button from the **Style** area.

The **Propagate to parent view** check box will be available only when the broken view is created for a projected view. This check box, if selected, removes material from the projected view and will also display the parent view as a broken view with the same amount of material removed.

You will notice that when you select the view to be broken, two lines with a break symbol will be attached to the cursor and you will be prompted to specify the start point for the material to be removed. This will be the point where the first cutting plane will be placed. After you specify the first point, you will notice that the two break lines are placed at that point. These break lines will be based on the style that you have selected from the **Style** area. You will now be prompted to specify the endpoint for the material to be removed. This point will define the position of the second cutting plane. After you specify the location of the second cutting plane, notice that the view will shrink because the material between the two cutting planes is removed. Also, the break lines of the selected style will be displayed on the view. Figure 11-21 shows a broken view created using the rectangular style and Figure 11-22 shows a broken view created using the structural style with three symbols.

Figure 11-21 Broken view created using the rectangular style

Figure 11-22 Broken view created using the structural style with three symbols

Note
If you break a view that is used as a parent view for generating other views, the dependent views will also be converted into broken views. Note that the isometric view generated by projecting the lines from an existing view is not dependent on the parent view; therefore, it will not be converted into a broken view.

Generating Break Out Views

Ribbon:	Place Views > Modify > Break Out
Toolbar:	Drawing Views Panel > Break Out

Break Out

As mentioned earlier, break out views are generated to remove a portion of the drawing view and display the area that lies behind the removed portion. These views are generated using the closed sketches that are associated with the view. Therefore, first you need to create a closed sketch associated with the view by selecting the view and choosing the **Create Sketch** tool from the **Sketch** panel in the **Place Views** tab. Next, choose the **Break Out** tool; you will be prompted to select a view. Select the view that has the closed associated sketch with it; the **Break Out** dialog box will be displayed (see Figure 11-23) and the associated sketch will be highlighted in blue. If you select a view that has no sketch associated with it, a message box will be displayed, informing that the selected view has no sketch associated with it.

*Figure 11-23 The **Break Out** dialog box*

The options in the **Break Out** dialog box are discussed next.

Boundary Area

This area has the **Profile** button that is chosen to select the closed sketch associated with the view to create the break out view. When you invoke this dialog box, the **Profile** button is chosen automatically.

Depth Area

The options in the **Depth** area are used to select the method for specifying the depth of the break out view. You can select the method for specifying the depth from the drop-down list in this area. The options in this drop-down list are discussed next.

From Point

The **From Point** option is used to select a point from which you define the depth of a break out view. The depth is defined in the edit box available below this option. Figure 11-24 shows the point from which the depth is defined. Figure 11-25 shows the resulting break out view. The depth from the point in this view is 20 mm.

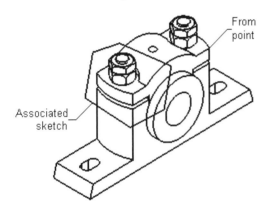

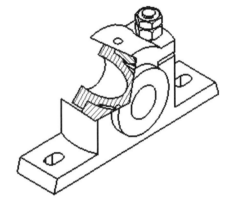

Figure 11-24 *The point to define the break out view*

Figure 11-25 *The resulting break out view*

To Sketch

This option is selected to use a sketch for defining the depth of a break out view. Note that to get a better view, it is recommended that you associate the sketch with a different view. Figure 11-26 shows the drawing views with the sketch used to specify the depth and the resulting break out view. Note that in this figure, the sketch used to define the depth is the one on the front view, and the sketch to define the break out is the same as that in Figure 11-24.

Tip. *You can open the part file for editing a component whose drawing views you are generating. To open the part file, right-click on the drawing view and then choose the* **Open** *option from the shortcut menu.*

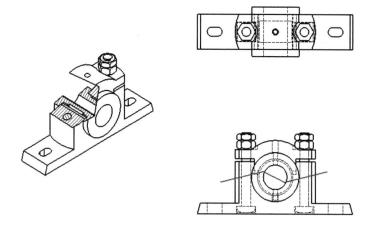

Figure 11-26   *Sketch to define the depth and the resulting break out view*

To Hole

This option is selected to use the hole on the selected view to define the depth of a break out view. Figure 11-27 shows a break out view created using the central hole of Brasses as the hole to define the depth of the break out view.

Through Part

This option is selected to use the depth of a selected part to define the depth of the break out view. When you select this option, you will be prompted to select a part to define the depth.

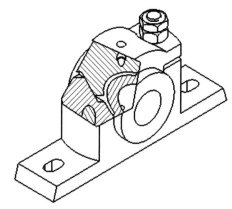

Figure 11-27   *Break out view generated up to the central hole of Brasses*

The **Display** area also has the **Show Hidden Edges** button that is selected to show the hidden edges in the selected view. The hidden edges help you define the depth of the break out view. Note that the display type of the view will change to the original one after the view is created.

Generating Overlay Views

Ribbon:	Place Views > Create > Overlay
Toolbar:	Drawing Views Panel > Overlay View

Overlay

As mentioned earlier, overlay views are used to show the alternative position of components in an assembly. This view can be generated only if you have created positional representations for the assembly in the assembly environment. The alternate position of the components is shown by dashed lines in an existing view.

To create an overlay view, choose the **Overlay** tool from the **Create** panel of the **Place Views** tab; you will be prompted to select a view. Select the drawing view of an assembly for which the positional representations were created; the **Overlay View** dialog box will be displayed, as shown in Figure 11-28. Most of the options in this dialog box are similar to those discussed while generating earlier drawing views. The remaining options are discussed next.

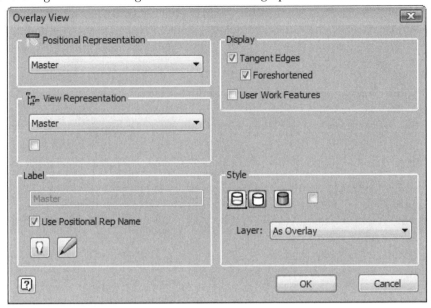

Figure 11-28 The **Overlay View** *dialog box*

Positional Representation Area

The drop-down list in this area lists all the available positional representations for the selected assembly. You can select the desired positional representation to generate the overlay view from this drop-down list.

View Representation Area

The drop-down list in this area lists all the available design views for the selected assembly. The overlay view will use the design view you select from this drop-down list.

After specifying the parameters in the **Overlay View** dialog box, choose **OK**; the overlay view will be generated in the selected view and the alternate position of the components will be displayed using the dashed lines. Figure 11-29 shows the overlay view generated on an isometric view. In this figure, the alternative position of the components is shown using dashed lines.

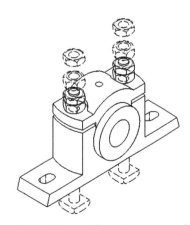

Figure 11-29 The overlay view generated on an isometric view

Generating Slice Views

Ribbon:	Place Views > Modify > Slice
Toolbar:	Drawing Views Panel > Slice

Slice

The **Slice** tool is used to create zero-depth sectional views. The sliced sectional views can be used in complex assemblies or part files to highlight a specific component or a feature. The sketch for the slice views is created on the parent views, and the resulting sliced view is created on the target view. The procedure to create slice views is discussed next.

Generate a base view and an associated projection. Next, select the base view and choose the **Create Sketch** tool from the **Sketch** panel of the **Place Views** tab; the sketching environment will be activated. Create the sketch that consists of one or more open profiles on the base view and exit the sketching environment. Choose the **Slice** tool from the **Modify** panel of the **Place Views** tab; you will be prompted to select a view. Select the projected view; the **Slice** dialog box will be displayed, as shown in Figure 11-30, and you will be prompted to select a sketch.

*Figure 11-30 The **Slice** dialog box*

The **Select Sketch** button is chosen by default in the **Slice Line Geometry** area. Select the sketch that is created on the parent view and choose the **OK** button from the **Slice** dialog box; the resultant sliced view will be created on the target view. The **Slice All Parts** check box will be available only when the slice view is created for an assembly and if selected, will slice all the parts that intersect the slice profile. Figure 11-31 shows the parent view with the sketch for the slice view and the resultant slice view.

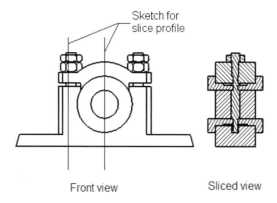

Sketch for
slice profile

Front view   Sliced view

Figure 11-31 The parent view and the slice side view of the Plummer Block assembly

DRAFTING DRAWING VIEWS

Ribbon: Place Views > Create > Draft
Toolbar: Drawing Views Panel > Draft

Draft

In addition to generating all above-mentioned views, Autodesk Inventor also allows you to draft a drawing view using the sketching tools. After sketching, these views will behave similar to the generated views.

The drawing views can be sketched using the **Draft** tool. On invoking this tool, the **Draft View** dialog box will be displayed, as shown in Figure 11-32. The options in the **View / Scale Label** area are similar to those discussed earlier in the **Drawing View** dialog box while generating drawing views. After you have set the parameters in this dialog box and chosen the **OK** button, the sketching environment will be activated and you can create a draft view.

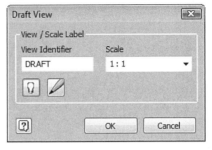

Figure 11-32 The **Draft View** *dialog box*

EDITING DRAWING VIEWS

Autodesk Inventor allows you to edit a drawing view according to your requirement. If you move the cursor over a drawing view in the sheet, you will notice that a red box with dotted lines is displayed around the view. This box is the bounding box of the view. To edit a view, double-click when the bounding box is displayed. Alternatively, right-click on the view when the bounding box is displayed and then choose **Edit View** from the shortcut menu; the **Drawing View** dialog box will be displayed. You can also invoke this dialog box by double-clicking on the required view in the **Browser Bar**. Figure 11-33 shows the **Drawing View** dialog box invoked for editing a drawing view.

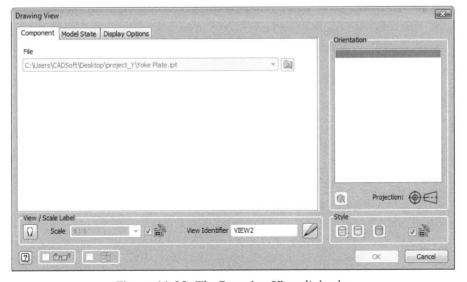

Figure 11-33 The **Drawing View** *dialog box*

While editing the dependent/projected view, you can change its display style by clearing the **Style from Base** check box in the **Style** area. If you clear this check box, the remaining buttons in this area will be activated. You can choose any of these buttons to change the display style of the dependent view based on your requirements.

Note
*The options in the **Component**, **Model State**, and **Display Options** tabs of this dialog box will be available based on the type of view selected for editing.*

DELETING DRAWING VIEWS

The unwanted drawing views can be deleted from the sheet using the **Browser Bar** or directly from the sheet. To delete a drawing view, move the cursor over the drawing view in the **Browser Bar** or on the drawing sheet; a dotted rectangle, which is actually the bounding box of the drawing view, will be displayed. Select the drawing view when the bounding box is displayed and then press the DELETE key; the **Autodesk Inventor Professional 2011** message box will be displayed. Choose **OK** from this message box; the selected view will be deleted. You can also delete a view by right-clicking on it and then choosing **Delete** from the shortcut menu.

If the selected drawing view has some dependent drawing views, the **Delete View** dialog box will be displayed. This dialog box will confirm whether you want to delete the selected view and its dependent views. Choose **OK** to delete the views. To display the views that are dependent on the selected view, choose the **More** button at the lower right corner of this dialog box. The dialog box will expand and provide the list of dependent views, see Figure 11-34.

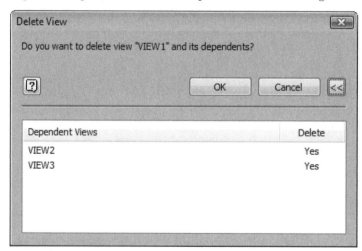

*Figure 11-34 The expanded **Delete View** dialog box*

By default, this dialog box will show **Yes** for all dependent views in the **Delete** column of the expanded area. This suggests that all dependent views will be deleted if you delete the parent view. If you do not want to delete a dependent view, click on **Yes** once; **Yes** will be replaced with **No**. This suggests that the selected dependent view will not be deleted if you delete the parent view.

Tip. *If you select a view to delete it, you will notice that red rectangles are drawn around all dependent views. If you change* **Yes** *to* **No** *for a view in the* **Delete View** *dialog box, refer to Figure 11-34, the red box will not be displayed. This indicates that the drawing view will not be deleted.*

MOVING DRAWING VIEWS

You can relocate the existing drawing view by moving it from its current location to a new location. However, remember that if the selected view has some dependent views, they will also move along with the parent view. To move the view, move the cursor over the view; the bounding box of the view is displayed. Move the cursor over one of the edges of the bounding box. Now, press and hold the left mouse button and drag the view to a new location in the sheet. Note that only section views, auxiliary views, and the projected orthographic views can be moved only along the axis, in which they were projected. The isometric views and detail views can be moved to any location in the drawing sheet.

Tip. *You can suppress option to move dependent views along with the parent view if you do not want to move them with the parent view. This is done by clearing the* **Align to Base** *check box in the* **Display Options** *tab of the* **Drawing View** *dialog box, which is displayed on double-clicking on the dependent views.*

COPYING DRAWING VIEWS

Autodesk Inventor allows you to copy an existing view at a new location in a new sheet. You can also copy the existing view in a new drawing file. To copy the view, move the cursor over the view and right-click when the bounding box of the view is displayed. Choose **Copy** from the shortcut menu that is displayed on right-clicking. You can also right-click on the drawing view in the **Browser Bar** and choose **Copy** from the shortcut menu. Now, paste this drawing view at a new location in a new sheet or in a new drawing file. Note that if the selected drawing view has some dependent views, they will not be copied along with the parent view.

Note
The process of adding more sheets will be discussed in the next chapter.

ROTATING DRAWING VIEWS

Autodesk Inventor allows you to rotate the selected drawing view about its center point. However, you cannot rotate a drawing view that has dependent sectional and auxiliary views, or an associated section. If you rotate a base view that has a dependent detail view, the detail view will also rotate to maintain its relationship with the base view. In any case, if you rotate the dependent view, the parent view will not be affected. You can rotate an existing drawing view by right-clicking on it in the **Browser Bar** or on the sheet and then by choosing **Rotate** from the shortcut menu. On choosing this option, the **Rotate View** dialog box will be displayed, as shown in Figure 11-35. The options in this dialog box are discussed next.

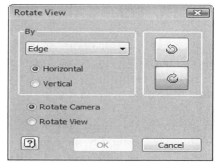

Figure 11-35 The **Rotate View** *dialog box*

By Area

The drop-down list in the **By** area is used to select the method of rotating the selected drawing view. There are three methods for rotating the drawing views. These methods are discussed next.

Edge

The **Edge** method is used to force the orientation of the selected view such that the selected edge becomes horizontal or vertical. Select the **Edge** option from the drop-down list in the **By** area; the **Horizontal** and **Vertical** radio buttons will be displayed in this area. The orientation will depend on whether you select the **Horizontal** or the **Vertical** radio button. To rotate the view using the **Edge** method, select the **Horizontal** or the **Vertical** radio button and then select the edge in the selected view.

Absolute angle

The **Absolute angle** method is used to rotate the drawing view with respect to the world coordinate system by specifying the rotation angle of the view. The angle can be specified in the **Angle** edit box that is displayed in the **By** area when you select the **Absolute angle** option from the drop-down list.

Relative angle

The **Relative angle** method is used to rotate the drawing view with respect to the current position of the drawing view by specifying the rotation angle of the view. The angle can be specified in the **Angle** edit box that is displayed in the **By** area when you select the **Relative angle** option from the drop-down list.

Counter clockwise

The **Counter clockwise** button is the first button in the area that is on the right of the **By** area. This button is chosen to rotate the selected view in the counterclockwise direction.

Clockwise

The **Clockwise** button is available below the **Counter clockwise** button and is chosen to rotate the selected view in the clockwise direction.

ASSIGNING DIFFERENT HATCH PATTERNS TO COMPONENTS IN ASSEMBLY SECTION VIEWS

Whenever you generate the section views of an assembly, by default, similar hatch patterns are assigned to all of them. Although the angle of hatching lines between the adjacent components is different yet it creates confusion, if the assembly has a number of components. For example, Figure 11-36 shows the drawing views of the Plummer Block assembly. In this figure, the components in the section view are assigned the similar hatch patterns.

You can avoid this confusion by assigning different hatch patterns to the components of the assembly. To modify the hatch pattern, move the cursor over the hatching lines in the component in the section view. The hatch pattern will turn red. Once the hatch pattern turns

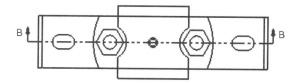

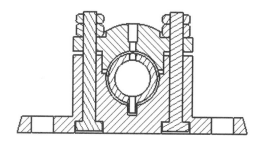

Figure 11-36   *Similar hatch patterns of components in the section view*

red, right-click to display the shortcut menu. In this shortcut menu, choose the **Edit** option; the **Edit Hatch Pattern** dialog box will be displayed, see Figure 11-37. The options in this dialog box are discussed next.

By Material

This check box, if selected, displays the hatch pattern defined for a particular type of material in the **Style and Standard Editor** dialog box.

Pattern

The **Pattern** drop-down list is used to select the hatch pattern for the selected hatching. You can select the required hatch pattern from the list of patterns in this drop-down list. The preview of the selected pattern will be displayed in the window to the right of this drop-down list and in the drawing sheet. The selected hatch pattern will be assigned to the selected component. However, note that this hatch pattern will not be assigned to the other instances of the selected component. The other instances of the selected component will still be hatched using the default hatch pattern.

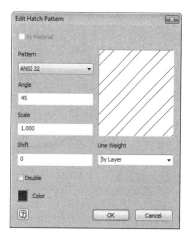

Figure 11-37   *The **Edit Hatch Pattern** dialog box*

Angle

The **Angle** edit box is used to specify the angle of the hatching lines.

Line Weight

The **Line Weight** drop-down list is used to specify the line weight of the hatching lines. You can specify the required line weight by selecting it from the predefined line weights available in this drop-down list.

Scale

The **Scale** edit box is used to specify the scale factor of the hatching lines.

Shift

The **Shift** edit box is used to offset the hatch pattern from its location through the specified distance. The hatch pattern is shifted to avoid confusion with the hatch pattern of the adjacent component. Generally, the shift value should lie between 1 and 5. You can view the effect of shifting the hatch pattern on the sheet when you enter a value in this edit box.

Color

The **Color** button is used to modify the color of the selected hatch pattern. When you choose this button, the **Color** dialog box is displayed. Select the required color for hatching lines from this dialog box.

Double

The **Double** check box is used to double the hatching lines by drawing another set of lines perpendicular to the original lines in the hatch pattern. Figure 11-38 shows the drawing views of the Plummer Block assembly with different hatch patterns assigned to the components.

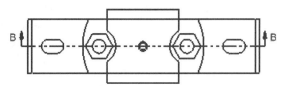

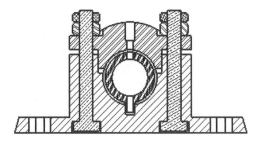

Figure 11-38 Different hatch patterns assigned to the components in the section view

EDITING THE DEFAULT HATCH STYLE OF THE SECTIONED OBJECTS

With this release of Autodesk Inventor, you can edit the default hatch style of the sectioned objects. You can change the default hatch pattern properties such as hatch angle, hatch pattern, hatch scale, and so on. Before changing the hatch properties, it is recommended to view the default hatch properties of the cut section. To do so, right-click on the hatching lines in the section view; a shortcut menu will be displayed. Choose **Edit** from the shortcut menu; the **Edit Hatch Pattern** dialog box will be displayed, refer to Figure 11-37. Using this dialog box, you can view or edit the hatch properties of the current section view. However, if you want to change the hatch pattern properties such that whenever you create a sectioned view the default hatch properties will be overridden by the new hatch pattern properties, then you need to invoke the **Style and Standard Editor** dialog box. To invoke this dialog box, right-click on the hatching lines and then choose the **Edit Hatch Style** option from the shortcut menu; the **Style and Standard Styles** dialog box will be displayed. Expand the **Hatch** node in this dialog box and click on a hatch style; the **New** button will be activated. Choose the **New** button; the **New Local Style** dialog box will be displayed. Enter the name of the hatch style in the **Name** edit box and select the **Add to standard** check box in this dialog box. Next, choose **OK** to create the hatch style. In the **Hatch Style** area of the **Style and Standard Editor** dialog box, specify different hatch properties such as hatch pattern, hatch angle, scale, and so on. After specifying the hatch properties, choose the **Save** button to save the hatch style.

Next, you need to modify the default hatch properties with the new hatch properties by using the **Object Defaults** node in the **Style and Standard Editor** dialog box. Expand the **Object Defaults** node to display the **Object Defaults (Current Units)** option. Select this option; the object types along with their default styles and layers will be listed in the **Style and Standard Editor** dialog box. Drag the vertical scroll bar located on the right of the dialog box to view all styles. Next, in the **Object Style** column, click on the object style corresponding to the **Section Hatch** object type; a drop-down list will be displayed. In this drop-down list, select the hatch style created earlier, as shown in Figure 11-39. Next, choose the **Save** button and then the **Done** button from the dialog box; the selected style will be set as the default hatching style.

Note

*1. You can create any number of hatch styles by using the **Style and Standard Editor** dialog box.*

*2. Make sure you select the **All Objects** or **Model/View Objects** option in the **Filter** drop-down list of the **Style and Standard Editor** dialog box. This will ensure that the **Section Hatch** along with its default style and default layer is displayed in the **Style and Standard Editor** dialog box.*

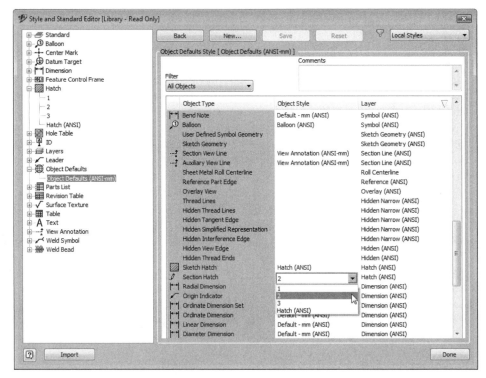

Figure 11-39 *Selecting the required object style for the **Section Hatch** object type*

EXCLUDING COMPONENTS FROM ASSEMBLY SECTION VIEWS

When you generate the section views of an assembly, all components that are intersected by the cutting plane are sectioned, as shown in Figure 11-40.

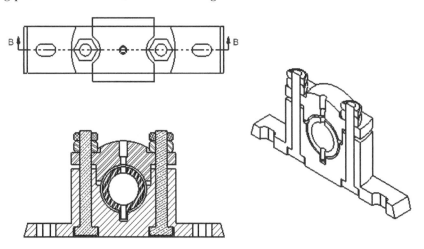

Figure 11-40 *All components intersected by the cutting plane*

However, according to the drawing standards, the components such as nuts, bolts, lock nuts, and so on should not be sectioned while generating the section view. Therefore, you will have to exclude these components before or after generating the assembly section view.

To prevent the components from being sectioned, click on the plus (+) sign located on the left of the section view; the name of the assembly will be displayed. Click on the plus (+) sign located on the left of the assembly name to display all the components of the assembly in the **Browser Bar**. Now, hold the CTRL key and using the left mouse button, select all the components that you want to exclude from sectioning. Once all the components are selected, they will be displayed with a blue background in the **Browser Bar**. Right-click on any of the selected components to display the shortcut menu. Choose **Section Participation > None** from the shortcut menu; all the selected components will be excluded from the section view, see Figure 11-41.

Note
*If the file that you have selected for generating the drawing views is not in the current project, the **Autodesk Inventor 2011** information box will be displayed. This box will inform that the location of the selected file is not in the current project folder.*

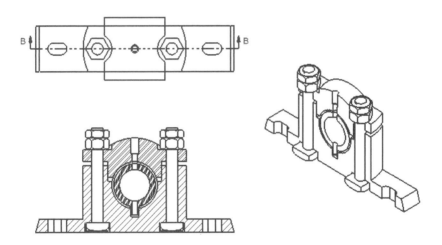

Figure 11-41 *Drawing views with components excluded from the section view*

TUTORIALS

Tutorial 1

In this tutorial, you will generate the top view, full sectioned front view, and isometric view of the sectioned front view of the model created in *Tutorial2* of the *c07* folder. Use the JIS standard template file for generating the views. **(Expected time: 30 min)**

The following steps are required to complete this tutorial:

a. Copy the model of *Tutorial2* of the *c07* folder to the current folder.
b. Open a JIS template file and generate the base view using the **Base** tool.
c. Generate the section view by sketching the section plane.
d. Use the **Projected** tool to project lines at an angle from the section view to generate the isometric view.

Copying the Model to the Current Folder

Before generating the drawing views of the model, it is important to copy the model to the current folder. The reason is that when you open the drawing file next time, the component will be searched in the current *c11* folder. As the component is not available in the current folder, the **Resolve Link** dialog box will be displayed. This dialog box will prompt you to specify the location and path of the component file. Therefore, all components or assemblies should be copied into the current folder, or the drawing file should be saved in the folder in which the component and assembly file are located.

1. Create a folder with the name *c11* at the location *C:\Inventor_2011* and then copy the *Tutorial 2.ipt* file from the location *C:\Inventor_2011\c07* to the *c11* folder. Next, rename this file *Tutorial 1.ipt*.

Starting a New Drawing File

As mentioned in the tutorial description, you need to use the JIS standard template for generating the drawing views. So, you will use the *JIS.idw* file for generating the drawing views.

1. Start a new session of Autodesk Inventor and choose the **New** tool from the **Launch** panel of the **Get Started** tab to invoke the **New File** dialog box.

2. Choose the **Metric** tab and then double-click on the **JIS.idw** option to open a JIS standard drawing file, see Figure 11-42.

Note
By default, the color of the drawing sheet on your screen will be in yellow shade. Here, the color has been changed to white for clarity.

Generating the Base View

As mentioned earlier, the base view is the first view in the drawing sheet. Once you have generated the base view, you can use it as the parent view for generating other views. The base view is generated using the **Base** tool.

1. Choose the **Base** tool from the **Create** panel of the **Place Views** tab; the **Drawing View** dialog box is displayed.

Base

The preview of the drawing view is not displayed on the sheet because you have not selected any part file. Therefore, first you need to select the part file, for which drawing view will be generated.

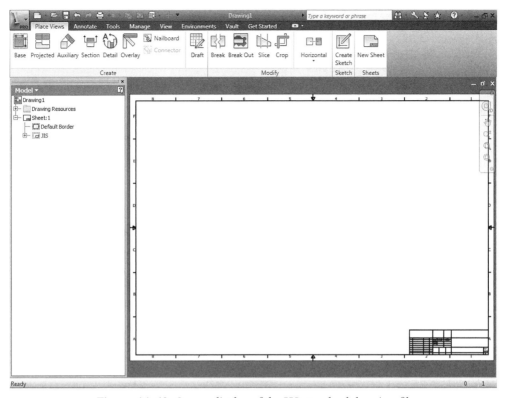

Figure 11-42 Screen display of the JIS standard drawing file

2. Choose the **Open an existing file** button on the right of the **File** drop-down list in the **Component** tab of the **Drawing View** dialog box; the **Open** dialog box is displayed.

3. In this dialog box, select *Tutorial1.ipt* from *C:\Inventor_2011\c11* and then choose the **Open** button.

   You will notice that the preview of the drawing view using the default orientation is now attached to the cursor. The preview moves as you move the cursor and will be generated at the point that you specify in the drawing window. In the default orientation, the cylindrical feature of the model is along the -Y axis of the sheet. First, you need to reorient the model such that the cylindrical feature of the model is along the -X axis.

4. Choose the **Change view orientation** button that is provided below the list box in the **Orientation** area.

   As soon as you choose this button, the **Custom View** tab gets activated. The tools in this tab are used to reorient the model. As mentioned earlier, the orientation that is achieved in this window will be selected as the orientation of the drawing view.

5. Choose the **Rotate at Angle** tool from the **Navigate** panel of the **Custom View** tab; the **Incremental View Rotate** dialog box is displayed.

Rotate
at Angle

6. Enter **90** in the **Increment** edit box and then choose the **Clockwise** button. You will notice that as soon as you choose the **Clockwise** button, the view in the graphic window is rotated through an angle of 90-degree in the clockwise direction.

7. Choose **OK** to exit the **Incremental View Rotate** dialog box.

8. As the new orientation of the view is what you require, you can now exit the **Custom View** tab. Choose the **Finish Custom View** button from the **Exit** panel of the **Custom View** tab.

   When you exit the **Custom View** tab, the drawing sheet reappears. Also, the cylindrical feature of the model is shown along the X axis in the preview of the drawing view.

9. Modify the scale value to **1.5 : 1** in the **Scale** edit box. Clear the **Create projected views immediately after base view creation** check box as you do not need the projection view to be placed immediately.

10. Specify the placement point of the view close to the top right corner of the sheet, see Figure 11-43.

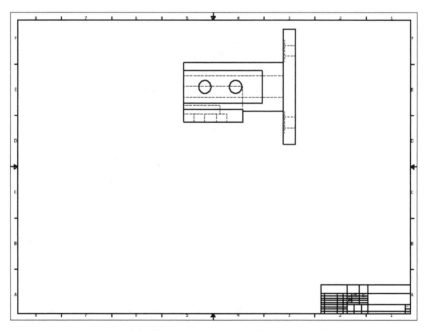

Figure 11-43 Drawing sheet with the base view

 Note
*If the **Drawing View** dialog box restricts you from specifying the point on the sheet, you can move it to the left side by holding it from the title bar.*

Generating the Section View

The section view can be generated using the **Section** tool. To generate the view using this tool, first you need to select the drawing view that has to be sectioned and then define the section plane. But, if you use the shortcut menu that is displayed by right-clicking on the base view in the **Browser Bar** or in the drawing sheet, you do not need to select the drawing view as it is already selected. So, you will use this shortcut menu to generate the section view.

1. Move the cursor over the base view on the sheet to display the red dotted box, which is the bounding box of the view. When the bounding box is displayed, right-click and choose **Create View > Section View** from the shortcut menu; the cursor changes to the sketch cursor and you are prompted to enter the endpoints of the section line.

2. Move the cursor close to the midpoint of the extreme left vertical edge of the base view; the cursor snaps to the midpoint and turns green.

3. After the cursor snaps to the midpoint of the edge, move the cursor horizontally toward the left of the view. You will notice that an imaginary horizontal line is being drawn from the midpoint of the left vertical edge. This is due to the temporary tracking option.

4. Click to specify a point after moving the cursor to a little distance horizontally toward the left of the view. The specified point is selected as the first point of the section plane.

   When you move the cursor toward the right, the symbol of the perpendicular constraint is attached to the cursor which confirms that the line defining the section view is horizontal. This symbol indicates that the line is normal to the extreme left vertical edge of the base view. This perpendicular constraint is applied because you snapped to the midpoint of the left vertical edge of the base view.

5. Move the cursor horizontally toward the right of the view. You will notice that a horizontal line is being drawn. Move the cursor to a little distance on the right of the extreme right vertical edge of the base view. Make sure that the cursor does not snap to the midpoint of the right vertical edge and the line being drawn is horizontal.

6. Specify a point on the right of the right vertical edge of the base view. This point is selected as the second point of the section plane.

7. Right-click and then choose **Continue** from the shortcut menu; the **Section View** dialog box is displayed and the preview of the section view attached to the cursor appears on the sheet. You are prompted to specify the location of the section view. Note that hatching lines will not be displayed in the preview of the section view.

8. Specify the location of the section view below the base view, see Figure 11-44. The **Section View** dialog box is automatically closed when you specify the location of the section view.

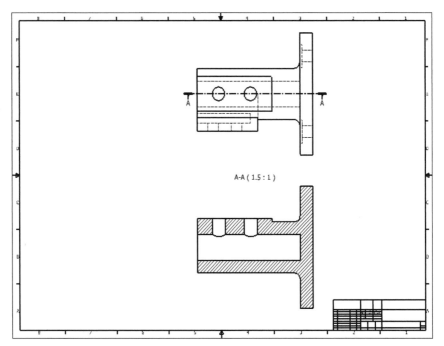

Figure 11-44 *Drawing sheet with the base and section views*

Generating the Isometric View of the Section View

The isometric view of the section view can be generated using the shortcut menu.

1. Move the cursor over the section view and right-click when the dotted rectangle is displayed, a shortcut menu is displayed.

2. Choose **Create View > Projected View** from the shortcut menu; you are prompted to select the view location.

3. Move the cursor toward the left of the section view and then move it upward until the preview of the isometric view appears. Now, specify the location of the view. Right-click on the view; a shortcut menu is displayed. Choose **Create** from the shortcut menu, the isometric view of the model is generated, as shown in Figure 11-45.

4. Save the drawing file with the name *Tutorial1.idw* at the location *C:\Inventor_2011\c11* and close it.

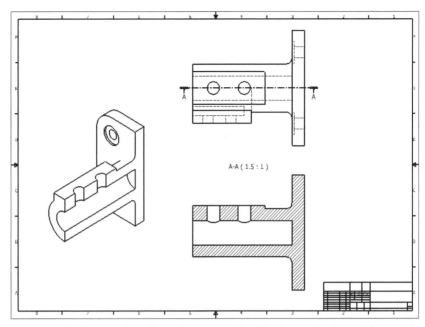

Figure 11-45 Drawing sheet after generating the isometric view of the model

Tutorial 2

In this tutorial, you will generate the top view, full sectioned front view, and isometric view of the section view of the Plummer Block assembly created in *Tutorial 2* of the *c09* folder. The Nuts and Bolts should be excluded from the section view. Also, all sectioned components should have different hatch patterns. Use the JIS standard drawing file for generating the drawing views of the assembly. **(Expected time: 45 min)**

The following steps are required to complete this tutorial:

a. Copy the *Plummer Block* folder from the *c09* folder to the *c11* folder.
b. Generate the top view of the assembly.
c. Show the contents of the base view and then suppress the Bolts, Nuts, and Lock Nuts so that they are not sectioned.
d. Use the top view as the parent view to generate the full section front view.
e. Modify the hatch of Casting and Cap.
f. Generate the projected isometric view of the sectioned front view.

Copying the Plummer Block Folder

As mentioned earlier, you will have to copy the file that will be used to generate drawing views in the current folder. To generate the drawing views of the assembly in this tutorial, you will have to copy the folder in which the files of the assembly are stored. Also, note that the drawing file will be saved in the folder of the assembly, and not in the *c11* folder.

1. Copy the *Plummer Block* folder from the location *C:\Inventor_2011\c09* to the location *C:\Inventor_2011\c11*.

Starting a New Drawing File

1. Choose the **New** tool from the **Launch** panel of the **Get Started** tab to invoke the **New File** dialog box.

2. In this dialog box, choose the **Metric** tab and then double-click on the **JIS.idw** option to open a JIS standard drawing file.

Generating the Top View of the Assembly

Base

1. Choose the **Base** tool from the **Create** panel of the **Place Views** tab; the **Drawing View** dialog box is displayed.

2. In the **Component** tab of this dialog box, choose the **Open an existing file** button on the right of the **File** drop-down list; the **Open** dialog box is displayed.

3. Browse to the *Plummer Block* folder at the location *C:\Inventor_2011\c11* and then select the *Plummer Block.iam* file from it.

4. Next, choose the **Open** button to select the assembly for generating the drawing views; the preview of the selected view of the assembly appears on the sheet. You are also prompted to specify the location of the view.

5. Modify the view scale to **1.25 : 1** in the **Scale** edit box. Clear the **Create projected views immediately after base view creation** check box as you do not need the projection view to be placed immediately.

6. Specify the location of the drawing view close to the upper right corner of the sheet, see Figure 11-46.

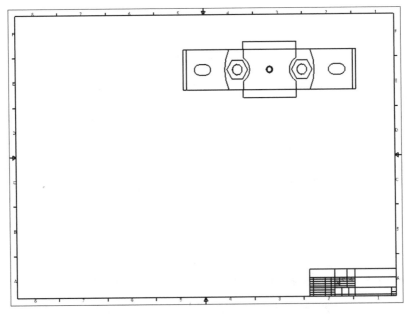

Figure 11-46 Top view of the assembly

Note
Depending upon the planes used for creating and assembling components, the orientation of the view may differ from the orientation shown in Figure 11-45. In this figure, the top view has been used as the orientation.

Suppressing Components from the Section Views

As mentioned in the tutorial description, the Nuts, Bolts, and Lock Nuts need to be excluded from the section view. Therefore, you need to suppress these components such that they are not sectioned in the section view.

1. Click on the + sign located on the left of the view in the **Browser Bar** to display the **Plummer Block.iam** assembly. Also, a plus (+) sign is displayed on the left of this assembly in the **Browser Bar**.

2. Click on the + sign located on the left of **Plummer Block.iam** to display all components of the assembly. Press and hold the CTRL key and select both instances of Nut, Bolt, and Lock Nut using the left mouse button. The selected components are displayed in blue background in the **Browser Bar**.

3. Right-click on any selected component in the **Browser Bar**; a shortcut menu is displayed. Choose **Section Participation > None** from the shortcut menu.

4. Pick a point on the sheet to clear the selection of components.

Generating the Section View

Since you have turned off the option for sectioning some of the components, they will not be sectioned when generating the section view.

1. Choose the **Section** tool from the **Create** panel of the **Place Views** tab; you are prompted to select the view to be sectioned.

2. Select the top view from the graphics window; the cursor turns into a sketch cursor and you are prompted to enter the endpoints of the section line.

3. Move the cursor close to the midpoint of the extreme left vertical edge of the top view; the cursor snaps to the midpoint and turns green.

4. When the cursor snaps to the midpoint, move it horizontally toward the left to a little distance and specify a point there as the start point of the section plane.

5. Now, move the cursor horizontally toward the right.

6. Specify a point on the right of the extreme right vertical edge of the top view as the second point of the section plane. Note that the line should be horizontal, and not inclined.

7. Right-click and then choose **Continue** from the shortcut menu to display the **Section View** dialog box. The preview of the section view attached to the cursor is displayed and you are prompted to specify the location of the section view. Specify the location below the top view, as shown in Figure 11-47.

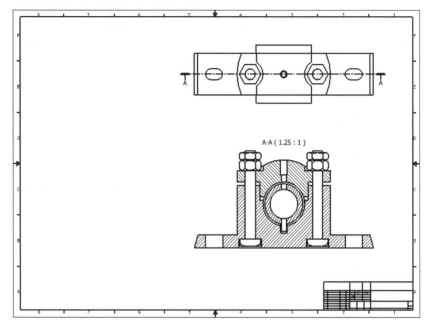

Figure 11-47 *Sheet with the top view and the sectioned front view*

Modifying Hatch Patterns

The section view displays three components in section: Casting, Cap, and Brasses. One of these components can retain the current hatching style and you need to modify the hatching style in the remaining two components. In this tutorial, Brasses will retain the current style and you will modify the hatching in Casting and Cap.

1. Move the cursor over the hatching in Casting; the hatching lines turn red. Next, right-click and choose **Edit** from the shortcut menu to display the **Edit Hatch Pattern** dialog box.

2. In this dialog box, select **ISO02W100** from the **Pattern** drop-down list and then select the **Double** check box. Choose **OK** to exit this dialog box; the hatching style of the selected component is modified.

3. Move the cursor over the hatching in Cap; the hatching lines turn red. Next, right-click to display the shortcut menu. Choose **Edit** from the shortcut menu to display the **Edit Hatch Pattern** dialog box.

4. Select the **Double** check box and then choose **OK** to exit this dialog box. All three components that are sectioned have different hatch patterns now.

Generating the Isometric View of the Section View

The third view that you need to generate is the isometric view of the section view. This view is generated using the shortcut menu.

1. Move the cursor on the section view to display the bounding box. Note that the cursor should not be over any hatch pattern. When the bounding box is displayed, right-click to display the shortcut menu. Choose **Create View > Projected View** from the shortcut menu; the preview of the projected view is attached to the cursor.

2. Move the cursor toward the left of the section view in the horizontal direction and then move the cursor upward until the preview of the isometric view attached to the cursor is displayed. When the isometric view is displayed, click to specify the point to define the location of this view.

3. Right-click and then choose **Create** from the shortcut menu; the isometric view of the section view is generated. The drawing sheet with all drawing views is shown in Figure 11-48.

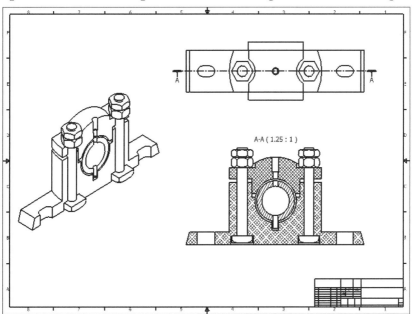

Figure 11-48 *Drawing sheet after generating all three views*

4. Save the drawing sheet with the name *Tutorial2.idw* at the location below and then close the file.

C:\Inventor_2011\c11\Plummer Block

The file is saved in the *Plummer Block* folder because the Plummer Block assembly file that was used to generate drawing views is stored in it.

Self-Evaluation Test

Answer the following questions and then compare them to those given at the end of this chapter:

1. You cannot generate the drawing views of an assembly file. (T/F)

2. The **Drawing** module of Autodesk Inventor is not bidirectional in nature. (T/F)

3. You can add more sheets for generating drawing views. (T/F)

4. The display type of a view set once can be modified later. (T/F)

5. In Autodesk Inventor, the cutting plane is defined by sketching one or more than one line. (T/F)

6. While generating the base view, you can display model dimensions by selecting the _____ check box in the **Display Options** tab of the **Drawing View** dialog box.

7. By default, the display type of the projected views is the same as that of the _____.

8. _____ views are generated by projecting the lines normal to a specified edge in the parent view.

9. The part of the original view that is sectioned will be displayed with _____ in the section view.

10. The **Slice** tool is used to create the _____ section views.

Review Questions

Answer the following questions:

1. You cannot prevent dependent views from getting deleted if the parent view is deleted. (T/F)

2. The hatch pattern of a component can be modified in the section view. (T/F)

3. You can prevent some components from getting sectioned in the section view. (T/F)

4. You can suppress the option to move the dependent views along with the parent view if you do not want to move them with the parent view. (T/F)

5. You can copy a selected drawing view in a new drawing file. (T/F)

6. Which of the following tools is used to sketch a drawing view?

   (a) **Draft**   (b) **Base**
   (c) **Section**   (d) None of these

7. Which of the following tabs is used to modify the orientation of the base view by using the **Drawing View** dialog box?

   (a) **Place Views**   (b) **Getting Started**
   (c) **Custom View**   (d) None of these

8. Which of the following tools is used to generate a drawing view by removing a small portion from its middle, keeping the ends of the component intact?

   (a) **Draft**   (b) **Base**
   (c) **Break**   (d) None of these

9. Which of the following tools is used to display the details of a portion of an existing view by magnifying that portion and displaying it as a separate view?

   (a) **Detail**   (b) **Base**
   (c) **Overlay**   (d) None of these

10. Which of the following tools in Autodesk Inventor can be used to generate isometric views?

   (a) **Draft**   (b) **Base**
   (c) **Projected**   (d) None of these

Exercise

Exercise 1

Generate the top view, right half sectioned front view, isometric view, and overlay view of the Double Bearing assembly with a scale of 2.5:1. Note that the overlay view should be created using positional reference. This assembly was created in *Tutorial 3* of the *c10* folder. The Nut that is intersected by the cutting plane should not be sectioned and the components should have different hatch patterns, as shown in Figure 11-49. Use the JIS standards for generating the views. **(Expected time: 45 min)**

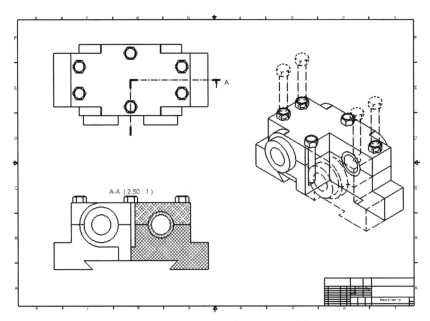

Figure 11-49 *Drawing views to be generated for Exercise 1*

Answers to Self-Evaluation Test

1. F, **2.** F, **3.** T, **4.** T, **5.** T, **6. Get Model Dimensions**, **7.** parent view, **8.** Auxiliary, **9.** hatching lines, **10.** zero-depth

Chapter 12

Working with Drawing Views-II

Learning Objectives

After completing this chapter, you will be able to:
- *Modify drawing standards.*
- *Insert additional sheets in the current drawing.*
- *Activate a drawing sheet.*
- *Add parametric and reference dimensions to drawing views.*
- *Modify the current sheet style.*
- *Create dimension styles.*
- *Modify a dimension and its appearance using the shortcut menu.*
- *Create and edit the parts list for assembly drawing views.*
- *Set the standard of the parts list.*
- *Add balloons to assembly drawing views.*

MODIFYING DRAWING STANDARDS

As mentioned in Chapter 11, by default, a selected sheet follows its standards in generating and dimensioning the drawing views. However, you can modify the standards of the current sheet. For example, you can open a JIS standard drawing file and assign the ANSI standards to it such that when you generate the drawing views and dimension them, the ANSI drafting standards are followed. You can modify the standards of the current sheet by choosing the **Styles Editor** tool from the **Styles and Standards** panel of the **Manage** tab. On doing so, the **Style and Standard Editor [Library - Read Only]** dialog box will be displayed. Select **All Styles** from the **Filter Styles** drop-down list on the top right corner of this dialog box. All available standards will be displayed under the **Standard** heading in the left pane of this dialog box and the current sheet standard will be displayed in bold face, as shown in Figure 12-1.

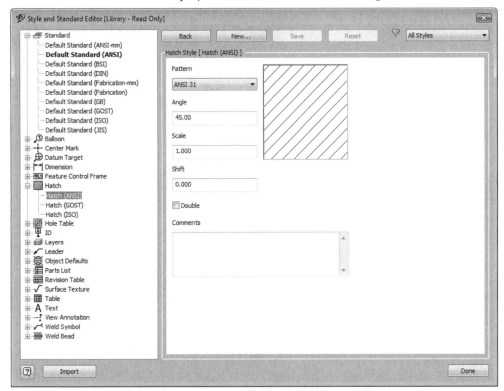

*Figure 12-1 The **Style and Standard Editor [Library - Read Only]** dialog box*

To assign a different standard to the current sheet, right-click on any standard and then choose the **Active** option from the shortcut menu; the selected standard will be assigned to the current sheet.

Using the options in the **Standard** area on the right pane of this dialog box, you can change the projection type from first angle to third angle in the **View Preferences** tab, and vice-versa. You can also select other headings from the left pane and expand them to display the standards for that heading. By selecting a standard, you can modify the options in it.

INSERTING ADDITIONAL SHEETS INTO DRAWING

Ribbon: Place Views > Sheets > New Sheet
Toolbar: Drawing Views Panel > New Sheet

New Sheet

When you open a new drawing file, only one sheet is available. However, you can insert more drawing sheets for generating the drawing views using the **New Sheet** tool. You can also insert a new drawing sheet by right-clicking in the **Browser Bar** or on the drawing sheet and choosing **New Sheet** from the shortcut menu. When you invoke this tool, a new sheet is automatically added. Note that the new sheet added will be the active sheet. An active sheet is the one on which you can generate the drawing views. The active sheet will be displayed with a white background in the **Browser Bar**. The other drawing sheets will be displayed with a gray background in the **Browser Bar**.

ACTIVATING A DRAWING SHEET

You can activate any drawing sheet by right-clicking on it in the **Browser Bar** and then choosing **Activate** from the shortcut menu, as shown in Figure 12-2. Note that if a sheet has already been activated, this option will not be available when you right-click on a sheet in the **Browser Bar**. You can also make a sheet active by double-clicking on it in the **Browser Bar**.

DISPLAYING DIMENSIONS IN DRAWING VIEWS

As mentioned in Chapter 11, you can display the model dimensions on the drawing views while generating them. Model dimensions are also called parametric dimensions and are the dimensions that were used to create the model in the part file. These are the dimensions that were applied on the sketches or in various dialog boxes while defining features. To display model dimensions while generating a

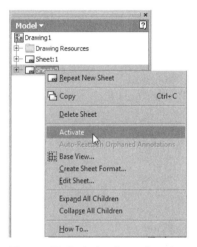

Figure 12-2 *Activating a drawing sheet using the **Browser Bar***

drawing view, select the **All Model Dimensions** check box in the **Display Options** tab of the **Drawing View** dialog box. Note that this option will not be activated when you generate the drawing views of an assembly.

You can retrieve the model dimensions after placing the drawing views and select the dimension that you need to retain. In addition to the model dimensions, Autodesk Inventor also allows you to add reference dimensions to the drawing views. The reference dimensions are those that were not applied to the model in the **Part** module. These dimensions are used only for reference and not during the manufacturing of a part. The methods of retrieving the model dimensions and placing the reference dimensions are discussed next.

Retrieving Parametric Dimensions in Drawing Views

Ribbon:	Annotate > Dimension > Retrieve
Toolbar:	Drawing Annotation Panel > Retrieve Dimensions

The **Retrieve** tool is used to retrieve the dimensions of a model after placing the drawing view. On invoking this tool, the **Retrieve Dimensions** dialog box will be displayed and you will be prompted to select a view, a draft view, or a drawing sheet sketch. When you select a view, the options in this dialog box will be enabled, refer to Figure 12-3. You can also select a drawing view and then right-click on it to display the shortcut menu. In the shortcut menu, choose

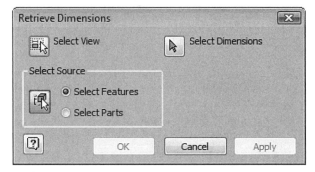

*Figure 12-3 The **Retrieve Dimensions** dialog box*

Retrieve Dimensions. You can use this dialog box to select the parts or features whose dimensions you want to retrieve. In this release of Autodesk Inventor, you can also retrieve dimensions from isometric drawing views and assembly views. The options in the **Retrieve Dimensions** dialog box are discussed next.

Tip. *Before retrieving dimensions, it is recommended that you first set the dimension style parameters first by expanding the **Dimension** option in the left pane of the **Style and Standard Editor [Library - Read Only]** dialog box and then modifying the required dimension style. You may have to select the **All Styles** option from the **Filter Style** drop-down list on the top right corner of the dialog box to display all styles. Before you exit this dialog box, choose the **Save** button to save the changes in the current style. Now, after invoking the **Retrieve Dimensions** dialog box, make the dimension style current by selecting it from the second drop-down list in the **Format** panel of the **Annotate** tab.*

Select View

This button is chosen to select the view, in which you want to retrieve the dimensions. Note that when you invoke the **Retrieve** tool using the **Ribbon** or using the toolbar, the **Select View** button is chosen by default and you are prompted to select the view, in which you want to retrieve the dimensions. Also, after retrieving the required dimensions in the selected view, you can choose this button again to select another view to retrieve the dimensions.

Select Source Area

The options in the **Select Source** area are used to specify whether you want to retrieve the dimensions of a selected feature or of the entire part. Depending on the source using which you want to retrieve the dimensions, select the radio button. Next, select the part or the feature in the view; the dimensions of the selected part or feature will be retrieved in that view.

Select Dimensions

You will notice that even after retrieving the dimensions of a selected feature or part, the **OK** button in the **Retrieve Dimensions** dialog box is not activated. This is because this command is not complete until you choose the **Select Dimensions** button and also select the dimensions that you want to retain. You can select the dimensions to be retained using a crossing or a window, or by selecting the dimensions individually.

After retrieving and selecting the dimensions, choose the **Apply** button to select another view to retrieve the dimensions. In this case, the retrieved dimensions will turn gray in color and the **Select View** button will be chosen to let you select another view for retrieving the dimensions. You can choose the **OK** button, if you do not want to select any other view to retrieve the dimensions.

Adding Reference Dimensions

Ribbon:	Annotate > Dimension > Dimension
Toolbar:	Drawing Annotation Panel > General Dimension

Dimension

Autodesk Inventor allows you to add reference dimensions to a drawing view. You can do so by using the **Dimension** tool of the drafting environment. The function of this tool is similar to that of the **Dimension** tool in the **Part** module. When you add a dimension to a drawing view, the **Edit Dimension** dialog box will be displayed. Using this dialog box, you can change different parameters of dimensions such as text, tolerance, and so on. The method of adding dimensions is also similar in both the tools.

MODIFYING THE MODEL DIMENSIONS

Autodesk Inventor allows you to modify model dimensions displayed in a drawing view. However, as mentioned earlier, all modules of Autodesk Inventor are bidirectionally associative. This nature of Autodesk Inventor ensures that if you modify a dimension value in the **Drawing** module, the modifications will be reflected on the model in the **Part** module. Therefore, you need to be very careful while modifying the model dimensions. To modify a model dimension, right-click on it and then choose **Edit Model Dimension** from the shortcut menu, see Figure 12-4. Based on the dimension selected to be edited, the dialog box or the **Edit Dimension** toolbar will be displayed with the current dimension value. You can modify the dimension value in the dialog box or in the toolbar and then exit the dialog box or the toolbar. You will notice that the dimension is modified and is reflected in the feature in the drawing views.

*Figure 12-4 Choosing **Edit Model Dimension** from the shortcut menu*

EDITING DRAWING SHEETS

Autodesk Inventor allows you to edit a selected drawing sheet. You can modify the size of a sheet, relocate a title block, modify the orientation of a drawing sheet, and so on. To edit a drawing sheet, right-click on its name in the **Browser Bar** and then choose **Edit Sheet** from the shortcut menu; the **Edit Sheet** dialog box will be displayed, as shown in Figure 12-5. The options in this dialog box are discussed next.

Format Area

The options in the **Format** area are used to define the name and size of the drawing sheet. These options are discussed next.

Name

The **Name** edit box is used to enter the name of the drawing sheet. The name you enter in this edit box will be displayed in the **Browser Bar**.

Size

The **Size** drop-down list is used to define the size of the drawing sheet. You can select predefined drawing sheet sizes from this drop-down list. To specify a user-defined size, select **Custom Size** (inches) or **Custom Size (mm)** from this drop-down list. Using these options, you can specify a user-defined size in inches or in millimeters. The height and width of the user-defined size will be defined in the **Height** and **Width** edit boxes. These edit boxes will be available below the **Size** drop-down list when you select the option to specify the user-defined size.

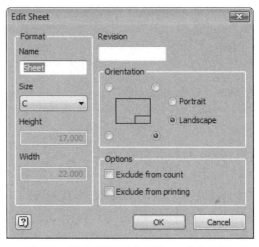

*Figure 12-5 The **Edit Sheet** dialog box*

Revision

The **Revision** edit box allows you to specify the revision number of the drawing sheets.

Orientation Area

The options in the **Orientation** area are used to specify the orientation of the sheet and the location of the title block. This area displays a sheet and has four radio buttons close to the four corners of the sheet. These radio buttons define the location of the title block in the sheet. By default, the radio button provided close to the lower right corner of the sheet is selected. This forces the title block to be placed on the lower right corner of the sheet. You can place the title block on any of the four corners by selecting their respective radio buttons. You can also define whether the orientation of the drawing sheet should be portrait or landscape by selecting the **Portrait** or **Landscape** radio button.

Options Area

The options in the **Options** area are discussed next.

Exclude from count

By default, when you open a drawing file, one sheet is available. This sheet is assigned number 1. If you add more sheets, they will be numbered 2, 3, and so on. Select the **Exclude from count** check box if you do not want the current sheet to be included in this count. On selecting this check box, the current sheet will not be assigned any number and the sheet numbers of the other sheets will be adjusted accordingly.

Exclude from printing

The **Exclude from printing** check box is selected to exclude the current sheet from printing. If this check box is selected, the current sheet will not be considered while printing.

CREATING DIMENSION STYLES

Dimension styles are used to control the appearance and positioning of the parameters related to dimensions. Autodesk Inventor provides a number of dimension styles that can be used to display dimensions. However, if a predefined dimension style does not meet your requirements, you can define a new dimension style and set its options based on your requirement. To create a new dimension style, choose the **Styles Editor** tool from the **Styles and Standards** panel of the **Manage** tab; the **Style and Standard Editor [Library - Read Only]** dialog box will be displayed. Expand the **Dimension** option from the left pane and then select the required dimension style. The options related to the **Default - mm (ANSI)** dimension style will be displayed in the right pane of the dialog box, as shown in Figure 12-6.

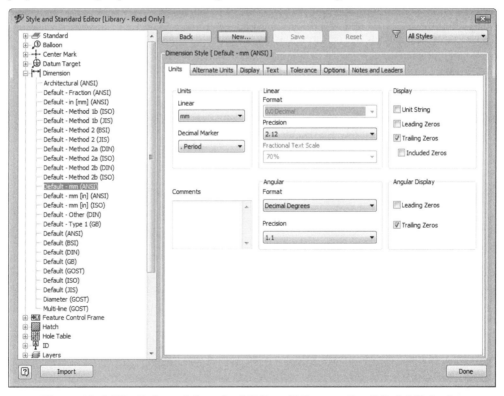

*Figure 12-6 The **Style and Standard Editor [Library - Read Only]** dialog box*

As evident from this figure, the right pane of the dialog box provides various tabs to set the options related to a dimension style. You can also create a new dimension style using this dialog box. To do so, choose the **New** button; the **New Local Style** dialog box will be displayed. Enter the name of the dimension style in this dialog box. Now, make the necessary changes in the parameters related to dimensions in the tabs of the **Style and Standard Editor [Library - Read**

Only] dialog box. After making all necessary changes, choose the **Save** button. The new drawing views will be dimensioned using this dimension style.

APPLYING DIMENSION STYLES

To apply a new dimension style to a dimension, select the required dimension from the drawing view and then right-click; a shortcut menu will be displayed. Choose **New Dimension Style** from the shortcut menu; the **New Dimension Style** dialog box will be displayed. Select the required dimension style from the list box in this dialog box; the options in the dialog box will modify accordingly. Next, choose **OK** to apply the selected dimension style to the dimension.

MODIFYING A DIMENSION AND ITS APPEARANCE USING THE SHORTCUT MENU

You can also modify a dimension and its appearance using the shortcut menu. This shortcut menu is displayed when you right-click on a dimension. Depending upon the type of dimension selected, the options are displayed in the shortcut menu. For example, Figure 12-7 shows the shortcut menu that will be displayed when you right-click on a linear dimension.

You can use this menu to control the display of extension lines, dimension text, leaders, arrowheads, and so on. To modify the dimension text, choose the **Edit** option from the shortcut menu; the **Edit Dimension** dialog box will be displayed, as shown in Figure 12-8. Select the **Hide Dimension Value** check box from the **Text** tab in this dialog box and enter the required value in the text box. Next, choose the **OK** button to exit this dialog box. To hide the extension lines of a dimension, select the required dimension from the drawing view and right-click to invoke the shortcut menu. Next, choose the **Hide Extension Line** option from the shortcut menu; the extension lines will be hidden.

ADDING THE PARTS LIST

Ribbon:	Annotate > Table > Parts List
Toolbar:	Drawing Annotation Panel > Parts List

Parts List

The parts list is a table, which provides information about the items, quantity, and other related description of components in an assembly. It is extremely useful for providing information related to the components of an assembly in the drawing views. On invoking the **Parts List** tool, the **Parts List** dialog box will be displayed, as shown in Figure 12-9. The options in this dialog box are discussed next.

Source Area

This area provides the options for selecting the source for generating the parts list. These options are discussed next.

Select View

This button is chosen by default in the **Parts List** dialog box and is used to select an existing drawing view as the source for generating the parts list.

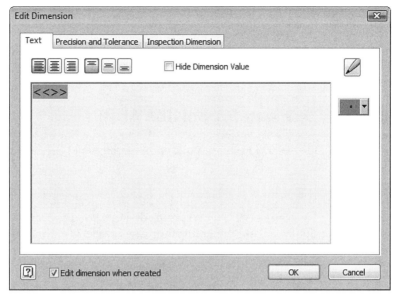

Figure 12-7 *Shortcut menu displayed*

Figure 12-8 *The* **Edit Dimension** *dialog box*

Figure 12-9 *The* **Parts List** *dialog box*

Browse for file

This button is chosen to select a file that will be used as a source to generate the parts list. When you choose this button, the **Open** dialog box will be displayed that can be used to select the file for generating the parts list. The name and location of the selected file is displayed in the drop-down list on the left of this button.

BOM Settings and Properties Area

The options in this area are used to specify the related to settings and properties related to BOM (Bill of Materials). These options are discussed next.

BOM View

This drop-down list is used to specify the Bill of Material view to be used for generating the parts list. You can select the **Structured**, **Parts Only**, **Structured (legacy)**, or **Parts Only (legacy)** options. If the **Structured** option is selected, the subassemblies in the main assembly will be displayed as a single item in the parts list and the individual components of the subassemblies will not be listed. However, if you select the **Parts Only** option, the components of the subassemblies will also be displayed. The **Structured (legacy)** option, if selected, determines and displays the nested components in an assembly and the changes made to them.

 Note

*If the **Parts Only** option is not turned on in the assembly document, an error message box will be displayed, stating that this option is not enabled. You can enable this option in the assembly document using this error message box.*

*The view properties are not available for the **Parts only (legacy)** option.*

Level/Numbering

The **Level** drop-down list is available when you select the **Structured** option from the **BOM View** drop-down list. This drop-down list is used to specify whether only the first level components will be displayed or all level components will be displayed in the BOM. The **Numbering** drop-down list is available when you select the **Parts Only** option from the **BOM View** drop-down list. You can specify whether the numbering for the components will be numeric or alpha.

Min. Digits

This drop-down list is used to set the minimum digits for numbering the components in the BOM. The range varies from 1 to 6.

Table Wrapping Area

The options in the **Table Wrapping** area are used to specify the format of the parts list. These options are generally used for the assemblies that have a large number of components. The parts list of such an assembly gets very lengthy. You can split it into two or three sections to reduce its length. However, in such parts lists, the width increases as the columns are increased by two or three times. The options in this area are discussed next.

Direction to Wrap Table

The **Left** and **Right** radio buttons in this area are used to specify the side of the parts list to which the additional section will be added if the number of sections are more than 1.

Enable Automatic Wrap

This check box is used to set the option for enabling automatic wrapping. When you select this check box, the **Maximum Rows** and **Number of Sections** radio buttons are enabled. The **Maximum Rows** radio button is used to specify the maximum number of rows after which the parts list will be wrapped to the specified side. You can specify the number of rows in the edit box available on the right of this radio button. The **Number of Sections** radio button is used to specify the number of sections in which the parts list will be split.

After setting the options in the **Part List** dialog box, choose the **OK** button; the dialog box will close and you will return to the drawing sheet. Also, you will notice that the parts list is attached to the cursor. Place the parts list at the desired point. Figure 12-10 shows the drawing views of the Double Bearing assembly with the parts list.

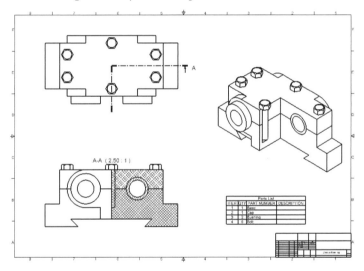

Figure 12-10 *Drawing views of an assembly with the parts list*

EDITING THE PARTS LIST

The default parts list, which is placed in an assembly, has only selected columns. To add more columns to the parts list or delete some of the columns from it, you need to edit it. To edit a parts list, right-click on it; a shortcut menu will be displayed. Choose **Edit Parts List** from the shortcut menu; the **Parts List** dialog box will be displayed, as shown in Figure 12-11. Alternatively, double-click on the parts list to invoke the **Parts List** dialog box.

In this dialog box, the default columns and values are displayed. You will notice that some of the values are displayed in red color and some in black color. To modify the value of any field, click on it and enter the new value. However, note that the fields displayed in red color cannot be modified. The other options in this dialog box are discussed next.

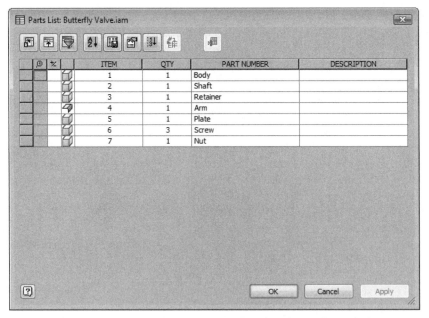

*Figure 12-11 The **Parts List** dialog box for editing the parts list*

Column Chooser

The **Column Chooser** button is used to select the columns that are displayed in the parts list. By default, the parts list displays some preselected columns. To display more columns in the parts list, choose this button; the **Parts List Column Chooser** dialog box will be displayed, as shown in Figure 12-12. This dialog box has two main areas: **Available Properties** and **Selected Properties**. The **Selected Properties** area displays all columns that are selected and displayed in the parts list. The **Available Properties** area displays all columns that can be selected for adding to the parts list. Select the column that you want to display in the parts list from the **Available Properties** area and then choose the **Add** button. On doing so, the selected column will be displayed in the **Selected Properties** area. Similarly, if you want to remove any column from the **Selected Properties** area, select the column and then choose the **Remove** button.

You can also define a new property by choosing the **New Property** button from this dialog box. On choosing this button, the **Define New Property** dialog box will be displayed. Enter the name of the property to be defined in the display box of this dialog box and then choose **OK**; the property will be added to the **Selected Properties** area of the **Parts List Column Chooser** dialog box. Next, choose **OK** from this dialog box; a new column with the defined property will be added to the **Parts List** dialog box.

Group Settings

The **Group Settings** button is chosen to invoke the **Group Settings** dialog box. You can use this dialog box to group similar items in the parts list.

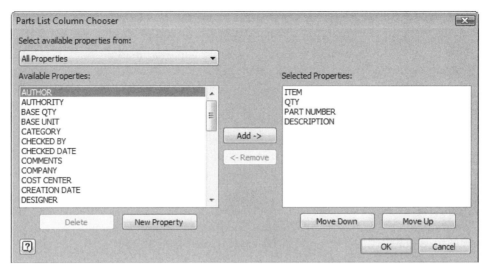

*Figure 12-12 The **Parts List Column Chooser** dialog box*

Filter Settings

The **Filter Settings** button is chosen to invoke the **Filter Settings** dialog box. You can use this dialog box to define the list of parts to be filtered. The **Filter Settings** dialog box updates the part list table according to the filtering conditions.

Sort

The **Sort** button is chosen to sort the items in the parts list. If you choose this button, the **Sort Parts List** dialog box will be displayed. Using this dialog box, you can sort the items in the parts list.

Export

The **Export** button is chosen to export the parts list to an external file. When you choose this button, the **Export Parts List** dialog box will be displayed. You can use this dialog box to specify the file type of the new file and its location.

Table Layout

The **Table Layout** button is chosen to define the heading of the parts list and its location in the table. When you choose this button, the **Parts List Table Layout** dialog box will be displayed. The name of the parts list can be specified in the edit box given below the **Title** check box and the location can be specified using the options which are displayed when you choose the button under the **Heading** area. If you choose the **No Heading** option, the heading of the parts list will not be displayed. This dialog box is also used to define the line spacing of the parts list.

Renumber Items

The **Renumber Items** button is chosen to renumber the items in the parts list. If the parts list has some items that are improperly numbered, they will be numbered according to their original numbering.

Save Item Overrides to BOM

 If you change the number of items in the **Item** column of the part list, then you need to choose this button to save the changes that you have made in the parts list to the assembly BOM.

Member Selection

 This button will be available only when you edit the parts list of an iAssembly. On choosing this button; the **Member Selection** dialog box will be displayed that allows you to select the members to be included in the parts list.

Adding/Removing Custom Parts

To add a custom part row, move the cursor over the gray color button on the extreme left of the **Parts List** dialog box; the cursor will be replaced by a small arrow pointing in the direction of the row. Next, right-click and choose the **Insert Custom Part** option from the shortcut menu; a new custom part row will be added.

To delete a custom part row, move the cursor over the gray color button on the extreme left of the custom row; the cursor will be replaced by a small arrow pointing in the direction of the row. Now, press the left mouse button. The custom row will be selected and highlighted in black color. Right-click on the selected row and choose **Remove Custom Part**; the custom part row will be removed.

Shortcut Menu Options

In addition to the buttons available in the **Parts List** dialog box, you can also use the shortcut menu to edit the parts list. This menu, shown in Figure 12-13, is displayed when you right-click on a column heading to modify the parts list. Most of the options in this shortcut menu are similar to those in the **Parts List** dialog box. The remaining options are discussed next.

Figure 12-13 Shortcut menu displayed by right-clicking on a column heading

Format Column

This option is used to modify the format of the columns in the parts list. When you choose this option, the **Format Column** dialog box will be displayed. You can use the **Column Format** tab of this dialog box to modify the justification and heading of the selected column. You can also modify the units formatting using this tab. You can use the **Substitution** tab of the **Format Column** dialog box to substitute the value of a selected field with that of the other selected field.

Column Width

This option is used to modify the width of the column. When you choose this option, the **Column Width** dialog box will be displayed. This dialog box will be used to modify the width of the columns in the parts list.

SETTING THE STANDARD FOR THE PARTS LIST

You can set the standard for the parts list using the **Style and Standard Editor [Library - Read Only]** dialog box. This dialog box is invoked when you choose the **Styles Editor** tool from the **Styles and Standards** panel of the **Manage** tab of the **Ribbon**. After invoking this dialog box, expand the **Parts List** option and then select the required parts list standard from it; the options related to the selected parts list standard will be displayed in the right pane, as shown in Figure 12-14. Using these options, you can set the parameters related to the parts list. After making the necessary modifications in the parts list standards, choose the **Save** button. You will notice that the changes are reflected in the parts list on the sheet.

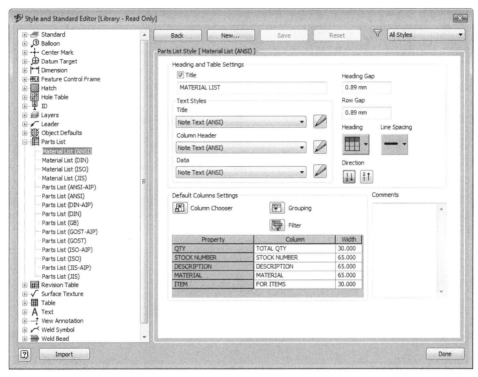

*Figure 12-14 The **Style and Standard Editor [Library - Read Only]** dialog box with the parts list options*

ADDING BALLOONS TO ASSEMBLY DRAWING VIEWS

Whenever you add the parts list to the assembly drawing views, all components in the assembly are listed in the parts list in a tabular form. You will notice that each component in the parts list is assigned a unique number. As a result, if an assembly has ten components, all of them will be listed in the parts list with a different serial number assigned to them. However, in the drawing views, there is no reference about these components. Therefore, if you are not familiar with the names of the components, it is difficult to recognize them in the drawing view. To avoid this confusion, Autodesk Inventor allows you to add callouts, called balloons, to the components in the drawing view. These callouts are based on the serial number of the components in the parts list. If the component is assigned serial number 1 in the parts list, the callout will also show number 1. Balloons make it convenient to relate the components in the parts list to those in the drawing view. You can add balloons to the selected components manually or automatically. The methods of adding balloons are discussed next.

Adding Balloons to Selected Components

Ribbon:	Annotate > Table > Balloon drop-down > Balloon
Toolbar:	Drawing Annotation Panel > Balloon

 You can add balloons to the selected components in a drawing view by using the **Balloon** tool, see Figure 12-15. To do so, you need to invoke the **Balloon** tool. After invoking this tool, move the cursor over one of the edges of the component to which you want to add the balloon; the component will be highlighted in red. Also, a plus sign (+) will be displayed on the right of the cursor. Select the edge and move the cursor away from the component; one end of the balloon will be attached to the component and the other end will be attached to the cursor. Specify a point for placing the balloon and right-click to display the shortcut menu. In the shortcut menu, choose **Continue** to place a balloon. You will notice that a callout is added to the selected component and the name of the callout is the same as that in the parts list. Remember that you can add as many balloons as you want by selecting the edges of components.

Remember that if you have not created the parts list of the component(s) before invoking this tool, the **BOM Properties** dialog box that will be displayed will look the one shown in Figure 12-16. This dialog box is used to define the source file and the BOM settings to create item number for balloons. The options in this dialog box are similar to those of the **Parts List** dialog box explained earlier in this chapter.

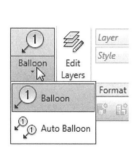

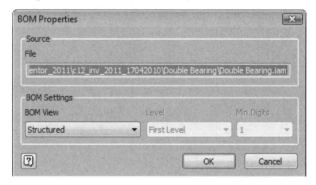

Figure 12-15 *Tools in the **Balloon** drop-down*

Figure 12-16 *The **BOM Properties** dialog box*

Adding Automatic Balloons

Ribbon:	Annotate > Table > Balloon drop-down > Auto Balloon
Toolbar:	Drawing Annotation Panel > Balloon > Auto Balloon

 You can also automatically add balloons to all components in a selected drawing view in a single attempt. To do so, choose the **Auto Balloon** tool from the **Table** panel in the **Annotate** tab, see Figure 12-15; the **Auto Balloon** dialog box will be displayed, as shown in Figure 12-17. The options in this dialog box are discussed next.

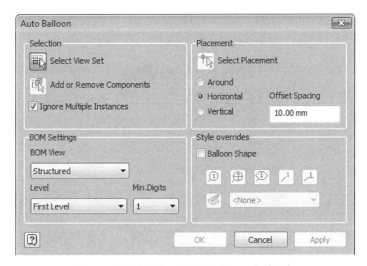

Figure 12-17 The **Auto Balloon** *dialog box*

Selection Area

This area provides the options to select the view and the components to which the balloons will be added. When you invoke the **Auto Balloon** dialog box, the **Select View Set** button in this area will be chosen automatically and you will be prompted to select the view to add balloons. As soon as you select the view, the **Add / Remove Components** button will be chosen and you will be prompted to select the components for ballooning. You can use window or crossing selection methods to select multiple components. The **Ignore Multiple Instances** check box is selected by default because of which the multiple instances of the same component are not ballooned.

Placement Area

The options in the **Placement** area are automatically enabled as soon as you select the components to be ballooned. Using the options in this area, you can specify whether the balloons should be placed along a horizontal or a vertical line, or around the view. The distance between the balloons can be set using the **Offset Spacing** edit box in this area. After selecting the option to place the balloon, choose the **Select Placement** button in this area; the preview of the balloons will be displayed and you will be prompted to select the balloon placement. If you are not satisfied with the orientations of the balloons after placing them, you can select any other option from the **Auto Balloon** dialog box. You can also choose the **Select Placement** button and place the balloons again.

BOM Settings Area

The options in this area are similar to those mentioned in the **Parts List** dialog box.

Style overrides Area

The options in this area are used to override the default balloon styles. To override the style, select the **Balloon Shape** check box and then select the required balloon shape. If the current drawing document has some sketch symbols, you can override them also by choosing the **User-Defined Symbol** button. When you choose this button, the drop-down list in this area becomes available and you can select the required sketch symbol.

After placing the balloons, choose **OK** from the **Auto Balloon** dialog box. Figure 12-18 shows a drawing sheet with the parts list and balloons added to the components in the drawing view.

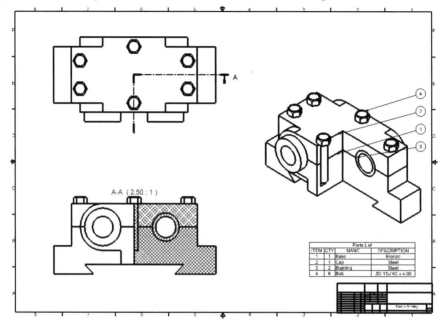

Figure 12-18 Drawing sheet with the parts list and balloons

Tip. *You can modify the styles of balloons using the **Style and Standard Editor** [**Library - Read Only**] dialog box. Invoke this dialog box and then expand the **Balloon** option. Now, select the desired balloon style and modify its parameters from the **Balloon Style** area in the right pane of the dialog box. Save the style before you exit.*

*Balloons use the default styles for arrowheads and text. Therefore, to modify these styles, you need to modify the respective sub-styles from the **Sub-styles** area in the right pane of the **Style and Standard Editor** [**Library - Read Only**] dialog box when the balloon options are displayed. After setting the sub-styles, you can choose the **Back** button to restore the balloon options.*

ADDING TEXT TO A DRAWING SHEET

Autodesk Inventor allows you to add user-defined text to a drawing sheet. Depending upon your requirement, you can add multiline text with or without a leader. The methods of adding both types of text are discussed next.

Adding Multiline Text without a Leader

Ribbon: Annotate > Text > Text
Toolbar: Drawing Annotation Panel > Text

You can add multiline text without a leader using the **Text** tool. On invoking this tool, you will be prompted to specify the location of the text or specify a rectangle by dragging the mouse to define the bounding box of the text. After you specify the location of the text or the bounding box of the text, the **Format Text** dialog box will be displayed, as shown in Figure 12-19. Enter text in the text box of this dialog box. You can also modify the format, style, and alignment of a text by using this dialog box.

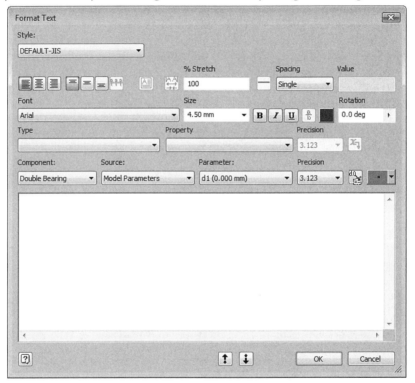

*Figure 12-19 The **Format Text** dialog box*

After writing the text in the text box, choose the **OK** button; the text will be placed at the specified location. Note that after placing the text, you will be prompted again to define the location of the text or define a box by using two points. This means you can define the text at as many locations as you want in a single attempt. You can exit this tool by pressing the ESC key.

Tip. *You can edit text by double-clicking on it. Alternatively, right-click on it and then choose the **Edit Text** option from the shortcut menu. On doing so, the **Format Text** dialog box is displayed with the current text. Next, you can modify it as required.*

Adding Multiline Text with Leader

Ribbon:	Annotate > Text > Leader Text
Toolbar:	Drawing Annotation Panel > Leader Text

A text with a leader is generally added to the entities to which you want to point and add some information. You can add the text with a leader using the **Leader Text** tool. After invoking this tool, select the entity to which you want to add the leader text. As you move the cursor close to an entity, it will be highlighted in red. Also, the symbol of the coincident constraint will be attached to the cursor. This symbol indicates that the coincident constraint will be added between the selected entity and the arrowhead of the leader. After selecting the entity, move the cursor away and define the second vertex of the leader. You can define as many vertices as you want in the leader line. Once you have defined the leader line, right-click to display the shortcut menu and choose **Continue**; the **Format Text** dialog box will be displayed. This dialog box is similar to the one that is displayed when you invoke the **Text** tool. You can enter the text in this dialog box and then choose **OK**. The leader text will be added to the drawing sheet. Figure 12-20 shows a drawing sheet after adding text with and without a leader.

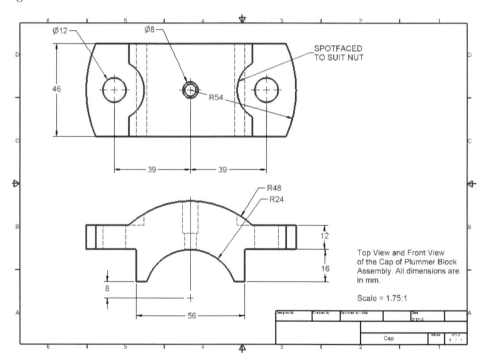

Figure 12-20 *Drawing sheet after adding text with and without a leader*

Note

*To add a center mark to a circle, choose the **Center Mark** tool from the **Symbols** panel of the **Annotate** tab in the **Ribbon** and then select the circle.*

TUTORIALS

Tutorial 1

In this tutorial, you will generate the top view, front view, right-side view, and isometric view of the model created in Exercise 1 of Chapter 5. You will use the ANSI mm standard drawing sheet of A2 size. Dimension the drawing views, as shown in Figure 12-21. You will create a new dimension style with the name **Custom** for dimensioning the drawing view. This dimension style has the following specifications: **(Expected time: 30 min)**

Dimension Units: **mm**
Linear Precision: **0**
Text Size: **5 mm**
Terminator Length: **5 mm**
Terminator Width: **2 mm**

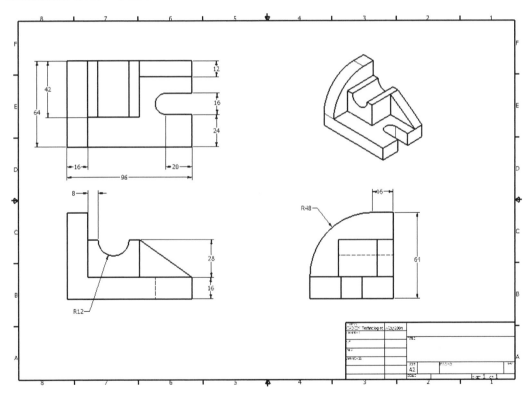

Figure 12-21 The dimensioned drawing views to be generated for Tutorial 1

The following steps are required to complete this tutorial:

a. Copy the model of Exercise 1 of Chapter 5 to the current folder and then start a new ANSI mm standard drawing file.
b. Create a new dimension style with the name **Custom** and modify the parameters as given in the tutorial description.
c. Generate the required drawing views.
d. Retrieve the model dimensions in the drawing views. Drag dimensions so that they are displayed as desired.

Copying the Model to the Current Folder

As mentioned in the previous chapter, you need to copy the model whose drawing views are being generating to the current folder.

1. Create a folder with the name *c12* at the location *C:\Inventor_2011*.

2. Copy the file *Exercise1.ipt* from *C:\Inventor_2011\c05* to the *c12* folder and then rename it *Tutorial1.ipt*.

Starting a New Drawing File

As mentioned in the tutorial description, you need to start a new ANSI mm standard drawing sheet for generating drawing views.

1. Choose the **New** tool to invoke the **New File** dialog box. Next, choose the **Metric** tab and double-click on the **ANSI (mm).idw** option; the default ANSI mm standard drawing sheet is displayed.

2. Right-click on **Sheet:1** in the **Browser Bar** and then choose **Edit Sheet** from the shortcut menu to invoke the **Edit Sheet** dialog box.

3. Select **A2** from the **Size** drop-down list and choose **OK** to close the **Edit Sheet** dialog box.

Creating the Dimension Style

As mentioned in the tutorial description, you need to create a new dimension style with the defined settings. You will create the new dimension style, taking the ANSI mm dimension style as the base style.

1. Choose the **Styles Editor** tool from the **Styles and Standards** panel of the **Manage** tab in the **Ribbon**; the **Style and Standard Editor [Library - Read Only]** dialog box is displayed.

2. Select **Local Styles** from the **Filter Styles** drop-down list at the upper right corner of the dialog box, if it has not already been selected.

3. Click on the plus sign (+) located on the left of **Dimension** in the left pane of the dialog box to display the available local dimension styles.

4. Select **Default - mm (ANSI)** from the list and then choose the **New** button; the **New Local Style** dialog box is displayed. Enter **Custom** as the name of the new dimension style in the **New Local Style** dialog box. Next, choose **OK** to exit this dialog box; a new dimension style is created with the name **Custom**. The parameters related to this dimension style are displayed in various tabs in the **Dimension Style [Custom]** area at the right pane of this dialog box.

5. Select **0** from the **Precision** drop-down list in the **Linear** area of the **Units** tab. The precision for a linear dimension is forced to 0. This means no digit will be displayed after decimal in dimensions.

6. Choose the **Text** tab to display the text options. Next, choose the **Vertical Dimensions** button in the **Orientation** area to display a flyout and then choose the first button from this flyout. This forces the text of the vertical dimension to be placed horizontally.

7. Similarly, choose the **Aligned Dimensions** button to display a flyout and then choose the first button from this flyout; the text of the aligned dimensions is also placed horizontally.

8. Choose the **Save** button to save these changes made in the dimension style.

9. Now, choose the **Edit Text Style** button provided on the right of the **Primary Text Style** drop-down list to display the text parameters.

10. Enter **5** in the **Text Height** edit box in the **Character Formatting** area and press ENTER.

11. Choose the **Save** button and then the **Back** button to redisplay the dimension style parameters.

12. Choose the **Display** tab to set attributes for terminators of dimensions. In the **Terminator** area, enter **5** as the value of size in the **Size (X)** edit box and enter **2** as the value of height in the **Height (Y)** edit box. Choose **Save** to save the changes made in the dimension style and then choose **Done** to exit the dialog box.

Generating the Drawing Views

In this tutorial, you need to generate four drawing views. The base view is the top view and the remaining views are the projected views. The front view is generated by using the top view as the parent view, and the right-side view and the isometric view are generated by using the front view as the parent view. Note that while generating drawing views, dimensions are not displayed. They are displayed only after generating drawing views.

1. Using the **Base** tool in the **Create** panel of the **Place Views** tab, generate the top view and then the front view of the *Tutorial1* part file that you have copied in the beginning of this tutorial. The scale of the views is 1.5. Place the top view close to the top left corner of the drawing sheet and the front view below the top view. Before placing the views, make sure that the **Create projected views immediately after the base view creation** check box is selected. Otherwise, you need to create the front view separately by using the **Projected** tool.

2. Taking the front view as the parent view, generate the right-side view and the isometric view. Modify the scale of the isometric view to **1**, see Figure 12-22.

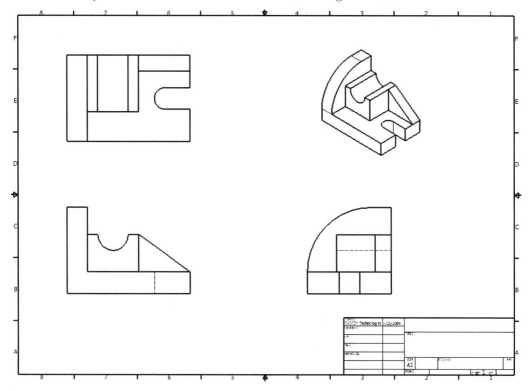

Figure 12-22 *Drawing sheet after generating the drawing views*

Retrieving the Model Dimensions

1. Move the cursor over the top view and right-click when the dotted rectangle is displayed; a shortcut menu is displayed.

2. Choose **Retrieve Dimensions** from the shortcut menu; the **Retrieve Dimensions** dialog box is displayed.

3. Select the **Custom** option from second drop-down list in the **Format** panel of the **Annotate** tab to apply the **Custom** dimension style to the dimensions to be retrieved.

4. Select the **Select Parts** radio button in the **Select Source** area and then select the part in the top view; dimensions are displayed.

5. Choose the **Select Dimensions** button from the **Retrieve Dimensions** dialog box and then drag the cursor around the dimensions to be retained. Next, choose the **Apply** button; the selected dimensions in the top view are retrieved and the **Select View** button is automatically chosen in the **Retrieve Dimensions** dialog box.

6. Select the front view, and then select the part in the front view; the dimensions in the front view are retrieved. Choose the **Select Dimensions** button and then drag a window around the dimensions to be retained. Next, choose the **Apply** button from the **Retrieve Dimensions** dialog box.

7. Similarly, retrieve the dimensions in the right-side view. Choose the **OK** button to exit the **Retrieve Dimensions** dialog box.

8. Use the **Dimension** tool to add the missing dimensions, refer to Figure 12-21.

   You will notice that the dimensions that are displayed on these drawing views are staggered and not aligned. You need to align these dimensions by dragging them.

9. Select the dimensions one by one and drag them to place them neatly in the drawing views. The sheet after aligning the dimensions is shown in Figure 12-23.

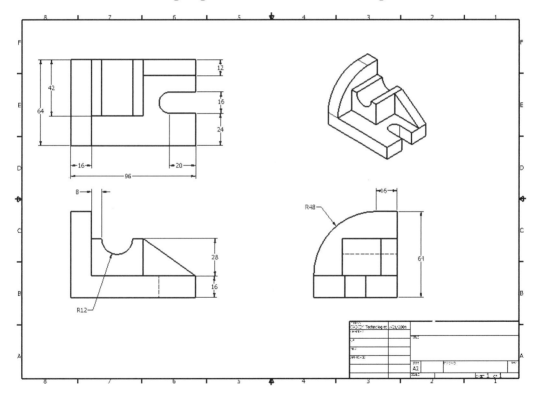

Figure 12-23 Drawing sheet after adding the dimensions

10. Save the file with the name *Tutorial1.idw* at the location *C:\Inventor_2011\c12* and then close the file.

Tutorial 2

In this tutorial, you will open the drawing views of the Double Bearing assembly generated in Exercise 1 of the *c11* folder. Note that in Exercise 1 of the *c11* folder, the drawing views were generated with positional representation. But, in this tutorial, you will create the parts list of the drawing views without positional representation. After opening the drawing views, you will add the parts list and balloons to components. Note that you will add the balloons to the isometric view of the sectioned front view. The final parts list should appear, as shown in Figure 12-24. **(Expected time: 45 min)**

Parts List			
ITEM	QTY	NAME	DESCRIPTION
1	1	Base	Bronze
2	1	Cap	Steel
3	2	Bushing	Steel
4	6	Bolt	.50–13UNC X 4.00

Figure 12-24 *Parts list for Tutorial 2*

The following steps are required to complete this tutorial:

a. Copy the *Double Bearing* folder from the *C:\Inventor_2011\c11* folder to the current folder.
b. Open the *Exercise1.idw* file in this folder.
c. Place the default parts list by using the **Parts List** tool. Use the isometric view of the sectioned front view for placing the parts list.
d. Modify the parts list such that it appears as the one shown in Figure 12-24.
e. Add balloons to the components in the isometric view by using the **Balloon** tool.

Copying the Double Bearing Folder to the Current Folder

1. Copy the *Double Bearing* folder from *C:\Inventor_2011\c11* to the current folder.

2. Open the *Exercise1.idw* file from the location *C:\Inventor_2011\c12*.

The drawing file is opened with the top view, sectioned front view, and isometric view generated in Exercise 1 of Chapter 11.

Placing the Parts List

As mentioned earlier, the parts list is placed using the **Parts List** tool. But, when you place the parts list, the data will be listed in it using the default parameters. For example, the fields under the **DESCRIPTION** column do not display any data. You need to modify the parts list after placing it so that it appears as the one shown in Figure 12-24.

1. Choose the **Parts List** tool from the **Table** panel of the **Annotate** tab; the **Parts List** dialog box is displayed.

    As mentioned earlier, the parts list can be placed taking the reference of a drawing view. It is recommended that the drawing view that you use as a reference for placing the parts list should have all components. On doing so, all components are listed in the parts list.

2. Select the isometric view as the reference view for placing the parts list.

3. Accept the other default options in this dialog box and choose the **OK** button to exit this dialog box.

    On exiting the dialog box, a rectangle attached to the cursor is displayed on the screen. This rectangle is the parts list that will be placed at the specified point.

4. Specify the location of the parts list at the bottom right corner of the sheet above the title block. The sheet with the default parts list is shown in Figure 12-25.

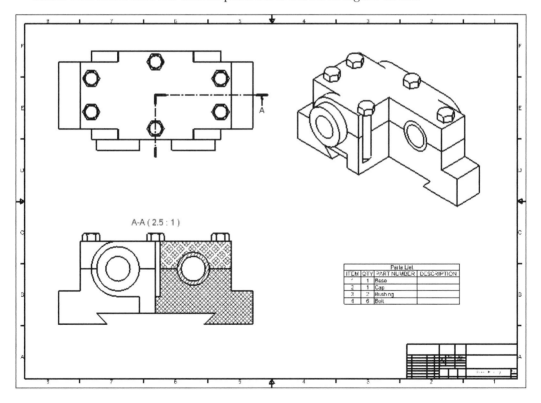

Figure 12-25 *Drawing sheet with the default parts list*

Modifying the Parts List

When you place a parts list in the drawing views, it is displayed in the drawing sheet and in the **Browser Bar**. You need to modify the parts list and the heading **PART NUMBER** to **NAME**. Also, you need to enter data in the fields below the **DESCRIPTION** column and center-align the data in this column.

1. Double-click on the parts list in the drawing sheet; the **Parts List** dialog box is displayed.

2. Click on the first field below the **DESCRIPTION** column and type **Bronze**.

3. Similarly, click on the remaining fields in the **DESCRIPTION** column and enter description about the remaining components. For more information about the data to be entered, refer to Figure 12-24.

   By default, the data in the **DESCRIPTION** column is left-aligned. You need to modify the alignment such that the text is center-aligned.

4. Move the cursor over the heading **DESCRIPTION**. You will notice that the cursor is replaced with an arrow pointing downward.

5. Right-click and then choose **Format Column** from the shortcut menu; the **Format Column : DESCRIPTION** dialog box is displayed.

6. Choose the **Center** button on the right of **Value** in the **Justification** area to center-align the data in the fields below the **DESCRIPTION** heading. Choose **OK** to exit this dialog box.

   You will notice that the data in the selected field is center-aligned.

7. Right-click on the **DESCRIPTION** heading again and then choose the **Column Width** option from the shortcut menu. Enter **60** in the **Column Width** edit box and choose **OK**. This increases the width of the fields below the **DESCRIPTION** heading.

   By default, the heading of the column that displays the name of the components is **PART NUMBER**. You need to modify this heading to **NAME**.

8. Move the cursor over the heading **PART NUMBER** and right-click when the cursor is replaced with an arrow. Next, choose **Format Column** from the shortcut menu; the **Format Column : PART NUMBER** dialog box is displayed.

9. Enter **NAME** in the **Heading** edit box and choose **OK** to exit the **Format Column : PART NUMBER** dialog box.

10. Next, choose the **OK** button to exit the **Parts List** dialog box. The sheet after editing the parts list is shown in Figure 12-26.

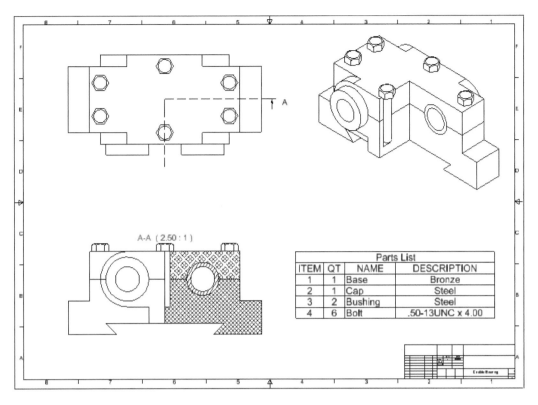

Figure 12-26 Drawing sheet after modifying the parts list

Adding Balloons to the Components

As mentioned earlier, balloons are the callouts that are attached to the components in the drawing view so that they can be referred to in the parts list. These balloons are based on the item numbers in the parts list. You can add balloons using the **Balloon** tool or the **Auto Balloon** tool. In this tutorial, balloons are added using the **Balloon** tool.

Before you add balloons, you need to set the parameters related to them.

1. Invoke the **Style and Standard Editor [Library - Read Only]** dialog box and then expand the **Balloon** option in the left pane.

2. Select the **Balloon (JIS)** option from the left pane; the parameters related to this balloon standard are displayed in the right pane of the dialog box.

3. Choose the **Edit Leader Style** button on the right of the **Leader Style** drop-down list.

4. Select the **Filled** option from the **Arrowhead** drop-down list in the **Terminator** area.

5. Enter **6** in the **Size (X)** edit box and **2** in the **Height (Y)** edit box in the **Terminator** area. Save the changes and then exit the dialog box.

6. Choose the **Balloon** tool from **Annotate > Table > Balloon** drop-down; you are prompted to select a component. Move the cursor over one of the edges of the Bolt at the upper left corner of the assembly in the isometric view; the component is highlighted and turns red. The plus sign is displayed on the left of the cursor.

7. Select the bolt; the start point of the balloon is attached to the selected edge of the bolt and the other end of the balloon is attached to the cursor.

 Tip. *If you have selected a wrong component for adding the balloon, you can deselect it from the current selection set before choosing **Continue** from the shortcut menu. To do so, right-click and then choose **Back** from the shortcut menu.*

8. Specify the location of the other end of the balloon above the view, refer to Figure 12-27.

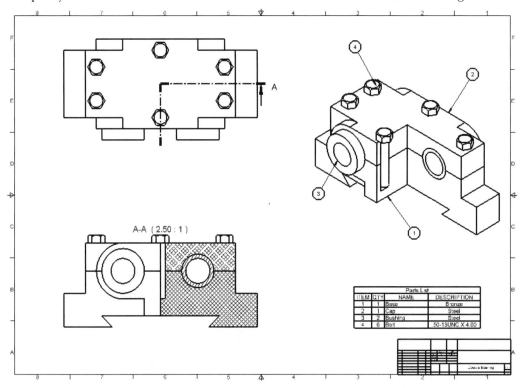

Figure 12-27 Drawing sheet after adding balloons

9. Now, right-click and then choose **Continue** from the shortcut menu; a balloon is created and it displays the number 4 inside the circle. Note that number 4 corresponds to the Bolt in the parts list.

10. Next, move the cursor over the circular edge of the Bushing, which is not sectioned in the isometric view. Select it when it is highlighted; one end of the balloon is attached to the edge.

11. Specify the location of the other end of the balloon on the left of the view, refer to Figure 12-27. Right-click to display the shortcut menu and then choose **Continue** from it to place the balloon.

12. Similarly, add balloons to the Base and the Cap, refer to Figure 12-27.

13. After placing balloons, right-click to display the shortcut menu. Choose **Done** from it to exit this tool. The drawing sheet after adding the parts list and balloons is shown in Figure 12-27.

Tip. *If you double-click on the parts list after adding balloons to components, you will notice that the symbols of the balloon is displayed in front of all components in the **Parts List** dialog box. These symbols suggest that the balloons corresponding to the components are added to the drawing sheet.*

*To change the arrowhead of a balloon, right-click on it and then choose **Edit Arrowhead**; the **Change Arrowhead** toolbar will be displayed with a drop-down list. Now, you can select the required arrowhead style from this drop-down list.*

14. Save the file with the name *Tutorial2.idw* at the location *C:\Inventor_2011\c12\Double Bearing* and then close the file.

Note

If the drawing file consists of more than one sheet, irrespective of which sheet was active while closing the file, the first sheet will be active when you open the drawing file next time.

Tutorial 3

In this tutorial, you will generate the drawing views of the Drill Press Vice assembly created in Exercise 1 of Chapter 9. The drawing views that need to be generated are shown in Figure 12-28. The parts list should appear as the one shown in Figure 12-29. You will use the ANSI mm standard sheet and the A3 size sheet for generating the drawing views.

(Expected time: 45 min)

The following steps are required to complete this tutorial:

a. Copy the *Drill Press Vice* folder from the *c09* folder to the *c12* folder. Start a new ANSI mm standard drawing file using the **Metric** tab of the **New File** dialog box.
b. Modify the sheet to the A3 size sheet.
c. Modify the drafting standards and generate the required drawing views.
d. Add the parts list and modify it such that it resembles the one shown in Figure 12-29.
e. Add balloons to components.

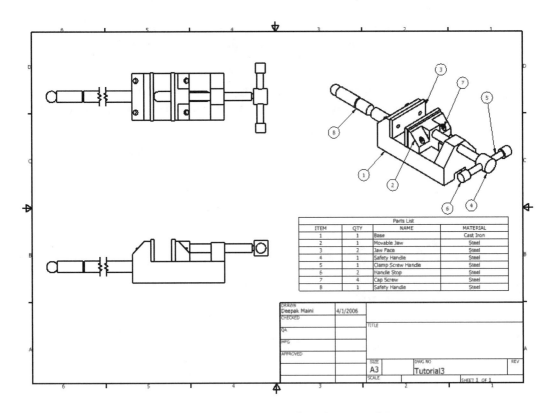

Figure 12-28 Drawing sheet for Tutorial 3

Parts List			
ITEM	QTY	NAME	MATERIAL
1	1	Base	Cast Iron
2	1	Movable Jaw	Steel
3	2	Jaw Face	Steel
4	1	Clamp Screw	Steel
5	1	Clamp Screw Handle	Steel
6	2	Handle Stop	Steel
7	4	Cap Screw	Steel
8	1	Safety Handle	Steel

Figure 12-29 Parts list to be added

Copying the Drill Press Vice Assembly

1. Copy the *Drill Press Vice* folder from the location *C:\Inventor_2011\c09* to the *c12* folder.

Starting a New ANSI mm Standard File

1. Start a new metric file with ANSI mm standards.

    The default ANSI mm standard drawing sheet is displayed. The size of the default sheet is C. You need to change this size to A3.

2. Right-click on **Sheet:1** in the **Browser Bar** and then choose **Edit Sheet** from the shortcut menu; the **Edit Sheet** dialog box is displayed.

3. Select **A3** from the **Size** drop-down list in the **Format** area. Choose **OK** to exit the dialog box; the sheet size changes to A3.

Generating the Drawing Views

1. Generate the top view of the Drill Press Vice assembly with a scale of 0.5. Break the view such that the length of the Safety Handle is reduced.

2. Generate the front and isometric views, as shown in Figure 12-30.

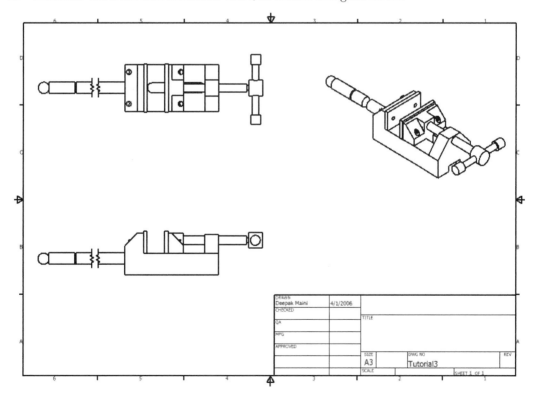

Figure 12-30 Drawing sheet after generating the drawing views

Placing the Parts List

Parts
List

1. Choose the **Parts List** tool from the **Table** panel of the **Annotate** tab; the **Parts List** dialog box is displayed

2. Select the isometric view as the reference view for placing the parts list.

3. Accept the default options in this dialog box and choose **OK**. A rectangle, which is actually the parts list, gets attached to the cursor and you are prompted to specify the location of the parts list.

4. Place the parts list above the title block.

Modifying the Parts List

1. Double-click on the parts list to display the **Parts List** dialog box.

2. Right-click on the **DESCRIPTION** heading and then choose the **Format Column** option from the shortcut menu; the **Format Column : DESCRIPTION** dialog box is displayed. Enter **MATERIAL** as the heading of this column in the **Heading** edit box.

3. Choose the **Center** button on the right of **Value** in the **Justification** area to center-align the data in the **MATERIAL** column. Next, choose **OK** to exit this dialog box.

4. Similarly, right-click on the **PART NUMBER** column and modify its heading to **NAME** in the **Heading** edit box of the **Format Column : PART NUMBER** dialog box.

5. Enter data in the **MATERIAL** field, based on the parts list shown in Figure 12-29. Choose **OK** to exit the dialog box.

Adding Balloons to the Components

The final step in this tutorial is to add balloons to the components in the isometric view. In this assembly, you will add balloons using the **Balloon** tool. Also, you need to drag balloons such that they are placed at proper locations in the drawing sheet. But before generating balloons, you need to modify the balloon style.

1. Invoke the **Style and Standard Editor [Library - Read Only]** dialog box and then expand the **Balloon** option in the left pane.

2. Select the **Balloon (ANSI)** option; the parameters related to this balloon standard are displayed on the right pane of the dialog box.

3. Choose the **Edit Leader Style** button on the right of the **Leader Style** drop-down list to display the leader parameters.

4. Enter **4** in the **Size (X)** edit box and **1.5** in the **Height (Y)** edit box. Choose **Save** and then **Done** to exit this dialog box; the size of arrowheads in the balloons is increased.

5. Choose the **Balloon** tool from **Annotate > Table > Balloon** drop-down; you are prompted to select a component.

6. Move the cursor over one of the edges of the Base in the isometric view for adding the balloon. Next, move the cursor away from the Base and place it below the component, refer to Figure 12-31. Right-click and then choose **Continue** from the shortcut menu.

7. Similarly, add balloons to the remaining components, refer to Figure 12-31.

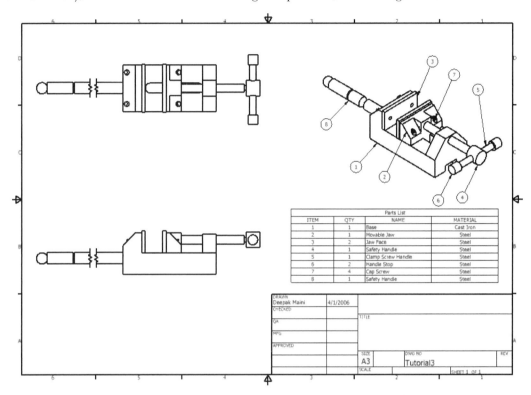

Parts List table content:

ITEM	QTY	NAME	MATERIAL
1	1	Base	Cast Iron
2	1	Movable Jaw	Steel
3	2	Jaw Face	Steel
4	1	Safety Handle	Steel
5	1	Clamp Screw Handle	Steel
6	2	Handle Stop	Steel
7	4	Cap Screw	Steel
8	1	Safety Handle	Steel

Title block:

DRAWN Deepak Maini	4/1/2006			
CHECKED		TITLE		
QA				
MFG				
APPROVED		SIZE A3	DWG NO Tutorial3	REV
		SCALE		SHEET 1 OF 1

Figure 12-31 Final drawing sheet for Tutorial 3

8. Drag balloons to a proper location in the drawing sheet. The final drawing sheet after adding the parts list and balloons is shown in Figure 12-31.

9. Save this file with the name *Tutorial3* at the location *C:\Inventor_2011\c12\Drill Press Vice* and then close the file.

Self-Evaluation Test

Answer the following questions and then compare them to those given at the end of this chapter:

1. The drafting standards of a drawing sheet can be modified using the **Style and Standard Editor [Library - Read Only]** dialog box. (T/F)

2. You can add parametric dimensions and reference dimensions to drawing views. (T/F)

3. You can modify an existing dimension style with a new dimension style. (T/F)

4. The default parts list cannot be modified. (T/F)

5. You can add the parts list to the assembly drawing views using the _____ tool.

6. You can add a multiline text without a leader using the _____ tool.

7. When you open a new drawing file, only _____ sheet is available by default.

8. The _____ make it convenient to relate the components in the parts list to the components in the drawing views.

9. You can modify the size of a drawing sheet by using the _____ dialog box.

10. If you assemble some of the components in a separate assembly file and insert the subassembly in the current assembly file, the components of the subassembly are called _____ components.

Review Questions

Answer the following questions:

1. You cannot control the line weight of lines in drawing views. (T/F)

2. Whenever you open an old drawing file that has more than one sheet, the sheet that was active last time is displayed as the active sheet. (T/F)

3. You can modify the size of the arrowheads of balloons using the **Style and Standards Editor [Library - Read Only]** dialog box. (T/F)

4. Autodesk Inventor allows you to add a user-defined text to a drawing sheet. (T/F)

5. You can edit text by double-clicking on it. (T/F)

6. Which of the following tools is used to add text along with a leader?

    (a) **Text**   (b) **Parts List**
    (c) **Leader Text**   (d) None of these

7. Which of the following tools is used to add center marks to circles in the drawing views?

    (a) **Center Mark**   (b) **Center Line**
    (c) **Center**   (d) None of these

8. Which of the following options of the **Style and Standard Editor [Library - Read Only]** dialog box is used to create a new dimension style?

    (a) **Dimension**   (b) **Terminator**
    (c) **Common**   (d) **Sheet**

9. Which of the following dialog boxes is used to create a new dimension style?

    (a) **Dimension Style**   (b) **Dimension Text**
    (c) **Drafting Standards**   (d) **Style and Standard Editor [Library - Read Only]**

10. Which of the following dialog boxes is displayed when you double-click on the parts list to edit it?

    (a) **Parts List**   (b) **Edit Sheet**
    (c) **Edit Dimension**   (d) None of these

Exercise

Exercise 1

Add the parts list and balloons to the drawing views of the Plummer Block assembly created in Tutorial 2 of Chapter 11, as shown in Figure 12-32. The parts list to be added is shown in Figure 12-33. **(Expected time: 45 min)**

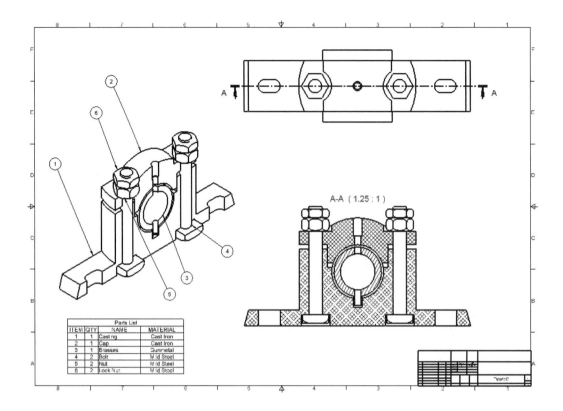

Figure 12-32 *Drawing sheet for Exercise 1*

Parts List			
ITEM	QTY	NAME	MATERIAL
1	1	Casting	Cast Iron
2	1	Cap	Cast Iron
3	1	Brasses	Gunmetal
4	2	Bolt	Mild Steel
5	2	Nut	Mild Steel
6	2	Lock Nut	Mild Steel

Figure 12-33 *Parts list for Exercise 1*

Answers to Self-Evaluation Test
1. T, **2.** T, **3.** T, **4.** F, **5. Parts List**, **6. Text**, **7.** one, **8.** Balloons, **9. Edit Sheet**, **10.** second-level

Chapter 13

Presentation Module

THE PRESENTATION MODULE

As mentioned earlier, Autodesk Inventor allows you to animate the assemblies created in the **Assembly** module. You can view some of the assemblies in motion by animating them. The animation of assemblies can be created in the **Presentation** module. You can use the **Presentation** module to create the exploded views of an assembly. An exploded view is the one in which the assembled components are moved to a defined distance from their original locations. To invoke the **Presentation** module, double-click on the **Standard (mm).ipn** file in the **Metric** tab of the **New File** dialog box, see Figure 13-1.

Figure 13-1 *Opening a new presentation file in the **Metric** tab of the **New File** dialog box*

The default screen appearance of the **Presentation** module is shown in Figure 13-2.

Note
*When you open a new presentation file, you will notice that only the **Create View** tool is available in the **Presentation** tab of the **Ribbon**. This is because first you need to create the presentation view of an assembly. Once the presentation view has been created, the other tools will become available in this module.*

*As mentioned earlier, all modules of Autodesk Inventor are bidirectionally associative. Therefore, if you make any modification in an assembly or the components of an assembly, the changes will automatically be reflected in the **Presentation** module.*

*You cannot modify an assembly or its components in the **Presentation** module.*

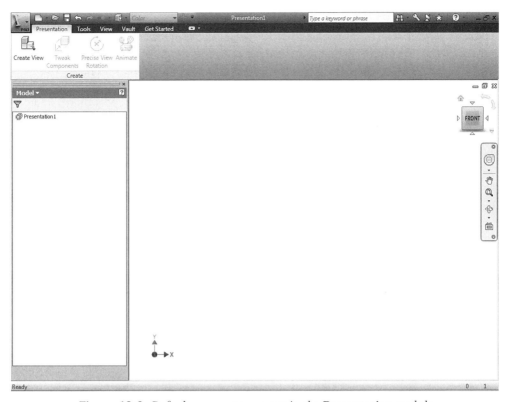

*Figure 13-2 Default screen appearance in the **Presentation** module*

CREATING THE PRESENTATION VIEW

Ribbon: Presentation > Create > Create View
Toolbar: Presentation Panel > Create View

Create View

The presentation view is used to animate an assembly or create its exploded state. You can create presentation views by using the **Create View** tool. You can invoke this tool by right-clicking in the drawing window and then choosing **Create View** from the shortcut menu. On invoking this tool, the **Select Assembly** dialog box will be displayed, as shown in Figure 13-3. The options in this dialog box are discussed next.

Assembly Area

The options in the **Assembly** area are used to select the assembly for creating the presentation view. These options are discussed next.

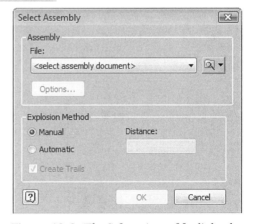

*Figure 13-3 The **Select Assembly** dialog box*

File

The **File** drop-down list displays the assembly file selected for creating the presentation view. By default, this drop-down list displays **<select assembly document>** as no assembly file is selected. To select an assembly file, choose the **Open an existing file** button on the right of this drop-down list; the **Open** dialog box will be displayed, see Figure 13-4. You can use this dialog box to select the assembly file to be used for creating the presentation view. The selected assembly file and its location will be displayed in the **File** drop-down list.

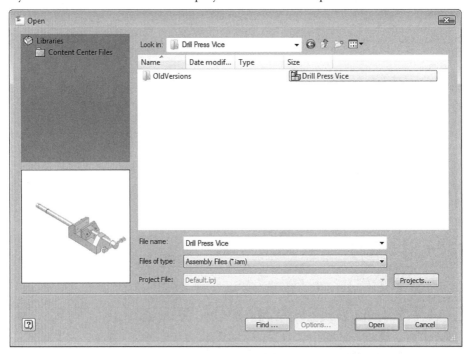

*Figure 13-4 The **Open** dialog box for selecting assembly file*

Tip. *In the **Open** dialog box, the **Files of type** drop-down list displays only the **Assembly Files (.iam)** option because you can create the presentation views of the assembly files only.*

Options

The **Options** button will be activated only after selecting a file for creating a presentation. Choose this button; the **File Open Options** dialog box will be displayed. Using this dialog box, you can select the design view representation, positional representation, or level of detail representation to be used for generating the presentation view.

Explosion Method Area

As mentioned earlier, an exploded view is the one in which all components of an assembly move to a specified distance from their original location in the assembly. The options in the **Explosion Method** area are used to select the method for exploding the selected assembly. These options are discussed next.

Manual

If the **Manual** radio button is selected, the assembly in the presentation view will not explode automatically. This option is selected when you want to explode the assembly manually using other tools such as **Tweak Components**, **Precise View Rotation**, and so on. Note that because the assembly will not be exploded, no other option in the **Explosion Method** area will be available if the **Manual** radio button is selected.

Automatic

The **Automatic** radio button is selected to automatically explode the assembly when the presentation view is created. The components of the assembly will move in the direction of the constraint that is used to assemble them. The distance to which the components will move is specified in the **Distance** edit box. This edit box will be available when you select the **Automatic** radio button.

Create Trails

Trails are defined as the parametric lines that display the path and direction of the assembled components. These lines can be used as a reference for determining the path and the direction in which the components are assembled. The **Create Trails** check box is selected to create the trails when the assembly is exploded. This check box will be available only when the **Automatic** radio button is selected.

Figure 13-5 shows the Drill Press Vice assembly exploded using the **Automatic** option. The distance of explosion is 25 mm. This figure also shows the trails that define the path and direction of the assembled components.

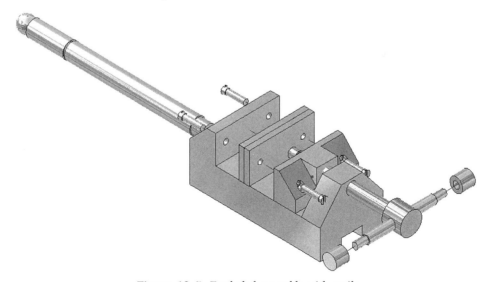

Figure 13-5 Exploded assembly with trails

Tip. *If the explosion distance is large, the result of exploding assemblies using the **Automatic** method may not be as desired. This is because with the large explosion distance, the components of an assembly will move to a large distance and start interfering with other components, refer to Figure 13-6. Therefore, it is recommended that if components need to be moved to a large distance, you should explode assemblies using the **Manual** method.*

*To increase the value of the automatic explosion after creating the presentation view, click on the + sign located on the left of the exploded view in the **Browser Bar** to display the name of the assembly. Right-click on the name and then choose **Auto Explode** from the shortcut menu to display the **Auto Explode** dialog box. Enter the value in the **Distance** edit box. The new distance value will be added to the previous distance value. Remember that you cannot enter a negative distance value.*

DEFINING UNITS FOR PRESENTATION FILES

Autodesk Inventor allows you to define the units in the presentation (*.ipn*) file. By defining the units in the presentation file, you can control the distance and angle while specifying the tweak. To define the units in the presentation file, choose the **Document Settings** tool from the **Options** panel of the **Tools** tab; the **Document Settings** dialog box will be displayed. Choose the **Units** tab and specify the length and angular units.

TWEAKING COMPONENTS IN THE PRESENTATION VIEW

Ribbon:	Presentation > Create > Tweak Components
Toolbar:	Presentation Panel > Tweak Components

Tweak
Components

As mentioned earlier, if the distance to which components move in the automatically exploded view is large, the components may interfere with one another. For example, refer to Figure 13-6. This figure shows an automatic exploded view, in which the components are moved to a distance of 42 mm. Notice the interference between the Movable Jaw and the Base, between the two Jaw Faces, and between the Clamp Screw and the Base. To avoid such interferences, it is recommended that if the components need to be exploded to a large distance, you should create the exploded view manually by tweaking the components. Tweaking is defined as the process of adjusting the position of the assembled components with respect to the other components of the assembly by transforming them in the specified direction. The components can be tweaked by using the **Tweak Components** tool. The tweaked components can also be animated, thus creating the animation of the assemblies.

Invoke this tool; the **Tweak Component** dialog box will be displayed, as shown in Figure 13-7. The options in this dialog box are discussed next.

Create Tweak Area

The options in the **Create Tweak** area are used to select the component to be tweaked, the direction of tweaking, and options related to the trails. These options are discussed next

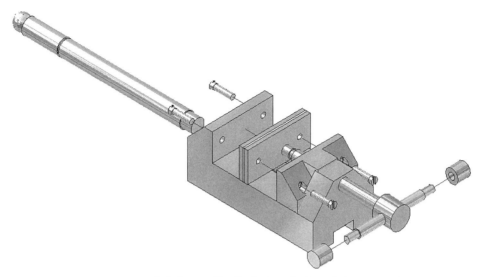

Figure 13-6 *Exploded assembly displaying the interfering components*

Direction

The **Direction** button is chosen by default and is used to specify the direction of movement or rotation of the components. When this button is chosen, you will notice that the direction symbol is attached to the cursor. This symbol will be visible when you move the cursor in the drawing window. You can define the direction of rotation or movement by using any linear edge, face, or feature of the components in the assembly. If you select a cylindrical component, you can use its central axis as the direction of tweaking. When you move the cursor close

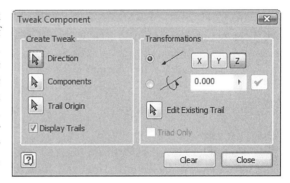

Figure 13-7 *The Tweak Component dialog box*

to any component for selecting the direction, you will notice that a triad is displayed. It displays the X, Y, and Z directions. Once you select the direction of tweaking, the triad will be fixed at the selected component. Also, the **Components** button will be chosen in the **Create Tweak** area. You can change the direction of tweaking by choosing the **Direction** button again and redefining the direction.

Components

The **Components** button is chosen to select the components that will be tweaked. This button will be automatically chosen when you define the direction of tweaking. When this button is chosen, you will notice that a symbol of a cube and an arrow is attached to the cursor. Also, you will be prompted to select the components to be tweaked.

Trail Origin

As mentioned earlier, trails are parametric lines defining the direction and path of the assembled components. By default, when you tweak the components, the trails are created at the center of the components. You can use the **Trail Origin** button to redefine the origin of trail using two points.

Display Trails

The **Display Trails** check box is selected to display the trails in the exploded view.

Transformations Area

The options in the **Transformations** area are used to specify the type of transformation, its direction, and distance. These options are discussed next.

Linear

 The **Linear** radio button is used to tweak the selected components in the linear direction. Whenever you select the direction of tweaking by using the **Direction** button in the **Create Tweak** area, a triad is displayed with three axes. If the **Linear** option is selected, the selected components will be tweaked in the linear direction along one of these three axes. By default, the components will be tweaked in the Z direction. This axis will be displayed in blue in the triad. The remaining two axes will be displayed in green. If you want to tweak the components in the X or Y direction, choose the respective button from the **Transformations** area. The selected axis will be displayed in blue and the remaining two axes will be displayed in green. The distance of tweaking will be entered in the edit box provided in this area. After entering the value in the edit box, choose the **Apply** button on the right of the edit box. Until you choose the **Apply** button, the components will not be tweaked.

Rotational

 The **Rotational** radio button is used to rotate the selected components around a specified axis of the triad. The triad is displayed when you select the direction by using the **Direction** button from the **Create Tweak** area. You can select the required axis by choosing its button from the **Transformations** area. The angle of rotation can be entered in the edit box provided on the right of the **Rotational** radio button. After entering the angle of rotation in the edit box, choose the **Apply** button to tweak the components.

Edit Existing Trail

This button is chosen to edit an existing trail. When you choose this button, most of the options in the **Tweak Component** dialog box will not be enabled. However, the **Direction** button in the **Create Tweak** area and the edit box in the **Transformations** area will be available. Choose the **Edit Existing Trail** button and then select the trail from the graphics screen. . You can modify the direction and distance/angle of the existing trail.

Triad Only

The **Triad Only** check box will be activated only when you select the **Rotational** radio button from the **Transformations** area. Select this radio button to rotate only the triad around the axis selected. Remember that you cannot move the triad without moving the components. However, you can rotate it without rotating the components. The angle of rotation is specified in the edit box provided on the right of the **Rotational** radio button. This check box is selected when you rotate the triad through a certain angle and then use the directions of the rotated triad to add tweaks to the components. After rotating the triad, you can add a linear or rotation tweak to the components. Figure 13-8 shows the exploded view of the Drill Press Vice assembly.

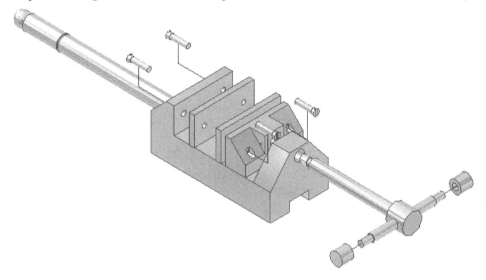

Figure 13-8 *Exploded view of the Drill Press Vice assembly*

Clear

The **Clear** button is chosen to clear the current settings in the **Tweak Component** dialog box. When you choose this button, all the current settings are reset to the default values and you can proceed with tweaking the other components.

> **Tip**. *To modify the tweak values of components, click on the + sign located on the left of the name of the assembly in the **Browser Bar**; all components in the assembly will be displayed. Click on the + sign located on the left of any component to display the tweak value. Select the tweak; an edit box will be displayed at the bottom of the Browser Bar. Modify the tweak value in this edit box.*

ANIMATING AN ASSEMBLY

Ribbon:	Presentation > Create > Animate
Toolbar:	Presentation Panel > Animate

You can animate the tweaked or exploded assemblies by using the **Animate** tool. On invoking this tool, the **Animation** dialog box will be displayed, as shown in Figure 13-9. The options in this dialog box are discussed next.

Figure 13-9 *The* *Animation* *dialog box*

Parameters Area

The options in the **Parameters** area are used to set the interval of a tweak in the animation and the number of repetitions in it. These options are discussed next.

Interval

The **Interval** spinner is used to specify the interval between the tweaks in an animation. You can use the spinner to specify the value or enter the value directly.

Repetitions

The **Repetitions** edit box is used to enter the number of repetitions in an animation. You can specify the number of repetitions by setting the value of the **Repetitions** spinner directly or entering a value in this edit box.

Motion Area

The options in the **Motion** area will be active only when you choose the **Apply** button. These options are used to set the motion of components or record the animation. These options are discussed next.

Forward By Tweak

The **Forward By Tweak** button is chosen to force the tweaked components to move to the end value of the tweak distance. If you have tweaked the selected components to a linear distance of 25 mm in the Z direction, then on choosing this button, all tweaked components will move forward by the complete tweak distance, that is 25 mm in this case.

Forward By Interval

Whenever you create an animation, the total tweak distance or tweak angle is automatically divided into small intervals that are used as the animation sequence. The **Forward By Interval** button is chosen to force the tweaked components to move forward by one interval in the animation.

Reverse By Interval

The **Reverse By Interval** button is chosen to force the tweaked components to move backward by one interval in the animation.

Reverse By Tweak

The **Reverse By Tweak** button is chosen to force the tweaked components to be moved to the start value of the tweak distance. This button will work only if one cycle of the animation is completed or the components are moved to the end position by using the **Forward By Tweak** button.

Play Forward

The **Play Forward** button is chosen to play the animation of the assembly in the forward direction. The number of cycles in the animation will be based on the value of **Repetitions** spinner in the **Parameter** area. If the number of repetitions is more than one, the components will be repositioned at the start point of the forward cycle after the first repetition is completed and the second repetition will again begin from the start point of animation.

Auto Reverse

If the **Auto Reverse** button is chosen, the animation of the assembly will be first played in the forward direction and then played automatically in the reverse direction. The number of forward and reverse cycles will depend upon the value of the **Repetitions** spinner. Note that in this case the forward and reverse movement of components is considered as one cycle.

 Tip. *If the components are already moved to the end value of the tweak distance, choosing the **Auto Reverse** button will animate the components in only the reverse direction in case the number of repetitions is one.*

Play Reverse

The **Play Reverse** button is used to play the animation of assembly in the backward direction. The number of cycles in the animation will be based on the value of **Repetitions** spinner in the **Parameters** area. If the number of repetitions is more than one, the components will be repositioned at the start point of the reverse cycle after the first repetition is completed and the second repetition will again begin from the end point of the animation.

Pause

The **Pause** button is used to temporarily stop the animation of the assembly.

Record

The **Record** button is used to store the animation of an assembly. You can record the animation in the *.wmv* or *.avi* format. On choosing this button, the **Save As** dialog box will be displayed, see Figure 13-10. This dialog box is used to specify the location and name of an animation file.

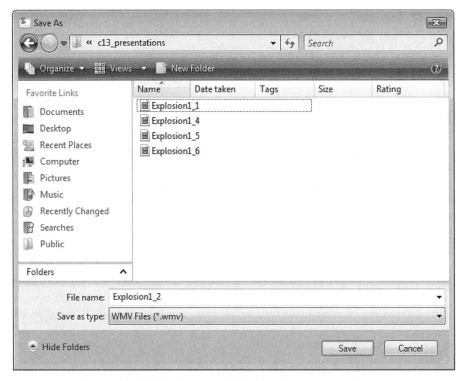

Figure 13-10 The Save As dialog box for saving animation

After specifying the location and name of the file, choose the **Save** button; the **ASF Export Properties** dialog box will be displayed, as shown in Figure 13-11. The options in this dialog box are used to set properties for saving the simulation of a file to the *.avi*, *.wmv*, or *.asf* file format. The **Profile** drop-down list is used to specify the profile for the animation file. If you select the **Custom Profile** option from this drop-down list, the other options in this dialog box will be activated. You can specify the bandwidth by using the option in the **Network Bandwidth** area of the **ASF Export Properties** dialog box. The options in the **Network Bandwidth** area control the output and quality of recording. The options in the **Image Size** area are used to specify the size of the recorded window. Set the required values in this dialog box and then choose the **OK** button.

Once the export properties are set, you can create the *.avi* file. Now, choose the **Play Forward**, **Play Reverse**, or **Auto Reverse** button to create the animation of the assembly. After the animation is recorded, choose this button again to exit the recording.

Note
If you select the .avi file format to save the animation of the presentation view for the first time, the ***Video Compression*** *dialog box will be displayed instead of the **ASF Export Properties** dialog box. Accept the default values in this dialog box and choose **OK** to record the animation.*

Minimize dialog during recording

The **Minimize dialog during recording** check box is selected to minimize the **Animation** dialog box while recording the animation. This is done because whatever appears on the graphics screen is also recorded in the avi file while recording the animation. If the dialog box is not minimized, it will also be recorded and will appear in the recorded file.

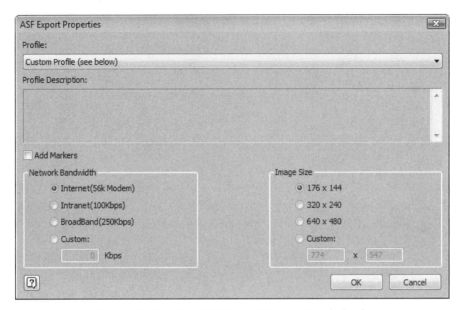

*Figure 13-11 The **ASF Export Properties** dialog box*

Apply

Choose the **Apply** button to apply the changes made to the parameters in this dialog box.

Reset

Choose the **Reset** button to reset the parameters in the **Animation** dialog box to the default values.

More

This button with two arrows provided at the lower right corner of the **Animation** dialog box is used to expand the **Animation** dialog box. The expanded dialog box displays the **Animation Sequence** area, see Figure 13-12. All tweaked components along with their tweak values are displayed in the list box in this area. Note that all components that were selected together while tweaking are displayed as a single sequence. The buttons in this area are discussed next.

Move Up

The **Move Up** button is chosen to move the selected sequence up in the order in the list box. Remember that the sequence that is displayed on top in the list box will be played first in the animation.

Move Down

The **Move Down** button is chosen to move the selected sequence down in the order in the list box.

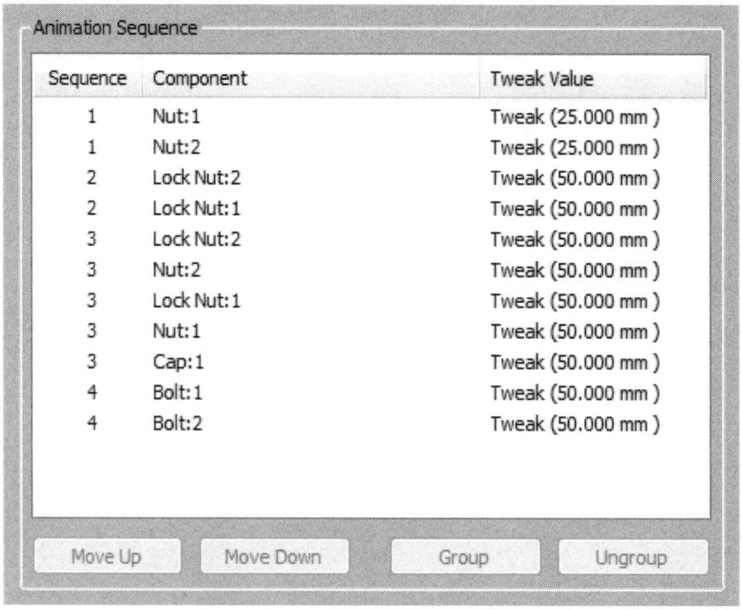

Sequence	Component	Tweak Value
1	Nut:1	Tweak (25.000 mm)
1	Nut:2	Tweak (25.000 mm)
2	Lock Nut:2	Tweak (50.000 mm)
2	Lock Nut:1	Tweak (50.000 mm)
3	Lock Nut:2	Tweak (50.000 mm)
3	Nut:2	Tweak (50.000 mm)
3	Lock Nut:1	Tweak (50.000 mm)
3	Nut:1	Tweak (50.000 mm)
3	Cap:1	Tweak (50.000 mm)
4	Bolt:1	Tweak (50.000 mm)
4	Bolt:2	Tweak (50.000 mm)

Move Up   Move Down   Group   Ungroup

*Figure 13-12 The **Animation Sequence** area displayed on choosing the **More** button*

Group

The **Group** button is chosen to group various sequences in the animation. All the grouped sequences will show the same sequence number after grouping. To create a group, you need to press and hold the CTRL or SHIFT key, select the components to be grouped, and then choose the **Group** button.

Tip. *The **Group** button is chosen when you want to club different tweak sequences together. Grouping a rotational tweak and a linear tweak provides the effect of linear and rotational movements together.*

Ungroup

The **Ungroup** button is chosen to ungroup the grouped sequences in the animation.

Note
*After grouping or ungrouping sequences, choose the **Apply** button. If you do not choose it, the buttons to start the animation in the **Motion** area will not be available.*

ROTATING THE PRESENTATION VIEW PRECISELY

Ribbon:	Presentation > Create > Precise View Rotation
Toolbar:	Presentation Panel > Precise View Rotation

 Autodesk Inventor allows you to rotate the presentation view precisely in the **Presentation** module. You can rotate a view by using the **Precise View Rotation** tool. On invoking this tool, the **Incremental View Rotate** dialog box will be displayed, see Figure 13-13. The options provided in this dialog box are discussed next.

*Figure 13-13 The **Incremental View Rotate** dialog box*

Increment
The **Increment** edit box is used to specify the angle through which the presentation view will be rotated.

Rotate Down
 The **Rotate Down** button is chosen to rotate the presentation view in the downward direction. The presentation will be rotated through the value entered in the **Increment** edit box.

Rotate Up
 The **Rotate Up** button is chosen to rotate the presentation view in the upward direction.

Rotate Left
 The **Rotate Left** button is chosen to rotate the presentation view toward the left through the values specified in the **Increment** edit box.

Rotate Right
 The **Rotate Right** button is chosen to rotate the presentation view toward the right through the values specified in the **Increment** edit box.

Roll Counter Clockwise
 The **Roll Counter Clockwise** button is chosen to rotate the presentation view in the counterclockwise direction through the value specified in the **Increment** edit box.

Roll Clockwise
 The **Roll Clockwise** button is chosen to rotate the presentation view in the clockwise direction through the value specified in the **Increment** edit box.

Reset
The **Reset** button is chosen to reset the current view to the default view.

TUTORIALS

Tutorial 1

In this tutorial, you will explode the Plummer Block assembly saved in the *c12* folder and then create the animation of disassembling (exploding) and assembling (unexploding) of the assembly. The exploded state of the Plummer Block assembly is shown in Figure 13-14.

(Expected time: 45 min)

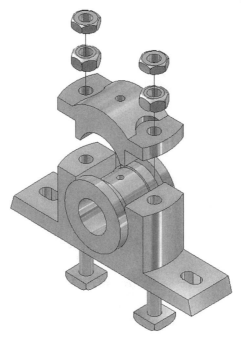

Figure 13-14 *Exploded view of the Plummer Block Assembly*

The following steps are required to complete this tutorial:

a. Copy the *Plummer Block* folder from the *c12* folder to the *c13* folder.
b. Open a new metric presentation file and create a new presentation view by using the **Create View** tool, refer to Figure 13-15.
c. Manually explode the assembly in four sequences. The first sequence will tweak the two Bolts and the second sequence will tweak the Cap, Lock Nuts, and Nuts. The third sequence will tweak the Lock Nuts. The final sequence will tweak the Nuts, refer to Figure 13-18.
d. Invoke the **Animate** tool and then combine all the four sequences.
e. Finally, animate the sequences by using the **Auto Reverse** button from the **Animation** dialog box.

Copying the Folder

The presentation view is generated by using the Plummer Block assembly. Therefore, you need to copy the *Plummer Block* folder from the *c12* folder to the *c13* folder.

1. Create a folder with the name *c13* at the location *C:\Inventor_2011*.

2. Copy the *Plummer Block* folder from the *c12* folder to the *c13* folder.

Starting a New Presentation File

1. Invoke the **New File** dialog box and then choose the **Metric** tab from it.

2. Double-click on the **Standard (mm).ipn** option; a new presentation file is started.

Creating the Presentation View

When you open a new presentation file, only the **Create View** tool is available in the **Create** panel of the **Presentation** tab in the **Ribbon**.

1. Choose the **Create View** tool from the **Create** panel of the **Presentation** tab; the **Select Assembly** dialog box is displayed.

Create View

2. In this dialog box, choose the **Open an existing file** button on the right of the **File** drop-down list in the **Assembly** area; the **Open** dialog box is displayed.

3. Open the folder *Plummer Block* from the location *C:\Inventor_2011\c13*.

   You will notice that only the *Plummer Block.iam* file is available in this folder because you can create the presentation view of an assembly file only.

4. Double-click on the *Plummer Block.iam* file to select the Plummer Block assembly for creating the presentation view.

   The **Open** dialog box is closed and the **File** drop-down list in the **Assembly** area of the **Select Assembly** dialog box displays the name and path of the selected assembly.

   By default, the **Manual** radio button is selected in the **Explosion Method** area. In this tutorial, you need to manually explode the assembly; therefore, you can accept the default options from the **Explosion Method** area.

5. Accept the default options from the **Explosion Method** area and choose the **OK** button.

   The presentation view is created and the current view is changed automatically to the isometric view. The file after creating the presentation view is shown in Figure 13-15.

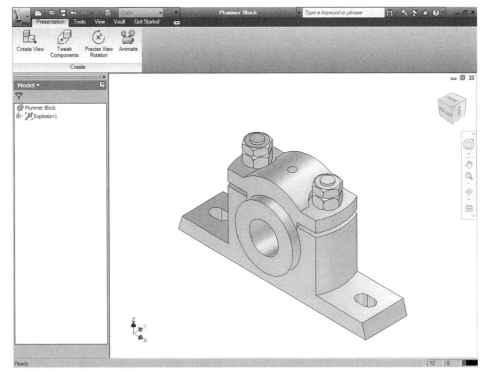

Figure 13-15 *Presentation file after creating the presentation view*

Tweaking the Components of the Assembly

Now, you need to explode the assembly or add tweaks to the components of the assembly using the **Tweak Components** tool.

1. Choose the **Tweak Components** tool from the **Create** panel of the **Presentation** tab to invoke the **Tweak Component** dialog box.

    In the **Tweak Component** dialog box, the **Direction** button in the **Create Tweak** area is chosen by default and you are prompted to select the direction of the tweak.

2. Select the vertical edge on the front face of the Casting as the direction of the tweak, see Figure 13-16.

    As soon as you select the direction of the tweak, a triad is displayed on the selected edge. The X, Y, and Z axes of the triad are along the X, Y, and Z axes of the current coordinate symbol displayed at the lower left corner of the drawing window. Also, the Z axis of the triad is displayed in blue. This indicates that the current tweak direction is along the Z axis.

Note that after defining the direction of the tweak, the **Components** button in the **Create Tweak** area is automatically chosen and you are prompted to select the components to be tweaked.

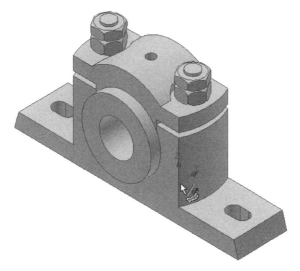

Figure 13-16 *Selecting the direction for the tweak*

3. Select both the bolts one by one to tweak from the portion where they extend out of the Lock Nuts.

   The top faces of the Bolts are displayed with a blue outline indicating that the components are selected and can be tweaked.

4. Make sure the **Display Trail** check box is selected in the **Create Tweak** area.

   You need to add the linear tweak to components. But, you need to tweak the components downward.

5. Enter **-50** in the **Tweak Distance** edit box on the right of the **Rotational** radio button. Next, choose the **Apply** button on the right of the edit box.

   The two Bolts move downward, see Figure 13-17. This is the first sequence of the tweak.

   As the **Tweak Components** tool is still active, you are prompted again to select the components to be tweaked. Also, notice that the two Bolts are still displayed with a blue outline. This indicates that the components are still selected, and if you enter a tweak value in the edit box, the components will be tweaked by the specified distance. Therefore, first you need to remove these components from the selected set.

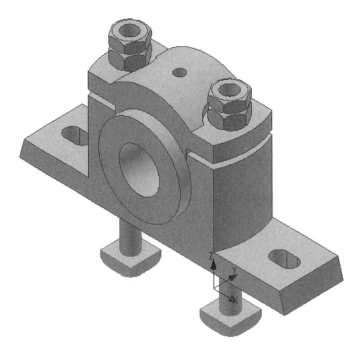

Figure 13-17 *Assembly after tweaking the two Bolts*

6. Press and hold the SHIFT key and click on the bolts one by one. You will notice that the blue outline is not displayed on the Bolts.

7. Select the Cap, two Nuts, and two Lock Nuts; all the selected components are displayed with a blue outline.

8. Enter **50** in the **Tweak Distance** edit box on the right of the **Rotational** radio button in the **Transformations** area and then choose the **Apply** button on the right of this edit box.

    The selected components move upward by a distance of 50 mm. This is the second tweak sequence.

9. Next, press and hold the SHIFT key and click on the Cap and both the Nuts one by one to remove them from the current selection set. Now, only the two Lock Nuts are displayed with a blue outline.

10. Choose the **Apply** button on the right of the edit box in the **Transformations** area to move the two Lock Nuts further up by a distance of 50 mm.

    This is the third tweak sequence. You will notice that blue trails are created as you tweak the components. This is because the **Display Trails** check box in the **Create Tweak** area is selected.

11. Choose the **Zoom All** button from the **Navigation Bar** on the right of the graphics window to increase the drawing display area. The complete exploded assembly is displayed on the graphics screen.

12. Press and hold the SHIFT key and click on the two Lock Nuts one by one to remove them from the selection set. Next, release the SHIFT key and select the two Nuts.

    You will notice that the Nuts are displayed with a blue outline.

13. Enter **25** in the **Tweak Distance** edit box on the right of the **Rotational** radio button in the **Transformations** area and then choose the **Apply** button on the right of this edit box. Both the Nuts move upward by a distance of 25 mm and are placed between the Cap and the two Lock Nuts. This is the fourth and final tweak sequence.

14. Choose the **Close** button to exit the **Tweak Component** dialog box.

    You will notice that the triad, which was displayed in the assembly, is removed from the drawing window. The assembly after creating four tweak sequences is shown in Figure 13-18.

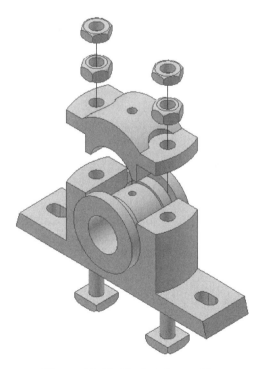

Figure 13-18 *Exploded assembly*

Animating the Assembly

The next step, after tweaking the assembly, is to animate it. The animation will carry out the simulation of exploding and unexploding the assembly. Note that when you tweak the components, the assembly is exploded and the components move to the tweaked position. Therefore, the first cycle in the animation is to unexplode the assembly by moving the components back to their original assembled position and the second cycle is to explode the assembly by moving the components to the tweaked position.

1. Choose the **Animate** tool from the **Create** panel of the **Presentation** tab to display the **Animation** dialog box.

2. Next, choose the **More** button provided at the lower right corner of the dialog box to expand it.

   You will notice that there are four sequences in the **Animation Sequence** area. If you animate the assembly now, the assembly will animate in four steps. These four steps are actually the four sequences displayed in the **Animation Sequence** area. Note that the next step will start only after the previous step has been completed. In order to animate the assembly such that all sequences animate together, you need to select and group them all.

3. Press and hold the SHIFT key and select all the sequences displayed in the **Animation Sequence** area.

   All sequences are displayed with a blue background. Also, only the **Group** button is activated in the **Animation Sequence** area.

4. Choose the **Group** button from the **Animation Sequence** area to group all sequences together.

   Now, all tweaks are grouped together as 1 under the **Sequence** column.

5. Choose the **Apply** button from the **Animation** dialog box to apply changes to the assembly.

6. Move the **Animation** dialog box to the left of the drawing window by dragging its title bar such that it does not overlap with the assembly.

7. Choose the **Auto Reverse** button from the **Motion** area.

   All tweaked components in the animation move together to their original assembled position and then move back to the tweaked position.

8. Choose the **Cancel** button from the **Animation** dialog box to exit it. Save the presentation file with the name *Tutorial1.ipn* at the location given below.

C:\Inventor_2011\c13\Plummer Block

Tutorial 2

In this tutorial, you will animate the Drill Press Vice assembly. The animation consists of a rotational tweak and a linear tweak. Save the animation in an *.avi* file with the name *Drill Press Vice*. **(Expected time: 1 hr)**

The following steps are required to complete this tutorial:

a. Copy the *Drill Press Vice* folder from the *c12* folder to the *c13* folder.
b. Start a new metric presentation file and create the presentation view of the Drill Press Vice assembly by using the **Create View** tool.
c. Tweak components by using the **Tweak Components** tool.
d. Invoke the **Animation** dialog box and group sequences.
e. Create an avi file and store the animation in it.

Copying the Drill Press Vice Assembly

1. Copy the *Drill Press Vice* folder from the *c12* folder to the *c13* folder.

Starting a New Presentation File

1. Choose the **New** tool from the **Standard** toolbar to invoke the **New File** dialog box.

2. In this dialog box, choose the **Metric** tab and double-click on the **Standard (mm).ipn** option to start a new metric presentation file.

Creating the Presentation View

1. Choose the **Create View** tool from the **Create** panel of the **Presentation** tab to invoke the **Select Assembly** dialog box.

Create View

2. Choose the **Open an existing file** button on the right of the **File** drop-down list in the **Assembly** area to invoke the **Open** dialog box.

3. Browse to *C:\Inventor_2011\c13\Drill Press Vice*; the *Drill Press Vice.iam* file is displayed.

4. Double-click on the *Drill Press Vice.iam* file.

The assembly is selected and displayed along with its path in the **File** drop-down list in the **Assembly** area.

5. Accept the remaining default options and choose the **OK** button.

The presentation view is created and the current view is changed to the isometric view, see Figure 13-19.

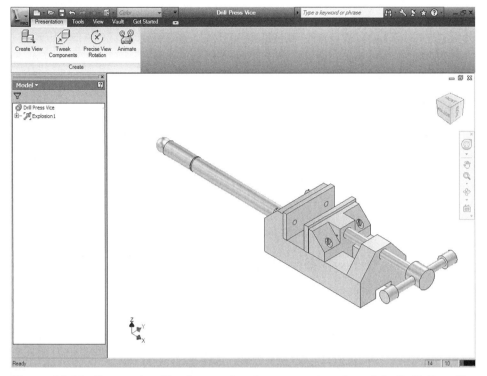

Figure 13-19 *Presentation file after creating the presentation view of the Drill Press Vice assembly*

Tweaking the Components of the Assembly

In this assembly, you need to apply the rotational tweak to the Clamp Screw, Clamp Screw Handle, and two Handle Stops. After that, you need to apply the linear tweak to the above-mentioned components and also to the Movable Jaw, the Jaw Face assembled with the Movable Jaw, and the two Cap Screws used to assemble the Jaw Face and the Movable Jaw.

1. Choose the **Tweak Components** tool from the **Create** panel of the **Presentation** tab to invoke the **Tweak Component** dialog box.

In this dialog box, the **Direction** button in the **Create Tweak** area is chosen by default and you are prompted to select the direction for the tweak.

2. Move the cursor close to the cylindrical face of the head of the Clamp Screw, see Figure 13-20.

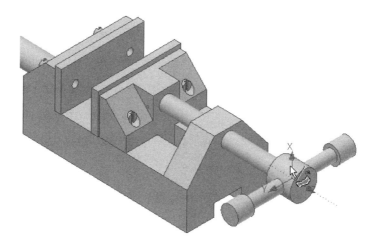

Figure 13-20 *Defining the tweak direction on the head of the Clamp Screw*

You will notice that the head of the Clamp Screw is displayed with a red outline and a triad is displayed on the component. Also, the Z axis of the triad coincides with the central axis of the Clamp Screw, refer to Figure 13-20.

3. Select the Clamp Screw when the triad is displayed and the central axis of the Clamp Screw is coincided with the Z axis of the triad.

    Note that the resultant animation will not be the required one if the Z axis of the triad does not coincide with the central axis of the Clamp Screw. If you have selected the wrong direction of tweaking, choose the **Direction** button in the **Create Tweak** area again and select the required axis.

    Now, you are prompted to select the components to be tweaked.

4. Select the Clamp Screw, Clamp Screw Handle, and two Handle Stops; the selected components are displayed with a blue outline.

5. Clear the **Display Trail** check box in the **Create Tweak** area.

    This ensures that the trails are not created when you tweak the components.

6. Select the **Rotational** radio button from the **Transformations** area.

Elliptical arrows indicating the positive direction of rotation are displayed on all the three axes of the triad. The Z axis of the triad and the elliptical arrow on it are displayed in blue.

7. Enter **720** in the **Tweak Angle** edit box on the right of the **Rotational** radio button. Choose the **Apply** button on the right of the edit box.

    The rotational tweak is applied to the selected components. This is the first sequence of the tweak. Note that the effect of rotational tweak is not visible on the screen at this time.

    Next, you need to apply the linear tweak to components. Some of the components have already been selected and you need to select the remaining components to apply the linear tweak.

8. Select the Movable Jaw, the Jaw Face assembled with the Movable Jaw, and the two Cap Screws used to fasten the Jaw Face with the Movable Jaw.

    All the selected components are displayed with a blue outline. But, the rotational tweak is still active and you need to change it to the linear tweak.

9. Select the **Linear** radio button from the **Transformations** area.

    The elliptical arrows disappear from the triad, but the Z axis of the triad is still displayed in blue. This indicates that the selected components will move along the Z axis of the triad.

10. Enter **25** in the **Tweak Distance** edit box in the **Transformations** area and then choose the **Apply** button on the right of the edit box.

    The selected components move to a distance of 25 mm along the Z axis of the triad. This is the second sequence of the tweak.

11. Choose the **Close** button to exit the **Tweak Component** dialog box. Now, choose the **Zoom All** button from the **Navigation Bar** to increase the drawing display area and fit the assembly into the current view. The assembly after tweaking is shown in Figure 13-21.

Animating the Assembly

1. Choose the **Animate** tool from the **Create** panel of the **Presentation** tab to invoke the **Animation** dialog box.

Animate

2. Choose the **More** button provided at the lower right corner of the dialog box to expand it.

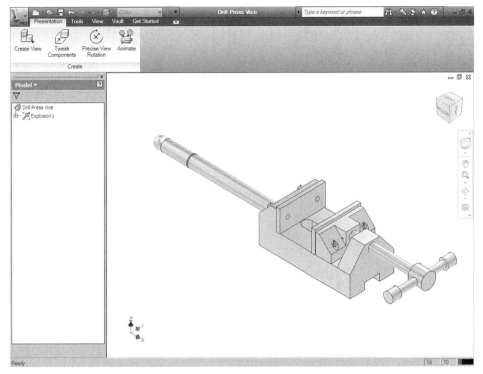

Figure 13-21 *Assembly after tweaking the components*

You will notice that two sets of sequences are displayed in the **Animation Sequence** area. You need to group these sequences to rotate and move the components simultaneously.

3. Press and hold the SHIFT key and select all sequences from the **Animation Sequence** area; all sequences are displayed with a blue background.

4. Choose the **Group** button to group all sequences in a single sequence.

5. Choose the **Apply** button to apply changes to all tweaked components.

   It is recommended that before you store the animation in the avi file, you should play it once to make sure the animation is correct.

6. Move the dialog box to the left of the screen such that it does not overlap the assembly. Now, choose the **Auto Reverse** button from the **Animation** dialog box to play the animation in the forward and reverse directions.

You will notice that all tweaked components are moving in the forward direction while the Clamp Screw, Clamp Screw Handle, and two Handle Stops are rotating around the central axis of the Clamp Screw in the clockwise direction. This is because you have applied the rotational tweak to the Clamp Screw, Clamp Screw Handle, and two Handle Stops. After the forward cycle is completed, all components move in the reverse direction and the components to which the rotational tweak has been applied rotate in the counterclockwise direction. This shows the effect of working of the Drill Press Vice assembly.

Now, you can store the animation of the assembly in an *.avi* file. Before you store the animation in an *.avi* file, it is recommended that you increase the interval of the sequence so that the *.avi* file is smooth.

7. Choose the **Cancel** button from the **Animation** dialog box to close it. Now, choose the **Browser Filters** button at the top left corner of the **Browser Bar** to display the flyout.

8. Choose the **Sequence View** option from the flyout. You will notice that the **Task1** and **Drill Press Vice.iam** sub nodes are displayed below the **Explosion1** node in the **Browser Bar**. Alternatively, click on the + sign located on the left of the **Explosion1** node to display them.

9. Right-click on **Task1** and then choose **Edit** from the shortcut menu displayed; the **Edit Task & Sequences** dialog box is displayed, see Figure 13-22.

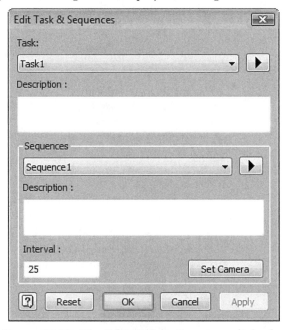

*Figure 13-22 The **Edit Task & Sequences** dialog box*

Tip. *Note that there is only one sequence named **Sequence1** in the drop-down list in the **Sequences** area. This is because you grouped the two sequences into a single sequence. If you invoke the **Edit Task** & **Sequences** dialog box before grouping the sequences, all the sequences that you have created will be displayed in the drop-down list.*

10. Enter **75** in the **Interval** edit box and then choose the **Apply** button. Next, choose **OK** to close this dialog box.

11. Invoke the **Animation** dialog box again and then choose the **Record** button from it; the **Save As** dialog box is displayed.

    The *Drill Press Vice* folder is open by default. Open this folder if it is not open.

12. Select **AVI Files (*.avi)** from the **Save as type** drop-down list. Enter **Drill Press Vice** as the name of the animation in the **File name** edit box and then choose the **Save** button.

    The animation file is saved with the name *Drill Press Vice.avi* in the folder *Drill Press Vice* at the location *C:\Inventor_2011\c13*

13. As soon as you choose the **Save** tool in the **Save As** dialog box, the **Video Compression** dialog box is displayed. Accept the default options in this dialog box and choose **OK** to close it.

14. Make sure the **Minimize dialog during recording** check box is selected in the **Motion** area of the **Animation** dialog box. Now, choose the **Auto Reverse** button.

    The assembly starts animating and the dialog box is minimized. After the animation is completed and the *.avi* file is created, the dialog box is restored on the screen.

15. Choose the **Record** button to record the animation and then close the **Animation** dialog box.

    The animation file is created and now you can view it by using the Windows Media Player.

16. Save the presentation file with the name *Tutorial2.ipn* at the location given below and then close the file.

    C:\Inventor_2011\c13\Drill Press Vice

Self-Evaluation Test

Answer the following questions and then compare them to those given at the end of this chapter:

1. Autodesk Inventor allows you to explode assemblies in a special environment called the **Presentation** module. (T/F)

2. Different presentation templates are available in the **Metric** tab of the **New File** dialog box for creating different presentations. (T/F)

3. If the explosion distance in the automatic explosion is large, components start interfering with each other. (T/F)

4. When you open a new presentation file, only the **Create View** tool is available. (T/F)

5. The **Open** dialog box that is displayed while creating a design view can be used to select only the _____ files.

6. The animation of assemblies can be stored in the _____ or _____ format.

7. There are two types of tweaks: _____ and _____.

8. You can animate assemblies in the forward direction as well as in the reverse direction by choosing the _____ button in the **Motion** area of the **Animation** dialog box.

9. _____ are defined as the parametric lines that display the path and direction of the assembled components.

10. The _____ button in the **Animation** dialog box is chosen to group different tweak sequences into a single sequence.

Review Questions

Answer the following questions:

1. You can modify the individual tweak values of components. (T/F)

2. You can modify the interval value of an animation. (T/F)

3. You cannot ungroup the sequences that have been grouped together. (T/F)

4. After grouping an animation, you need to choose the **Apply** button. (T/F)

5.   The *.avi* files can be viewed in the Windows Media Player. (T/F)

6.   You cannot move the triad without moving the components but can rotate it without rotating the components. (T/F)

7.   Which of the following tools is used to precisely rotate the presentation view in the **Presentation** module?

  (a) **Rotate View**   (b) **Precise View**
  (c) **Precise View Rotation** (d) None of these

8.   Which of the following tweaks is used to rotate the selected components about a specified rotational axis?

  (a) **Linear**   (b) **Circular**
  (c) **Rotational**   (d) None of these

9.   Which of the following dialog boxes is used to explode assemblies?

  (a) **Tweak Component**   (b) **Explode Component**
  (c) **Tweak Assemblies**   (d) None of these

10. Which of the following check boxes in the **Animation** dialog box is used to display trails in the exploded view?

  (a) **Trail**   (b) **Trail On**
  (c) **Display Trail**   (d) None of these

Exercise

Exercise 1

Create the animation of exploding and unexploding the Butterfly Valve assembly. The exploded view of the Butterfly Valve assembly is shown in Figure 13-23.   **(Expected time: 1 hr)**

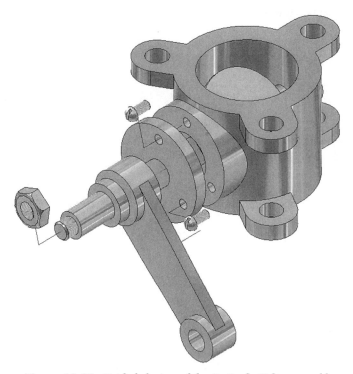

Figure 13-23 *Exploded view of the Butterfly Valve assembly*

Answers to Self-Evaluation Test
1. T, **2.** F, **3.** T, **4.** T, **5.** assembly, **6.** *.wmv*, *.avi*, **7.** linear, rotational, **8. Auto Reverse**, **9.** Trails,
10. Group

Chapter 14

Working with Special Design Tools

Learning Objectives

After completing this chapter, you will be able to:

- *Understand the concept of adaptivity and create adaptive parts.*
- *Define parameters for creating parts.*
- *Create standard and custom iPart factories.*
- *Place iParts using the custom and standard iPart factories.*
- *Create 3D Sketches.*
- *Understand hybrid surface-solid modeling.*

ADAPTIVE PARTS

Adaptive parts automatically update their adaptive features or driven dimensions based on the dimensions and constraints of the relative parts with which they are assembled. Note that while creating the adaptive parts or adaptive features, the corresponding sketch should be partially constrained. The missing dimension and adaptive features will then be modified based on the sizes, location of other components, and constraints applied between the components. You can remove the adaptivity of components at any time and add the missing dimensions so that the parts do not change their size. To convert a feature or sketch into an adaptive feature, right-click on it in the **Browser Bar** and choose **Adaptive** from the shortcut menu. Similarly, to convert a part into an adaptive part in the **Assembly** module, right-click on the part in the **Browser Bar** and choose **Adaptive** from the shortcut menu. Two semicircular arrows pointing in the counterclockwise direction will be displayed on the left of the adaptive part, feature, or sketch in the **Browser Bar**. Remember that components originally created in the other solid modeling tools and imported to the Inventor file cannot be converted into an adaptive part.

DEFINING PARAMETERS

Ribbon:	Manage > Parameters > Parameters
Toolbar:	2D Sketch Panel > Parameters

As mentioned earlier, every dimension in Autodesk Inventor is assigned a unique name, termed as parameter. When you specify the value for the dimension, the dimension parameter is equated in an expression with the value that you specified. Autodesk Inventor allows you to use parameters or expressions instead of entering the value while dimensioning a sketch. These parameters or expressions can also be entered in the edit boxes of a dialog box while creating a feature. You can create a new parameter by defining it in terms of the other parameter in an expression. The new parameters can be created before or after creating the sketch. You can use the **Parameters** tool to create new parameters. However, you can use this tool to control the relative position of the component in an assembly besides controlling the shape and size of the feature. When you invoke this tool, the **Parameters** dialog box will be displayed, see Figure 14-1. This dialog box has two types of parameters that are discussed next.

Model Parameters

Model parameters are those that are automatically created when you apply the dimensions to the entities or create a feature. The model parameters are displayed in a tabular form, as shown in Figure 14-1. The options in this table are discussed next.

Parameter Name

The **Parameter Name** column displays the names of parameters. To modify the name of a parameter, click on its field in the **Parameter Name** column. The field will change to an edit box and you can enter the new name in it. Note that you cannot duplicate the name of parameters. This means you cannot have two parameters with the same name.

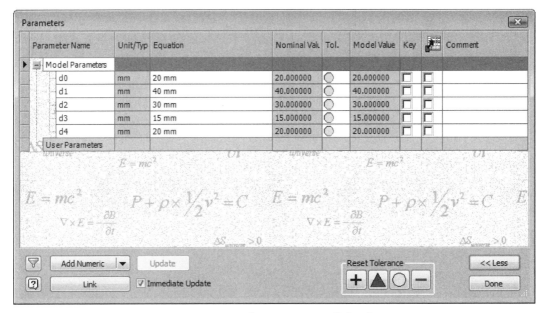

*Figure 14-1 The **Parameters** dialog box*

Unit/Type

The **Unit/Type** column displays the unit of measuring the parameters. Note that you cannot modify the unit of a parameter.

Equation

Equations are mathematical expressions, in which the parameters are equated with the algebraic or the trigonometric functions. Autodesk Inventor allows you to define the parameters using the existing parameters and equations. For example, to define a parameter d2, you can use the equation such as d2=(d0/2+d1/2), where d0 and d1 are the existing parameters. However, in the d2 field of the **Equation** column, you will not enter "d2=". All you need to enter is (d0/2+d1/2) as the equation. Since it is entered in the d2 field of the **Equation** column, Autodesk Inventor will automatically equate it with the d2 parameter.

You can also add tolerance to the parameter using the **Equation** column. To add tolerance, click on the field corresponding to the required parameter in the **Equation** column; the field changes into an edit box with an arrow on its right. Next, click on this arrow or right-click on the **Equation** field (edit box); a shortcut menu will be displayed. Choose **Tolerance** from this shortcut menu; the **Tolerance** dialog box will be displayed, as shown in Figure 14-2. You can set the tolerance parameters using the options in this dialog box.

Nominal Value

This column shows the resulting value of the equation and expressions entered in the equations column.

Tol.

The **Tol.** column is used to select the nominal, median, upper, or the lower tolerance size for the dimension. You can select the required tolerance size from the drop-down list that is displayed when you click on the field under the **Tol.** column.

Model Value

Generally, it is not possible for a component to be manufactured using the nominal values. As a result, you assign some tolerance to the dimension. The **Model Value** column shows the actual value after assigning the tolerance. The value in this column depends on the tolerance assigned to the dimension by using the **Tolerance** dialog box.

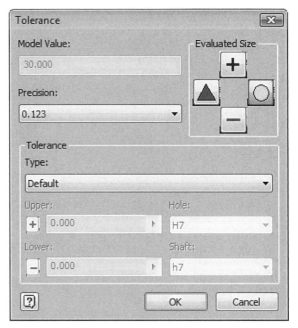

*Figure 14-2 The **Tolerance** dialog box*

Key

Select this check box to designate the selected parameter as a key parameter as these parameters are easy to identify. You will learn more about keys later in this chapter.

Export Parameter

The **Export Parameter** column displays the check boxes for each parameter. If you select the check box of a parameter, that parameter will be added to the custom properties and can be displayed in the parts list.

Comment

The **Comment** column is used to enter some information about the selected parameter. To enter a value, click on this field. The field is changed into a text box and you can enter the desired comment in it.

User Parameters

User parameters are parameters that are defined by the user for specifying the dimensions of entities and features. To create a user-defined parameter, choose the **Add Numeric** button in the **Parameters** dialog box; a new row will be displayed in the **User Parameters** table. You can specify the new settings of the user-defined parameters in the table. Note that you can modify the units of the user-defined parameter. To modify the units, click on the field below the **Unit** column; the **Unit Type** dialog box will be displayed, as shown in Figure 14-3. You can select the desired units from this dialog box. In addition to the **Add Numeric** option, there are two more options that can be used to create user parameters. These options are **Add Text** and **Add True/False**. These options can be invoked by clicking on the down arrow located on the right of the **Add Numeric** button and then choosing the required option from the flyout.

These options work in coordination with the iLogic features of Autodesk Inventor. The iLogic features will not be discussed in detail here as they are out of the scope of this textbook.

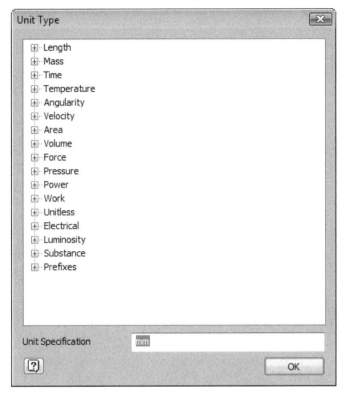

Figure 14-3 *The **Unit Type** dialog box*

Note
*The options in the **User Parameters** table are similar to those discussed in the **Model Parameters** table.*

Update
Choose this button to update the feature or the model when the parameters are changed.

Immediate Update
This check box is selected by default. As a result, the feature or the model is updated immediately when the parameters are changed. If you clear this check box, you need to choose the **Update** button whenever the parameters are changed.

Link
In addition to the model parameters and the user-defined parameters, Autodesk Inventor also allows you to create link parameters. The link parameters are created in a separate Microsoft Excel spreadsheet. Note that the model parameters and the user-defined parameters can be used only in the current file, whereas the link parameters can be used in as many number of

files as you require. This is because the link parameters are external parameters that can be imported to any file. To import a link parameter, choose the **Link** button; the **Open** dialog box is displayed, as shown in Figure 14-4. You can specify the name and the location of the Microsoft Excel spreadsheet by using the **Open** dialog box.

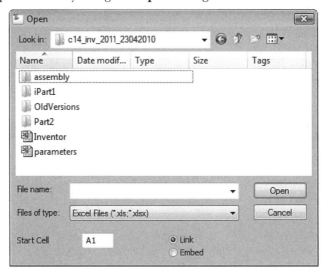

*Figure 14-4 The **Open** dialog box for selecting the spreadsheet*

When you select the spreadsheet, its location and name are displayed in the dialog box and a new table is displayed. This table shows the parameters imported from the selected spreadsheet.

The following table shows a sample of the spreadsheet that can be created in order to be used as link parameters.

LEN	60
LEN1	30
WID	20
HT	15

Filter

On choosing this button, a flyout will be displayed. The options in this flyout are used to limit the number of parameters displayed in the **Parameters** dialog box. You can choose the **All** option from the flyout if you want all parameters to be displayed. If you choose the **Key** option, only the parameters that have been assigned the keys will be displayed in the **Parameters** dialog box. But if you choose the **Non-Key** option, only the parameters that have not been assigned any key will be displayed. If you choose the **Renamed** option, only the parameters that have been renamed will be displayed. If you choose the **Equation** option, the parameters that have been defined using equations or the parameters that are used to define equations are displayed in the **Parameters** dialog box.

WORKING WITH iPARTS

While working on assemblies, you may need to create parts having identical designs but with different sizes, materials, or other variables. Autodesk Inventor allows you to create these parts and then use them with one or more variables. These parts are called as iParts.

There is a special technique for creating parts at the places where "**collaborative engineering**" is brought into use. This special technique is called iPart factories. The iPart factories can be shared by the members in the collaborative engineering environment to create iParts. The properties and dimensions of an iPart factories are saved in a table and you can use these dimensions to create an iPart in an assembly modeling environment.

Types of iPart Factories

In Autodesk Inventor, you can create two types of iPart factories. These are the Standard iPart factories and the Custom iPart factories. Both these types of iPart factories are discussed next.

Standard iPart Factories

The Standard iPart factories create iParts whose dimensions cannot be changed. This type of iPart factory is used to create standard parts. You can store these parts in the location of standard parts so that other members can also use them.

Custom iPart Factories

The Custom iPart factories create iParts with different dimensions. You can specify the dimension of the iPart while inserting it in the assembly modeling environment.

Creating iPart Factories

Ribbon:	Manage > Author > Create iPart
Toolbar:	ipart/iAssembly > iPart/iAssembly Author

Create
iPart

The iPart factories are created using the standard parts. However, it is recommended that the dimensions of the standard parts should be defined in terms of the model or user-defined parameters using the **Parameters** dialog box. To create the iPart factories, create a standard part using the parameters and then choose the **Create iPart** tool from the **Author** panel of the **Manage** tab in the **Ribbon**; the **iPart Author** dialog box will be displayed. The options in this dialog box are discussed next.

Parameters Tab

The options in the **Parameters** tab (Figure 14-5) are used to select the parameters and dimensions to be included in the iPart factory. When you invoke this tool, the **Parameters** tab is active. This tab of the **iPart Author** dialog box is divided into three areas. These areas are discussed next.

Part Parameters Pane

The **Part Parameters** pane is on the left side in the **Parameters** tab. This pane lists all the parameters and dimensions in the current part.

Selected Parameters Pane

The **Selected Parameters** pane is on the right of the **Parameters** tab. This pane lists all parameters included in the iPart factory. When you invoke the **iPart Author** dialog box, all user-defined parameters in the current file appear on this pane automatically. You can remove a parameter from this pane by selecting it and then choosing the **Remove (<<)** button on the left of this pane. Once the selected parameter is removed from the iPart factory, you cannot modify the value related to this parameter when you create an iPart using this iPart factory. Similarly, you can add a parameter by selecting it from the **Part Parameters** pane and then choosing the **Add (>>)** button.

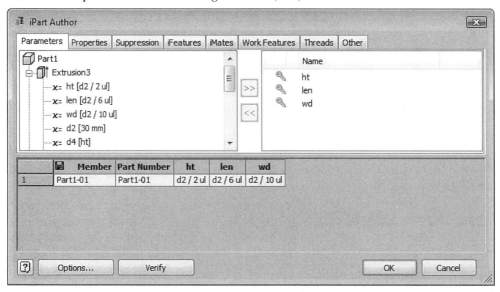

*Figure 14-5 The **Parameters** tab of the **iPart Author** dialog box*

Assigning Keys: By assigning a key to a parameter, you can recognize the values assigned to the parameter. Later on, you can change the attribute values of the parameters that have been assigned the keys. To assign a key to a parameter, click on the corresponding key of the parameter in the **Key** column; a key of numeric value 1 will be assigned to the parameter and the key of that parameter will turn blue. The keys of the remaining parameters will be gray. To modify the numeric value of the key, click on the value; a flyout will be displayed. Select the required key value from the flyout.

Making a Parameter Column Custom: Making a parameter column custom allows you to change its value while creating the iPart. To create a standard iPart factory, do not make any parameter column custom. However, to create a custom iPart factory, you need to make at least one parameter custom. To make a parameter column custom, first make sure no key is assigned to it. Next, right-click on it to display the shortcut menu. Choose **Custom Parameter Column** from the shortcut menu that is displayed; the selected parameter is made custom and the current iPart factory is made the custom iPart factory. Whenever you create an iPart using this factory, you can change the value of the custom parameter. The custom parameter column is displayed in blue in the **iPart Table** below the two list boxes in the **iPart Author** dialog box.

iPart Table

The **iPart Table** is available below the two list boxes. By default, this table has only one row with the default values of the parameters. The number of columns depend on the number of parameters in the **Selected Parameters** list box. You can add rows to this table by right-clicking on any cell of the table and choosing **Insert Row** from the shortcut menu. A new row is added to the table. Each row in the **iPart Table** represents a separate iPart in the iPart factory. You can edit the value of the iPart parameter by clicking on its field. The new iPart created using this iPart factory will use the value that you specify.

Note

*You can also make a particular cell of the **iPart Table** custom by right-clicking on it and choosing **Custom Parameter Cell** from the shortcut menu.*

Properties Tab

The options in the **Properties** tab (Figure 14-6) are used to select the summary of the component, project properties, and physical properties. You can select a property from the **File Properties** pane on the right and add it to the **Selected Properties** pane on the right.

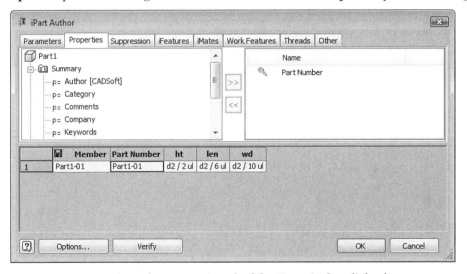

*Figure 14-6 The **Properties** tab of the **iPart Author** dialog box*

Suppression Tab

The options in the **Suppression** tab (Figure 14-7) are used to specify whether the selected features will be computed or suppressed while creating a part using the iPart factory.

If you want that a feature should be suppressed when you create a part using the iPart factory, select it from the **Model Features** pane and add it to the **Selected Features** pane. Next, right-click on it and choose **Custom Parameter Column** from the shortcut menu. The selected feature will be made custom and you can now specify whether the feature will be computed or suppressed while creating a part using the iPart factory. If you select to suppress the feature, it will not appear in the model.

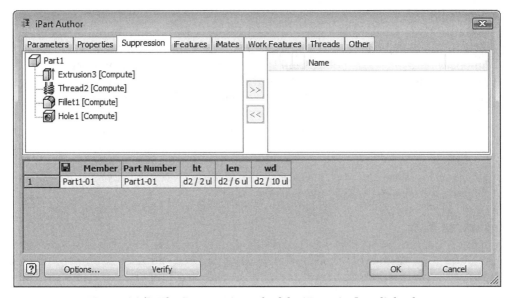

*Figure 14-7 The **Suppression** tab of the **iPart Author** dialog box*

iFeatures Tab

The options in the **iFeature** tab (Figure 14-8) are used to specify the table-driven iFeatures to be included in the iPart table. You can specify a unique iFeature row for each iPart row of the included iFeature. By using the iPart table, you can control the suppression status of the iFeature. iFeatures will be discussed in detail in Chapter 17.

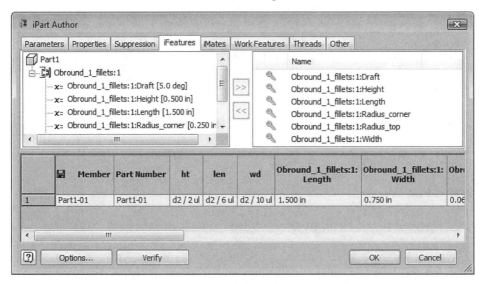

*Figure 14-8 The **iFeatures** tab of the **iPart Author** dialog box*

iMates Tab

The **iMates** tab (Figure 14-9) is used to select the iMates applied to the part that will be included in the iPart factory. iMates are created on the parts to be assembled. Creating iMates allows you to assemble parts automatically in the assembly environment. iMates will be discussed in detail in Chapter 17. iMates will be displayed in the **Model iMates** pane if you have created them on the part. To include iMates in the iPart factory, select them from the **Model iMates** pane and add to the **Selected iMates** pane. The selected iMates will be added to the iPart factory.

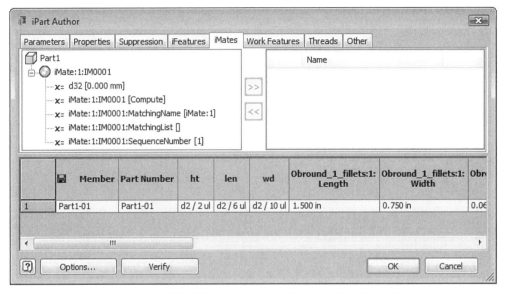

*Figure 14-9 The **iMates** tab of the **iPart Author** dialog box*

Work Features Tab

The options in the **Work Features** tab (Figure 14-10) are used to add work features to the iPart factory. The work features of a component include work planes, work axes, and work points. These work features are displayed on the left pane of the **iPart Author** dialog box only when they are created in the part. You can turn on or off the visibility of work features by selecting the required check boxes from the **Object Visibility** drop-down in the **Visibility** panel of the **View** tab.

Threads Tab

The options in the **Threads** tab (Figure 14-11) are used to add the parameters related to threads in the iPart factory. Threads are displayed on the left pane of the **iPart Author** dialog box only if you have created them in the part. You can select threads parameters from the **Thread definition tree** and add them to the **Selected thread variable** pane.

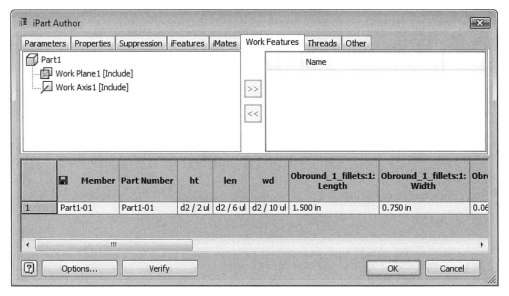

*Figure 14-10 The **Work Features** tab of the **iPart Author** dialog box*

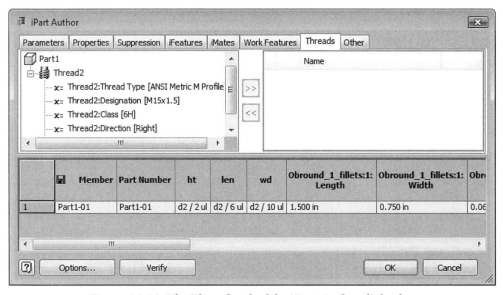

*Figure 14-11 The **Threads** tab of the **iPart Author** dialog box*

Other Tab

The options in the **Other** tab (Figure 14-12) are used to add other parameters to iPart factories. Note that these parameters cannot control the size of the part created using the iPart factory.

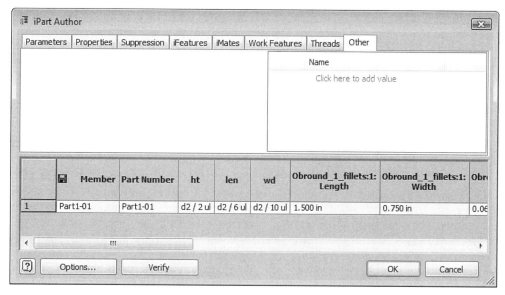

*Figure 14-12 The **Other** tab of the **iPart Author** dialog box*

To add the other parameter, click on **Click here to add value** and then enter the value of the other parameter in the text box that appears in the **Other Parameters** pane. You will notice that the parameter that you add in the **Other Parameters** pane is also added to the **iPart Table**. You can modify the value of the individual cells by selecting each field of the new parameter in the **iPart Table**.

After setting the options in various tabs of the **iPart Author** dialog box, choose **OK** to exit the dialog box and to save the file. The saved file will act as the iPart factory to place the parts in the assembly files.

Note
*When you create an iPart factory, an item **Table** is added to the **Browser Bar** above the **Origin** folder. If you click on the + sign located on the left of the **Table** in the **Browser Bar**, the tree view will expand and the parameters in the iPart factory will be displayed.*

Procedure to Create an iPart

The procedure to create an iPart is discussed next.

1. Create a component in the Part environment using parameters.

2. Invoke the **iPart Author** dialog box by choosing the **Create iPart** tool from the **Author** panel of the **Manage** tab. By default, the **Parameters** tab is chosen in this dialog box. You can include iMates, work features, threads, and other customized properties in the part by using the tabs displayed in the **iPart Author** dialog box.

3. Select the required parameter from the left pane of the **iPart Author** dialog box and then choose the **Add (>>)** button; the selected parameter will be added to the right pane of

the dialog box. Repeat the same procedure in other tabs of the **iPart Author** dialog box to add the required parameters to the right pane. You can also remove parameters from the right pane by first selecting them and then choosing the **Remove (<<)** button from the dialog box. Using different tabs in the **iPart Author** dialog box, you can control the suppression and visibility of the created features.

4. Next, assign keys to the parameters that you want to identify later. You can change the values of the parameters that have been assigned the keys. To assign a key to a parameter, click on its corresponding key in the **Key** column.

5. After assigning keys, you need to add the number of rows that is equal to the number of iParts you want to create in the **iPart Table**. Add the required number of rows in the **iPart Table** and then change the parameter value in the required parameter. Note that you need to change the parameter values of the parameters that have been assigned the keys. The size of other parameters will vary according to the expressions used in defining the parameters.

6. After adding the required number of rows in the **iPart Table**, you need to verify the table for errors. If there are any errors in the table, they will be highlighted in yellow. Rectify the error, if any, found in the table.

7. Next, save the table by choosing **OK** from the **iPart Author** dialog box and then exit the part file.

Inserting an iPart into an Assembly

You can insert an iPart into an assembly file using the **Place** tool. The number of iParts that can be inserted into the graphics window depends upon the number of rows added to the **iPart Table**. Depending on whether you select a standard iPart factory or custom iPart factory, the dialog box for placing the part will differ. The procedure for placing both these types of iPart factories is discussed next.

Placing Standard iParts in an Assembly

To place a part using the standard iPart factory, choose the **Place** tool from the **Component** panel of the **Assemble** tab; the **Place Component** dialog box will be displayed. Select the required standard iPart and choose the **Open** button from the **Place Component** dialog box; the **Place Standard iPart** dialog box will be displayed. The options in the three tabs of this dialog box are discussed next.

Keys Tab

The **Keys** tab (Figure 14-13) consists of the **Predefined values** pane that displays the name and value of the parameters that were assigned the keys in the **Selected Parameters** pane of the **iPart Author** dialog box. Note that because it is a standard iPart, you cannot modify the value of any of the parameters in this dialog box. However, if more than one rows were created in the **iPart Table**, you can select the standard values from the list of available values. This list is displayed when you click on one of the values and select the **All Values** check box.

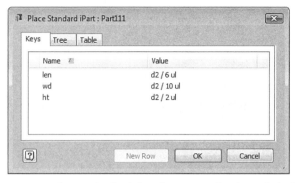

Figure 14-13 *The **Keys** tab of the **Place Standard iPart** dialog box*

Tree Tab

The **Tree** tab (Figure 14-14) displays the name and values of the parameters that were assigned the keys in the form of a tree view in the **iPart Author** dialog box. You can click on the + sign on the left of each parameter to expand the tree view.

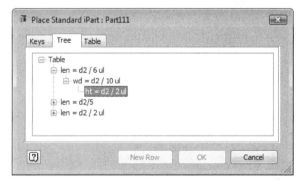

Figure 14-14 *The **Tree** tab of the **Place Standard iPart** dialog box*

Table Tab

The **Table** tab (Figure 14-15) displays the iPart table created in the **iPart Author** dialog box. As mentioned earlier, each row in this table represents a part. Also, different fields in the rows can be set to different values in the **iPart Author** dialog box. As a result, you can select any row from this tab to insert the iPart. Depending on the value of the parameters defined for the selected row in the **iPart Author** dialog box, the part will be placed.

Placing Custom iParts in an Assembly

To place a part using the custom iPart factory, invoke the **Place** tool. Next, select the custom iPart; the **Place Custom iPart** dialog box will be displayed. The options in the three tabs of this dialog box are discussed next.

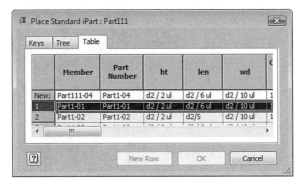

*Figure 14-15 The **Table** tab of the **Place Standard iPart** dialog box*

Keys Tab

The **Keys** tab of the **Place Custom iPart** dialog box (Figure 14-16) has two panes. The pane on the left is the **Predefined values** pane and displays all parameters that were not made custom in the **iPart Author** dialog box. Note that you cannot modify the values of the parameters available in this pane. The pane on the right is called the **Custom values** pane. It displays all the parameters that were made custom using the **iPart Author** dialog box. To modify the value of the parameter, click on the **Value** field of that parameter in the **Custom values** pane; the field will change to an edit box. Enter the new value in it. The part that will be placed using this iPart factory will have the specified value of the parameter.

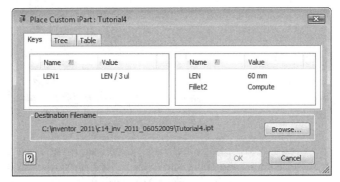

*Figure 14-16 The **Keys** tab of the **Place Custom iPart** dialog box*

Tree Tab

The **Tree** tab (Figure 14-17) also has two panes. The left pane displays the name and values in the form of a tree view of the parameters that were assigned keys in the **iPart Author** dialog box. The right pane displays the parameters that were made custom using the **iPart Author** dialog box.

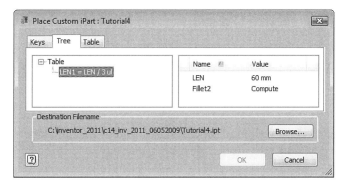

Figure 14-17 The **Tree** *tab of the* **Place Custom iPart** *dialog box*

Table Tab

The **Table** tab of the **Place Custom iPart** dialog box (Figure 14-18) is similar to that of the **Place Standard iPart** dialog box. It displays the iPart table that was created in the **iPart Author** dialog box. You can select the table to place the part based on the values in that table.

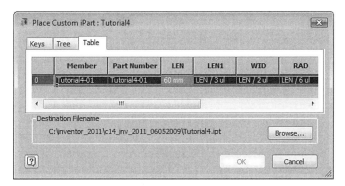

Figure 14-18 The **Table** *tab of the* **Place Custom iPart** *dialog box*

Changing the iParts in the Assembly File

If the iPart factory used to place the iPart in the assembly file has more than one row in the iPart table, you can replace the iPart with the other iPart defined in the rows. To change the iPart, right-click on **Table** under **iPart** in the **Browser Bar**; a shortcut menu will be displayed. Choose **Change Component** from the shortcut menu; the **Place Standard iPart** dialog box or the **Place Custom iPart** dialog box will be displayed. Choose the **Table** tab and then select the row of the required iPart; the previous iPart will be replaced by the other iPart whose row you select.

CREATING 3D SKETCHES

| **Ribbon:** | Model > Sketch drop-down > Create 3D Sketch |

In the earlier chapters, you have learned about creating 2D sweeps by defining the path in 2D space. In this chapter, you will learn about creating a 3D sketch that can be used for creating sweep features in 3D space, as shown in Figure 14-19.

To create a 3D sketch, choose the **Create 3D Sketch** tool from the **Sketch** drop-down in the **Sketch** panel of the **Model** tab; the 3D sketching environment will be activated. Note that because a 3D sketch has to be created, you will not be prompted to select the sketching plane. As soon as you enter the 3D sketching environment, the **3D Sketch** tab will be activated. Some of the tools in this tab are the same as those discussed in 2D sketching. The functions of the remaining tools are discussed next.

Line

The **Line** tool is used to create a line in the 3D space. Note that similar to drawing the line in a 2D sketch, you can create a line by specifying the points on the graphics screen. The 3D line can also be created by using work points, vertices of an existing model, or center points of a cylindrical feature or hole. You can also turn on the option of creating bends at the corners of a 3D line. By default, this option is turned off. To turn this option on, invoke the **Line** tool in the 3D sketching environment and then right-click in the drawing window to display the shortcut menu. Choose the **Auto-Bend** option. Now, when you draw a 3D line, it will automatically be bent at the corners and the bend radius will be displayed, as the value of the first instance. At the remaining instances, the value will be displayed as the function of the first value. As a result, when you modify the first value, the remaining values will be modified automatically. If you want to modify any other value, double-click on it and modify it using the **Edit Dimension** toolbar. However, in this case, the modified value will no more be the function of the first value. Figure 14-20 shows a 3D line created by using the vertices of an existing model and the center points of the holes. Note that after invoking the **Line** tool, the **Inventor Precise Input** toolbar is displayed. You can also specify the points of 3D line using this toolbar.

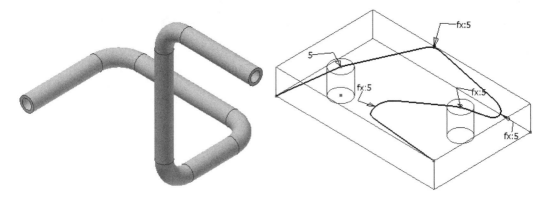

Figure 14-19 *Pipe created by sweeping a profile along a 3D path*

Figure 14-20 *3D line created using work points and vertices of a model*

Spline

 Spline   The **Spline** tool is used to create splines in the 3D sketching environment. This tool works similar to the **Spline** tool of 2D sketching environment. You can use work points, vertices of an existing feature, or center points of holes or cylindrical features for creating a 3D spline.

Bend

 Bend   The **Bend** tool is used to create bends manually at the corners of the 3D line. When you invoke this tool, the **Bend** toolbar will be displayed, as shown in Figure 14-21. You can specify the radius of the bend in this toolbar and then select the two lines that comprise of the corner where the bend will be created. Note that the corners at which the bend cannot be created, a cross will be displayed when you move the cursor over the line to select it. This cross suggests that you cannot select this line for creating a bend.

*Figure 14-21 The **Bend** toolbar*

Include Geometry

The **Include Geometry** tool is used to include an existing 2D geometry in the 3D sketch. You can also select the edge of an existing model to be included in the 3D sketch. This is similar to projecting geometries or cutting edges. The only difference is that in this case, the selected entities are projected in a 3D sketching environment.

Intersection Curve

The **Intersection Curve** tool is used to create a 3D curve using the intersection of two surfaces, work planes, or existing components. When you invoke this tool, the **3D Intersection Curve** dialog box will be displayed, as shown in Figure 14-22.

When you invoke this dialog box, the **Select intersecting geometry** button is chosen by default. Select the first intersecting geometry; the **Select geometry to be intersected** button will be chosen automatically. Now, select the other intersecting surface; a 3D curve will be created at the intersection of the two selected geometries. Figure 14-23 shows two intersecting surfaces and Figure 14-24 shows the resultant 3D curve created using the intersecting surfaces.

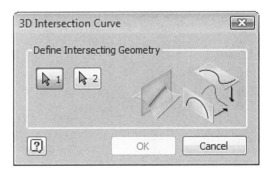

*Figure 14-22 The **3D Intersection Curve** dialog box*

Helical Curve

 Helical Curve   The **Helical Curve** tool allows you to create 3D helical curves that consist of a helical curve and a centerline. The dimensions of the curve are also displayed in the drawing area. To create a 3D helical curve, choose the **Helical Curve** tool from the **3D Sketch** tab; the **Helical Curve** dialog box will be displayed, as shown in Figure 14-25. Also, you will be prompted to select a start point for the helix axis. The **Inventor Precise Input** toolbar that is displayed along with the **Helical Curve** dialog box can be used to specify the start point and endpoint of the helix axis. The rest of the options that are used to create the helical curve are similar to those discussed while creating coil feature in Chapter 8. Figure 14-26 shows a helical curve along with the other components that are displayed in the drawing area.

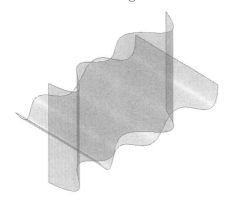

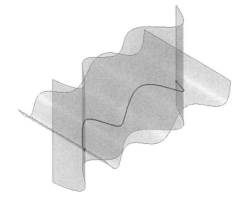

Figure 14-23 Intersecting surfaces   *Figure 14-24* 3D curve created using the surfaces

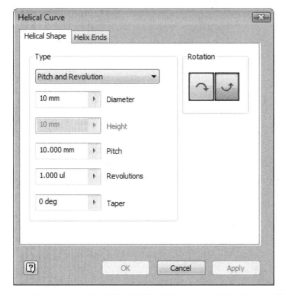

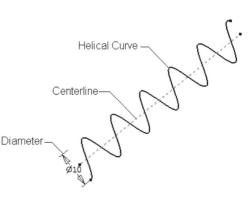

Figure 14-25 The **Helical Curve** dialog box   *Figure 14-26* Helical curve with its components

Note
You cannot save a file in the 3D Sketching environment. Therefore, you need to exit the 3D sketching environment to save the part file.

The other options in this environment are similar to those discussed in the 2D Sketching environment and Part modeling environment.

TUTORIALS

Tutorial 1

In this tutorial, you will create new parameters and then use them for sketching and extruding the model shown in Figure 14-27. The dimensioned sketch is shown in Figure 14-28. The sketch should be extruded to a distance of EXT. The dimensions in the sketch should be displayed as equations, as shown in Figure 14-28. **(Expected time: 30 min)**

The numeric values of parameters are given below.

LEN = 60
WID = LEN/2
RAD = LEN/6
EXT = LEN/3

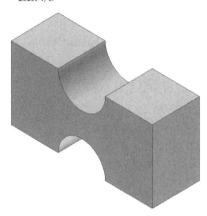

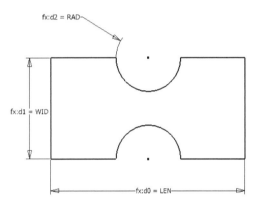

Figure 14-27 *Model for Tutorial 1*   **Figure 14-28** *Sketch for the model*

The following steps are required to complete this tutorial:

a. Start Autodesk Inventor and then start a new metric standard part file.
b. Create the sketch and add required constraints to it, refer to Figure 14-29.
c. Invoke the **Parameters** tool and create required parameters, refer to Figure 14-30.
d. Invoke the **Document Settings** dialog box and select the option to display the dimensions as equations.
e. Invoke the **Dimension** tool and dimension the sketch by entering parameters instead of entering values in the **Edit Dimension** toolbar, refer to Figure 14-31.
f. Exit the sketching environment and extrude the sketch. Enter the parameters instead of entering value in the extrusion distance edit box.

Starting a New Part File

1. Start Autodesk Inventor and invoke the **New File** dialog box.

2. Choose the **Metric** tab and start a new metric part file. Exit the sketching environment and define a new sketch plane on the XZ plane.

Drawing the Sketch

1. Draw the sketch for the model by using the sketching tools. Add the required constraints to it. The sketch is shown in Figure 14-29.

Creating Parameters

As mentioned earlier, parameters are created by using the **Parameters** dialog box. You can invoke this dialog box by using the **Parameters** tool.

1. Choose the **Parameters** tool from the **Parameters** panel of the **Manage** tab to invoke the **Parameters** dialog box.

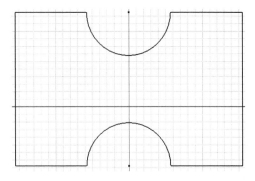

Figure 14-29 *Sketch after adding the constraints*

2. Choose the **Add Numeric** button from this dialog box to enter a new row in the **User Parameters** table. Enter the name of the parameter as **LEN** in the **Parameter Name** field and then press ENTER.

   You will notice that a new row with the name LEN is created. The unit of the parameter is mm, and the equation and value is 1. Now, you need to modify the value of the parameter.

Note
*Note that the parameter names are case sensitive. Therefore, if you enter a name in uppercase characters, you need to enter the parameters in the same case while specifying them in the **Edit Dimension** toolbar or in any dialog box.*

3. Click on the **Equation** field of the LEN row. It changes into an edit box. Enter **60** in this edit box and then press ENTER.

   You will notice that the values of the **Nominal Value** field and the **Model Value** field are automatically changed to 60.000000.

4. Again, choose the **Add Numeric** button to add another row in the **User Parameters** table.

5. Enter **WID** in the **Parameter Name** field.

6. Click on the **Equation** field of the WID row and enter **LEN/2** in this field. Next, press ENTER.

   You will notice that the value in the **Model Value** field has automatically changed to 30.000000. This is because the value of the LEN parameter is 60 and WID = LEN/2 = 60/2 = 30. Also, notice that **ul** has automatically been added on the right of the equation. You do not need to enter this value while defining the equation as it is automatically added by Autodesk Inventor.

7. Similarly, create the remaining parameters. The **Parameters** dialog box after creating all parameters is shown in Figure 14-30. Choose **Done** to exit the **Parameters** dialog box.

Note

*As you have not dimensioned the sketch until now, no row will be displayed in the **Model Parameters** table. Once you add dimensions to the sketch, the parameters will be added in the **Model Parameters** table.*

Displaying Dimensions as Equations

As mentioned in the tutorial description, you need to display dimensions as equations. Therefore, you need to select this option from the **Document Settings** dialog box.

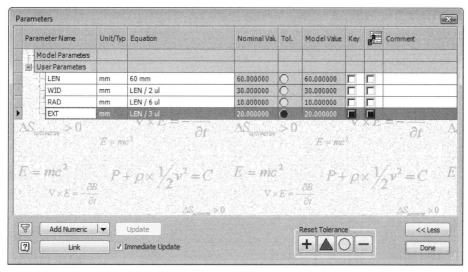

*Figure 14-30 The **Parameters** dialog box after adding the user-defined parameters*

1. Choose the **Document Settings** tool from the **Options** panel of the **Tools** tab to invoke the **Document Settings** dialog box.

2. In this dialog box, choose the **Units** tab and select the **Display as expression** radio button from the **Modeling Dimension Display** area. Next, choose **Apply** and then choose **Close** to exit the dialog box.

Dimensioning the Sketch

Now, you need to dimension the sketch by using parameters. As mentioned earlier, parameters are case sensitive. This means if you have specified the name of the parameter in capital letters, you need to enter the name in capital letters in the **Edit Dimension** toolbar, else you will be informed through Autodesk Inventor dialog box that this expression cannot be evaluated.

1. Invoke the **Dimension** tool and then select the vertical lines one by one at the two ends of the sketch. Place the dimension below the sketch; the **Edit Dimension** toolbar is displayed.

2. Enter **LEN** in the **Edit Dimension** toolbar and press ENTER.

   You will notice that the dimension is automatically modified and displayed as an equation on the graphics screen. This happens because you have selected the option of displaying dimensions as equations.

3. Select the left vertical line and then place the dimension on the left of the sketch. Enter **WID** in the **Edit Dimension** toolbar and press ENTER.

4. Select the upper arc and then place the dimension on the left of the arc. Enter **RAD** in the **Edit Dimension** toolbar and press ENTER.

   This completes the dimensioning of the sketch. The sketch after adding all dimensions is shown in Figure 14-31. In this figure, the grid lines and axes have not been displayed for better visibility of the sketch.

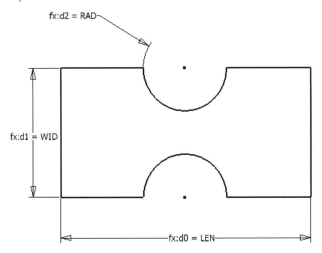

Figure 14-31 Sketch displaying the dimensions as equations

Note
If you do not dimension the sketch in the same sequence as mentioned above, the name of the model parameters with which the user parameters are equated will be different from those shown in Figure 14-28.

Extruding the Sketch

1. Exit the sketching environment and then change the current view to the isometric view.

2. Invoke the **Extrude** dialog box and then enter **EXT** in the edit box provided in the **Extents** area. Accept the remaining default options and then choose the **OK** button.

   The sketch is extruded through a distance defined by the EXT parameter. You can also specify the parameters of the extruded feature using the mini toolbar that is displayed on invoking the **Extrude** tool.

3. Save the model with the name *Tutorial1.ipt* at the location given below and then close the file.

C:\Inventor_2011\c14

Tutorial 2

In this tutorial, you will create the assembly of the Outer Plate and the Inner Plate shown in Figure 14-32. The dimensions of the Outer Plate are shown in Figure 14-33. Create the Inner Plate as an adaptive part such that it automatically adjusts its size to fit inside the Outer Plate. Apply the **Mate** constraint with an offset of 10 mm to all the outer faces of the Inner Plate and the inner faces of the groove in the Outer Plate. After assembling the components, edit the inner cavity of the Outer Plate such that the Inner Plate again automatically adjusts its size.

(Expected time: 1 hr)

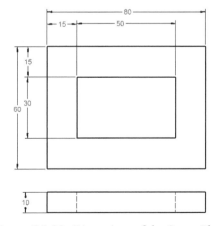

Figure 14-32 *Assembly for Tutorial 2*

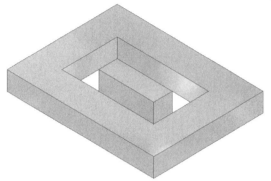

Figure 14-33 *Dimensions of the Outer Plate*

 Note
As the Inner Plate has to be an adaptive part, its dimensions are not required.

The following steps are required to complete this tutorial:

a. Start a new metric assembly file and then create the Outer Plate, refer to Figure 14-34.
b. Invoke the **Create** tool and then select the top face of the Outer Plate as the sketching plane for the Inner Plate.
c. Make the sketch of the Inner Plate adaptive and then set the parameters in the **Assembly** tab of the **Options** dialog box.
d. Sketch the Inner Plate and then extrude it up to the bottom face of the Outer Plate.
e. Save the model and then exit the Part environment.
f. Add the **Mate** constraint between all inner faces of the groove in the Outer Plate and the outer faces of the Inner Plate. The size of the Inner Plate automatically changes in order to adjust inside the Outer Plate, refer to Figure 14-35.
g. Modify the dimensions of the inner cavity of the Outer Plate. The size of the Inner Plate again changes automatically to retain the design intent, refer to Figure 14-38.

Creating the Outer Plate

You can directly create the Outer Plate and the Inner Plate in the assembly file. Before creating the Outer Plate, you need to change the measurement unit to mm.

1. Start a new metric standard assembly file. Next, choose the **Document Settings** button from the **Options** panel of the **Tools** tab; the **Document Settings** dialog box is displayed.

2. Choose the **Units** tab and then select **millimeters** from the **Length** drop-down list in the **Units** area. Next, choose **OK** to close the dialog box.

3. Create the Outer Plate on the XY plane. After creating the Outer Plate, return to the assembly file. The assembly file after creating the Outer Plate is shown in Figure 14-34. For dimensions, refer to Figure 14-33.

Creating the Inner Plate

You will sketch the Inner Plate by taking the top face of the Outer Plate as the sketching plane. Note that the sketch plane should be constrained to the selected face.

1. Invoke the **Create** tool. Make sure that the **Constrain sketch plane to selected face or plane** check box is selected in the **Create In-Place Component** dialog box.

2. Enter **Inner Plate** as the name of the component in the **New Component Name** edit box in the **Create In-Place Component** dialog box. Choose **OK** from the dialog box and then select the top face of the Outer Plate as the sketching plane.

3. Right-click on **Sketch1** in the **Browser Bar** and then choose **Adaptive** from the shortcut menu. This makes the Inner Plate adaptive and therefore its size is adjusted automatically based on the surrounding.

4. Choose the **Application Options** tool from the **Options** panel of the **Tools** tab to display the **Application Options** dialog box. Choose the **Assembly** tab from this dialog box to display the options in this tab.

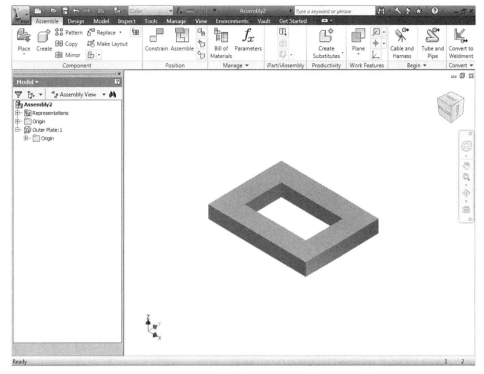

Figure 14-34 *Assembly after creating the Outer Plate*

5. Select all check boxes in the **In-place features** area to make the model adaptive. As a result, on extruding the model up to the bottom face of the Inner Plate, the new part is automatically modified.

6. Choose **Apply** and then choose **Close** from the **Application Options** dialog box. Next, draw the sketch for the Inner Plate and then extrude it up to the bottom face of the Outer Plate. Save the part file and then exit the part modeling environment.

   You do not need to add dimensions to the Inner Plate as it is an adaptive part. The assembly after creating the Inner Plate is shown in Figure 14-35.

7. Now, apply the **Mate** constraint with an offset value of 10 mm on the inner left vertical face of the Outer Plate and the outer left vertical face of the Inner Plate. The Inner Plate shifts toward the right.

8. Change the display type of both plates to wireframe and then apply the **Mate** constraint with an offset of 10 mm on the inner lower horizontal face of the Outer Plate and the outer lower horizontal face of the Inner Plate; the Inner Plate shifts upward.

9. Now, apply the **Mate** constraint with an offset value of 10 mm on the inner right vertical face of the Outer Plate and the outer right vertical face of the Inner Plate.

You will see that the size of the Inner Plate has reduced in order to fit inside the cavity of the Outer Plate. This is because of the adaptive property of the Inner Plate.

10. Similarly, apply the **Mate** constraint with an offset value of 10 mm between the inner upper horizontal face of the Outer Plate and the outer upper horizontal face of the Inner Plate.

Notice the size of the Inner Plate. It has further reduced in order to fit inside the cavity of the Outer Plate.

11. Close the **Place Constraint** dialog box and then change the display type back to shaded. The assembly after applying the constraint is shown in Figure 14-36. Notice the change in the size of the Inner Plate.

Figure 14-35 Assembly after creating the Inner Plate   *Figure 14-36* Assembly after applying the constraint

Modifying the Dimensions of the Cavity of the Outer Plate

You can edit the dimensions of the cavity of the Outer Plate in the assembly file. Since the Inner Plate is an adaptive part, it will automatically change its dimensions when the dimensions of the cavity are modified.

1. Double-click on **Outer Plate:1** in the **Browser Bar** to activate this component.

2. Modify the dimensions of the cavity, as shown in Figure 14-37.

3. Choose **Return** from the **Quick Access Toolbar** to exit the sketching environment. You may need to add the **Return** tool to the **Quick Access Toolbar**, if it is not displayed by default.

4. Again, choose **Return** from the **Quick Access Toolbar** toolbar to exit the part modeling environment. Change the current view to the isometric view.

On doing so, you will notice that the dimensions of the Inner Plate are modified in order to retain the design intent of the assembly. The assembly after modifying the dimensions of the cavity is shown in Figure 14-38. Notice the change in the dimensions of the Inner Plate.

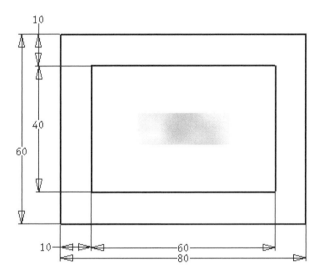

Figure 14-37 *Modifying the dimensions of the cavity*

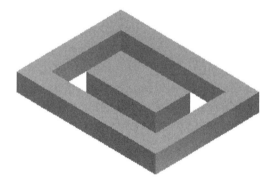

Figure 14-38 *Modified assembly*

5. Save the assembly with the name *Tutorial2.iam* at the location *C:\Inventor_2011\c14*. You are prompted to save the individual part files. Save the changes in the part files.

Tutorial 3

In this tutorial, you will create a pipe in 3D space, as shown in Figure 14-39. Assume the dimensions of the pipe.   **(Expected time: 30 min)**

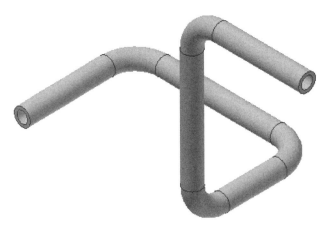

Figure 14-39 *Pipe for Tutorial 3*

The following steps are required to complete this tutorial:

a. Create a 2D sketch consisting of three lines on the XY plane and then exit the sketching environment, refer to Figure 14-40.
b. Define a new work plane normal to the existing sketch and then create the second 2D sketch on this new work plane, refer to Figure 14-41. The start point of the first line in the second sketch should be the endpoint of the right vertical line in the first sketch.
c. Exit the sketching environment and then invoke the 3D sketching environment.
d. Select all lines to be included in the 3D sketch using the **Include Geometry** tool.
e. Add bends at all corners and then exit the 3D sketching environment, refer to Figure 14-42.
f. Define a new work plane at the start point of the path and then sketch the profile of the pipe. Take the reference of the start point of the first line for drawing the sketch.
g. Exit the sketching environment and sweep the sketch along the 3D path.

Drawing the First 2D Sketch
1. Invoke the **New File** dialog box and then choose the **Metric** tab from it.

2. Start a new metric part file and then draw the first sketch on the XY plane, as shown in Figure 14-40.

3. Exit the sketching environment by choosing the **Finish Sketch** button.

Drawing the Second 2D Sketch
You need to create the second 2D sketch on a work plane that is normal to the third line of the first 2D sketch. Therefore, first you need to define a new work plane normal to the third line of the sketch.

1. Define a new work plane normal to the right vertical line in the sketch and then select it as the sketching plane for drawing the next 2D sketch.

2. Draw the next sketch starting from the origin of the sketch plane. The origin of the sketch plane is the endpoint of the right vertical line of the first sketch, see Figure 14-41.

   To ensure that the start point of the line is at the origin, you need to project the third line of the sketch. The line will be projected as a point that will be placed at the origin. Now, apply the **Coincident** constraint between the endpoint of the line and the projected point.

3. Exit the sketching environment and turn off the display of the work plane. The first and second 2D sketches are shown in Figure 14-41.

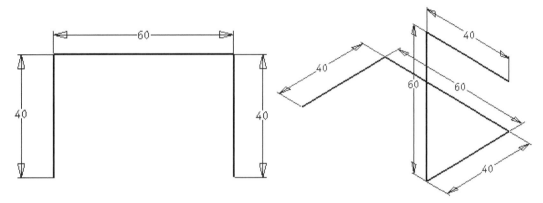

Figure 14-40 First 2D sketch   *Figure 14-41* First and second 2D sketches

Creating the 3D Sketch

1. Choose the **Create 3D Sketch** tool from **Model > Sketch > Sketch** drop-down to invoke the 3D Sketching environment.

2. Choose the **Include Geometry** tool from the **Draw** panel of the **3D Sketch** tab.

3. Select all lines in the first 2D sketch and the second 2D sketch, one by one.

4. Choose the **Bend** tool from the **Draw** panel of the **3D Sketch** tab to display the **Bend** toolbar. Enter **10** in this toolbar and then select all lines that form the corners of the 3D sketch.

   You will notice that a fillet kind of bend is created at all corners of the 3D sketch and the dimension is displayed on all bends.

5. Exit the 3D sketching environment.

6. Now, turn off the visibility of two 2D sketches using the **Browser Bar**.

   The 3D sketch after turning off the visibility of 2D sketches is shown in Figure 14-42.

Note

If you are not able to fillet the vertex at the intersection of the first and second 2D sketches, it implies that the endpoint of the first 2D sketch is not coincident with that of the second 2D sketch. In other words, the start point of the first line of the second 2D sketch is not at the origin. Therefore, you need to edit the second 2D sketch and move it to the origin.

Creating the Profile for the Sweep Feature

To create the profile for the sweep feature, you need to define a new work plane at the start point of the first 2D sketch. Next, you need to select this work plane as the new sketching plane and draw the sketch of the profile.

1. Define a new work plane at the start point of the 3D path from where the first 2D sketch was started. Select this work plane as the new sketching plane.

2. Draw the 2D sketch of the profile of the sweep feature. The sketch of the profile consists of two concentric circles. The center of the circles should be at the start point of the first line of the 3D path. Specify 6 mm as the diameter of the outer circle and 4 mm as the diameter of the inner circle. Make sure that the center point of the circles lie at the origin.

3. Exit the sketching environment.

Sweeping the Profile along the 3D Path

1. Invoke the **Sweep** dialog box and select the area between the two circles as the profile of the sweep feature. The area between the two circles turns blue and the **Path** button gets activated in the **Sweep** dialog box.

2. Select the 3D path as the path of the sweep feature. The complete 3D path turns blue.

3. Choose **OK** to close the **Sweep** dialog box. The final pipe for Tutorial 3 is shown in Figure 14-43.

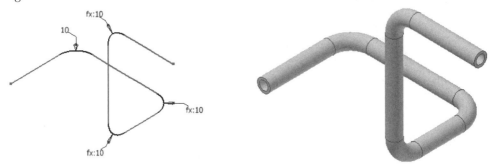

Figure 14-42   *3D Sketch after turning off the visibility of the 2D sketches*   *Figure 14-43*   *Pipe for Tutorial 3*

4. Save this model with the name *Tutorial3* at the location *C:\Inventor_2011\c14*.

Tutorial 4

In this tutorial, you will open the model saved in Tutorial 1 and add another parameter to it with the name FILLET, where FILLET = LEN/10. Using this parameter, you will fillet the model. Figure 14-44 shows the final filleted model. Next, you will change this model into a custom iPart factory. Make the LEN and FILLET as custom variables, and then suppress the FILLET variable. Finally, place the two iParts in an assembly file using the custom iPart factory that you created. The details of the two iParts that you need to place in the assembly are given below. **(Expected time: 30 min)**

iPart 1
Value of LEN = 60
Suppress the fillet in the model

iPart 2
Value of LEN = 100

Figure 14-44 Model after filleting the edges using the FILLET parameter

The following steps are required to complete this tutorial:

a. Open the *Tutorial1.ipt* file and save it with the name *Tutorial4.ipt*.
b. Create a new user-defined parameter, FILLET in the part. The value of this parameter is LEN/10.
c. Fillet the model using the FILLET parameter.
d. Invoke the **iPart Author** dialog box and make the LEN parameter custom.
e. Add one more row in the iPart table. Change the value of the LEN parameter to 100.
f. Invoke the **Suppression** tab and suppress the FILLET variable.
g. Make the FILLET variable custom.

h.   Save the file and then open a new assembly file.

i.   Place iParts in an assembly file using the custom iPart factory created earlier.

Opening the Tutorial 1 File

1.   Open the *Tutorial1.ipt* file created earlier in this chapter.

2.   Next, save it with the name *Tutorial4.ipt*.

Adding a User-defined Parameter

You need to add a user-defined parameter in the current file. This parameter will be used to fillet the model. You do not need to invoke the sketching environment as the **Parameters** dialog box can be invoked from the **Parameters** panel of the **Manage** tab in the modeling environment.

1.   Choose the **Parameters** tool from the **Parameters** panel of the **Manage** tab to invoke the **Parameters** dialog box.

2.   Choose the **Add Numeric** button to enter a new row in the **User Parameters** table. Enter **FILLET** in the **Parameter Name** field and then press ENTER.

A new row of the user-defined parameter is added. At this stage, the value of this parameter is 1.00 mm in the **Equation** column. You need to equate this parameter in terms of the LEN parameter.

3.   Click on the **Equation** field in the FILLET row; the field changes to an edit box.

4.   Enter **LEN/10** in the edit box and then press ENTER. You will notice that the value of this parameter automatically changes to 6.000000 in the **Nominal Value** and **Model Value** edit boxes.

5.   Exit the **Parameters** dialog box.

Adding a Fillet to the Model Using the FILLET Parameter

1.   Choose the **Fillet** tool from the **Modify** panel of the **Model** tab to invoke the **Fillet** dialog box.

2.   Select the four edges to be filleted from the model.

3.   Enter **FILLET** in the **Radius** field of the **Constant** tab in the **Fillet** dialog box.

Note that when you enter values in terms of parameters, you need to delete **mm** from the edit boxes.

4.   Choose **OK**; the fillet is added to the model and looks similar to the one shown in Figure 14-45.

Creating the Custom iPart Factory

Next, you need to create the custom iPart factory. You will create it by customizing the LEN parameter and suppressing the fillet feature.

1. Choose the **Create iPart** tool from the **Author** panel of the **Manage** tab; the **iPart Author** dialog box is displayed with the **Parameters** tab chosen.

   All the user-defined parameters are displayed on the **Selected Parameters** pane. You will also notice that only one row is available in the iPart table. This row has the default values of variables.

Figure 14-45 *Filleted model viewed from a different direction*

2. Right-click on the LEN variable in the **iPart Table**; a shortcut menu is displayed. Choose **Custom Parameter Column** from the shortcut menu.

   The **LEN** column in the **iPart Table** turns blue and the key on the left of this parameter in the **Selected Parameters** pane is removed.

3. Click on the key corresponding to the WID parameter; a key with numeric value 1 is assigned to the WID parameter.

4. Choose the **Suppression** tab and then select **Fillet1** from the **Model Features** pane. Choose the **Add** button (**>>**) to add this feature to the **Selected Features** pane.

5. Next, right-click on **Fillet1** in the **iPart Table**, and then choose **Custom Parameter Column** from the shortcut menu; this feature is made custom. Now, you can suppress or compute it while inserting iParts using this iPart factory. Choose the **OK** button from the **iPart Author** dialog box to create the iPart factory. Now, you can save it and use it to place iParts.

6. Choose the **Save** button from the **Quick Access Toolbar** and then close this file.

Placing iParts Using the Custom iPart Factory

Generally, iParts are placed in assembly files. This is the reason you need to start a new assembly file to place iParts in it.

1. Start a new assembly file and then invoke the **Place** tool from the **Component** panel of the **Assemble** tab; the **Place Component** dialog box is displayed.

2. Select the *Tutorial4.ipt* file from this dialog box to place the iPart and then choose the **Open** button; the **Place Custom iPart** dialog box is displayed.

The **Predefined values** pane shows only the WID parameter because only this parameter was assigned the key. On the other hand, the custom values pane shows the LEN parameter and the **Fillet1** feature. As a result, you can modify the value of the LEN parameter and suppress or compute the **Fillet1** feature.

3. Click on the **Value** field of the **Fillet1** feature in the **Custom values** pane; the field is changed into a drop-down list.

4. Select **Suppress** from this drop-down list. Next, click anywhere on the screen to place the component.

5. Choose **OK** to close the dialog box.

   Notice that an iPart is placed in the assembly file and the fillet in this part is suppressed.

 Tip: *If you want to unsuppress the fillet in the iPart placed in the current assembly file, click on the + sign located on the left of the part in the **Browser Bar**; the tree view expands, and **Table** and **Origin** appear in the **Browser Bar**. Next, right-click on the **Table**, and then choose **Change Component** from the shortcut menu; the **Place Custom iPart** dialog box will be displayed. Change **Suppress** to **Compute** in the **Value** field of **Fillet1**. Choose **OK** to exit the dialog box; the fillet will be computed and then shown in the model.*

6. Next, you need to place another iPart with a different value in the assembly. Invoke the **Place** tool to display the **Place Component** dialog box.

7. Next, select the *Tutorial4.ipt* in this dialog box to place the iPart; the **Place Custom iPart** dialog box is displayed. Click on the **Value** field of the **LEN** parameter; the field changes into an edit box.

8. Enter **100** in this edit box and then click anywhere on the graphics screen. Next, right-click, and then choose **Done** from the shortcut menu; the component is placed and the dialog box is closed.

9. Next, save the file.

   You can now use these components to create an assembly.

Tutorial 5

In this tutorial, you will use the hybrid surface-solid modeling to create the model shown in Figure 14-46. Figure 14-47 shows another view of this model. The dimensions of this model are given in the tutorial steps.   **(Expected time: 45 min)**

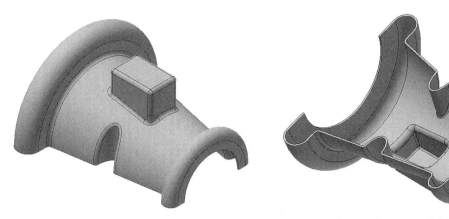

Figure 14-46 Model for Tutorial 5

Figure 14-47 Another view of the model for Tutorial 5

The following steps are required to complete this tutorial:

a. Open a new part file and then create the sketch shown in Figure 14-48 on the default XY plane.
b. Revolve this sketch through an angle of 180-degree so that the final output is a surface, refer to Figure 14-49.
c. Create two extruded surfaces, refer to Figure 14-51.
d. Split surfaces using the **Face Split** option, refer to Figure 14-52.
e. Delete faces using the **Delete Face** tool, refer to Figure 14-54.
f. Define a new work plane at an offset distance of 45 mm and then create the sketch shown in Figure 14-56.
g. Split the base surface using the last sketch, and then delete the face, refer to Figure 14-57.
h. Create a 3D sketch on the deleted face and then share the sketch that was used in splitting the base surface. Create a lofted surface using the shared sketch and the 3D sketch, as shown in Figure 14-59.
i. Create a boundary patch to close the top face of the lofted surface, refer to Figure 14-60.
j. Stitch all surfaces together and fillet all sharp edges, refer to Figure 14-62.
k. Thicken the surface using the **Thicken/Offset** tool, refer to Figure 14-63.

Creating the Base Surface

You will create the base surface using the sketch drawn on the XY plane. Next, you will revolve this sketch by an angle of 180-degree.

1. Open a new metric standard part file and then draw the sketch on the XY plane, as shown in Figure 14-48. Note that a sketch point is placed at the origin and is fixed using the **Fix** constraint. The sketch is dimensioned using this point to make it a fully constrained sketch. Note that a sketch is fully constrained only when all its entities are displayed in blue.

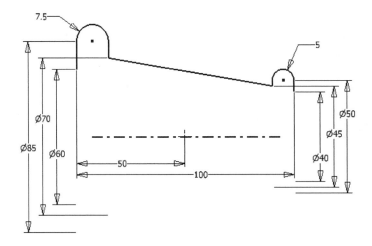

Figure 14-48 *Fully constrained sketch for the base surface*

2. Exit the sketching environment and then invoke the **Revolve** dialog box; the **Surface** button is automatically chosen in the **Output** area.

   Since there is only one sketch in the drawing window, it is automatically selected and you are prompted to select the axis.

3. Select the centerline as the axis of revolution; the preview of the resultant surface is displayed.

4. Select **Angle** from the drop-down list in the **Extents** area and set the value of the angle to 180-degree. Next, choose **OK**; the base surface is created, as shown in Figure 14-49.

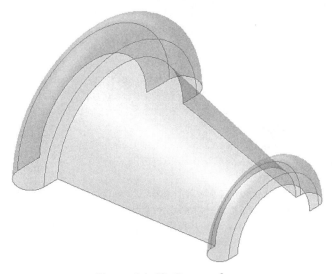

Figure 14-49 *Base surface*

Creating Side Surfaces

The two cuts on both sides of the base surface are created by splitting the base surface using the two surfaces at sides. Therefore, first you need to create side surfaces.

1. Define a new sketch plane on the XY plane and then create an ellipse, as shown in Figure 14-50. Note that the center point of the ellipse should be coincident with the edge of the base surface.

   Next, you need to extrude the ellipse to create a surface.

2. Exit the sketching environment and then extrude the ellipse as a surface through a distance of 30 mm.

3. Choose the **Mirror** tool from the **Pattern** panel of the **Model** tab; the **Mirror** dialog box is displayed and you are prompted to select a feature to pattern.

4. Select the extruded elliptical surface and then select **XZ Plane** as the mirror plane. Next, choose **OK** from the **Mirror** dialog box; the feature is mirrored, as shown in Figure 14-51.

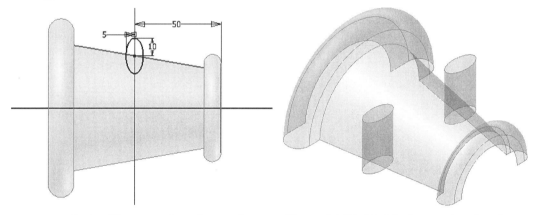

Figure 14-50 Ellipse created on the XY plane　　*Figure 14-51 Model after creating the mirror feature*

Creating Cuts on Sides by Using Side Surfaces

To create cuts on sides, first you will use the two side surfaces to split the base surface. Next, you will use the base surface to split the side surfaces. Finally, all unwanted surfaces will be deleted using the **Delete Face** tool.

1. Invoke the **Trim Surface** tool from the **Surface** panel of the **Model** tab and select one of the extruded ellipse surfaces as the trim tool.

2. Select the portion common between the base surface and the extruded surface as the portion to be trimmed, as shown in Figure 14-52. Choose **OK** from the dialog box.

3. Similarly, using the second extruded surface as the trimming tool, trim the revolved base surface.

4. Now, using the base surface as the trim tool, trim the remaining portion of the extruded surface on left of the base surface, as shown in Figure 14-53.

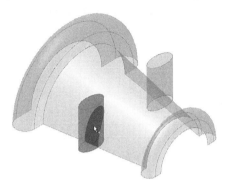

Figure 14-52 *Trimming the base surface*

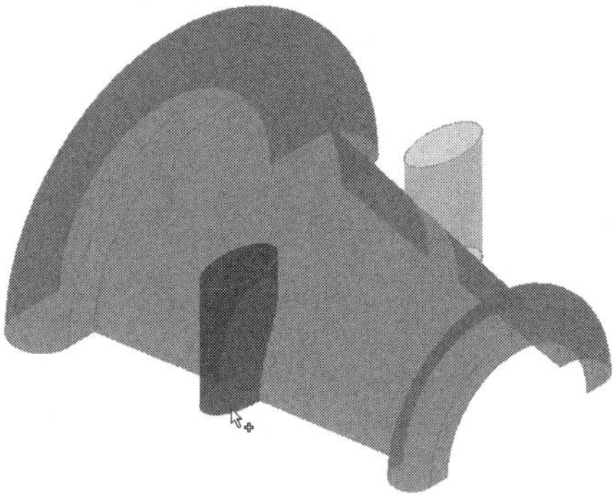

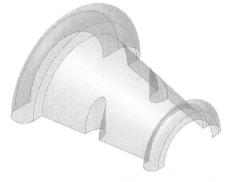

Figure 14-53 *Trimming one of the extruded surfaces*

5. Similarly, trim the other extruded ellipse surface using the base surface as the trim tool. Note that you need to select the outer portion of the extruded surface to trim, as shown in Figure 14-54.

The model after trimming all unwanted surfaces is shown in Figure 14-55.

Figure 14-54 *Trimming the other extruded surface*

Figure 14-55 *Model after trimming unwanted surfaces*

Creating the Lofted Surface

Next, you need to create the lofted surface. To create this surface, you need to create a work plane at an offset from the XY plane.

1. Create a new work plane at an offset distance of 45 mm above the XY plane.

2. Select this plane as the sketching plane and draw the sketch, as shown in Figure 14-56.

3. Exit the sketching environment and invoke the **Split** tool from the **Modify** panel of the **Model** tab.

4. Select the sketch as the split tool and select the base surface as the face to be split.

5. Choose **OK**; the base surface is split using the sketch.

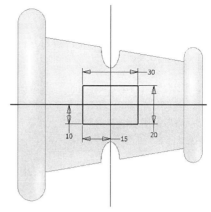

Figure 14-56 Sketch drawn on the offset plane

6. Delete the split surface from the base surface using the **Delete Face** tool. The model after deleting the split surface is shown in Figure 14-57.

   Next, you will create a 3D sketch using the edges of the surface that are removed from the base surface.

7. Invoke the 3D sketching environment and then choose the **Include Geometry** tool from the **Draw** panel of the **3D Sketch** tab.

8. Select the four edges that resulted from the split surface which was removed from the base surface, see Figure 14-58.

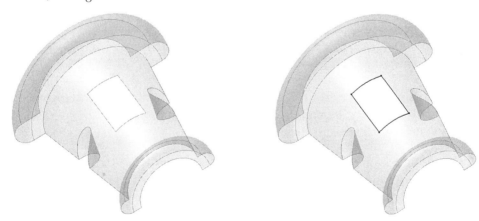

Figure 14-57 Model after deleting the split surface *Figure 14-58 3D Sketch created using the edges*

9. Exit the 3D sketching environment.

Note
*In case, the rectangular sketch that was used to split the base surface (Figure 14-56) is not visible, you need to turn on its visibility by using the **Browser Bar**.*

10. Create a lofted surface between the two sketches.

11. Turn off the visibility of the sketches. The model after creating the lofted surface is shown in Figure 14-59.

    Next, you need to cover the top face of the lofted surface using the **Patch** tool.

12. Choose the **Boundary Patch** tool from the **Surface** panel of the **Model** tab to invoke the **Boundary Patch** dialog box.

13. Select the top edges of the lofted surface and choose **OK** from the **Boundary Patch** dialog box; a boundary patch covering the top of the lofted surface is created, see Figure 14-60.

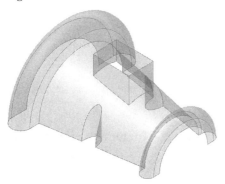
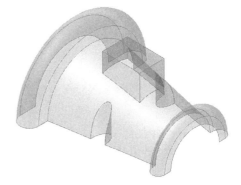

Figure 14-59 Model after creating the lofted surface

Figure 14-60 Model after covering the top face of the lofted surface

Stitching Surfaces and Hiding Original Surfaces

After creating all surfaces, you need to stitch them together and hide the original surfaces. The surfaces are stitched using the **Stitch Surface** tool.

1. Invoke the **Stitch Surface** tool. Select all surfaces so that they are stitched together. Next, choose **Apply** and then **Done** from the **Stitch** dialog box. Figure 14-61 shows the model after stitching surfaces.

    When you stitch surfaces, a stitched surface is created above the original surfaces and the visibility of original surfaces is automatically turned off.

2. Fillet all sharp edges of the stitched surface with a radius of 2 mm. The surface, after creating fillets, is shown in Figure 14-62.

Thickening the Surface

The final step in creating the hybrid surface-solid model is to thicken the complex surface created in the previous steps. By thickening, you can add material to the surface model so as to make it a solid model. The model can be thickened using the **Thicken/Offset** tool.

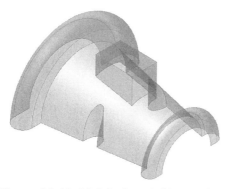
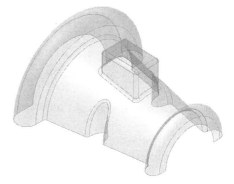

Figure 14-61 *Model after stitching surfaces*   *Figure 14-62* *Model after filleting surfaces*

1. Invoke the **Thicken/Offset** dialog box and select the **Quilt** radio button from it.

2. Set the value in the **Distance** spinner to **1**, if it is not already set. Select the stitched surface.

   As you have selected the **Quilt** radio button, you will notice that the entire stitched surface is selected in a single click.

3. Choose **OK** to exit the dialog box. Now, turn off the visibility of the stitched surface using the **Browser Bar**. The final model for Tutorial 5 is shown in Figure 14-63. Figure 14-64 shows the rotated view of the same model.

Figure 14-63 *Final hybrid model*   *Figure 14-64* *Another view of the hybrid model*

Self-Evaluation Test

Answer the following questions and then compare them to those given at the end of this chapter:

1. Autodesk Inventor allows you to create custom and standard iParts. (T/F)

2. You cannot turn off the display of surfaces. (T/F)

3. In Autodesk Inventor, the hybrid surface-solid modeling is used to create complex surfaces. (T/F)

4. The options in the _____ tab of the **iPart Author** dialog box are used to add the thread parameters to the iPart factory.

5. Autodesk Inventor does not allow you to display dimensions as equations. (T/F)

6. _____ parameters are automatically created when you apply dimensions to entities or create a feature.

7. _____ are mathematical expressions in which parameters are equated with algebraic or trigonometric functions.

8. _____ parts automatically change their dimensions based on the dimensions and functions of other parts to which they are assembled.

9. In Autodesk Inventor, every dimension is assigned a unique name called _____.

10. The _____ tool is used to create bends manually at the corners of the 3D line.

Review Questions

Answer the following questions:

1. You can modify dimensions while inserting custom iParts to an assembly. (T/F)

2. You can specify sketch points using the **Inventor Precise Input** toolbar in the 3D sketching environment. (T/F)

3. Unlike the 2D sketching environment, you can save a file in the 3D sketching environment. (T/F)

4. The Link parameters are created in a separate Microsoft Excel spreadsheet. (T/F)

5. The user parameters are defined by the user for specifying the dimensions of entities and features. (T/F)

6. Which of the following tabs in the **iPart Author** dialog box is used to select the parameters and dimensions to be included in the iPart factory?

    (a) **Parameters**   (b) **Threads**
    (c) **Work Plane**   (d) None of these

7. Which of the following is not a parameter?

    (a) Drawing   (b) Model
    (c) User   (d) Link

8. Which of the following tabs in the **Document Settings** dialog box is used to display dimensions as equations?

    (a) **Units**   (b) **Sketch**
    (c) **Modeling**   (d) None of these

9. Which of the following tabs in the **iPart Authors** dialog box is used to specify whether the selected features will be computed or suppressed while creating a part using the iPart factory?

    (a) **Parameters**   (b) **Threads**
    (c) **Work Plane**   (d) **Suppression**

10. Which of the following tools is used to merge a 2D sketch entity into a 3D sketch?

    (a) **Line**   (b) **Bend**
    (c) **Include Geometry** (d) None of these

Exercise

Exercise 1

Create the following sketch with the help of parameters. After dimensioning the sketch, display the dimensions as expressions, as shown in Figure 14-65. The numeric values of the parameters are given below.   **(Expected time: 30 min)**

LEN = 60
LEN1 = LEN/3
LEN2 = LEN/2.5
WID = LEN*0.75
WID1 = WID/5
WID2 = WID1

After displaying the dimensions as expressions, display them as names.

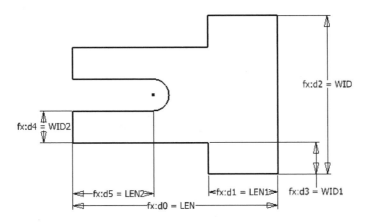

Figure 14-65 *Sketch with dimensions as equations*

Chapter 15

Working with Sheet Metal Components

Learning Objectives

After completing this chapter, you will be able to:

- *Set parameters for creating sheet metal parts.*
- *Create the base of a sheet metal component.*
- *Fold a part of a sheet metal part.*
- *Add a flange to a Sheet metal component.*
- *Create a cut feature in a sheet metal part.*
- *Add a corner seam to sheet metal parts.*
- *Round the corners of a sheet metal part.*
- *Chamfer the corners of a sheet metal part.*
- *Punch 3D shapes into sheet metal components.*
- *Add a hem to a sheet metal part.*
- *Create the flat pattern of a sheet metal component.*

THE SHEET METAL MODULE

A component having a thickness greater than 0 and less than 12 mm is called a sheet metal component. A sheet metal component is created by bending, cutting, or deforming a sheet of metal that has uniform thickness, see Figure 15-1.

As it is not possible to machine such a model, therefore after creating a sheet metal component, you need to flatten it for its manufacturing. Figure 15-2 shows the flattened view of the sheet metal component shown in Figure 15-1.

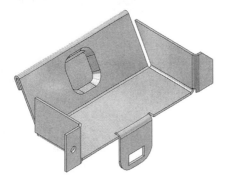

Figure 15-1 *A sheet metal component*

Figure 15-2 *The flattened view of the sheet metal component*

Autodesk Inventor allows you to create sheet metal components in a module, called the **Sheet Metal** module. This module is provided specially for sheet metal components. This environment provides all tools required for creating the sheet metal components. To invoke the **Sheet Metal** module, double-click on **Sheet Metal (mm).ipt** in the **Metric** tab of the **New File** dialog box, see Figure 15-3.

After invoking the **Sheet Metal** module, you will notice that when you open a new sheet metal file, the sketching environment is activated by default, as shown in Figure 15-4. This is because similar to the part modeling environment, first you need to create the sketch of the base feature of a sheet metal component. After creating it, the remaining tools will be available in the **Sheet Metal** module.

Note
Sheet metal files are saved in the *.ipt format.

*You can convert a sheet metal part into a solid part. To do so, choose the **Convert to Standard Part** button from the **Convert** panel of the **Model** tab of the **Sheet Metal** environment; the sheet metal component is converted into solid part and the **Modeling** environment is invoked.*

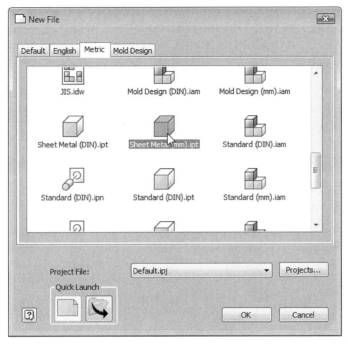

*Figure 15-3 Starting a new sheet metal file from the **Metric** tab of the **New File** dialog box*

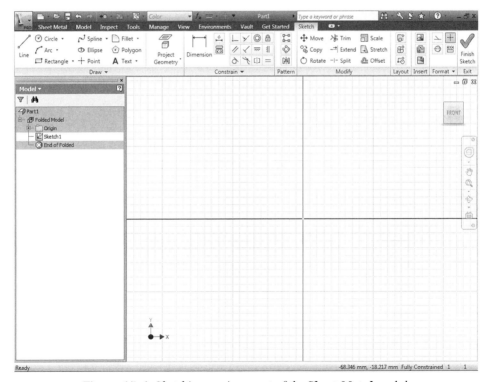

*Figure 15-4 Sketching environment of the **Sheet Metal** module*

After creating the sketch for the base of the sheet metal component, exit the sketching environment. You will notice that the **Sheet Metal** tab is activated in the **Ribbon**. Note that very few tools are available in this tab. More tools will be available after you create the base of the sheet metal part.

Before converting the sketch into the sheet metal base, it is recommended that you set the parameters related to the sheet metal components by using the **Sheet Metal Defaults** tool. This tool is discussed next.

SETTING SHEET METAL COMPONENT PARAMETERS

Ribbon: Sheet Metal > Setup > Sheet Metal Defaults
Toolbar: Sheet Metal Features > Sheet Metal Defaults

You can set the parameters related to a sheet metal component by using the **Sheet Metal Defaults** tool. On invoking this tool, the **Sheet Metal Defaults** dialog box will be displayed, as shown in Figure 15-5. The procedure to specify parameters, material style, and unfolding rule by using the options in this dialog box is discussed next.

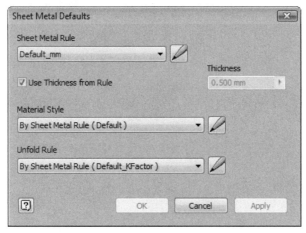

*Figure 15-5 The **Sheet Metal Defaults** dialog box*

Setting the Sheet Metal Rule

The sheet metal rule is set by choosing the **Edit Sheet Metal Rule** button, which is available on the right of the **Sheet Metal Rule** drop-down list. On choosing this button, the **Style and Standard Editor [Library-Read Only]** dialog box will be displayed, as shown in Figure 15-6. Choose the **New** button; the **New Local Style** dialog box will be displayed. Enter the name to create a new rule in this dialog box and choose the **OK** button; the new name will be displayed in the left pane of the dialog box. Right-click on the name and choose **Active** from the shortcut menu, so that if you modify the settings, they are stored in this name. The options related to the selected name will be displayed in the right pane of the **Style and Standard Editor [Library - Read Only]** dialog box. This dialog box provides three tabs for setting the parameters of the sheet metal components. The options in these three tabs are discussed next.

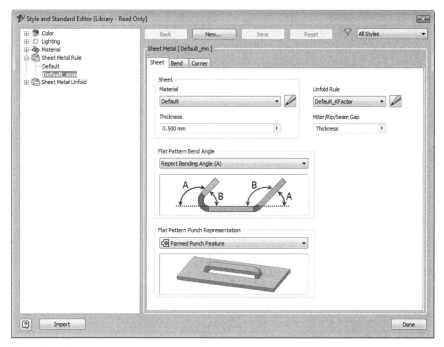

*Figure 15-6 The **Sheet** tab of the **Style and Standard Editor [Library - Read Only]** dialog box*

Sheet Tab

The options in the **Sheet** tab (Figure 15-6) are discussed next.

Sheet Area

The options in the **Sheet** area are used to specify the material and thickness of the sheet as discussed next.

Material: The **Material** drop-down list is used to specify the material of the sheet. You can select the desired predefined material in this drop-down list.

Thickness: The **Thickness** edit box is used to specify the thickness of the sheet. You can enter the thickness of the sheet in this edit box or select from the predefined thicknesses by choosing the arrow on the right of this edit box.

Note

*If the **Use Thickness from Rule** check box is selected in the **Sheet Metal Defaults** dialog box, the value entered in the **Thickness** edit box will be used as the default thickness. However, you can change the thickness by clearing the **Use Thickness from Rule** check box and entering a new value in the **Thickness** edit box. Alternatively, to change the thickness, enter a new value in the **Thickness** edit box in the **Sheet** area of the **Style and Standard Editor [Library - Read Only]** dialog box.*

Unfolding Rule Area

The drop-down list in this area is used to select the predefined unfolding rule.

Miter/Rip/Seam Gap

This edit box is used to specify the gap to be used for miter/rip/seam. By default, the thickness value specified in the **Thickness** edit box is used as the value of the miter/rip/seam for the sheet metal component. Enter a new value in this edit box to change the gap value.

Flat Pattern Bend Angle Area

The options in this area determine how the reported bend angle will be measured when the folded model is displayed as a flat pattern. The options in this area are discussed next.

Report Bending Angle (A): This option is selected by default in the drop-down list below the **Flat Pattern Bend Angle** area. As a result, the bend angle will be measured between the selected face and the outside face of the bend.

Report Open Angle (B): If you select this option, the bend angle will be measured between the selected face and the inside face of the bend.

You can preview these reported bend angles in the window given below the **Flat Pattern Bend Angle** area.

Flat Pattern Punch Representation Area

The options in this area determine how the sheet metal punch features will be displayed when the folded model is displayed as a flat pattern. The options in this area are discussed next.

Formed Punch Feature: This option, if selected, displays the sheet metal punch features as 3D features in the flat pattern of the component.

2D Sketch Representation: This option, if selected, displays the sheet metal punch features using a previously created 2D sketch in the flat pattern of the component.

2D Sketch Rep and Center Mark: This option, if selected, displays the sheet metal punch features using a previously defined 2D sketch along with a Center Mark in the flat pattern of the component.

Center Mark Only: This option, if selected, displays the sheet metal punch features using only the center mark of the sketch, when the flat pattern of the component is displayed.

After setting the parameters, choose the **Save** button.

Bend Tab

The options in the **Bend** tab (Figure 15-7) are used to set the parameters related to the bending of a sheet. These options are discussed next.

Bend Relief Area

The options in this area are used to control the bend width, bend depth, and so on. These options are discussed next.

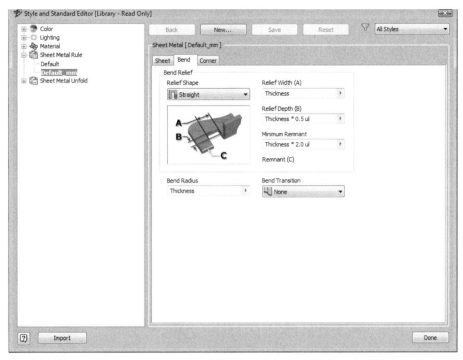

Figure 15-7 The **Bend** tab of the **Style and Standard Editor [Library - Read Only]** dialog box

Relief Shape: Whenever you bend or fold a sheet metal component such that the bend does not extend throughout the length of the edge, a groove is added at the end of the bend so that the walls of the sheet metal part do not intersect when folded or unfolded. This groove is known as relief. The **Relief Shape** drop-down list is used to select the shape of the relief. By default, a straight relief is added, as shown in Figure 15-8. You can add a round relief by selecting the **Round** option from this drop-down list. Figure 15-9 shows a round relief. You can also add a tear relief by selecting the **Tear** option from this drop-down list. A tear relief is added when tight bends are required in the sheet metal component.

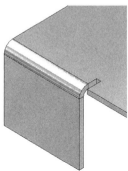

Figure 15-8 Straight relief added

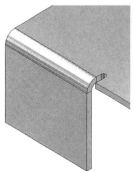

Figure 15-9 Round relief added

Relief Width (A): The **Relief Width (A)** edit box is used to enter the value of the width of the relief. The default value of the relief width is equal to the thickness of the sheet. You can enter the value of the relief width in this edit box. Figure 15-10 shows a sheet metal component with a relief width of 1 mm and Figure 15-11 shows a sheet metal component with a relief width of 4 mm.

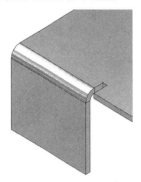
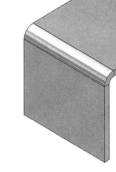

Figure 15-10 *Relief width = 1 mm*   *Figure 15-11* *Relief width = 4 mm*

Relief Depth (B): The **Relief Depth (B)** edit box is used to enter the value of the depth of the relief.

Minimum Remnant: The **Minimum Remnant** edit box is used to set the value of the material between the relief created by bending or folding and the edge of the sheet metal component.

Bend Radius

The **Bend Radius** edit box is used to set the radius of the bend or the fold. The default value of the radius of the bend is equal to the thickness of a sheet. You can enter a numeric value in this edit box to set it as the bend radius. Figure 15-12 shows a sheet folded with a radius of 1 mm and Figure 15-13 shows a sheet folded with a radius of 5 mm.

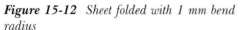

Figure 15-12 *Sheet folded with 1 mm bend radius*   *Figure 15-13* *Sheet folded with 5 mm bend radius*

Tip. *If you modify the bend radius after bending or folding a sheet metal component, the model will be automatically updated and will acquire the new bend radius when you choose the **Save** button and exit the **Style and Standard Editor** dialog box.*

Bend Transition

The **Bend Transition** drop-down list is used to specify the transition type in the unfolded view when no relief is specified. The default value of this drop-down list is **None**. You can select the **Intersection**, **Straight Line**, **Arc**, or **Trim to Bend** transition type from this drop-down list.

After setting the parameters, choose the **Save** button.

Corner Tab

The options in the **Corner** tab (Figure 15-14) are used to set the parameters related to the relief at the corners where the three faces of a sheet metal component are folded. These options are discussed next.

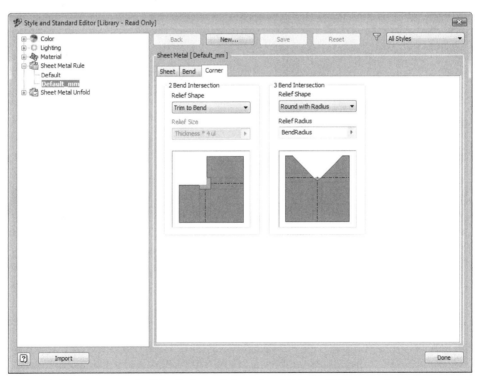

Figure 15-14 *The **Corner** tab of the **Style and Standard Editor [Library - Read Only]** dialog box*

2 Bend Intersection Area

The options in the **2 Bend Intersection** area allow you to specify the corner relief when two bends intersect. These options are discussed next.

Relief Shape: The **Relief Shape** drop-down list is used to specify the shape of the relief at the corner where the two faces are folded. The preview of the selected type of relief will be displayed in the preview window below the **Relief Size** edit box in the **2 Bend Intersection** area. Remember that the options in this drop-down list will work only when one of the two faces is created by using the **Corner Seam** tool, which is discussed later in this chapter. The options in this drop-down list are discussed next.

Note

*It is recommended that to view a better effect of various corner relief shapes, the sheet metal component should be flattened using the **Flat Pattern** tool. This tool will be discussed later in the chapter.*

Trim to Bend: The **Trim to Bend** is the default option in the **Relief Shape** drop-down list. It appears as a polygonal cut bounded by bend lines. Figure 15-15 shows the flattened sheet metal part with no relief at the corner.

Round: The **Round** option is used to create a round corner relief, which is centered at the intersection of bend lines. Figure 15-16 shows a sheet metal part with a round relief.

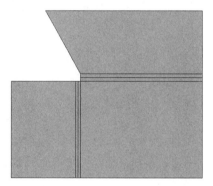

Figure 15-15 *Flattened sheet metal part with no corner relief*

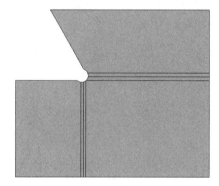

Figure 15-16 *Flattened sheet metal part with round corner relief*

Square: The **Square** option is used to create a square corner relief, which is centered at the intersection of bend lines. Figure 15-17 shows a sheet metal part with a square corner relief.

Tear: The **Tear** option is used to create a corner relief that appears torn at the corners. Figure 15-18 shows a flattened sheet metal part with a tear corner relief.

Linear Weld: This option is used to apply a linear weld type of relief at the corners and appears as a V-shaped cutout. It lies at the intersection of the inner bend zone lines to the outer bend zone line's intersection with the flange, refer to Figure 15-19.

Arc Weld: This option is used to create a relief that is suitable for the components that need to be created by arc welding, refer to Figure 15-20.

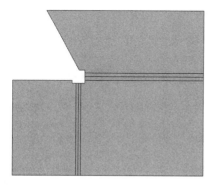

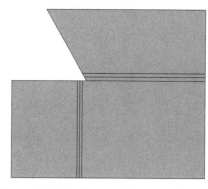

Figure 15-17 *Flattened sheet metal part with square corner relief*

Figure 15-18 *Flattened sheet metal part with tear corner relief*

Figure 15-19 *Flattened sheet metal part with linear weld*

Figure 15-20 *Flattened sheet metal part with arc weld*

Relief Size: The **Relief Size** edit box is used to specify the size of the corner relief. You can enter the value as an equation in terms of the thickness of the sheet or as a numeric value. This edit box will be activated only when you select the **Round** or **Square** option in the **Relief Shape** drop-down list.

3 Bend Intersection Area

The options in the **3 Bend Intersection** area allow you to specify the corner relief when three bends intersect at a common point. These options are discussed next.

Relief Shape: The **Relief Shape** drop-down list is used to specify the shape of the relief at the corner where all faces are folded. The preview of the selected type of relief will be displayed in the preview window below the **Relief Radius** edit box in the **3 Bend Intersection** area. The options in this drop-down list are discussed next.

Intersection: This option is used to create relief by extending and intersecting all flange edges.

No Replacement: This option, if selected, retains the default corner relief that was selected before creating the component.

Full Round: This option, if selected, creates a corner relief by extending the flange edges to their intersection and then, creates a fillet tangent to the bend zone tangent lines.

Round with Radius: This option is selected by default. As a result, a corner relief will be created by extending the flange edges to their intersection and then creates a tangent fillet of specified radius. The radius of the fillet created using the **Round with Radius** option is smaller compared to the fillet created by using the **Full Round** option.

Relief Radius: The **Relief Radius** edit box will be available only when the **Round with Radius** option is selected from the **Relief Shape** drop-down list. This edit box is used to specify the radius of the fillet.

After making the necessary modifications, choose the **Save** button to save the changes and then choose the **Done** button to close the **Style and Standard Editor [Library - Read only]** dialog box.

Once you have made necessary initial settings, you are ready to create the sheet metal component.

Setting the Material Style

You can set material for a sheet metal component by using the **Material Style** drop-down list in the **Sheet Metal Defaults** dialog box. You can also edit an existing material style. To do so, choose the **Edit Material Style** button located on the right of this drop-down list; the **Style and Standard Editor [Library - Read Only]** dialog box will be displayed along with the list of materials on its left. Also, the properties of the selected material will be listed in the **Material Style** area, as shown in Figure 15-21. Set the parameters such as density, Young's Modulus, Poison's Ratio, units, and so on for the current material style. After setting the parameters, first choose the **Save** button and then the **Done** button to save the new material style.

Setting the Unfolding Rule

You can apply the available unfolding rule to a sheet metal component using the **Unfold Rule** drop-down list in the **Sheet Metal Defaults** dialog box. To do so, select the required unfolding rule from this drop-down list. You can also edit an existing unfolding rule. To do so, choose the **Edit Unfold Rule** button on the right of this drop-down list; the **Style and Standard Editor [Library - Read Only]** dialog box will be displayed, as shown in Figure 15-22. You can edit the default parameters in this dialog box and then choose the **Save** button to save the settings. The options in the **Sheet Metal Unfold** area are used to specify parameters to unfold the sheet metal component for manufacturing. These options are discussed next.

Unfold Method

The **Unfold Method** drop-down list consists of three options for unfolding the sheet metal component. The first option is the **Linear** method. This method uses a simple unfolding technique for flattening the component. You can set the KFactor value manually using the **KFactor Value** edit box. Note that the KFactor value should be between 0 and 1. You can specify the spline factor value in the **Spline Factor Value** edit box. This value is significant in case of contour flanges, contour rolls, and lofted flanges. After setting the required parameters, choose **Save** and then the **Done** button.

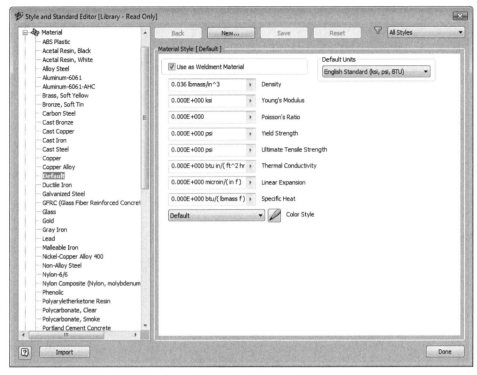

Figure 15-21 The modified Style and Standard Editor [Library - Read Only] dialog box displayed on choosing the Edit Material Style button

Figure 15-22 The partial view of the Style and Standard Editor [Library - Read Only] dialog box

The second option is the **Bend Table** method. On selecting this option, all parameters related to the unfolding rule will be displayed, as shown in Figure 15-23. You can set these parameters based on your requirement. After setting the required parameters, choose **Save** and then the **Done** button.

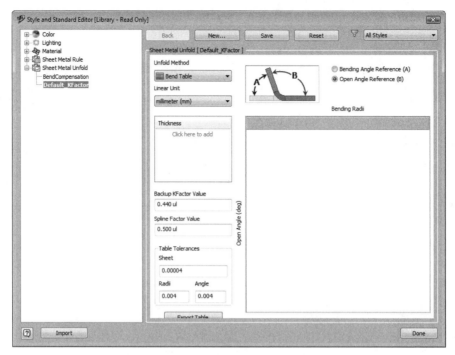

*Figure 15-23 The **Style and Standard Editor [Library - Read Only]** dialog box with the options related to the **Bend Table** method*

The third option is the **Custom Equation** method. When you select this option, you can use different types of equations for calculating the size of bend zone. These equations can be selected from the **Equation Type** drop-down list in the **Style and Standard Editor [Library - Read Only]** dialog box. You can select the **Bend Allowance**, **Bend Compensation**, **Bend Deduction**, or **KFactor** option from the **Equation Type** drop-down list as per your requirement. Figure 15-24 shows different options related to the **Custom Equation** option. After setting the required parameters, choose **Save** and then the **Done** button.

CREATING SHEET METAL COMPONENTS

Ribbon:	Sheet Metal > Create > Face
Toolbar:	Sheet Metal Features > Face

The **Face** tool is used to create the base of a sheet metal component or to add additional faces to it. As mentioned earlier, when you open a new sheet metal file, the Sketching environment becomes active. After creating sketch for the base of the sheet metal component, exit the sketching environment and invoke this tool. On invoking this tool, the **Face** dialog box will be displayed, as shown in Figure 5-25. This dialog box has three tabs. But, since you are creating the base, the options in these tabs are not required. If there is a single sketch in the graphics screen, it will be selected automatically for creating the sheet metal part. The thickness of the sheet will be taken as the thickness defined in the **Sheet** tab of the **Style and Standard Editor [Library - Read Only]** dialog box. Figure 15-26 shows a sketch and Figure 15-27 shows the sheet metal component created using the same sketch.

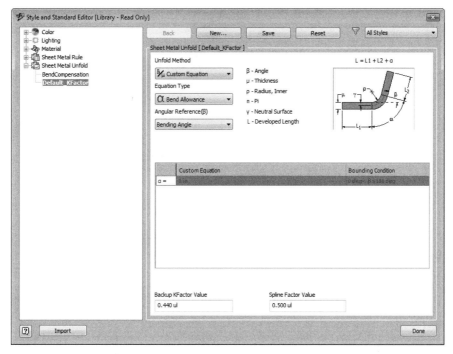

*Figure 15-24 The **Style and Standard Editor [Library - Read Only]** dialog box with the options related to the **Custom Equation** option*

An alternative method to invoke the **Face** tool is by using the mini toolbar. The mini toolbar is displayed if you select a sketched entity after exiting the Sketching environment. To create the base of the sheet metal component, choose the **Create Face** button from the mini toolbar; the preview of the base of sheet metal will be displayed in the drawing window. Also, the **Face** dialog box will be displayed, refer to Figure 15-25. Specify the required parameters and then choose the **OK** button to create the base of the sheet metal.

After creating the base of the sheet metal component, if you create a sketch and invoke the **Face** tool again, the other options in the **Face** dialog box will be available. The other options in the **Face** dialog box are discussed next.

*Figure 15-25 The **Shape** tab of the **Face** dialog box*

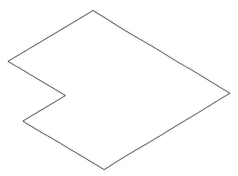

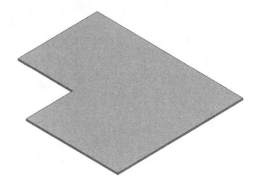

Figure 15-26 *Sketch for creating the sheet metal part*

Figure 15-27 *Sheet metal part created using the same sketch*

Shape Tab

The options in the **Shape** tab (Figure 15-25) are used to define the shape and bend radius of the face. These options are discussed next.

Shape Area

The options in the **Shape** area are used to specify the shape of the face. These options are discussed next.

Profile

The **Profile** button is chosen to select the sketch of the face. If there is only one unconsumed sketch on the screen, it will be automatically selected. However, if there are more than one unconsumed sketches or the sketch consists of multiple closed loops, you will have to select them manually by using this button.

Offset

The **Offset** button is chosen to reverse the direction of the face creation.

Bend Area

Whenever you create a face on an existing sheet metal component, a bend is created at the edge where the new face joins the existing component. Also, a bend relief is added to the new face. The options related to the bend and the bend relief are available in the **Bend** area. These options are discussed next.

Radius

The **Radius** edit box is used to specify the radius of the bend. By default, the bend radius value defined in the **Bend** tab of the **Style and Standard Editor [Library - Read Only]** dialog box is selected. You can also specify a new bend radius by entering a numeric value in this edit box.

Edges

The **Edges** button is chosen to select the edge that will be joined with the existing sheet metal component. If one of the edges of the sketch is coincident with an edge of the existing sheet metal part, the common edge will be automatically selected. However, if the edge of the sketch is not coincident with an edge of the sheet metal component, you will have to select the edge manually. You can also use this button to select additional faces that you want to add to the bend.

Extend Bend Aligned to Side Faces

If you choose the **Extend Bend Aligned to Side Faces** button, the material will be added on the sides of the edges along the faces and not normal to the axis of the bend.

Figure 15-28 shows the sketch to be used for creating the face of a sheet metal component and Figure 15-29 shows the sheet metal component created after adding the face. Notice the bend and the bend relief created with the face.

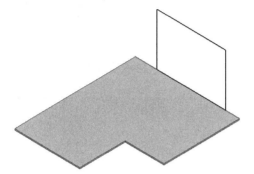

Figure 15-28 Sketch before converting into a new face of the sheet metal part

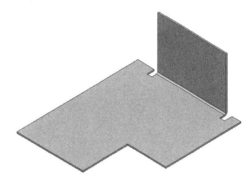

Figure 15-29 Sheet metal part after adding the new face

Figure 15-30 shows a sketch that has no edge coincident with the edge of the sheet metal part. Notice that in this figure, the edge of the sheet metal base is selected for creating the face. Figure 15-31 shows the sheet metal component created by using the given sketch.

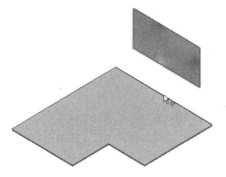

Figure 15-30 Selecting the sketch and the edge for creating the face of the sheet metal part

Figure 15-31 Sheet metal part after creating the new face

Extend Bend Perpendicular to Side Faces

If you choose the **Extend Bend Perpendicular to Side Faces** button, the material will be added perpendicular to the side faces.

Unfold Options Tab

Choose the **Unfold Options** tab to specify the unfold style using the **Unfold Rule** drop-down list. If you have created a new unfold style as discussed earlier, then you can select it by using the **Unfold Rule** drop-down list, as shown in Figure 15-32.

Bend Tab

The options in the **Bend** tab are used to specify the parameters related to bend relief. By default, the options specified in the **Bend** tab of the **Style and Standard Editor [Library - Read Only]** dialog box are used. If you want to override the options specified in this dialog box, select an option other than the **Default** option in the **Relief Shape** drop-down list. The options available in the **Bend** tab are shown in Figure 15-33. These options are similar to those discussed in the **Style and Standard Editor [Library - Read Only]** dialog box, refer to Figure 15-7.

*Figure 15-32 The **Unfold Options** tab of the Face dialog box*

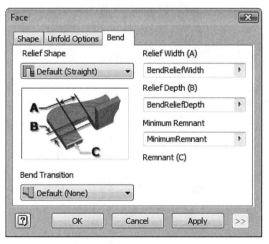

*Figure 15-33 The **Bend** tab of the **Face** dialog box*

FOLDING SHEET METAL COMPONENTS

Ribbon:	Sheet Metal > Create > Fold
Toolbar:	Sheet Metal Features > Fold

Autodesk Inventor allows you to fold sheet metal component by using the **Fold** tool. Remember that the sheet metal part will be folded with the help of a sketched line. Note that the line that you want to use should not extend beyond the face that you want to fold. On choosing the **Fold** tool from the **Create** panel of the **Sheet Metal** tab, the **Fold** dialog box will be displayed. The options in the **Fold** dialog box are discussed next.

Shape Tab

The options in the **Shape** tab (Figure 15-34) are used to specify the shape of the fold. These options are discussed next.

Bend Line

The **Bend Line** button is chosen to select the bend line that will be used to fold the component. When you invoke the **Fold** dialog box, this button is chosen by default. Note that only the line that has both its endpoints at the edges of the sheet metal component can be selected to bend the component. As soon as you select the bend line, two green arrows are displayed on it. The straight arrow points in the direction of the portion of the sheet metal part that will be folded and the curved arrow points in the direction of bending.

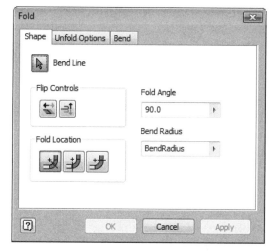

*Figure 15-34 The **Shape** tab of the **Fold** dialog box*

Flip Controls Area

The buttons in this area allow you to reverse the direction of folding and the side of the sheet metal component to be folded. The **Flip Side** button is chosen to reverse the side of the sheet metal part that will be folded and the **Flip Direction** button is chosen to reverse the direction in which the sheet metal component will be folded.

Fold Location Area

The buttons in this area are chosen to specify the location of the bend with respect to the sketch line selected as the bend line. The three buttons in this area are discussed next.

Centerline of Bend

 By default, the **Centerline of Bend** button is chosen in the **Fold Location** area. So, the bend line will be considered as the centerline of the bend and the bend will be created equally in both the directions of the bend line.

Start of Bend

 If the **Start of Bend** button is chosen, the bend will be created such that the bend line is located at the start of the bend.

End of Bend

 If the **End of Bend** button is chosen, the bend will be created such that the bend line is located at the end of the bend.

Fold Angle

The **Fold Angle** edit box is used to specify the angle of the fold for the sheet metal component. The default value in this edit box is 90.0. You can specify desired value in this edit box.

Bend Radius

The **Bend Radius** edit box is used to specify the radius of a bend. By default, the value specified in the **Bend** tab of the **Style and Standard Editor [Library - Read Only]** dialog box is taken as the bend radius. You can also enter any desired value in this edit box.

Figure 15-35 shows a line that will be used to fold the sheet metal part and Figure 15-36 shows the sheet metal part folded through an angle of 60-degree.

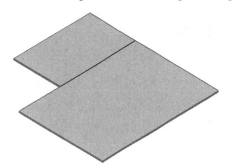

Figure 15-35 *Line for folding the sheet metal part*

Figure 15-36 *Sheet metal part folded through an angle of 60-degree*

Note
*The options in the **Unfold Options** and **Bend** tabs are the same as those discussed in the previous sections of this chapter.*

ADDING FLANGES TO SHEET METAL COMPONENTS

Ribbon:	Sheet Metal > Create > Flange
Toolbar:	Sheet Metal Features > Flange

Autodesk Inventor allows you to directly add a folded face to the existing sheet metal component. This is done using the **Flange** tool. On invoking this tool, the
Flange   **Flange** dialog box will be displayed. The options in the **Flange** dialog box are discussed next.

Shape Tab

The options in the **Shape** tab (Figure 15-37) are used to set the parameters related to the shape of the flange. These options are discussed next.

Edge Select Mode

The **Edge Select Mode** button is chosen by default and allows you to select the edges on which the flanges will be attached.

Loop Select Mode

 The **Loop Select Mode** button is used to select an edge loop and to create a flange on this loop. Figure 15-38 shows the edge loop selected on the top face of the base wall for creating flange and Figure 15-39 shows the flanges created on the selected loop.

Edges Area

The **Edges** area displays all the edges that have been selected to create a flange. Click in the **Edges** area to add new edges to attach the flange.

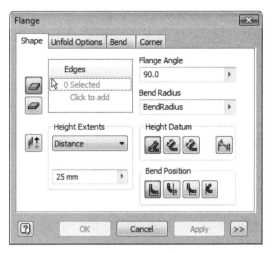

*Figure 15-37 The **Shape** tab of the **Flange** dialog box*

Height Extents Area

The **Height Extents** area allows you to specify the height of the flange wall. The drop-down list in this area has two options, **Distance** and **To**, that determine the height of the flange. If the **Distance** option is selected from the drop-down list, the height of the flange can be entered in the edit box below the drop-down list. If the **To** option is selected from the drop-down list, you will be prompted to select a point or vertex that terminates the flange.

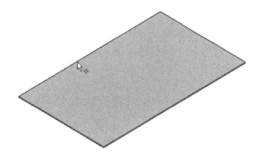

Figure 15-38 Edge loop selected on the top face of the base wall

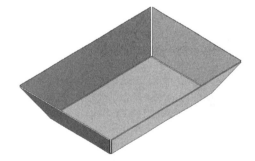

Figure 15-39 Flanges created at an angle of 60-degree on the selected loop

Flip Direction

 The **Flip Direction** button is chosen to reverse the direction of the flange. If you select an edge on the top face of the sheet metal component, by default, the flange will be created in the upward direction. But if you choose the **Flip Direction** button, the flange will be created in the downward direction. However, note that the selected edge will still be the starting edge of the flange.

Flange Angle

The **Flange Angle** edit box is used to specify the angle through which the flange will be bent with respect to the sheet metal component. The default value in this edit box is 90.0 and therefore, the flange will be bent through an angle of 90-degree. The value of flange angle can vary from 0 to 180 degrees.

Tip. *If a flange is created through an angle of 180-degree, it will merge with the face of the sheet metal component and therefore will not be visible. However, if a flange is created through an angle of 170-degree, it will create a face similar to a hem. The hems will be discussed later in this chapter.*

Bend Radius

The **Bend Radius** edit box is used to enter the radius of the bend. By default, the value set in the **Sheet Metal Defaults** dialog box is taken as the bend value. However, you can set any bend radius by entering its value in this edit box.

Height Datum Area

The options in this area allow you to specify the datum reference for measuring the height of the flange. These options are discussed next.

Bend from the intersection of the two outer faces

This button, if chosen, measures the height of the flange from the intersection of the outer faces.

Bend from the intersection of the two inner faces

This button, if chosen, measures the height of the flange from the intersection of the inner faces.

Parallel to the flange termination detail face

This button, if chosen, measures the height of the flange parallel to its face and tangent to the bend.

Aligned VS Orthogonal

This button, if chosen, measures the height of the flange aligned with the flange face or orthogonal to the base face.

Bend Position Area

The buttons in this area allow you to specify the position of the bend relative to the face containing the selected edge. These options are discussed next.

Inside of base face extents

This button, if chosen, creates the bend in such a way that the inner face of the flange is aligned with the extended selected edge.

Bend from adjacent face

This button, if chosen, creates the bend starting from the selected edge.

Outside of base face extents

 This button, if chosen, aligns the outer face of the flange with the intersection of the outer face and the selected edge.

Bend Tangent To Side Face

 The **Bend Tangent To Side Face** button is chosen to create a flange that is tangent to the side face of a sheet metal component.

Figure 15-40 shows the edge being selected for creating a flange and Figure 15-41 shows the sheet metal component after creating flange.

Figure 15-40 *Selecting the edge for creating the flange*

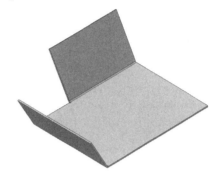

Figure 15-41 *Sheet metal component after creating flange at an angle of 60-degree*

More Button

The **More** button is available at the lower right corner of the **Flange** dialog box. When you choose this button, the **Flange** dialog box expands with more options. These options are discussed next.

Width Extents Area

The options in the **Width Extents** area (Figure 15-42) are used to set the parameters related to the width of a flange. These options are provided in the **Type** drop-down list and are discussed next.

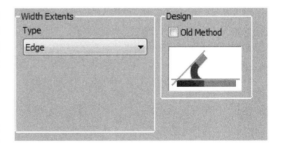

Figure 15-42 *The **Width Extents** area of the **Flange** dialog box*

Edge

The **Edge** option is selected by default in the **Type** drop-down list. This option ensures that the flange is created along the whole length of the edge selected from the sheet metal component.

Width

The **Width** option is used to create a flange of specified width on the selected edge and at a specified offset distance. If you select this option, the **Centered** and **Offset** radio buttons will be available. The **Centered** radio button will be selected by default and the **Width** edit box will be displayed. On specifying the width of the flange in the **Width** edit box, the flange will be created at the center of the specified width on the selected edge. If the **Offset** radio button is selected, you can create flange by specifying the offset distance from the faces of the selected edge. You can select a face for specifying the offset by choosing the **Offset1** button from the **Width Extents** area of the **Flange** dialog box. Figure 15-43 shows a flange created at an offset of 10 mm from the selected start point and with a width of 25 mm. Notice the bend relief that is automatically created on both the sides.

Offset

The **Offset** option is selected to define the width of a flange in terms of offset from two points on the selected edge. On invoking this option, the **Offset1** and **Offset2** edit boxes will be displayed in the **Width Extents** area. By default, the start point and endpoint of the flange will be selected. You can change the start point and endpoint of the flange by choosing the **Offset 1** and **Offset 2** buttons and then selecting the required points/ vertices from the sheet metal part. You can define the offset from the start point and the endpoint in the **Offset1** and **Offset2** edit boxes, respectively. Based on the two offset values and the known length of the edge, the width of the flange is automatically calculated. Figure 15-44 shows a flange created with the **Offset1** value 20 mm and the **Offset2** value 10 mm.

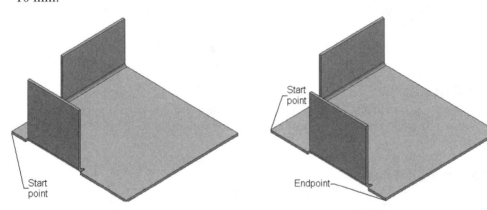

Figure 15-43 *Flange created with an offset of 10 mm and width of 25 mm*

Figure 15-44 *Flange created with Offset1=20 mm and Offset2=10 mm*

From To

This option, if selected, allows you to create a flange with the width defined by selecting an existing geometry.

Design Area

The **Old Method** check box allows you to edit the flanges that were created in releases prior to the Autodesk Inventor 2009 release, by using the options used when the component was first created. This check box remains clear for all the components created in Autodesk Inventor 2009. As a result, you have more control over the bend measurement and its positioning. However, the check box will be selected by default if a component has been created in the earlier releases of Autodesk Inventor. If you want to edit the component with the features available in Autodesk Inventor 2009, clear this check box and continue editing it.

Note
*The options in the **Unfold Options**, **Bend**, and **Corner** tabs of the **Flange** dialog box are similar to those discussed in the previous sections of this chapter.*

Tip. *You can create two flanges using the **Flange** tool such that they form a corner. When you do so, the Corner Seam icon will be displayed at the corner. If you click on this icon, the **Corner Edit** dialog box will be displayed. You can specify the required corner seam and corner type using this dialog box.*

CREATING CUTS IN SHEET METAL COMPONENTS

Ribbon:	Sheet Metal > Modify > Cut
Toolbar:	Sheet Metal Features > Cut

You can create any type of cut in a sheet metal component by drawing its sketch and then cutting it by using the **Cut** tool. Note that if you invoke this tool without creating a sketch, you will be informed that there is no unconsumed sketch. On invoking this tool, the **Cut** dialog box will be displayed, as shown in Figure 15-45. The options in this dialog box are discussed next.

Shape Area

The options in the **Shape** area are used to specify the shape of the cut. These options are discussed next.

Profile

The **Profile** button is chosen to select the profile of the cut. This button is chosen by default in the **Cut** dialog box. If there is only one unconsumed sketch on the sheet metal part, it will be automatically selected for creating the cut. However, if there are more than one unconsumed sketches, you will be prompted to select the profile.

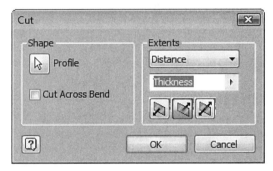

*Figure 15-45 The **Cut** dialog box*

Cut Across Bend

The **Cut Across Bend** check box is selected to cut the material to a required depth or throughout the thickness of the sheet. If you select this check box, the drop-down list in the **Extents** area will not be available. The edit box below the drop-down list allows you to specify the thickness for the cut feature.

Extents Area

The options in the **Extents** area are used to specify the extents of the cut. The options in this drop-down list are similar to those discussed for the solid model components.

Figure 15-46 shows two unconsumed sketches in the sheet metal component and Figure 15-47 shows the sheet metal component after creating the cut by using the two sketches.

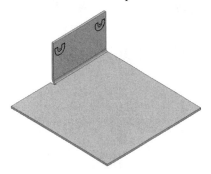

Figure 15-46 Unconsumed sketches before creating the cut

Figure 15-47 Sheet metal component after creating the cut

CREATING SEAMS AT THE CORNERS OF SHEET METAL COMPONENTS

Ribbon: Sheet Metal > Modify > Corner Seam
Toolbar: Sheet Metal Features > Corner Seam

Corner
Seam

Autodesk Inventor allows you to create corner seams in a sheet metal component with the help of the **Corner Seam** tool. On invoking this tool, the **Corner Seam** dialog box will be displayed. The options in this dialog box are discussed next.

Shape Tab

The options in the **Shape** tab (Figure 15-48) are used to set the parameters related to the shape of a seam. These options are discussed next.

Shape Area

The options in the **Shape** area are used to create a corner seam or a corner rip by selecting edges using the **Edges** button. These options are discussed next.

Seam

The **Seam** radio button is selected when you want to create a seam between two existing coplanar or intersecting faces of a sheet metal component.

*Figure 15-48 The **Shape** tab of the **Corner Seam** dialog box*

Rip

The **Rip** radio button is selected when you want to rip a corner of a solid component that has three faces meeting at a corner. This is generally used when you want to convert a shelled solid model into a sheet metal component and rip its corner in order to open it. Note that the thickness of the component must be equal to the thickness specified in the **Sheet Metal Defaults** dialog box. To rip a corner of such a component, select the vertical edge at the corner. Figure 15-49 shows a shelled solid model component before ripping the corners and Figure 15-50 shows a solid model component converted into a sheet metal component with the ripped corners. The **Flat Pattern** and **Bend** tools are discussed later in this chapter.

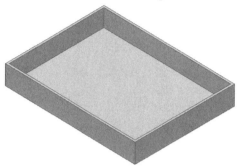

Figure 15-49 Model before ripping the corners

Figure 15-50 Model after ripping the corners

Edge

The **Edges** button is chosen to select the edges for creating the corner seam. In the **Corner Seam** dialog box, the **Edges** button is chosen by default and no option is available in the **Seam** area. The options in the **Seam** area will be available only after you have selected the edges for creating the corner seam.

Tip. *To convert a solid model into a sheet metal component, first you need to shell it. Remember that the wall thickness in the shell should be equal to or less than the thickness of the active sheet specified in the **Style and Standard Editor [Library - Read Only]** dialog box or the **Sheet Metal Defaults** dialog box. After shelling the component, choose the **Convert to Sheet Metal** button from the **Convert** panel of the **Model** tab. Next, rip its corners by using the **Corner Seam** tool.*

Seam Area

The options in this area are discussed next.

Maximum Gap Distance

Select this radio button to create a seam between two edges.

Face/Edge Distance

Select this radio button to create a seam between an edge and a face.

Symmetric Gap

This button will be available only when the **Maximum Gap Distance** radio button is selected. This is the first button in the **Seam** area and if chosen, creates a seam in such a way that the distance between the seamed material and the nearest intersecting corner is symmetric.

No Overlap

This button will be available only when the **Face/Edge Distance** radio button is selected. This button is chosen by default and ensures that there is no overlapping of the faces whose edges are selected for creating the corner seam. Figure 15-51 shows the two edges to be selected for creating the corner seam and Figure 15-52 shows the sheet metal component after creating the corner seam. Notice that there is no overlapping of the faces. Also, the bend relief in both the faces is automatically adjusted with reference to the corner seam.

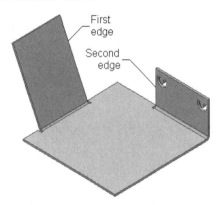

Figure 15-51 *Edges to be selected for creating a corner seam*

Figure 15-52 *Model after creating the corner seam*

For example, to create a corner seam between the edges (refer to Figure 15-53), select the **Maximum Gap Distance** radio button and then choose the **Symmetric Gap** button. Next, specify the gap of 1mm in the **Gap** edit box; the gap between Edge 1 and Edge 2 in the resultant model will become 1mm.

Similarly, to create a corner seam between the edges (refer to Figure 15-53), select the **Edge/Face Distance** radio button and then choose the **No Overlap** button. Next, specify the gap of 1mm in the **Gap** edit box; the gap between Edge 1 and Face 2 in the resultant model will become 1mm.

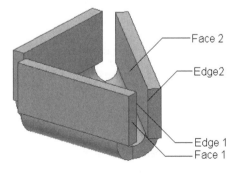

Figure 15-53 *Reference edges and faces for creating the corner seam*

Overlap

The **Overlap** button is provided on the right of the **No Overlap/Symmetric Gap** button. If this button is chosen, the face defined by the first selected edge will overlap the face defined by the second selected edge, see Figure 15-54. In this figure, the sequence of selection of edges is the same as that of selection of edges in Figure 15-51.

Reverse Overlap

If the **Reverse Overlap** button is chosen, the face defined by the second selected edge will overlap the face defined by the first selected edge, as shown in Figure 15-55. The sequence of selection of edges is the same as that of selection of edges in Figure 15-51.

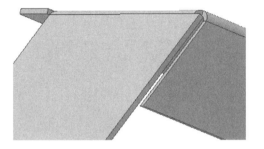 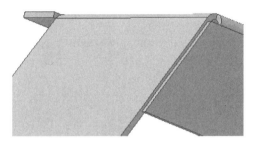

Figure 15-54 Overlapping of faces   *Figure 15-55* Reverse overlapping of faces

Percent Overlap

This edit box is available if you choose the **Overlap** or the **Reverse Overlap** button. This edit box is used to specify the percentage of the overlap using the decimal values 0 to 1.

Gap

The **Gap** edit box is used to specify the gap between two faces in the corner seam. You can enter any desired value in this edit box.

Miter Area

The **Seam** area is replaced by the **Miter** area, if the edges selected to define corner seam are coplanar and perpendicular to each other, as shown in Figure 15-56. The options in this area are similar to those discussed earlier in the **Seam** area.

You can create different models using different buttons in the **Miter** area, as shown in Figures 15-57 through 15-59.

Note

*The options in the **Bend** and **Corner** tabs are the same as those discussed in the previous sections of this chapter.*

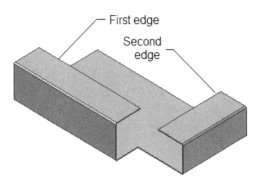

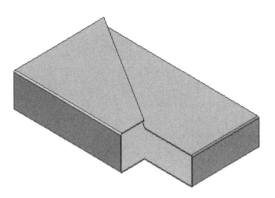

Figure 15-56 *Selecting the edges to create a miter corner*

Figure 15-57 *A 45-degree miter corner*

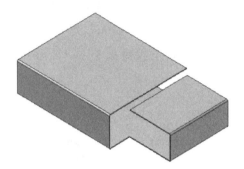

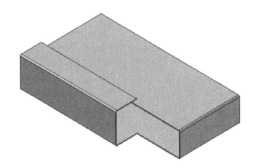

Figure 15-58 *Overlap miter corner*

Figure 15-59 *Reverse overlap miter corner*

BENDING THE FACES OF A SHEET METAL COMPONENT

Ribbon:	Sheet Metal > Create > Bend
Toolbar:	Sheet Metal Features > Bend

 Autodesk Inventor allows you to add a new bent face between two existing faces. This is done by using the **Bend** tool. On invoking this tool, the **Bend** dialog box will be displayed. The options in this dialog box are discussed next.

Shape Tab

The options in the **Shape** tab (Figure 15-60) are used to set the parameters related to the shape of a bent face. These options are discussed next.

Bend Area

The options in this area are discussed next.

Edges

The **Edges** button is chosen to select the edges on the two faces between which the bent face will be added. By default, this button is chosen in the **Bend** dialog box and you are prompted to select the edge. Remember that until you select the edges for creating the bent face, the options in the **Double Bend** area will not be available.

Bend Radius

The **Bend Radius** edit box is used to specify the radius of the bend. The default value of this edit box is the bend radius specified in the **Style and Standard Editor [Library - Read Only]** dialog box. However, you can override this value by entering a new value in the **Bend Radius** edit box.

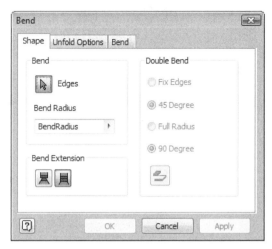

*Figure 15-60 The **Shape** tab of the **Bend** dialog box*

Double Bend Area

The options in the **Double Bend** area are used to specify the shape of bend.

Fix Edges

The **Fix Edges** radio button is selected to create bends of equal dimensions at the selected edges.

45 Degree

The **45 Degree** radio button is selected to create 45-degree bend between the selected edges. Note that when you select the edges for defining the bend, the edge selected first is taken as the fixed edge. While creating the bent face, if the sizes of the two selected edges are different, the size of the fixed edge and the face defined by this edge remains constant by default. However, the size of the other edge and the face defined by it is either trimmed or extended in order to adjust the new face.

Full Radius

The **Full Radius** radio button is selected to create a half circle bent face between two selected edges. Figure 15-61 shows the two edges to be selected for creating bend and Figure 15-62 shows a full radius bend created between the selected faces. Notice that in Figure 15-62, the face defined by the second edge has been modified to adjust the new bent face.

90 Degree

The **90 Degree** radio button is selected to create a 90-degree bend between selected edges, as shown in Figure 15-63. In this figure, the sequence of selecting edges is the same as that of selecting edges in Figure 15-61.

Flip Fixed Edge

The **Flip Fixed Edge** check box is chosen to change the fixed edge. As mentioned earlier, the edge selected first is taken as the fixed edge and the face defined by the other edge is modified to adjust the new bent face. However, if you choose this button, the edge selected second will be taken as the fixed edge and the face defined by the first edge will be modified to adjust the new bent face. Figure 15-64 shows a bent face added by selecting two edges in an order similar to that shown in Figure 15-61 and flipping the fixed edges. Notice that the size of the face defined by the first edge has been modified to adjust the new bent face.

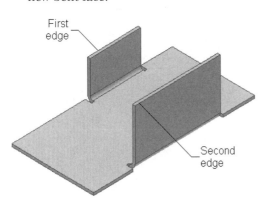

Figure 15-61 Edges to be selected to create bend

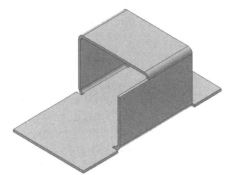

Figure 15-62 A full radius bent face

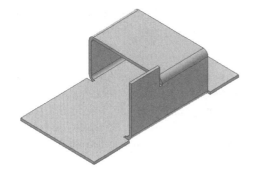

Figure 15-63 The 90-degree bend

Figure 15-64 The 90-degree bend after flipping the fixed edge

Bend Extension Area

The options in this area are discussed next.

Extend Bend Aligned to Side Faces

 If you choose the **Extend Bend Aligned to Side Faces** button, material will be added on the sides of the edges along the faces and not normal to the axis of the bend.

Extend Bend

 This button is chosen by default when the **Bend** dialog box is invoked and extends the bend material perpendicular to the bend axis.

 Note

*The options in the **Unfold Options** and **Bend** tabs are the same as those discussed in the previous sections of this chapter.*

ROUNDING THE CORNERS OF SHEET METAL COMPONENTS

Ribbon:	Sheet Metal > Modify > Corner Round
Toolbar:	Sheet Metal Feature> Corner Round

The corners of a sheet metal component can be rounded by using the **Corner Round** tool. You can use this tool to round a single selected corner or all corners of a selected face. On invoking this tool, the **Corner Round** dialog box will be displayed, as shown in Figure 15-65. The options in this dialog box are discussed next.

Corner

The **Corner** column lists the number of corners that are selected to be rounded. When you invoke the **Corner Round** dialog box, you are prompted to select a corner to be rounded. By default, this column displays 0 Selected as no corner is selected for rounding. To round a corner, select the edge that defines the corner of the sheet metal plate. When you select a corner, this column displays **1 Selected**. Similarly, if you select more corners, the **Corner** column lists the number of corners that you have selected. You can preview the corner round on the graphics screen.

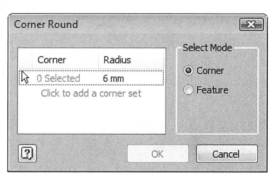

*Figure 15-65 The **Corner Round** dialog box*

Radius

The **Radius** column displays the radius of the corner round. To modify the radius, enter new radius in the edit box that is displayed when you click on the value in the **Radius** column.

Select Mode Area

The options in the **Select Mode** area are used to specify the mode for selecting object to be filleted. The options in this area are discussed next.

Corner

The **Corner** radio button is selected by default in the **Select Mode** area and it allows you to individually select the corners to be rounded.

Feature

The **Feature** radio button is selected to select a feature whose all corners will be rounded. On selecting this radio button, you will be prompted to select the feature to be rounded. As soon as you select a feature, you will notice that all its corners are selected. Note that if a feature has some faces that are folded, even the corners at the folded faces will be selected. Figure 15-66 shows a feature being selected for rounding the corners. Notice that the dotted lines display the original feature before the face is folded. Figure 15-67 shows the sheet metal component after all corners of the selected feature are rounded. Because the two flanges were not a part of the actual base feature, their corners are not rounded.

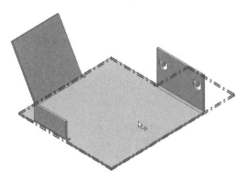

Figure 15-66 Selecting the feature to be rounded   *Figure 15-67 Feature after rounding all corners*

CHAMFERING THE CORNERS OF SHEET METAL COMPONENTS

Ribbon:	Sheet Metal > Modify > Corner Chamfer
Toolbar:	Sheet Metal Features > Corner Chamfer

Corner Chamfer   You can chamfer the corners of a sheet metal component by using the **Corner Chamfer** tool. On invoking this tool, the **Corner Chamfer** dialog box will be displayed, as shown in Figure 15-68. The options in this dialog box are discussed next.

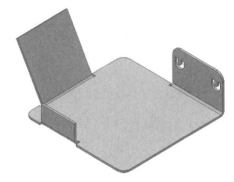

One Distance

The **One Distance** is the first button in the **Corner Chamfer** dialog box. This button is chosen by default and is used to create a chamfer with an equal distance in both the

*Figure 15-68 The **Corner Chamfer** dialog box*

directions of the chamfer corner. This option is used to create a chamfer at a 45-degree angle. The chamfer distance can be specified in the **Distance** edit box that is available in the area that is on the extreme right of this dialog box.

Distance and Angle

The **Distance and Angle** button is provided below the **One Distance** button. This button is chosen to define the chamfer by using one distance and one angle value. When you choose this button, the **Edge** button will be displayed in the area that is in the middle of the **Corner Chamfer** dialog box and you are prompted to select a face to be chamfered. This is the face along which the distance value will be calculated. On selecting the face, you will be prompted to select the corner to be chamfered. Select the edge from the sheet metal component; the corner chamfer will be created. You can define the distance value in the **Distance** edit box and the angle value in the **Angle** edit box. These edit boxes will be displayed in the area located on the extreme right of the **Corner Chamfer** dialog box.

Two Distances

The **Two Distances** button below the **Distance and Angle** button is used to create a chamfer by defining the two distances of the chamfer. The two distances can be entered in the **Distance1** and **Distance2** edit boxes. These edit boxes are displayed in the area located on the extreme right of the **Corner Chamfer** dialog box. Choose the **Flip Direction** button available below the **Corner** button to flip the distance values. Figure 15-69 shows a sheet metal component before chamfering the corners and Figure 15-70 shows the component after chamfering the corners.

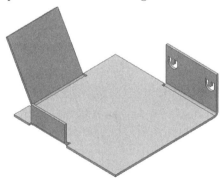

Figure 15-69 *Component before chamfering*

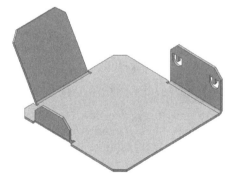

Figure 15-70 *Component after chamfering*

PUNCHING 3D SHAPES INTO SHEET METAL COMPONENTS

Ribbon:	Sheet Metal > Modify > Punch Tool
Toolbar:	Sheet Metal Features > Punch Tool

Punch
Tool

You can punch a 3D shape into a sheet metal component using the **Punch Tool** tool. Note that a 3D shape can be punched only on a sketched point, endpoints of a line or an arc, or center points of arcs and circles. Therefore, you need to create any of these entities before invoking this tool. On invoking this tool, the **PunchTool**

Directory dialog box will be displayed, as shown in Figure 15-71. Using this dialog box, you can select a predefined punch tool from the punch tool library.

Select a predefined punch tool and then choose the **Open** button from the **PunchTool Directory** dialog box; the **PunchTool** dialog box will be displayed. This dialog box has three tabs that allow you to set the parameters for the punch. You can also choose the **Cancel** button from the **PunchTool Directory** dialog box to exit it and accept the default punch tool.

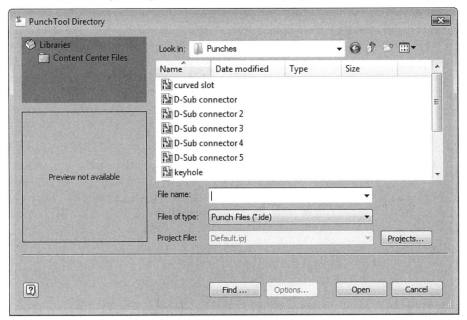

*Figure 15-71 The **PunchTool Directory** dialog box*

Preview Tab

The **Preview** tab is the first tab that is displayed when you invoke this dialog box, see Figure 15-72. The options in this tab allow you to select the shape to be punched on the sheet metal component. The options in this tab are discussed next.

Location

The **Location** display box is activated only when you choose the **Cancel** button from the **PunchTool Directory** dialog box. It displays the name and path of the selected 3D punch shape. To select a new punch shape library file, choose the **Select PunchTool Library Folder** button. When you choose this button, the **PunchTool Directory** dialog box is displayed. You can use this dialog box to select the library file that stores the punch shapes. The library file and its path will be displayed in the **Location** display box. If you have already selected the 3D punch shape in the **PunchTool Directory** dialog box, then the **Location** display box and the **Select PunchTool Library Folder** will not be available.

Punch Area

The list box in the **Punch** area displays the list of the punch shapes available in the selected library file. You can select the required punch shape from the list box. On doing so, its preview will be displayed in the preview window on left of this list box.

Geometry Tab

The options in the **Geometry** tab (Figure 15-73) are used to specify the location and orientation of the punch shape. As soon as you select the location of the punch shape, its preview will be displayed on the screen. You can change the orientation of the punch shape by entering its value in the **Angle** edit box.

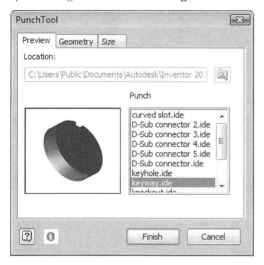

Figure 15-72 *The **Preview** tab of the* ***PunchTool*** *dialog box*

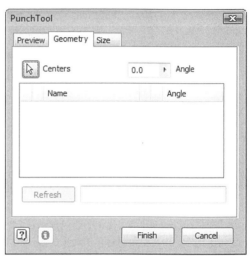

Figure 15-73 *The **Geometry** tab of the* ***PunchTool*** *dialog box*

Size Tab

The **Size** tab of the **PunchTool** dialog box is used to modify the dimensions of the punch shape. The name and the value of the dimension are displayed under the **Name** column and the **Value** column, respectively, as shown in Figure 15-74. To modify a dimension value, click on its field; the field will turn into an edit box or a drop-down list. If it turns into an edit box, you can enter value in it. If the field turns into a drop-down list, you can select value from the drop-down list. After setting dimensions, choose the **Finish** button to exit the dialog box and punch the shape into the sheet metal component.

Figure 15-75 shows a sheet metal component after punching the keyway into the flange face.

Figure 15-74 *The* **Size** *tab of the* **PunchTool** *dialog box*

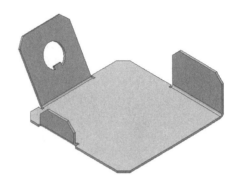

Figure 15-75 *Sheet metal component after punching the keyway*

CREATING HEMS

Ribbon:	Sheet Metal > Create > Hem
Toolbar:	Sheet Metal Features > Hem

Hem is a folded part created on a face of a sheet metal component. Hems are created to strengthen a sheet metal component or to remove its sharp edges. Hems make a sheet metal component easy to handle and assemble. You can create hems by using the **Hem** tool. Choose the **Hem** tool from the **Create** panel of the **Sheet Metal** tab; the **Hem** dialog box will be invoked. The options in this dialog box are discussed next.

Shape Tab

The options in the **Shape** tab (Figure 15-76) are used to set the parameters related to the shape of a hem. These options are discussed next.

Type

The **Type** drop-down list provides the types of hems that can be created. These options are discussed next.

Single

The **Single** is the default hem type and is used to create a single hem, as shown in Figure 15-77

Figure 15-76 *The* **Shape** *tab of the* **Hem** *dialog box*

Teardrop

The **Teardrop** type is used to create a teardrop hem, as shown in Figure 15-78.

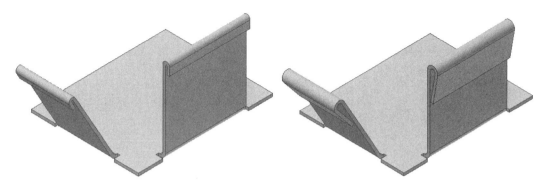

Figure 15-77 *Single hem on flanges*   *Figure 15-78* *Teardrop hem on flanges*

Rolled

The **Rolled** type is used to creates a rolled hem that does not have a face extending beyond a curve, as shown in Figure 15-79.

Double

The **Double** type is used to create a double hem by rotating the hem twice, as shown in Figure 15-80. This type of hem does not have any shared edge; therefore, it is very easy to handle.

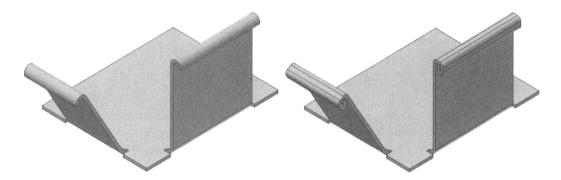

Figure 15-79 *Rolled hem on flanges*   *Figure 15-80* *Double hem on flanges*

Shape Area

The options in this area are discussed next.

Select Edge

When you invoke the **Hem** dialog box, this button is chosen by default and you are prompted to select the edge. Selecting the required edge; the hem will be created. Note that you can select only one edge at a time for creating hem. After selecting an edge, set parameters and choose the **Apply** button to create hem. Once the hem has been created on one edge, this button will be chosen automatically and you will be prompted to select another edge to create hem.

Flip Direction
The **Flip Direction** button is chosen to reverse the direction of a hem.

Gap/Radius
The **Gap** edit box is used to set the value of the gap of a hem for single hem type or double hem type. The default value in this edit box is Thickness*0.50. You can enter any desired value as the gap of the hem in this edit box. This edit box is replaced with the **Radius** edit box for the teardrop and rolled hems and is used to define the radius of the teardrop or rolled hem.

Length/Angle
The **Length** edit box is used to set the length of hem for a single hem type or double hem type. The default value in this edit box is Thickness*4.0. You can enter any desired value as the length of the hem in this edit box. This edit box is replaced with the **Angle** edit box for the teardrop and rolled hems and is used to define the angle of teardrop or rolled hem. The angle value can vary from 181-degree to 359-degree.

Note
*The options in the **More** area are the same as those discussed in the **Flange** dialog box.*

*The options in the **Unfold Options** and **Bend** tabs are the same as those discussed in the **Sheet Metal Defaults** dialog box.*

CREATING CONTOUR FLANGES

Ribbon:	Sheet Metal > Create > Contour Flange
Toolbar:	Sheet Metal Features > Contour Flange

Contour flanges are created by using an open sketch. To create a contour flange, first you need to create an open sketch. After creating the sketch, invoke the **Contour Flange** tool; the **Contour Flange** dialog box will be displayed. The options in this dialog box are discussed next.

Shape Tab
The options in the **Shape** tab (Figure 15-81) are used to set the parameters related to the shape of a contour flange. These options are discussed next.

Shape Area
The options in this area are discussed next.

Profile

The **Profile** button is chosen to select the profile that will be used to create the contour flange. When you invoke the **Contour Flange** dialog box, this button is chosen by default and you are prompted to select an open profile.

Edge Select Mode

 The **Edge Select Mode** button is chosen by default and allows you to specify the edges on which the flanges will be attached.

Loop Select Mode

 This button allows you to select an edge loop and creates a flange attached to all selected edges.

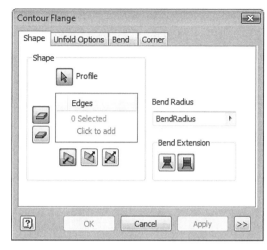

*Figure 15-81 The **Shape** tab of the **Contour Flange** dialog box*

Edges Area

The **Edges** area displays the number of edges that have been selected to create a flange. Click in the **Edges** area and select new edges from the drawing window to attach the flange.

Direction Area

This area is located below the **Edges** area. The three buttons in this area are used to specify the direction for adding material to create a counter flange.

Bend Radius

The **Bend Radius** edit box is used to set the value of the radius of the bend in the contour flange.

Bend Extension Area

The options in this area are discussed next.

Extend Bend Aligned to Side Faces

If you choose the **Extend Bend Aligned to Side Faces** button, the material is added on the sides of the edges along the faces and not normal to the axis of the bend.

Extend Bend

This button is chosen by default when the **Contour Flange** dialog box is invoked and extends the bend material perpendicular to the bend axis.

More

The **More** button is the button with two arrows and is available at the lower right corner of the **Contour Flange** dialog box. When you choose this button, the **Contour Flange** dialog box expands and displays the **Width Extents** area. This area has the **Type** drop-down list for specifying the extents of the flange. All the options in this drop-down list, except for the **Distance** option, are the same as those discussed in the previous sections of this chapter. The **Distance** option is discussed below.

Distance

The **Distance** option is used to specify the distance of the contour flange. When you select this option, the **Distance** edit box appears in the **Width Extents** area. You can define the distance of the contour flange in this edit box. You can reverse the direction of the flange creation by choosing the buttons available below the **Distance** edit box.

Figure 15-82 shows the profile and the edge selected for creating contour flange and Figure 15-83 shows the resulting contour flange.

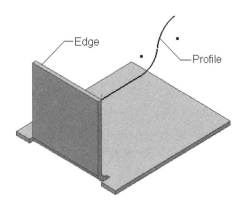
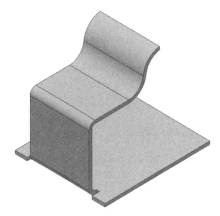

Figure 15-82 The profile and the edge selected   *Figure 15-83 The resulting contour flange*

 Note
*The options in the **Unfold Options**, **Bend**, and **Corner** tabs are the same as those discussed in the previous sections of this chapter.*

CREATING THE FLAT PATTERNS OF SHEET METAL COMPONENTS

Ribbon:	Sheet Metal > Flat Pattern > Create Flat Pattern
Toolbar:	Sheet Metal Features > Flat Pattern

Create Flat Pattern

You can unfold the sheet metal components by using the **Create Flat Pattern** tool. On invoking this tool, the sheet metal component will be unfolded and displayed in the graphics window. Note that the modifications made in the unfolded sheet metal component will not be reflected in the folded model. However, if you make any changes in the sheet metal component, they will be reflected in the flat pattern.

When you create the flat pattern, it is added in the **Browser Bar** below all features of the sheet metal component. Figure 15-84 shows a sheet metal component and Figure 15-85 shows the flat pattern of the same component.

Figure 15-84 *Sheet metal part*

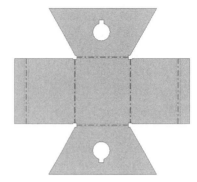

Figure 15-85 *Flat pattern of the sheet metal part*

Adding or Removing Material from the Flat Pattern

This is one of the enhancements introduced in Autodesk Inventor. This feature allows you to add or remove material from the flat patterned sheet metal component. When you create the flat pattern of a component, notice that the **Sheet Metal** tab is replaced by the **Flat Pattern** tab, displaying the tools that can be to add or remove material from the flat pattern sheet metal component. The tools that can be used for this purpose are **Extrude**, **Revolve**, **Hole**, and so on. After creating the flat pattern, choose the **Create 2D Sketch** tool from the **Sketch** panel of the **Flat Pattern** tab and select the required face as the sketching plane. Remember that you cannot select the existing default datum planes from the **Browser Bar**. On selecting a face to create a feature, the **Autodesk Inventor 2011** message box will be displayed informing you about the exclusive application of the edits to the flat pattern without affecting the folded model. Choose the **OK** button from the **Autodesk Inventor 2011** message box; the sketcher environment will be activated. Create the sketch and exit the sketched environment. Now, invoke the flat pattern editing feature tools such as **Extrude**, **Revolve**, or other features from the **Flat Pattern** tab and complete creating the feature. Figure 15-86 shows a sheet metal component with flange walls and Figure 15-87 shows its flat pattern with an extruded cut feature and two hole features.

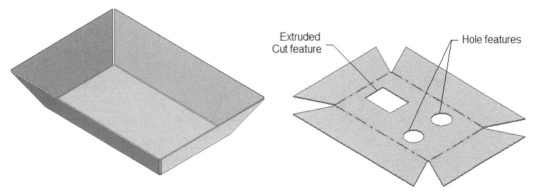

Figure 15-86 *Sheet metal component with flange walls*

Figure 15-87 *Flat pattern with an extruded cut and two hole features*

Tip. *To activate a folded model after creating the flat pattern of a sheet metal component, double-click on the* **Folded Model** *node in the* **Browser Bar**. *Similarly, to invoke the flat pattern of a sheet metal, double-click on the* **Flat Pattern** *node in the* **Browser Bar**. *You can also use the* **Ribbon** *to switch between the folded model and flat pattern of a sheel metal component. To activate a folded model, choose the* **Go To Folded Part** *tool from the* **Folded Part** *panel of the* **Flat Pattern** *tab in the* **Ribbon**. *To switch to the flat pattern of the model, choose the* **Go To Flat Pattern** *tool from the* **Flat Pattern** *panel of the* **Sheet Metal** *tab.*

TUTORIALS

Tutorial 1

In this tutorial, you will create the sheet metal component of the Holder Clip shown in Figure 15-88a. The flat pattern of the component is shown in Figure 15-88c. Its views and dimensions are shown in Figures 15-88b and 15-88d. The thickness of the sheet is 1 mm. After creating the sheet metal component, create its flat pattern. **(Expected time: 45 min)**

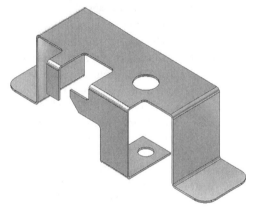

Figure 15-88a *Sheet metal component of the Holder Clip*

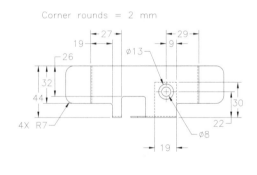

Figure 15-88b *Top view of the Holder Clip*

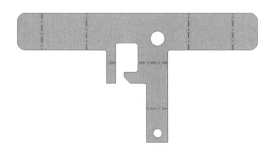

Figure 15-88c *Flat pattern of the component*

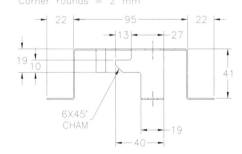

Figure 15-88d *Front view of the Holder Clip*

The following steps are required to complete this tutorial:

a. Start a new metric sheet metal file and then draw the sketch of the top face of the sheet metal component.
b. Set parameters in the **Sheet Metal Defaults** dialog box and convert the sketch into the sheet metal face.
c. Add the contour flange on the right and left faces of the top feature.
d. Add the contour flange on the front face of the feature.
e. Create a cut feature on the front face of the new flange and then add another face and add chamfer to it.
f. Create the last flange and then create two holes. Finally, create the flat pattern.

Opening a New Metric Sheet Metal File

1. Start Autodesk Inventor 2011 and invoke the **New File** dialog box.

2. Choose the **Metric** tab and then double-click on the **Sheet Metal (mm).ipt** option to start a new metric sheet metal file.

   The sketching environment is invoked. Now, you can draw sketch of the top face of the sheet metal component.

3. Draw the sketch of the top face of the Holder Clip, as shown in Figure 15-89.

Note
In Figure 15-89, grid lines are hidden for the sake of clarity of the sketch.

4. Exit the sketching environment by choosing the **Finish Sketch** button from the **Exit** panel of the **Sketch** tab.

Converting the Sketch into the Sheet Metal Face

Before converting the sketch into the sheet metal face, it is recommended that you set parameters in the **Style and Standard Editor [Library- Read Only]** dialog box. These parameters control the thickness of sheet, radius of bend, parameters of relief, and so on.

1. Choose the **Sheet Metal Defaults** tool from the **Setup** panel of the **Sheet Metal** tab to invoke the **Sheet Metal Defaults** dialog box. Choose the **Edit Sheet Metal Rule** button from the dialog box to invoke the **Style and Standard Editor [Library- Read Only]** dialog box.

   On invoking the **Style and Standard Editor [Library- Read Only]** dialog box, the **Sheet** tab is chosen by default. You can set the parameters related to the thickness of the sheet using this tab. Since all other parameters are based on the thickness of the sheet, they automatically change when you change the thickness of the sheet.

2. Enter **1** in the **Thickness** edit box of the **Sheet** area.

3. Choose **Save** and then **Done** to save the changes and exit the **Style and Standard Editor [Library- Read Only]** dialog box. Next, choose the **Cancel** button from the **Sheet Metal Defaults** dialog box and exit the dialog box.

4. Choose the **Face** tool from the **Create** panel of the **Sheet Metal** tab to invoke the **Face** dialog box.

    Face

    As there is only one unconsumed sketch, it is automatically selected and highlighted.

5. Choose **OK** to create the face and exit the **Face** dialog box. Change the current view to the isometric view. The isometric view of the Holder Clip is shown in Figure 15-90.

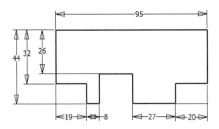

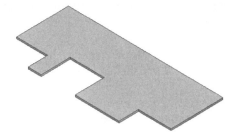

Figure 15-89 *Sketch of the top face of the Holder Clip*

Figure 15-90 *Isometric view of the Holder Clip*

Creating the First Contour Flange

As mentioned earlier, a contour flange is created with the help of a sketched contour. Therefore, first you need to sketch the contour so that it will be used to create a flange.

1. Choose the **Create 2D Sketch** tool from the **Sketch** panel of the **Model** tab and then select the face as the sketching plane, as shown in Figure 15-91.

2. Draw the sketch of the contour flange, as shown in Figure 15-92.

3. Exit the sketching environment. Choose the **Contour Flange** tool from the **Create** panel of the **Sheet Metal** tab; the **Contour Flange** dialog box is invoked. In this dialog box, the **Profile** button in the **Shape** area of the **Shape** tab is chosen by default. As a result, you are prompted to select the profile for creating the contour flange.

    Contour
    Flange

4. Select one of the two sketched lines as the profile for creating the flange. As the other line is a part of the same sketch, it is selected automatically and turns blue.

    As soon as you select the profile, the **Edge Select Mode** button in the **Shape** area is chosen and you are prompted to select the edge on which the flange will be created.

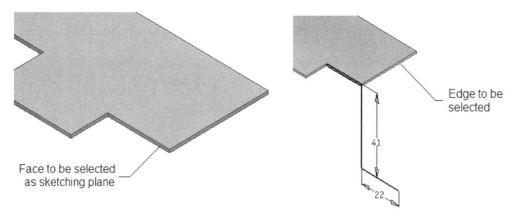

Figure 15-91 *Face to be selected as the sketching plane*

Figure 15-92 *Sketch of the contour flange*

5. Select the edge on the right of the top face to create the flange, refer to Figure 15-92.

6. Accept the remaining default options and choose **OK** to create the flange. You will notice that a bend is automatically created between the base sheet and the flange. The dimensions and parameters of this bend are taken from the parameters defined in the **Style and Standard Editor [Library - Read Only]** dialog box.

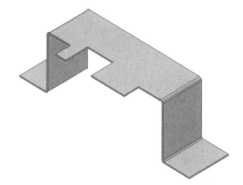

7. Similarly, create second contour flange on the other side of the top face. You may need to flip the direction of the contour flange by using the **Flip Side** button, which is the middle button in the **Shape** area of the **Shape** tab. On choosing this button, the front face of the flange becomes coplanar with the left face of the base sheet. The sheet metal model of the Holder Clip after creating the two contour flanges is shown in Figure 15-93.

Figure 15-93 *Sheet metal component after creating the two contour flanges*

Creating the Third Contour Flange

1. Define a new sketch plane on the planar face of the base feature and then create the sketch for the contour flange, as shown in Figure 15-94.

2. Exit the sketching environment. Next, choose the **Contour Flange** tool from the **Create** panel of the **Sheet Metal** tab; the **Contour Flange** dialog box is invoked. In this dialog box, the **Profile** button in the **Shape** area of the **Shape** tab is chosen by default. As a result, you are prompted to select the profile for creating the contour flange.

Contour Flange

3. Select one of the two sketched lines as the contour for creating the flange. As the other line is a part of the same sketch, it is also automatically selected and turns blue.

    As soon as you select the profile, the **Edge Select Mode** button in the **Shape** area is chosen and you are prompted to select the edge on which the flange will be created.

4. Select the horizontal edge on the top face to create the flange.

5. Choose the middle **Flip Side** button to reverse the direction along which the face of the flange needs to be created.

6. Accept the remaining default options and choose **OK** to create the flange. The sheet metal component after creating the third contour flange is shown in Figure 15-95.

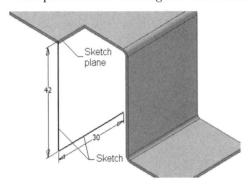

Figure 15-94 *The sketch plane and the sketch for the contour flange*

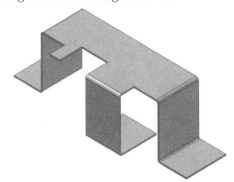

Figure 15-95 *Sheet metal component after creating the contour flange*

Creating a Cut and a New Face on the Front Face of the Third Contour Flange

1. Define a new sketch plane on the front face of the third contour flange and create the sketch of the cut feature, as shown in Figure 15-96. After creating the sketch, exit the sketching environment.

2. Invoke the **Cut** tool and then create the cut feature by selecting the **All** option from the drop-down list in the **Extents** area of the **Cut** dialog box. The sheet metal component after creating the cut is shown in Figure 15-97.

3. Similarly, define a sketch plane on the front face of the third contour flange and create a new rectangular face by using the **Face** tool, refer to Figure 15-88d for dimensions.

4. Next, add the corner chamfer by using the **Corner Chamfer** tool, as shown in Figure 15-98, refer to Figure 15-88d for dimensions.

Creating the Flange

1. Choose the **Flange** tool from the **Create** panel of the **Sheet Metal** tab; the **Flange** dialog box is displayed and you are prompted to select the edge for creating the flange.

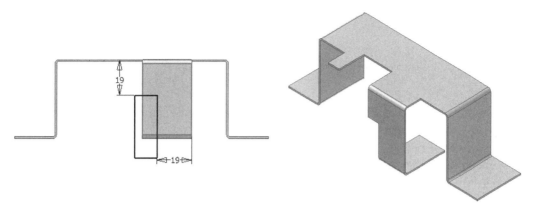

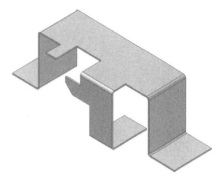

Figure 15-96 *Sketch of the cut feature*   **Figure 15-97** *Model after creating the cut feature*

2. Select the edge on the top face of the base feature, as shown in Figure 15-99.

3. Enter **19** in the **Distance** edit box; the size of the flange in the preview is modified.

4. Choose the **Flip Direction** button from the **Flange** dialog box to flip the direction of the flange.

5. Accept the remaining default options and choose the **OK** button to create the flange and exit the dialog box. The sheet metal component after creating the flange is shown in Figure 15-100.

Figure 15-98 *Sheet metal component after creating the new face and the corner chamfer*

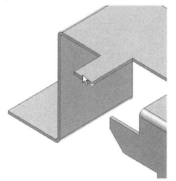

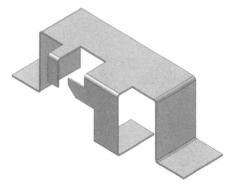

Figure 15-99 *Selecting the edge to create the flange*   **Figure 15-100** *Model after creating the flange*

Creating Rounds and Holes

1. Create all rounds by using the **Corner Round** tool, refer to Figures 15-88b and 15-88d for dimensions.

2. Create two holes by using the **Hole** tool from the **Modify** panel of the **Sheet Metal** tab.

This completes the creation of the sheet metal component of the Holder Clip. The final sheet metal component of the Holder Clip is shown in Figure 15-101.

3. Save the sheet metal component with the name *Tutorial1.ipt* at the location *C:\Inventor_2011\c15*.

Creating the Flat Pattern

The flattened view of a sheet metal component plays a very important role in the process of planning and designing the punch tools and dies for creating a sheet metal component. Therefore, the flattened view is a very important part of any sheet metal component. As mentioned earlier, you can unfold a sheet metal component and display its flattened view in a separate graphics window by using the **Create Flat Pattern** tool.

1. Choose the **Create Flat Pattern** tool from the **Flat Pattern** panel of the **Sheet Metal** tab; the sheet metal component is unfolded and displayed as a flat component, as shown in Figure 15-102.

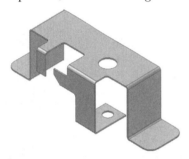

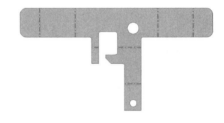

Figure 15-101 *Final model of the Holder Clip*

Figure 15-102 *Flat pattern of the sheet metal part*

Note

*1. You can also use the **Measure** tool to measure distances in the flat pattern. To measure distances, right-click in the graphics window, and then choose **Measure** > **Measure Distance** from the shortcut menu.*

2. The orientation of the flat pattern in your case may be different from the orientation shown in Figure 15-102.

Tutorial 2

In this tutorial, you will create the sheet metal component shown in Figure 15-103a. Its dimensions are shown in Figures 15-103b through 15-103d. The flat pattern of the component is shown in Figure 15-104. The thickness of the sheet is 1 mm and the radius of corner bends is 3 mm. The dimensions of hems are not given. Select the default parameters as the dimensions for creating hems on the two faces. **(Expected time: 45 min)**

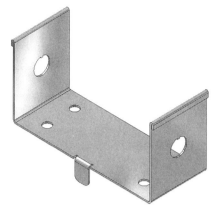

Figure 15-103a *Sheet metal component*

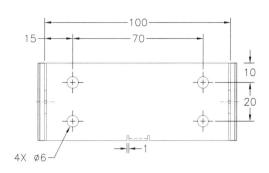

Figure 15-103b *Top view of the component*

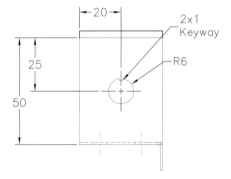

Figure 15-103c *Left view of the component*

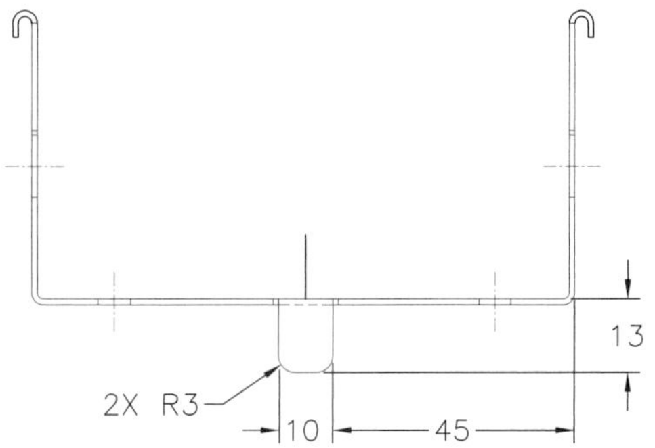

Figure 15-103d *Front view of the component*

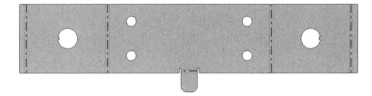

Figure 15-104 *Flat pattern of the sheet metal component*

The following steps are required to complete this tutorial:

a. Start a new metric sheet metal file and create the sketch for the base of the sheet metal component on the XY plane.
b. Exit the sketching environment and convert the sketch into a face by using the **Face** tool.
c. Create one hole and then pattern it to create the remaining three instances.
d. Create flanges on the left and right faces of the sheet metal base.

e. Create hems on both flanges and then create two keyways using the **PunchTool** dialog box.

f. Create flange on the front face of the base.

Drawing the Sketch for the Base Feature

1. Choose the **New** tool from the **Quick Access Toolbar** to invoke the **New File** dialog box.

2. Choose the **Metric** tab and start a new metric sheet metal file.

3. Draw the sketch for the base, as shown in Figure 15-105, and then exit the Sketching environment.

Converting the Sketch into a Sheet Metal Face

As mentioned earlier, first you need to set parameters in the **Sheet Metal Defaults** dialog box and then convert the sketch into a face.

1. Choose the **Sheet Metal Defaults** tool from the **Setup** panel of the **Sheet Metal** tab; the **Sheet Metal Defaults** dialog box is displayed. Choose the **Edit Sheet Metal Rule** button from this dialog box to invoke the **Style and Standard Editor [Library - Read Only]** dialog box.

2. Enter **1** in the **Thickness** edit box in the **Sheet** area. Choose **Save** and then choose **Done** to close the dialog box.

3. Choose the **Cancel** button from the **Sheet Metal Defaults** dialog box to close it.

4. Choose the **Face** tool from the **Create** panel of the **Sheet Metal** tab to invoke the **Face** dialog box.

    As there is only one unconsumed sketch, it is automatically selected and the preview of the face of the sheet metal component is displayed in the drawing window.

5. Choose **OK** to create the face and exit the **Face** dialog box.

6. Invoke the **Hole** dialog box and create a hole at the lower left corner of the base using the **Linear** option, refer to Figure 15-103b for dimensions.

7. Create the rectangular pattern of the hole, refer to Figure 15-103b for dimensions. Change the current view to the isometric view. The base of the sheet metal component after creating the hole pattern is shown in Figure 15-106.

Creating the Two Flanges

1. Choose the **Flange** tool from the **Create** panel of the **Sheet Metal** tab; the **Flange** dialog box is invoked and you are prompted to select the edge for creating flange.

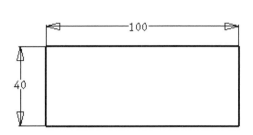

Figure 15-105 *Sketch for the base feature*   ***Figure 15-106*** *Base after creating the hole pattern*

2. Select the right edge of the bottom face on the base feature. You will notice that the preview of the flange is shown in the downward direction.

3. Choose the **Flip Direction** button and enter **50** in the **Distance** edit box.

4. Next, choose the **Apply** button.

    You will notice that the flange is created on the right edge and the **Flange** dialog box is still available. This is because you did not exit the dialog box after creating the flange.

5. Press and hold the F4 key and rotate the model such that the left edge of the bottom face of the base is visible.

6. Release the F4 key and select the left edge on the bottom face of the base.

    You will notice that the flange is created in the upward direction. This is because the parameters have already been set in the **Flange** dialog box.

7. Choose the **OK** button from the **Flange** dialog box to create the flange and exit the dialog box. Change the current view to the isometric view. The sheet metal component after creating flanges is shown in Figure 15-107.

Creating Hems

1. Choose the **Hem** tool from the **Create** panel of the **Sheet Metal** tab; the **Hem** dialog box is invoked and you are prompted to select an edge to create hem.

2. Select the outer edge on the top face of the right flange. You will notice that the preview of the hem is displayed.

3. Accept the default parameters in the **Hem** dialog box and choose **Apply** to create hem.

4. Now, select the outer edge of the left flange; the preview of the hem is displayed. Choose the **OK** button to create the hem and exit the dialog box. The sheet metal component after creating hems is shown in Figure 15-108.

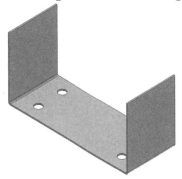   

Figure 15-107 *Model after creating flanges*   *Figure 15-108* *Model after creating hems*

Creating Keyways

Next, you will create keyways by created by punching the predefined shape on both the flanges. As mentioned earlier, the shapes are punched by using a sketched point. Therefore, first you need to sketch a point in the middle of one of the flanges.

Before creating keyways, it is recommended that you suppress hems. This is because after creating hems, the actual dimensions of the face are reduced and you cannot get the proper locations of keyways.

1. Using the **Browser Bar**, suppress the two hems. Now, define a new sketch plane on the outer face of the right flange.

2. Create a sketch point at the center of the face. Note that the vertical dimension of the point from the top edge should be 25 mm and its horizontal dimension from the left edge of the flange should be 20 mm.

3. Exit the Sketching environment and then choose the **Punch Tool** from the **Modify** panel of the **Sheet Metal** tab; the **PunchTool Directory** dialog box is displayed. Choose the **Cancel** button to exit the **PunchTool Directory** and display the **PunchTool** dialog box.

    Punch
    Tool

4. Select **keyway.ide** from the list box. The preview of the keyway is displayed in the preview window.

5. Choose the **Geometry** tab from the **PunchTool** dialog box. Since there is only one sketched point, this point is selected as the center of the keyway and the preview of the keyway is displayed on the graphics screen. In the preview, you will notice that the keyway pointing toward the right of the circle. You need to rotate it to get the proper orientation.

6. Enter **90** in the **Angle** edit box of the **Geometry** tab. Choose the **Size** tab from the **PunchTool** dialog box, accept the other default dimension values, and then choose **Finish** to create the keyway.

   If units of the keyway in the preview are different, then set the following parameters in the **Size** tab of the **PunchTool** dialog box:

   bottom_fillet: 0 mm   **top_fillet:** 0 mm   **keyway_depth:** 5 mm
   keyway_width: 2 mm   **diameter:** 12 mm.

Note
*The punched 3D shapes are displayed as iFeature in the **Browser Bar**.*

7. Similarly, define a new sketch plane on the outer face of the left flange and then project the last sketch point on this face. Using this projected point, create the keyway on the left flange. The model after creating both keyways is shown in Figure 15-109.

Creating the Next Flange

1. Choose the **Flange** tool from the **Create** panel of the **Sheet Metal** tab; the **Flange** dialog box is invoked and you are prompted to select the edge for creating the flange.

Flange

2. Select the upper edge on the front face of the base of the sheet metal component; the preview of the flange is displayed on the graphics screen.

3. Enter **13** in the **Distance** edit box and then choose the **Flip Direction** button to reverse the direction of feature creation. Choose the **More** button at the lower right corner of the dialog box to expand it.

4. Select **Width** from the **Type** drop-down list in the **Width Extents** area and then select the **Centered** radio button; the **Width** edit box appears in the **Width Extents** area and the preview of the flange is displayed.

5. Enter **10** in the **Width** edit box and then choose **OK** to create the flange and exit the dialog box.

6. Create rounds on the two corners of the flange created previously, by using the **Corner Round** tool. The radius of the corner round is 3 mm.

   This completes the creation of the sheet metal component. Unsuppress the hem features by using the **Browser Bar**. The final sheet metal component is shown in Figure 15-110.

Creating the Flat Pattern

1. Choose the **Create Flat Pattern** tool from the **Flat Pattern** panel of the **Sheet Metal** tab; the flat pattern of the sheet metal component is displayed, as shown in Figure 15-111.

Figure 15-109 Sheet metal component after creating the keyways

Figure 15-110 Completed sheet metal component for Tutorial 2

Note

The orientation of the flat pattern in your case may be different from the orientation shown in Figure 15-111.

2. Choose the **Save** tool from the **Quick Access Toolbar**; a message box is displayed, informing that the model cannot be saved in the flat pattern edit mode.

3. Choose the **OK** button from the message box and save the model with the name *Tutorial2.ipt* at the location given below and then close the file.

Figure 15-111 Flat pattern of the component

C:\Inventor_2011\c15

Self-Evaluation Test

Answer the following questions and then compare them to those given at the end of this chapter:

1. The sheet metal files are saved as the *.ipt* files. (T/F)

2. When you start a new sheet metal file, the sketching environment is invoked. (T/F)

3. A contour flange is created only with the help of a sketched contour. (T/F)

4. A sketched point is automatically selected as the center of the punched 3D shape. (T/F)

5. You can unfold a sheet metal component by using the _____ tool.

6. By default, the value of the bend radius is equal to the _____ of a sheet.

7. In Autodesk Inventor, you can fold a sheet metal face only by using a _____ line that acts as the _____ line.

8. Autodesk Inventor allows you to create corner seams in a sheet metal component with the help of the _____ tool.

9. If a flange is created through an angle of _____, it will not be visible as it merges with the face of a sheet metal component.

10. To convert a solid model into a sheet metal component, first you need to _____ it.

Review Questions

Answer the following questions:

1. If you modify a value in the **Style and Standard Editor [Library - Read Only]** dialog box after creating a sheet metal component, the changes will reflect in the sheet metal component when you exit the dialog box after saving the changes. (T/F)

2. You can measure the dimensions of a sheet metal component by using different measuring tools. (T/F)

3. You can set material for a sheet metal component from the **Material Style** drop-down list in the **Sheet Metal Defaults** dialog box. (T/F)

4. The values of the bend and unfold parameters that are set in the **Style and Standard Editor [Library - Read Only]** dialog box cannot be overridden from the dialog boxes of any tool. (T/F)

5. You can set value in an edit box as an equation in terms of thickness of a sheet. (T/F)

6. A punched 3D shape cannot be mirrored. (T/F)

7. The **Contour Flange** tool is used to create a flange that follows a sketched shape in a sheet metal component. (T/F)

8. You can create an Obround hem in Autodesk Inventor. (T/F)

9. Which of the following tools is used to create the base of a sheet metal component?

    (a) **Flange**   (b) **Contour Flange**
    (c) **Face**   (d) **Hem**

10. Which of the following tools is used to round all corners of the base feature?

    (a) **Round**   (b) **Corner Round**
    (c) **Face**   (d) **Hem**

Exercise

Exercise 1

Create the sheet metal component shown in Figure 15-112a. The flat pattern of the component is shown in Figure 15-112c. The dimensions of the model are shown in Figures 15-112b and 15-112d. Assume the missing dimensions.   **(Expected time: 30 min)**

Hint
*Create the flanges of same width on the top face and the left face and then by using the **Corner Seam** tool, you can force them to close together. This way the corner relief will also be created.*

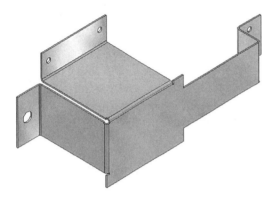

Figure 15-112a *Sheet metal component for Exercise 1*

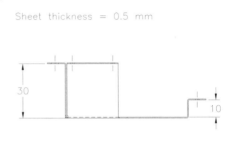

Figure 15-112b *Top view of the component*

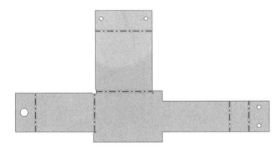

Figure 15-112c *Flat pattern of the component*

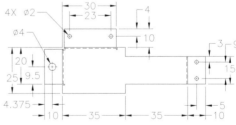

Figure 15-112d *Front view of the component*

Answers to Self-Evaluation Test
1. T, **2.** T, **3.** T, **4.** T, **5. Flat Pattern**, **6.** thickness, **7.** sketched, folding, **8. Corner Seam**, **9.** 180-degree, **10.** shell

Chapter 16

Introduction to Weldments

Learning Objectives

After completing this chapter, you will be able to:
- *Understand weldment assemblies and weldment environment.*
- *Create a cosmetic weld.*
- *Create a fillet weld.*
- *Create a groove weld.*

UNDERSTANDING WELDMENT ASSEMBLIES

Weldment assemblies are those in which you can weld a component with another component using various types of welds. These assemblies are also called weldments. Autodesk Inventor provides you with a dedicated environment for creating weldments, called the Weldment environment. This environment is similar to the Assembly environment. This environment provides tools to assemble components as well as to weld components. In this environment, you can also make some initial preparations to weld components. The initial preparations include creating cut features by using the tools available in the Assembly environment.

Similar to various types of drawing templates, you are also provided with various weldment templates. To invoke the Weldment assembly environment, double-click on any of the weldment assembly templates in the **New File** dialog box, see Figure 16-1.

Figure 16-1 *Various types of weldment templates in the **New File** dialog box*

Figure 16-2 shows the weldment assembly environment invoked using the **Weldment (ANSI - mm).iam** template.

Note
*You can convert an assembly created in the Assembly modeling environment into a Weldment assembly by choosing the **Convert to Weldment** tool from the **Convert** panel of the **Assemble** tab. However, remember that an assembly once converted into a weldment cannot be converted back into a simple assembly.*

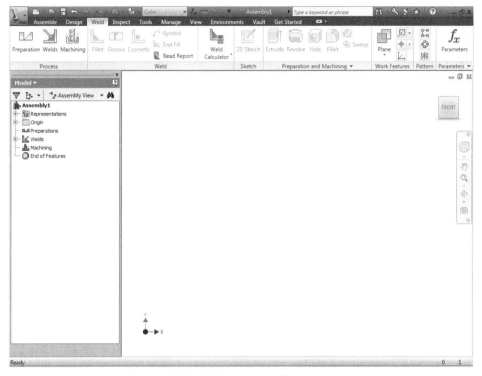

Figure 16-2 *Weldment assembly environment*

MAIN TYPES OF WELDS IN Autodesk Inventor

Autodesk Inventor allows you to create three main types of welds: cosmetic, fillet, and groove. In addition to these, there are some other types of welds that can be used to create weldments. But, they are not discussed in this book. The three main types of welds are discussed next.

Cosmetic Welds

Cosmetic welds are artificial welds added to the selected edge. These types of welds are not actual welds and as a result, no weld bead is added to the model. To create a cosmetic weld, you just need to select the edge that requires welding.

Note
Adding cosmetic welds does not modify the physical properties of an assembly. This is because adding cosmetic welds does not physically add any material to a model. It only adds a convention that gives an impression of welding.

Figure 16-3 shows a part of the Shock assembly in which a cylinder is assembled with a bracket. Note that as there is no physical bonding between these two components, they cannot be held together. Therefore, you need to weld these two components together. Figure 16-4 shows the same assembly after creating a cosmetic weld. The cosmetic weld symbol is also shown in the assembly.

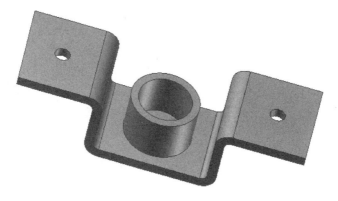

Figure 16-3 Assembly before welding

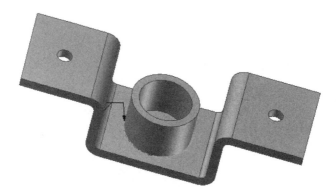

Figure 16-4 Assembly after creating the cosmetic weld

Fillet Welds

Fillet welds are actual welds and are represented by a solid feature in an assembly. When you add fillet welds, a solid feature representing the weld bead is added in the assembly. Also, the physical properties of the assembly are modified. To create a fillet weld, you need two surfaces. Figure 16-5 shows the Shock assembly after adding a fillet weld to the bracket and cylinder. Figure 16-6 shows a butt-joint with a fillet weld.

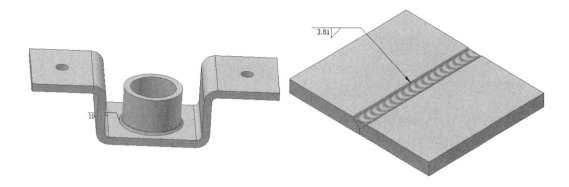

Figure 16-5 *Assembly with a fillet weld*   **Figure 16-6** *Butt-joint with a fillet weld*

Groove Welds

Groove welds are used to weld the parts that are placed at a certain offset from each other or have some grooves between them. These are also known as actual welds and are represented by a solid feature in an assembly. Figure 16-7 shows a partial three-quarter section view of the Shock assembly after adding a groove weld to the bracket and cylinder. Note that in this case, the cylinder is assembled at some offset from the bracket. As evident from this figure, the groove weld bead is filled in this offset space. Figure 16-8 shows a butt-joint with a groove weld. As is evident from this figure also, some offset is maintained between the two mating faces of the plates between which the groove weld bead is filled.

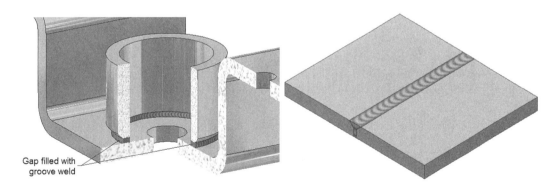

Figure 16-7 *Assembly with a groove weld*   **Figure 16-8** *Butt-joint with a groove weld*

ADDING WELDS TO ASSEMBLIES

The process of creating weldment assemblies is completed in three steps: assembling the components, preparing components for welding, and creating welds. These three steps are discussed next.

Assembling the Components of Weldment Assemblies

As mentioned earlier, you can create the weldment assemblies in the weldment environment. Alternatively, you can assemble the components in the assembly modeling environment and then switch to the weldment environment to add welds to the components. Remember that once you shift from the assembly modeling environment to the weldment environment, you cannot switch back.

Preparing Assemblies for Weldments

Once you have assembled components of the weldment assemblies, you need to prepare them for welding by removing material from the components to accommodate the weld beads. You can create cut features, holes, fillets, and chamfers to remove the material. For example, to create a butt-joint, you need to chamfer the two edges of the plates between which the weld bead will be added. This step is not required if the components were chamfered during their creation. Note that similar to the assembly features, these features are also limited to the assembly and are not made on the individual part files.

To prepare weldments, choose the **Preparation** tool from the **Process** panel of the **Weld** tab. Alternatively, double-click on the **Preparations** node in the **Browser Bar**; various material removal tools will get activated in the **Weld** tab of the **Ribbon**. Next, use the required preparation tool from the **Preparation and Machining** panel of the **Weld** tab and then choose the **Return** tool from the **Return** panel to return to the **Weldment** environment.

Note
*While preparing weldments, the **Extrude** and **Revolve** tools provide only the **Cut** option.*

Adding Welds

The final step in creating weldments is to add welds. To do so, choose the **Welds** tool from the **Process** panel of the **Weld** tab. Alternatively, double-click on the **Welds** node in the **Browser Bar**; various weldment tools will be activated in the **Weld** panel of the **Weld** tab. You can add the fillet symbol either while adding welds or separately using the **Symbol** tool.

The tools to create all three types of welds are discussed next.

CREATING FILLET WELDS

Ribbon:	Weld > Weld > Fillet
Toolbar:	Weldment Features Panel > Fillet Weld

Fillet

To create a fillet weld between components, choose the **Fillet** tool from the **Weld** panel of the **Weld** tab; the **Fillet Weld** dialog box will be displayed, as shown in Figure 16-9.

Bead Area

To create a fillet weld, you need to select the two faces that will be welded together. This is the reason, the **1** button in the **Bead** area will automatically be chosen on invoking the **Fillet Weld** dialog box. Also, you will be prompted to select a face to be welded. After selecting the first face to weld, choose the **2** button; you will again be prompted to select the face to weld. Select the second face; the second face will turn green and the preview of the fillet weld will appear. Selecting the **Chain** check box ensures all faces that are tangent to the selected face are also selected.

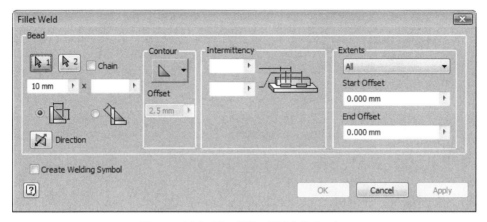

Figure 16-9 *The* **Fillet Weld** *dialog box*

You can specify the dimension of the weld in terms of leg length or in terms of throat measurement by selecting their respective radio buttons from this area. The value of the weld leg or the throat measurement can be entered in the edit boxes below the **1** and **2** buttons.

Contour Area

The options in this area are used to specify the contour of the resulting weld bead. By default, the **Flat** button is chosen. To use any other button, click on the down arrow on the right of the **Flat** button in this area; a flyout will be displayed. Choose the **Convex** or **Concave** button to specify the required contour of weld bead. Specify the offset value of the convex or concave surface in the **Offset** edit box in this area. Figure 16-10 shows a fillet weld with a convex contour.

Intermittency Area

The options in this area are used to create an intermittent fillet weld. You can specify the length and pitch of the intermittent fillet in the **Length** and **Pitch** edit boxes, respectively. Figure 16-11 shows an intermittent fillet weld in a butt-joint. In this case, the length value is 10 mm and the pitch value is 20 mm.

Extents Area

The options in this area are used to specify the extents of a fillet weld. The **All** option is used to create the fillet weld throughout the selected faces. You can also specify the start and end offsets of the fillet weld. The **From-To** option is used to define the extent of the intermittent weld. You can create work planes to specify the "from" and "to" faces. The **Start-Length** option is used to create a weld that starts from a selected face and ends at a specified length.

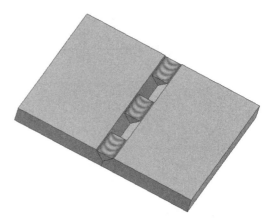

Figure 16-10 *Fillet weld with a convex contour*

Figure 16-11 *Intermittent fillet weld in a butt-joint*

Start Offset/End Offset

The **Start Offset** and **End Offset** edit boxes will be available only when you select the **All** option from the drop-down list in the **Extents** area. These edit boxes are used to specify the distance value of a weld from the start/end edge of the components on which you want to create a fillet weld, as shown in Figure 16-12. If you select the **From-To** option from the drop-down list in the **Extents** area, the **From** and **To** buttons will be available. You can select faces or planes for the start and end of the fillet. If you select the **Start-Length** option from the drop-down list, the **Start Offset** and **Length** edit boxes will be available. You can specify the start offset and the length of the fillet weld in these edit boxes.

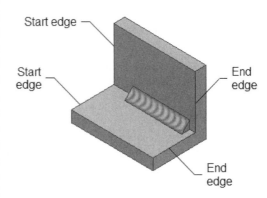

Figure 16-12 *Fillet weld offset from the start and end edges*

Create Welding Symbol

When you select this check box, the **Fillet Weld** dialog box expands and provides option to add weld symbols.

CREATING COSMETIC WELDS

Ribbon:	Weld > Weld > Cosmetic
Toolbar:	Weldment Features Panel > Cosmetic Weld

To create cosmetic weld between components, choose the **Cosmetic** tool from the **Weld** panel of the **Weld** tab; the **Cosmetic Weld** dialog box will be displayed, as shown in Figure 16-13.

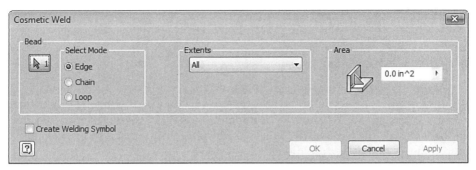

Figure 16-13 The **Cosmetic Weld** *dialog box*

Bead Area

When you invoke the **Cosmetic Weld** dialog box, the **1** button will be chosen and you will be prompted to select an edge or loop for the weld. You can set the selection mode using the options in the **Select Mode** area on the right of the **1** button. The selected edge turns blue.

Extents Area

The options in this area are used to create a cosmetic weld up to a specified extent. The extent of the weld can be specified by selecting the **From-To** option from the drop-down list in this area. You can create work planes to specify the "from" and "to" faces.

Area

The edit box in this area is used to specify the cross-sectional area of the fillet weld. Note that even when you increase this value, there will be no change in the display of the fillet weld in the model. This is because this value is used only for calculating the physical properties of the model after welding.

Figure 16-14 shows two components welded together using the cosmetic weld.

Figure 16-14 Two components welded using the cosmetic weld

Note
*All welds are listed in the **Beads** folder under **Welds** in the **Browser Bar**.*

CREATING GROOVE WELDS

Ribbon:	Weld > Weld > Groove
Toolbar:	Weldment Features Panel > Groove Weld

As mentioned earlier, groove welds are created between the components assembled at some offset or having some grooves between them. After assembling components and invoking the Welding environment, choose the **Groove** tool from the **Weld** panel of the **Weld** tab; the **Groove Weld** dialog box will be displayed, as shown in Figure 16-15. The options in this dialog box are discussed next.

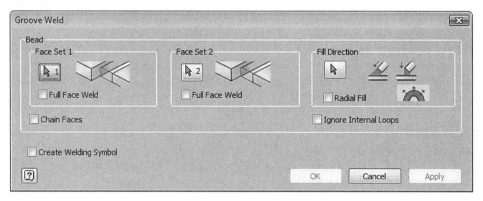

Figure 16-15 The Groove Weld dialog box

Bead Area

The options in this area are used to specify the faces to be groove welded. You can also specify the direction of the groove weld. These options are discussed next.

Face Set 1 Area

The options in this area are used to select the first face for applying the groove weld. When you invoke the **Groove Weld** dialog box, the **1** button in the **Face Set 1** area will be chosen and you will be prompted to the select the face to be welded. The face selected as face set 1 turns blue. You can select the **Full Face Weld** check box to add the weld bead to the entire face.

Face Set 2 Area

The options in this area are used to select the second face for applying the groove weld. The face selected as face set 2 turns green. You can select the **Full Face Weld** check box to add the weld bead to the entire face.

Fill Direction Area

If you are not creating a full face weld, you need to specify the direction of a groove weld. You can specify the direction by using a linear edge, cylindrical face, or planar face, or by using two vertices.

Figure 16-16 shows the quarter section view of a full face groove weld. Note that in this case, the cylinder is assembled at an offset from the bracket.

Radial Fill

Select this check box to project the groove weld for the cylindrical or hole feature, as no fill direction is required for welding these features.

Ignore Internal Loops

This check box is selected to create a groove weld by ignoring the internal loop. Figure 16-17 shows the quarter section view of a groove weld created by ignoring the internal loop, which is the hole in the bracket.

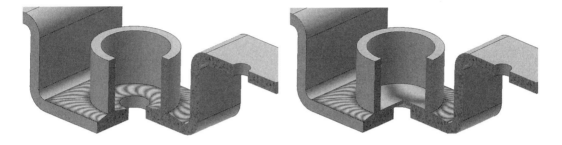

Figure 16-16 Full face groove weld   *Figure 16-17* Groove weld created by ignoring the internal loop

TUTORIALS

Tutorial 1

In this tutorial, you will create the welded butt-joint shown in Figure 16-18. To create this weldment, you will use the **Weldment (ANSI - mm).iam** template and the top-down approach for assembling Plates. Next, you will prepare Plates for welding in the weldment environment by chamfering their edges. The Plate to be used for creating the butt-joint is 30 mm long and 50 mm wide. The thickness of the Plate is 5 mm and the chamfer is a 3 mm equal distance chamfer.   **(Expected time: 30 min)**

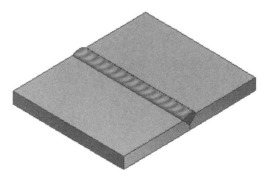

Figure 16-18 Welded butt-joint for Tutorial 1

The following steps are required to complete this tutorial:

a. Open a new **Weldment (ANSI - mm).iam** template and then create a plate using the top-down assembly approach.
b. Exit the part modeling environment and insert another instance of the Plate into the weldment environment.
c. Prepare Plates for welding by creating chamfers.
d. Assemble two plates by using assembly constraints.
e. Invoke the welding options and create the butt-joint using the fillet weld.

Opening a New Weldment File and Creating a Plate

As mentioned in the tutorial description, you need to use the **Weldment (ANSI - mm).iam** file for creating the butt-joint. Therefore, you need to select this file from the **Open** dialog box.

1. Start Autodesk Inventor and invoke the **New File** dialog box. Next, double-click on the **Weldment (ANSI - mm).iam** template from the **Metric** tab to invoke the Weldment environment.

2. Invoke the **Create** tool from the **Assemble** tab and then create a plate of dimensions 30 x 50 x 5 mm. Save the file and then choose the **Return** tool from the **Return** panel to return to the Assembly environment. The Weldment assembly after creating the Plate is shown in Figure 16-19.

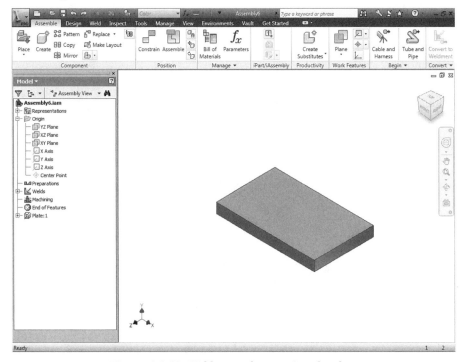

Figure 16-19 Weldment after creating the plate

3. Choose the **Save** tool from the **Quick Access Toolbar**; the **Save As** dialog box is displayed.

4. Specify **Plate** as the name of the part in this dialog box and then choose the **Save** button; the **Save** message box is displayed.

5. Choose **Yes to All** and then **OK** from the **Save** message box to save both part and assembly files.

Placing another Instance of the Plate

Next, you need to place another instance of the Plate in the Weldment (assembly) environment. Note that you will not assemble the two plates at this stage. First, you need to prepare them for welding by chamfering their edges.

1. Choose the **Place** tool from the **Component** panel of the **Assemble** tab to invoke the **Place Component** dialog box.

2. Double-click on *Plate.ipt* to select this file; the **Place Component** dialog box is closed and you are prompted to place the component.

3. Specify a point on the screen at a location where the second instance will not interfere with the previous instance. Right-click and then choose **Done** from the shortcut menu.

4. Choose **Zoom All** from the **Navigation Bar** to modify the drawing display area.

Preparing the Two Plates for Welding

Next, you need to prepare the two Plates for welding by chamfering them. To chamfer the edges, you need to activate the **Weld** tab.

1. Choose the **Preparation** tool from the **Weld** tab or double-click on **Preparations** in the **Browser Bar** to activate various preparation and machining tools in the **Ribbon**.

2. Choose the **Chamfer** tool from the **Preparation and Machining** panel of the **Weld** tab to invoke the **Chamfer** dialog box.

3. Enter **3** in the **Distance** edit box and then select one of the edges (of 50 mm length) of one of the Plates. Choose **OK** to create the chamfer and exit the dialog box.

4. Similarly, chamfer the edge on the top face of the other plate.

You will notice that **Chamfer 1** and **Chamfer 2** are added under **Preparations** in the **Browser Bar**. This is because you have created both the chamfers in the two plates as two different features.

5. Choose the **Return** tool from the **Return** panel of the **Weld** tab to finish the preparation (chamfering) of the component for weldment. The weldment assembly after chamfering the edges of the two plates is shown in Figure 16-20.

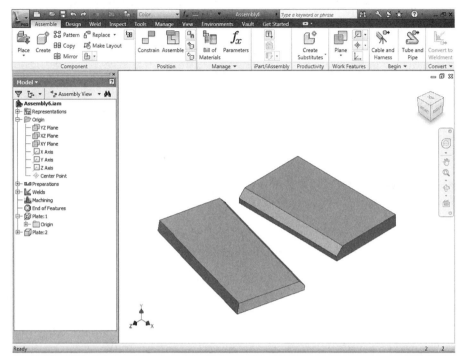

Figure 16-20 *Weldment after chamfering the two plates*

Assembling the Two Plates

1. Apply multiple instances of the **Mate** constraint to the two instances of the Plate and assemble them. The assembly of the two plates is shown in Figure 16-21.

Creating the Fillet Weld

Next, you need to create the fillet weld. To weld components, you need to activate the welding tools.

1. Choose the **Welds** tool from the **Process** panel of the **Weld** tab or double-click on **Welds** in the **Browser Bar**; various welding tools are activated.

    Remember that when you double-click on **Preparations** in the **Browser Bar**, the welding tools in this panel do not get activated. But, when you double-click on **Welds** in the **Browser Bar**, these tools get activated.

2. Choose the **Fillet** tool from the **Weld** panel of the **Weld** tab; the **Fillet Weld** dialog box is displayed and you are prompted to select the face to weld.

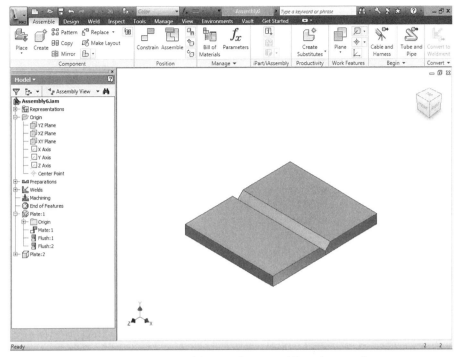

Figure 16-21 Weldment after assembling the two plates

3. Select the chamfered face on one of the Plates; the selected face turns blue.

4. Now, choose the **2** button from the **Bead** area of the **Fillet Weld** dialog box to select the second face; you are prompted again to select the face to weld.

5. Rotate the model using the **Rotate** tool and select the chamfered face on the other plate.

    The second selected face turns green. Also, the preview of the weld appears on the plates. You will notice that the weld extends beyond the V groove created in the two plates. If you apply the weld at this stage, a warning box will appear, informing that the face selected for the leg of the bead is recomputed to be smaller than the specified leg size. Therefore, you need to reduce the leg size of the bead.

6. Enter **4.2** in the **Leg 1** edit box below the **1** button.

    The welding shown in the preview will not extend beyond the V groove. As is evident from Figure 16-18, the fillet weld has a convex contour. Therefore, you need to select the **Convex** option from the **Fillet Weld** dialog box.

7. Choose the down arrow on the right of the **Flat** button in the **Contour** area; a flyout is displayed. Next, choose the **Convex** button from the flyout to apply the contour. On doing so, the **Offset** edit box is also enabled.

8. Enter **1** in the **Offset** edit box.

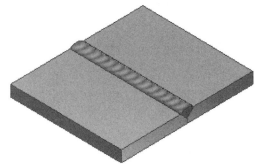

   With this, all welding options are defined and you can now apply the weld.

9. Choose the **Apply** button and then the **Cancel** button to exit the dialog box. Next, choose the **Return** button to finish the creation of the fillet weld. The welded Plates are shown in Figure 16-22.

10. Save the assembly with the name *Butt Joint.iam* at the location *C:\Inventor_2011\ c16\Tutorial1*.

Figure 16-22 *Final weldment assembly after creating the fillet weld*

Tutorial 2

In this tutorial, you will create the Bracket and Cylinder assembly in the Assembly modeling environment. Also, you will switch to the weldment environment and weld components, as shown in Figure 16-23. The dimensions of the two components are given in Figures 16-24a and 16-24b, 16-25a and 16-25b.   **(Expected time: 45 min)**

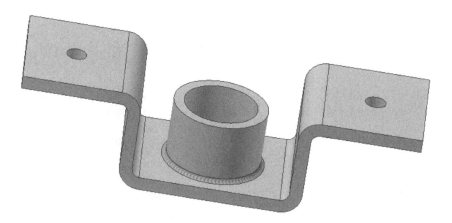

Figure 16-23 *Weldment assembly of the Bracket and the Cylinder*

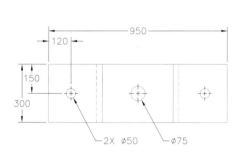

Figure 16-24a *Top view of the Bracket*

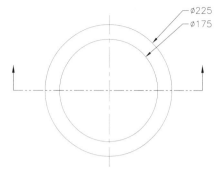

Figure 16-24b *Top view of the Cylinder*

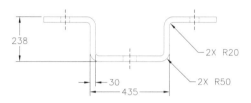

Figure 16-25a *Front view of the Bracket*

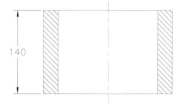

Figure 16-25b *Sectioned front view of the Cylinder*

The following steps are required to complete this tutorial:

a. Create the Bracket and the Cylinder as separate part files.
b. Start a new assembly file and then place the Bracket and the Cylinder in the assembly file.
c. Assemble both components by using the assembly constraints.
d. Switch to the Weldment environment.
e. Weld components using the fillet weld.

Creating Components

1. Create two components in separate part files and then save them at the location *C/Inventor_2011/c16\Shock Assembly*.

Assembling the Components

As mentioned in the tutorial description, you need to assemble the components in the Assembly modeling environment and then switch to the Weldment environment. Therefore, you need to start a new assembly file using the **New File** dialog box to assemble the components.

1. Start a new assembly file using the **New File** dialog box. Now, place one instance each of the Bracket and the Cylinder in the current assembly file.

2. Assemble the Cylinder with the Bracket using the assembly constraints. The assembly file after assembling the components is shown in Figure 16-26.

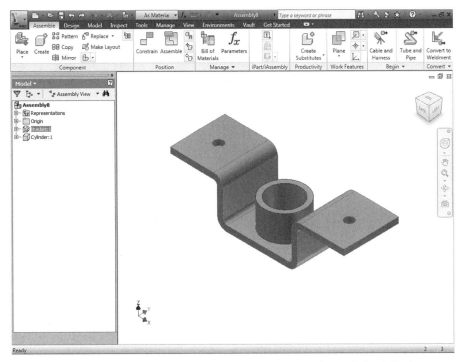

Figure 16-26 Assembly file after assembling the Bracket and the Cylinder

Welding the Components

Components can be welded in the Weldment assembly environment. Therefore, you need to switch from the Assembly modeling environment to the Weldment assembly environment.

1. Choose the **Convert to Weldment** tool from the **Convert** panel of the **Assemble** tab; the **Autodesk Inventor 2011** warning box is displayed, informing that once an assembly has been converted into a weldment, you cannot convert it back to an assembly.

2. Choose **Yes** from the warning box; the **Convert to Weldment** dialog box is displayed, as shown in Figure 16-27.

    This dialog box allows you to convert an assembly into a weldment of specified standard. You can also change the color of weldment using this dialog box.

3. Select the **ANSI** radio button from the **Standard** area of this dialog box. Accept the remaining default options and choose **OK** to close this dialog box.

On doing so, the Weldment environment is invoked and the **Weld** tab is activated. Since you do not need to make any preparations for welding the components, you can directly weld the components.

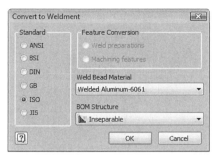

*Figure 16-27 The **Convert to Weldment** dialog box*

4. Choose the **Welds** tool from the **Process** panel of the **Weld** tab to activate the welding tools.

5. Choose the **Fillet** tool from the **Weld** panel of the **Weld** tab; the **Fillet Weld** dialog box is invoked and you are prompted to select the face to be welded.

6. Select the outer face of the Cylinder as the first face to be welded; the selected face turns blue.

7. Choose the **2** button from the **Fillet Weld** dialog box; you are prompted again to select the face to be welded.

8. Select the upper face of the Bracket with which the Cylinder needs to be assembled; the preview of the weld appears on the assembly.

9. Enter **10** in the **Leg 1** edit box below the **1** button.

The fillet contour shown in Figure 16-23 is concave. Therefore, you need to specify the corresponding options from the **Contour** area.

10. Click on the down arrow on the right of the **Flat** button in the **Contour** area to invoke a flyout. Next, choose the **Concave** button from the flyout.

11. Enter **2** in the **Offset** edit box. Choose **Apply** and then **Cancel** to exit the dialog box. Next, choose the **Return** tool from the **Return** panel of the **Weld** tab to finish the welding.

The final weldment assembly is shown in Figure 16-28.

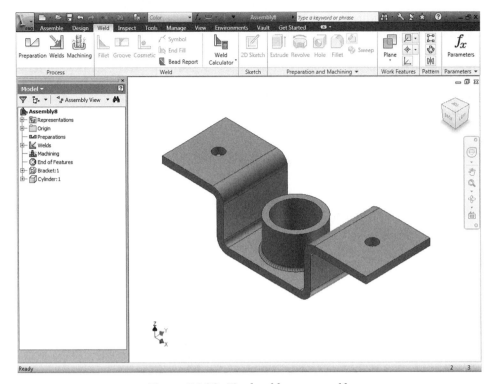

Figure 16-28 *Final weldment assembly*

12. Save the assembly with the name *Shock Assembly.iam* at the location *C:\Inventor_2011\c16\ Tutorial 2*.

Self-Evaluation Test

Answer the following questions and then compare them to those given at the end of this chapter:

1. The Weldment environment is used to weld the components of an assembly. (T/F)

2. You can convert a weldment file into an assembly file. (T/F)

3. Groove welds are added to the parts that are placed at a certain offset from each other or have grooves between them. (T/F)

4. You can create the extruded and revolved join features while preparing welds. (T/F)

5. Which of the following types of weld does not affect the physical properties of an assembly?

    (a) **Cosmetic**   (b) **Groove**
    (c) **Fillet**   (c) None of these

6. Which of the following contours is not a type of weld bead?

    (a) Flat   (b) Convex
    (c) Concave   (d) Round

7. Which of the following welds is not considered as an actual weld?

    (a) **Fillet**   (b) **Cosmetic**
    (c) **Groove**   (c) None of these

8. You can convert an assembly created in the Assembly modeling environment to a Weldment assembly by choosing the _____ tool from the **Convert** panel of the **Assemble** tab.

9. You can create a _____ weld between two parts with or without including internal loops.

10. Select the _____ check box to add weld symbols to a welded assembly.

Review Questions

Answer the following questions:

1. To create a cosmetic weld, you just need to select the edge that requires welding. (T/F)

2. The process of creating weldment assemblies is performed in four steps. (T/F)

3. You can prepare the assembled components for welding by removing material from them to accommodate weld beads. (T/F)

4. Which of the following options is used to create a fillet that extends throughout the selected edges of components?

    (a) **All**   (b) **From-To**
    (c) **Start-Length**   (d) None of these

5. Which of the following sub-nodes of the **Browser Bar** lists all welds of a weldment assembly?

    (a) **Preparations**   (b) **Welds**
    (c) **Machining**   (d) **Representations**

6. You can add a fillet symbol by using **Fillet** tool or by using the _____ tool.

Exercise

Exercise 1

In this exercise, you will create the Base Plate and the Top Mounting as separate part files and then assemble them using the assembly constraints in the Weldment environment. The weldment assembly is shown in Figure 16-29. The dimensions of both components are shown in Figures 16-30 and 16-31. **(Expected time: 45 min)**

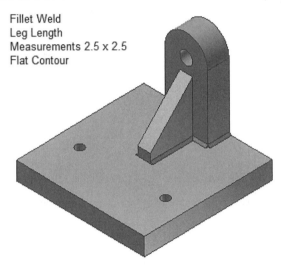

Figure 16-29   *Weldment assembly for Exercise 1*

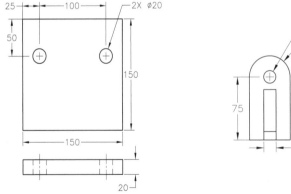

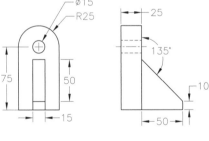

Figure 16-30   *Dimensions of the Base Plate*   *Figure 16-31*   *Dimensions of the Top Mounting*

Answers to Self-Evaluation Test
1. T, **2.** F, **3.** T, **4.** F, **5.** Cosmetic, **6.** Round, **7.** Cosmetic, **8. Convert to Weldment**, **9.** groove, **10. Create Welding Symbol**

Chapter 17

Miscellaneous Tools

Learning Objectives

After completing this chapter, you will be able to:
- *Find the Center of Gravity of a model.*
- *Extract an iFeature.*
- *Insert an iFeature.*
- *Create an iMate.*
- *Understand the use of iProperties.*
- *Create user-defined drawing sheets.*
- *Import AutoCAD blocks into Inventor.*

INTRODUCTION

In this chapter, you will learn about some of the tools that help in enhancing your working efficiency.

COPYING THE SKETCHES

Ribbon:	Sketch > Modify > Copy
Toolbar:	2D Sketch Panel > Copy

 The **Copy** tool is available in the sketching environment and allows you to copy and paste the sketched entities from one location to the other. Note that if dimensions are also selected along with the entities to be copied, then the selected dimensions will also be copied along with the sketched entities. To copy the sketched entities, invoke the **Copy** tool from the **Modify** panel of the **Sketch** tab; the **Copy** dialog box will be displayed, as shown in the Figure 17-1. The options in this dialog box are discussed next.

*Figure 17-1 The **Copy** dialog box*

Select

This button is used to select the entities to be copied. On invoking the **Copy** tool, this button is automatically chosen and you are prompted to select the geometry to copy. You can select individual entities using the mouse button or select more than one entity using the Window or Crossing options.

Base Point

This button is chosen to specify the point that will act as the base point for moving the copied entities. Once you have selected all the entities to be copied, choose this button to select the point from where the movement will start.

Clipboard [Ctrl-C]

This check box, if selected, temporarily saves the selected geometry or the clipboard so that after choosing the **Done** button, you can paste the selected geometry by pressing CTRL+V keys from the keyboard.

Precise Input

This check box, if selected, allows you to specify the coordinates for the base point and the destination point using the **Inventor Precise Input** toolbar.

Optimize for Single Selection

If this check box is selected, the **Base Point** button will be activated automatically after making a single selection or the window selection of geometry. But if you clear this check box, you can make multiple geometry selections before choosing the **Base Point** button.

After selecting the geometry and the base point, you will be prompted to specify the endpoint for copy. Specify the end point in the drawing window; the copied geometry will be pasted. You will notice the **Copy** tool is still active. If you need multiple copies, specify more endpoints, else right-click and choose **Done**.

SCALING THE SKETCHES

| **Ribbon:** | Sketch > Modify > Scale |
| **Toolbar:** | 2D Sketch Panel > Scale |

The **Scale** tool is available in the sketching environment and is used to resize the sketched entities with respect to the specified base point. On invoking this tool, the **Scale** dialog box will be displayed, as shown in Figure 17-2. Most of the options in this dialog box are similar to those discussed in the **Move** dialog box in Chapter 4.

*Figure 17-2 The **Scale** dialog box*

Select the sketched entities to be scaled. After selecting the sketched entities, choose the **Base Point** button; you will be prompted to select the base point. Select a base point; the **Scale Factor** edit box will be highlighted. As you move the cursor in the drawing window, the entities will be resized with respect to the cursor position and the value in the **Scale Factor** edit box will change dynamically. You can also enter the required value manually in the **Scale Factor** edit box to resize the entities.

FINDING THE CENTER OF GRAVITY

| **Ribbon:** | View > Visibility > Center of Gravity |

This tool allows you to find the Center of Gravity (COG) of a model or an assembly. To invoke this tool, choose the **Center of Gravity** tool from the **Visibility** panel of the **View** tab; the **Autodesk Inventor 2011** dialog box will be displayed, as shown in Figure 17-3.

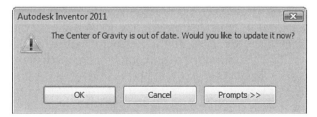

*Figure 17-3 The **Autodesk Inventor 2011** dialog box*

Choose the **OK** button from the dialog box; the Center of Gravity triad will be displayed, as shown in the Figure 17-4. The red arrow indicates the X-axis, the green arrow indicates the Y-axis, the blue arrow indicates the Z-axis, and the yellow sphere indicates the location of the Center of Gravity of the selected component. This triad also includes three selectable work planes and a selectable work point at the origin of COG.

You can use the COG symbol as a virtual reference in the designing process. The triad can be used for measuring the distances. To measure the distances, choose the **Distance** tool from the **Measure** panel of the **Inspect** tab. Next, select one of the planes of the triad, and then select a face of the model; the measurements will be displayed in the **Measure Distance** dialog box. For more information on measurement tools, refer to Chapter 3. If you modify the model, the triad becomes fade. For updating the Center of Gravity, you need to remove the existing COG triad. To do so, choose the **Center of Gravity** tool from the **View** tab again; the COG will disappear. Repeat the above procedure to display the updated COG.

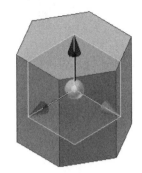

Figure 17-4 Center of Gravity triad

EXTRACTING THE iFEATURE

Ribbon:	Manage > Author > Extract iFeature

 Features such as slot and keyways are used in most of the designs with the variation in dimensions. In Autodesk Inventor, you can create these features as sketched features in one design, and then extract and place them in other designs. These extracted features are called as iFeature. The iFeature is created by using the **Extract iFeature** tool. Note that if a feature created using the join operation is extracted as an iFeature and placed on the other model, the material will be added to the model. Similarly, if the feature created using the cut operation is extracted as an iFeature and placed on the other model, the material will be removed from the model.

> **Note**
> *The features created using the 2D sketches are known as Sketched Features. Extrude, revolve, and sweep are some of the examples of the sketched features. The features that do not require a sketch are known as Placed Features. Fillet, chamfer, threads, and shells are some of the examples of the placed features.*

After creating the required sketched features on the model, choose the **Extract iFeature** tool from the **Author** panel of the **Manage** tab; the **Extract iFeature** dialog box will be displayed, as shown in Figure 17-5. The options in this dialog box are discussed next.

Type Area

In this area, there are two radio buttons, **Standard iFeature** and **Sheet Metal Punch iFeature**. Select the **Standard iFeature** radio button, if you want to create the iFeature that has to be placed in the part environment. Select the **Sheet Metal Punch iFeature** radio button, if you want to create the iFeature that has to be placed in the part or sheet metal environment. Also, note that if you want to create an iFeature using the **Sheet Metal Punch iFeature** radio button, then the sketch of the original feature must have a center point.

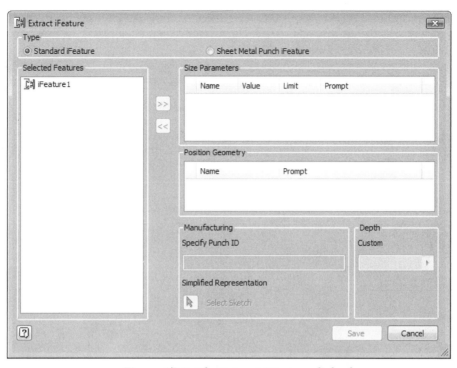

Figure 17-5 The **Extract iFeature** *dialog box*

Selected Features Area

After invoking the **Extract iFeature** dialog box, you need to select the sketched feature to be extracted as iFeature. Select a sketched feature from the **Browser Bar**; the feature will be displayed in the **Selected Features** area along with all its dimensions. If you select the feature in this area, its dependent geometry, dimensions, as well as two buttons on the right of this area will get activated. Next, choose the button with arrows pointing toward right, the dimensions of the selected feature will be displayed in the **Size Parameters** area.

Size Parameters Area

This area displays the dimensions and parameters to be edited at the time of inserting an iFeature in another design. If you need to edit a particular parameter, then click in its corresponding column and edit it.

Position Geometry Area

This area displays the reference geometry that defines the position of the iFeature. It is recommended to include all the depended geometries in this area, so that they can be used to define the position of the iFeature while inserting it.

Manufacturing Area

The options in this area will be activated only when you select the **Sheet Metal Punch iFeature** radio button in the **Type** area. Using these options, you can specify the punch ID in the **Specify Punch ID** edit box. If you have selected multiple features to create the sheet metal punch iFeature, then you can specify the reference center point by choosing the **Select Sketch** button.

Depth Area

The **Custom** edit box in this area is used to specify the punching depth.

After defining all parameters, choose the **Save** button; the **Save As** dialog box will be displayed. This dialog box is used to save the iFeature created. The iFeature file will be saved in *.ide* file format.

INSERTING THE iFEATURE

| **Ribbon:** | Manage > Insert > Insert iFeature |
| **Toolbar:** | Part Features > Insert iFeature |

 This tool is used to insert the iFeatures into a model. To insert an iFeature, choose the **Insert iFeature** tool from the **Insert** panel of the **Manage** tab; the **Insert iFeature** dialog box will be displayed, as shown in Figure 17-6.

Figure 17-6   *The **Insert iFeature** dialog box*

The flow chart on the left of this box indicates four indicators and their names. The active indicator turns green and the information of the respective indicator is displayed in the right pane of this dialog box. These indicators are discussed next.

Select

This indicator is chosen by default. On the right pane of this indicator, the **Browse** button is available. Choose this button; the **Open** dialog box will be displayed. You can open the required *.ide* file using this dialog box.

Position

When you open the required *.ide* file, the **Position** indicator will be activated and names of the reference geometry such as work plane, point, axis, and line will be displayed in the list box. You need to define the reference geometry in the model where you need to place it. To do so, click once on the name of the reference geometry in the dialog box and then specify its position in the drawing window.

Size

After defining the position of the reference geometry, choose the **Next** button; the **Size** indicator will be activated and the dimensions will be displayed along with their names on the right pane of the indicator. You can modify these dimensions according to your requirement.

Precise Pos.

After defining all the dimensions of the iFeature, choose the **Next** button; the **Precise Pos.** indicator will be activated and two radio buttons will be displayed in the **Upon Completion of Placement** area on the right side of the pane. These radio buttons are discussed next.

Activate Sketch Edit Immediately

If you select this radio button and then choose the **Finish** button, the sketching environment will be activated.

Do Not Activate Sketch Edit

If you select this radio button, the sketching environment will not be activated.

Choose the **Finish** button to place the iFeature.

CREATING iMates

Ribbon:	Manage > Author > Create iMate
Toolbar:	Part Features > Create iMate

Some parts such as bolts, rods, washers, nuts, and flanges are used in many assemblies in the same way. So, if you specify the mate references on parts before they are assembled, assembling these parts will be easier. These mates references are called as iMates. After defining an iMate on a part, if you place it in the Assembly environment, it will be placed in its position automatically. To create an iMate, first create the part or subassembly and then invoke the **Create iMate** tool from the **Author** panel of the **Manage** tab; the **Create iMate** dialog box will be displayed, as shown in Figure 17-7. This dialog

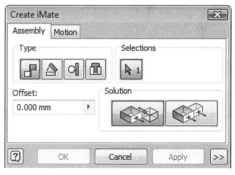

*Figure 17-7 The **Create iMate** dialog box*

box is similar to the **Place Constraints** dialog box discussed in Chapters 9 and 10. However, in this dialog box, the **Translation** tab is not available. Select the type of mate to be applied to the part from the **Type** area and then select the face to which the mate has to be applied. Note that you can select the type of mate from the **Type** area available in the **Assembly** or **Motion** tab. At the lower right corner of this dialog box, the **More** button is provided. If you choose this button, the **Create iMate** dialog box will expand. Figure 17-8 shows the partial

view of the expanded **Create iMate** dialog box. This
expanded dialog box can be used to increase the
accuracy of the mate. The options in the
expanded dialog box are discussed next.

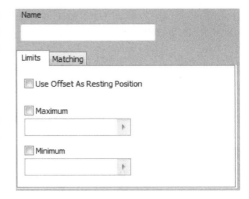

Name Area

You can specify the name of the current iMate in
the edit box of this area. If you leave this area blank,
then the name will be created automatically.

Limits Tab

With this release of Autodesk Inventor, you can
specify the maximum and minimum limits of the
constraint to be applied to an iMate component.

Figure 17-8 More options in the **Create**
iMate *dialog box*

You can specify these limits in the **Maximum** and **Minimum** edit boxes in the **Limits** tab.
These options of the **Limits** tab have already been discussed in detail in Chapter 9.

Matching Tab

In this tab, you can list the name of iMate with which the part will mate. When a part is placed
in the assembly, the system will first try to mate the part with the iMate located in the **Match
List** area. For adding, deleting, and moving the name in the list box, four buttons are provided
at the right side of this list box. These buttons are discussed next.

Add name to list

 If you choose this button, the **New Name** edit box will be displayed in the **Match List**
list box. In the edit box, you can specify the name of the iMate to which this part has
to be assembled. For adding another name, you need to choose this button again.

Delete selected name

 This button is used to remove the selected name from the **Match List** list box.

Move selected name up in priority

 This button is used to move the selected name one step up in the **Match List** list box
to change the priority of matching.

Move selected name down in priority

 This button is used to move the selected name one step down in the **Match List** list
box to change the priority of matching.

After setting the parameters, choose the **OK** button to apply the iMates. You will observe
that a circular symbol is attached to a face of the part. Also, the **iMates** node is created in the
Browser Bar.

APPLYING iMATES IN THE ASSEMBLY ENVIRONMENT

For applying iMates in an assembly, place the first component to which iMates are specified. Next, you need to place the second component to which the respective iMates are specified. To place the second component, choose the **Place** tool from the **Component** panel in the **Assemble** tab; the **Place Component** dialog box will be displayed. The buttons in the **iMates** area of this dialog box can be used to place the component using different methods, refer to Figure 17-9. These methods are discussed next.

Figure 17-9 The iMates area in the Place Component dialog box

Interactively place with iMates

 This button is used to insert the component with matching iMates in an assembly. It also enables you to place the number of instances in an assembly.

Automatically generate iMates on place

 If you choose this button, then you will exit the **Place** tool after placing a single instance in an assembly. This button is also used to insert the component with matching iMates in an assembly.

Choose the **Open** button after selecting the component and specifying the method; the part will be placed in its position automatically. If you have chosen the **Interactively Place with iMates** button, then you will be prompted to specify the next location. Else, the tool will be terminated.

VIEWING THE iPROPERTIES

Application Menu:	iProperties

The properties of the component created in the Assembly environment in Autodesk Inventor are known as iProperties. iProperties can be used for creating reports, updating BOM, updating title block, and to display all the related information of the component created. The options of iProperties are internally linked with the related component. Therefore, whenever you update information in iProperties, it will be reflected in the related component. You can invoke this tool by choosing the **iProperties** option from the **Application Menu**. Alternatively, right-click on the name of the component in the **Browser Bar** of the current assembly and choose **iProperties** from the shortcut menu displayed; the **iProperties** dialog box of the corresponding component will be displayed, as shown in Figure 17-10. The tabs in this dialog box are discussed next.

General Tab

This tab displays the name, size, and type of the file. It also displays the date when the file was created, modified, and accessed.

Summary Tab

This tab is used for classifying and managing files. This tab displays seven edit boxes: **Title**, **Subject**, **Author**, **Manager**, **Company**, **Category**, **Keywords**, and **Comments**. You can enter the required information in these edit boxes. On choosing the **Apply** button, this information updates the Title blocks and BOM in the drawing file.

*Figure 17-10 The **iProperties** dialog box*

Project Tab

This tab is used to define the project iProperties of the component.

Status Tab

This tab is used to define the status of the component.

Custom Tab

This tab is used to add the custom iProperties of the component.

Save Tab

This tab is used for setting the saving options of the image of the component. In this tab, the **Save Preview Picture** check box is selected by default. Therefore, it saves the thumbnail image of the model that will be displayed in the **Open File** dialog box. You can turn off the image from the **Open File** dialog box by clearing this check box.

Physical Tab

This tab is used to calculate and display the physical and inertial properties of the model. This helps you analyze how the differences in materials, tolerances, and dimensions can affect the model. To analyze the physical properties, select the required material from the **Material** drop-down list; it displays the values of density, mass, area, and volume of the model for the applied material. It also displays coordinates of the COG in the **General Properties** area. In the **Inertial Properties** area, the **Principal**, **Global** and **Center Of Gravity** buttons are available. By choosing these buttons, you can view the inertial properties of the component for the applied materials.

CREATING USER-DEFINED DRAWING SHEETS

Autodesk Inventor provides you an option to create user-defined drawing sheets by defining border and title block according to your requirement. The procedures to create the user-defined drawing sheets are discussed next.

Whenever you open a drawing (*.idw*) file, the **Drawing Resources** node will be displayed in the **Browser Bar**. Click on the plus (+) sign beside the **Drawing Resources** node to expand it. Three sub-nodes will be displayed under this node. These sub-nodes and their options are discussed next.

Sheet Formats

Click on the plus (+) sign of this sub-node; a list of drawing sheets will be displayed. If you right-click on any of these sheets; a shortcut menu will be displayed, as shown in Figure 17-11. Choose **New Sheet** from the shortcut menu; the **Select Component** dialog box will be displayed, as shown in Figure 17-12. In this dialog box, choose the button on right of the **Document Name** drop-down list and open a part or an assembly; the path of the selected component will be displayed in the **Document Name** drop-down list. Choose the **OK** button from the **Select Component** dialog box; the selected model will be drafted in the new sheet with a number of views. Note that the number of views and the size of the new sheet depend upon the name of the sheet selected in the **Browser Bar**.

Borders

The **Borders** sub-node has a predefined border style, which will be applied to the sheet. You can also define and insert a new border and new zone border in the drawing sheet using this node. The procedures to define a new border, border zone, and inserting a new border zone are discussed next.

Defining a New Border

To define a new border, choose the **Define New Border** option from the shortcut menu that is displayed on right-clicking on the **Borders** sub-node, refer to Figure 17-13; the sketching environment will be activated. You can draw a border in the sketching environment based on your requirement. After drawing the border, choose the **Return** tool from the **Quick Access Toolbar** or choose the **Finish Sketch** button from the **Exit** panel of the **Sketch** tab; the **Border** dialog box will be displayed, as shown in Figure 17-14. Enter a new name in the **Name** edit box and choose the **Save** button; the new name will be displayed in the **Browser Bar** below the **Borders** node.

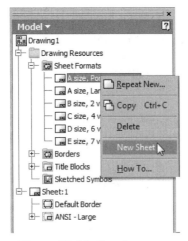

Figure 17-11 *Creating a new sheet using the shortcut menu*

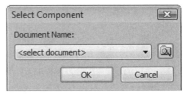

Figure 17-12 *The Select Component dialog box*

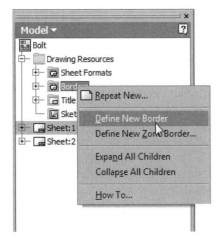

Figure 17-13 *The Borders shortcut menu*

Figure 17-14 *The Border dialog box*

Defining a New Zone Border

To define a new zone border, choose the **Define New Zone Border** option from the shortcut menu that is displayed on right-clicking on the **Borders** sub-node; the **Default Drawing Border Parameters** dialog box will be displayed. In this dialog box, you can set the horizontal and vertical zones of the border from the respective areas. If you choose the **>>** button from the lower right corner of this dialog box, the **Default Drawing Border Parameters** dialog box will expand, as shown in Figure 17-15. In the expanded area, you can set the appearance of the border. After setting all parameters, choose the **OK** button; the new border with its dimensions will be displayed in the sketching environment, where you can edit these dimensions. You can modify the border using the tools provided in the sketching environment. After modifying the border according to the requirements, choose the **Return** button from the **Quick Access Toolbar**; the **Borders** dialog box will be displayed again, refer to Figure 17-14. Enter a new name in the **Name** edit box and choose the **Save** button; the new name will be displayed in the **Browser Bar** below the **Borders** sub-node.

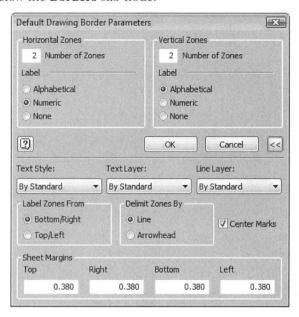

*Figure 17-15 The **Default Drawing Border Parameters** dialog box*

Inserting a New Border

For inserting a new border, you need to delete the existing border. To do so, right-click on the **Default Border** option available in the **Sheet:1** node of the **Browser Bar**; a shortcut menu will be displayed, as shown in Figure 17-16. Choose the **Delete** option from the shortcut menu; the existing border will be deleted from the drawing sheet as well as from the **Browser Bar**. After deleting the border, click on the **Borders** sub-node; all available borders will be displayed. Double-click on any of the borders; the selected border will be displayed in the active drawing sheet.

Title Blocks

The **Title Blocks** sub-node has a predefined title block. You can define a new title block using the procedure given next.

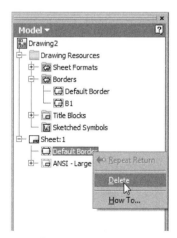

Figure 17-16 Deleting the existing border using the shortcut menu

Defining a New Title Block

Choose the **Define New Title Block** option from the shortcut menu of the **Title Blocks** sub-node, as shown in Figure 17-17; the sketching environment will be activated. You can draw a title block in the sketching environment based on your requirements. After drawing the title block, choose the **Return** tool from the **Quick Access Toolbar**; the **Title Block** dialog box will be displayed, as shown in Figure 17-18. Enter a new name in the **Name** edit box and choose the **Save** button; the name will be displayed in the **Browser Bar** below the **Title Blocks** sub-node. You can insert a new title block in a way similar to inserting a new border.

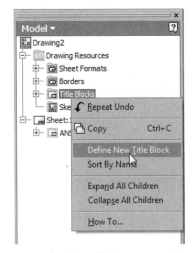

Figure 17-17 *Defining a new title block using the shortcut menu*

Figure 17-18 *The **Title Block** dialog box*

Creating a Customized Title Block that Updates with iProperties

You can create a customized title block based on your requirements that gets updated when its iProperties change. To do so, right-click on the name of the title block that is available in the **Browser Bar** below the **Title Blocks** sub-node; a shortcut menu will be displayed, as shown in Figure 17-19. Choose the **Edit** option from the shortcut menu; the sketching environment will be activated. Also, the title block along with the dimensions and names will be displayed in the drawing window, as shown in Figure 17-20. These names are internally linked with the iProperties of the active drawing file. Therefore, it is recommended that while editing the title block, keep the required names and delete the remaining portion of the title block.

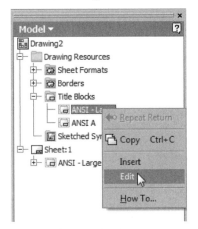

Figure 17-19 *The shortcut menu of the existing title block*

If you try to move the name of the title block, then the complete title block will be moved. To avoid this movement, right-click on the required name and then choose the **Text Box** option from the shortcut menu, as shown in Figure 17-21. Now, you can move the required name. In this way, you can move all the required names and delete the remaining portion of the title block.

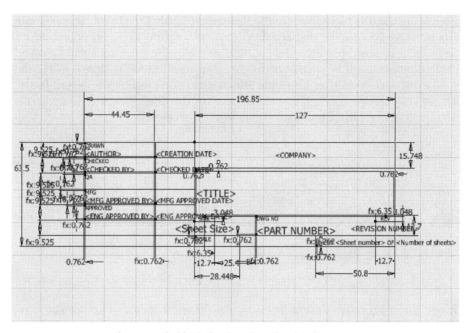

Figure 17-20 *Title block displayed in the sketching environment*

Draw a new layout for the title block using the tools provided in the **Draw** panel of the **Sketch** tab and move the names to the required area, refer to Figure 17-22.

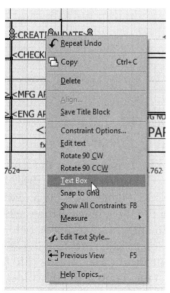

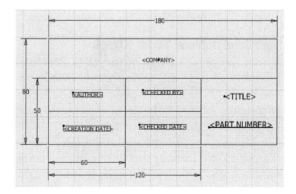

Figure 17-21 *Choosing the* **Text Box** *option from the shortcut menu*

Figure 17-22 *Editing a title block in the sketching environment*

After customizing the title block, choose the **Return** tool from the **Quick Access Toolbar**; the **Save Edits** message box will be displayed, as shown in Figure 17-23. If you choose the **Yes** button from this message box, then the changes made to the title block will be saved in the existing title block and will be displayed in the drawing window, as shown in Figure 17-24. If you choose the **Save As** button, the **Title Block** dialog box will be displayed. In the **Name** edit box of this dialog box, you can enter the name for the title block. On doing so, the name will be displayed in the **Title Blocks** sub-node in the **Browser Bar**.

Figure 17-23 The Save Edits message box

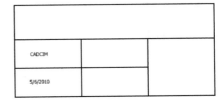

Figure 17-24 Customized title block created

Next, choose the **iProperties** option from the **Application Menu** to invoke the **iProperties** dialog box. Enter the required information in different tabs of the dialog box for the current drawing. Now, choose the **Apply** button and then the **Close** button from the **iProperties** dialog box; the information will be displayed in the title block, see Figure 17-25.

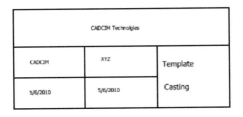

Figure 17-25 The updated title block with the change in its iProperties

Inserting a New Title Block

Click on the plus (+) sign of the **Title Blocks** sub-node in the **Browser Bar**; the list of all available title blocks will be displayed in the **Browser Bar**. You can insert any of the title blocks from this list. Note that you need to delete the existing title block before inserting a new one. To delete the existing title block, click on the plus (+) sign of the sheet in the **Browser Bar**; a node list will be displayed. Next, right-click on the name of the title block available below the name of the sheet **Sheet:1** in the **Browser Bar**; a shortcut menu will be displayed, as shown in Figure 17-26. Choose the **Delete** option from the shortcut menu; the existing title block will be deleted. To activate another title block, double-click on the name of the title block that is available in the **Title Blocks** sub-node in the **Browser Bar**; the selected title block will be displayed in the drawing window.

Tip. *It is recommended that you save the file after creating the customized border and title block so that you can use it as a template file.*

Creating Sketch Symbols

Sometimes in the drafting process, you need to use some special symbols frequently. For this, Autodesk Inventor provides a special sub-node, named **Sketched Symbols**. You can use this option to create a customized sketch symbol that can be used whenever you want. To do so, right-click on the **Sketched Symbols** sub-node in the **Browser Bar**; a shortcut menu will be displayed, as shown in Figure 17-27. If you choose **Define New Symbol** from the shortcut menu, the sketching environment will be activated. You can draw any symbol by using the sketching tools of the **Draw** panel in the **Sketch** tab. After creating a symbol, if you choose the **Return** tool from the **Quick Access Toolbar**, the **Sketched Symbol** dialog box will be displayed. Enter a name for the symbol in the **Name** edit box and choose the **Save** button; the name will be displayed below the **Sketched Symbols** in the **Browser Bar** and the drawing environment will be activated. If you double-click on that name in the **Browser Bar**, then the cursor will be changed to a plus (+) sign. Next, if you click anywhere in the drawing window, the sketch symbol that you created will be placed at that point. You can place a number of sketch symbols in the drawing window by clicking at various points.

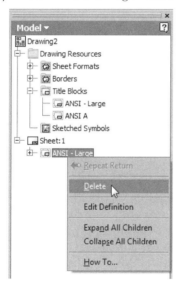

*Figure 17-26 Choosing the **Delete** option from the shortcut menu*

*Figure 17-27 The shortcut menu of the **Sketched Symbols** sub-node*

Tip. *If you have generated the drawing views of a model or an assembly, you can display the COG mark on it. To do so, click on the (+) sign on the right of the **View** node; the model or assembly node will be displayed. Next, right-click on the corresponding model or assembly node to invoke a shortcut menu. Choose the **Center of Gravity** option from this shortcut menu; a plus (+) sign will be displayed on the related drawing view indicating the position of the COG of that model.*

IMPORTING AutoCAD BLOCKS INTO Inventor

Ribbon: Annotate > Symbols > User > Import AutoCAD Block

With this release of Autodesk Inventor, you can import the blocks created in AutoCAD into the drawing sheets of Inventor. Also, you can move, scale, and rotate them in Inventor. To import an AutoCAD block into Inventor, first create it in AutoCAD and then save it. Next, start a new drawing (dwg) file in Inventor and choose the **Import AutoCAD Block** tool from **Annotate > Symbols > User** drop-down in the **Ribbon**; the **Import Block** dialog box will be displayed, as shown in Figure 17-28.

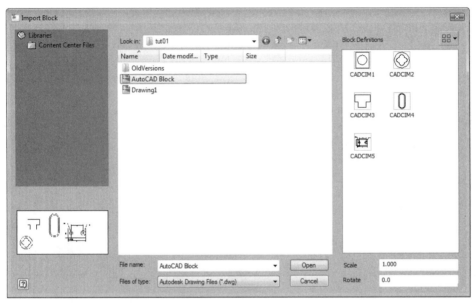

*Figure 17-28 The **Import Block** dialog box*

Browse to the required AutoCAD file and then select it; all blocks created in the file will be displayed in the form of icons in the **Block Definitions** area of the **Import Block** dialog box, see Figure 17-28. Select the required block from the **Block Definitions** area and then specify the scale and rotation angle values in the **Scale** and **Rotate** edit boxes at the bottom of the dialog box. Next, choose the **Insert** button; the **Import Block** dialog box will disappear and you will be prompted to insert the AutoCAD block. Note that the **Insert** button will be available only when you select a block from the **Block Definitions** area. Click on the drawing sheet at the location where you want to place the block; the block will be placed at the specified location. You can place any number of AutoCAD blocks in the drawing sheet. After inserting the required block, right-click and then choose **Done** from the shortcut menu; the inserted blocks will be displayed in the **AutoCAD Blocks** node under the **Sheet** node in the **Browser Bar**, refer to Figure 17-29. Expand the **AutoCAD Blocks** node to display the inserted blocks.

If you double-click on a block, the **AutoCAD Blocks** dialog box will be displayed, as shown in Figure 17-30. In this dialog box, you can specify the scale and rotation angle values in their respective edit boxes. By default, the **Static** check box is selected in this dialog box. As a result, the AutoCAD block behaves as static entity and you cannot rotate or scale it manually. However, you can move it by using the base point grip that is displayed in green in the drawing sheet. If you clear this check box, the grips surrounding the block will be displayed. With the help of these grips, you can scale, move, and rotate a block manually. The yellow, green, and blue grips are used to scale, move, and rotate the block, respectively.

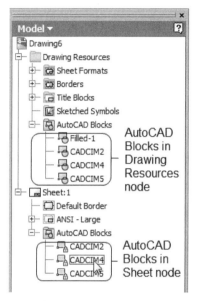

Figure 17-29 *AutoCAD Blocks in the* ***Sheet*** *and* ***Drawing Resources*** *nodes in the* ***Browser Bar***

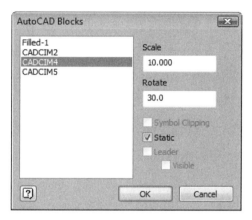

Figure 17-30 *The* ***AutoCAD Blocks*** *dialog box*

Figure 17-31 shows an AutoCAD block with grips displayed on it in the drawing sheet.

Note
You can also invoke the ***AutoCAD Blocks*** *dialog box by using the* ***Drawing Resources*** *node of the* ***Browser Bar***. *To do so, expand the* ***Drawing Resources*** *node; the sub-nodes of this node will be displayed, refer to Figure 17-29. Expand the* ***AutoCAD Blocks*** *node; all inserted blocks will be displayed under this node. Next, right-click on the required block and choose the* ***AutoCAD Blocks*** *option from the shortcut menu; the* ***AutoCAD Blocks*** *dialog box will be displayed, refer to Figure 17-30.*

Figure 17-31 *Grips displayed on an AutoCAD block*

TUTORIALS

Tutorial 1

In this tutorial, you will create a shaft with a groove, as shown in Figure 17- 32. Extract the groove as an iFeature and place it on a hexagonal bar, as shown in Figure 17-33.

(Expected time: 45 min)

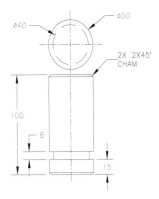

Figure 17-32 *A shaft with a groove*

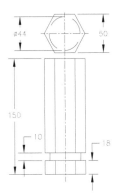

Figure 17-33 *Hexagonal bar with a groove*

The following steps are required to complete this tutorial:

a. Create a circular shaft and chamfer the sharp edges.
b. Draw the profile for the groove on the XZ-plane and apply the dimensions to the profile, refer to Figure 17-34.
c. Revolve the profile about the Z-axis using the **Cut** option, refer to Figure 17-35.
d. Extract the iFeature of the groove using the **Extract iFeature** tool.
e. Create a hexagonal shaft and place the iFeature by using the **Insert iFeature** tool.
f. Save the model.

Creating the Shaft

First, you need to create a shaft and then create an iFeature from it. It is recommended that you do not use the reference objects such as points, planes, and axes while creating iFeatures.

1. Start a new metric file; the Sketching environment is invoked with the XY-plane as the sketching plane. By default, a reference point is displayed at the origin (0,0).

2. Select the reference point and press DELETE to delete it.

3. Choose the **Point** tool from the **Draw** panel of the **Sketch** tab and place a point at the origin.

4. Choose the **Fix** tool from the **Constrain** panel of the **Sketch** tab and select the sketched point; the sketched point is fixed to the origin.

5. On the XY plane, create a circle of 50 mm diameter such that its center point coincides with the sketched point. Next, exit the Sketching environment.

6. Extrude the profile to 100 mm using the **Extrude** tool.

7. Apply the chamfer of 2 mm at the ends of the shaft.

Creating the Groove

1. Choose the **Create 2D Sketch** tool from **Model > Sketch > Sketch** drop-down and select the **XZ Plane** as the sketch plane; the Sketching environment is invoked.

2. Use the ViewCube to orient the model, as shown in Figure 17-34. Change the display of the model to wireframe by choosing the **Wireframe** tool from **View > Appearance > Visual Style** drop-down.

3. By default, a reference point is displayed at the origin (0,0). Select this point and press DELETE to delete it.

4. Choose the **Point** tool from the **Draw** panel of the **Sketch** tab and place a point at the origin.

5. Next, choose the **Fix** tool from the **Constrain** panel of the **Sketch** tab and select the sketched point; the sketched point is fixed to the origin.

6. Draw a rectangle and apply vertical dimensions (20 mm and 25 mm) to it with respect to the sketched point, refer to Figure 17-34. Apply the horizontal dimension (15 mm) to it with respect to the vertical edge on the right of the model, see Figure 17-34. You need to dimension the length (8 mm) of the rectangle.

7. Draw a horizontal line that passes through the origin.

8. Choose the **Centerline** tool from the **Format** panel of the **Sketch** tab and select the horizontal line; the line is converted to a center line. This center line will be used as the axis for the groove.

9. Choose the **Return** tool from the **Quick Access Toolbar**; the part modeling environment is displayed.

10. Invoke the **Revolve** tool. Next, choose the **Cut** option from the **Operation** area and create the groove, see Figure 17-35.

11. Choose the **Shaded with Edges** tool from **View > Appearance > Visual Style** drop-down; the model is shaded, see Figure 17-35.

12. Save the part with the name *shaft_iFeature.ipt* at the following location:

C:\Inventor_2011\c17\Tutorial1

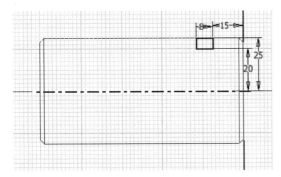

Figure 17-34 *Dimensions applied to the profile for creating a groove*

Figure 17-35 *The shaft after creating the groove*

Creating the iFeature

1. Choose the **Extract iFeature** tool from the **Author** panel of the **Manage** tab; the **Extract iFeature** dialog box is displayed.

2. Select the **Revolution1** node in the **Browser Bar**; the name of the feature and its related dimensions and references are displayed in the **Selected Features** area of the **Extract iFeature** dialog box.

3. Select the **Revolution1** node from the **Selected Features** area and choose the double arrow pointing toward the right; all related dimensions are displayed in the **Size Parameters** area and **Sketch Plane1** is displayed in the **Position Geometry** area.

4. Select **Center Point** from the **Browser Bar**; the **Center Point** is displayed in the **Selected Features** area. It is also displayed in the **Position Geometry** area with the name Point1.

5. Select **Z Axis** from the **Browser Bar**; the **Z Axis** is displayed in the **Selected Features** area. It is also displayed in the **Position Geometry** area with the name Axis1.

    You will notice that in the **Size Parameters** area, default names are displayed in the **Prompt** column. You need to change these names. Changing the default names will make identifying and modifying a parameter easy when you insert iFeatures. Follow the steps given next to edit default names.

6. Click once in the field corresponding to the value 20 mm in the **Prompt** column; an edit box is displayed.

7. Enter **ID** in the edit box.

8. Similarly, change the default names for the remaining values in the **Prompt** column as given next in the table.

Value	Prompt to be modified as
15	REF
25	OD
8	GW

9. Change the field corresponding to **Point1** to **Center Point** in the **Prompt** column of the **Position Geometry** area.

10. Similarly, change the fields corresponding to **Axis1** and **Sketch Plane 1** to **Z-Axis** and **Sketch Plane**, respectively in the **Prompt** column of the **Position Geometry** area. After changing the prompts, the **Extract iFeature** dialog box appears, as shown in Figure 17-36.

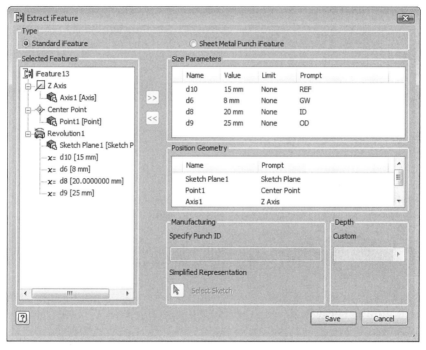

*Figure 17-36 The **Extract iFeature** dialog box*

11. Choose the **Save** button from the **Extract iFeature** dialog box; the **Save As** dialog box is displayed.

12. Save the iFeature with the name *groove_iFeature.ide* at the following location:

C:\Inventor_2011\c17\Tutorial1

13. Save the part file and close it.

Creating the Hexagonal Shaft

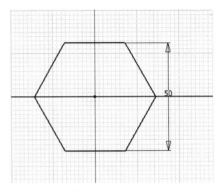

1. Start a new part file.

2. Create a hexagon on the default XY-plane, as shown in Figure 17-37.

3. Extrude the profile up to 150 mm in the downward direction.

4. Choose the **Insert iFeature** tool from the **Insert** panel of the **Manage** tab; the **Insert iFeature** dialog box is displayed.

Figure 17-37 Sketch for creating the Hexagonal shaft

5. Choose the **Browse** button; the **Open** dialog box is displayed.

6. Open the *groove_iFeature.ide* file from *C:\Inventor_2011\c17\Tutorial1*; the **Position** indicator is activated. Also, on the right of the pane, **Sketch Plane1** is highlighted in red. On the lower side of the dialog box, **Sketch Plane** is displayed in the prompt box indicating that you need to select the plane for placing the iFeature.

7. Select **XZ Plane** from the **Browser Bar**.

8. Select **Point1** from the right pane of the dialog box; it turns red and you are prompted to select the center point. Select **Center Point** from the **Browser Bar**.

9. Select **Axis1** from the right pane of the dialog box; it turns red and you are prompted to select the Z axis. Select the **Z Axis** from the **Browser Bar**.

10. On selecting the axis, you will observe that after defining the position of geometry, the **Refresh** button will be activated on the left of the prompt box. Choose this button to view the updated position of the iFeature.

11. Choose the **Next** button in the **Insert iFeature** dialog box; the **Size** indicator is highlighted on the left pane of the dialog box. Similarly, on the right pane of the dialog box, the dimensions of the iFeature are displayed and the dimension with 20 mm is highlighted in it. Also, **ID** is displayed in the prompt box, which is available on right of the **Refresh** button.

12. Enter **22 mm** in place of 20 mm.

13. Click on 15 mm; **REF** is displayed in the prompt box. Enter **18 mm** in place of 15 mm.

14. Click on 25 mm; **OD** is displayed in the prompt box. Enter **30 mm** in place of 25 mm.

15. Click on 8 mm; **GW** is displayed in the prompt box. Enter **10 mm** in place of 8 mm.

16. Choose the **Next** button; the **Precise Pos.** indicator is activated on the left in the dialog box and the **Do Not Activate Sketch Edit** radio button is selected automatically.

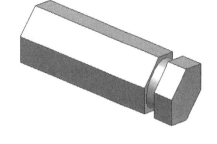

17. Choose the **Finish** button; the iFeature is applied to the model, as shown in Figure 17-38. You can notice that the **iFeature** node is created in the **Browser Bar**.

Figure 17-38 *The iFeature applied to the model*

18. Save the model with the name *applied_iFeature* at the location *C:\Inventor_2011\c17\Tutorial1* and then close the file.

Tutorial 2

In this tutorial, you will create a circlip and a shaft using the dimensions given in Figures 17-39 and 17-40. Apply iMates to the circlip and the groove of the shaft. Then, assemble the parts using the **Insert** constraint, as shown in Figure 17-41.   **(Expected time: 45 min)**

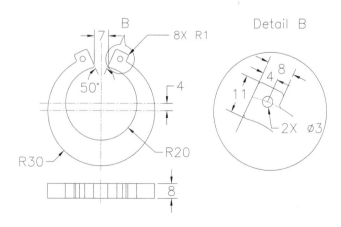

Figure 17-39 *The Circlip for Tutorial 2*

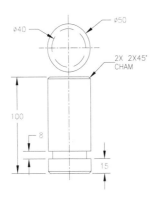

Figure 17-40 A shaft with a groove   *Figure 17-41 Final assembly*

The following steps are required to complete this tutorial:

a.   Create the shaft.
b.   Apply iMates to the groove of the shaft using the **Create iMates** tool.
c.   Create the circlip and apply fillets according to dimensions.
d.   Apply iMates to the circlip using the **Create iMates** tool.
e.   Place the shaft in the new assembly file.
f.   Place the circlip into the assembly using the **Automatically generate iMates on place** button from the **Place Component** dialog box.
g.   Save the Assembly.

Applying iMates to the Shaft

1.   Create the shaft with groove, refer to Figure 17-40 for dimensions.

2.   Choose the **Create iMate** tool from the **Author** panel of the **Manage** tab; the **Create iMate** dialog box is displayed. Choose the **Insert** button from the **Type** area.

3.   Choose the **>>** button available at the lower right corner of the dialog box; the dialog box expands.

4.   Enter **insert_1** in the **Name** edit box and then choose the **Matching** tab; the **Match List** area is displayed, see Figure 17-42.

5.   Choose the **Add name to list** button from the **Match List** area; an edit box is displayed in the list box.

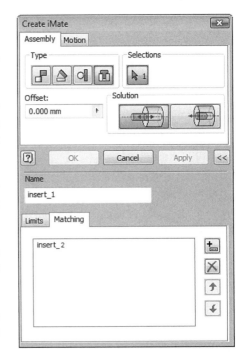

*Figure 17-42 The **Create iMate** dialog box*

6. Enter **insert_2** in the edit box displayed, refer to Figure 17-42.

7. Accept the default settings for the rest of the options and select the inner edge of the groove from the drawing area.

8. Choose the **Apply** button and then the **Cancel** button.

9. Save the model with the name *shaft.ipt* and close the file.

Creating the Circlip

1. Start a new part file; the sketching environment is displayed with the default XY-plane.

2. Draw the profile for creating a circlip and then apply dimensions to it, as shown in Figure 17-43.

3. After drawing the sketch, extrude the profile up to 8 mm.

4. Apply the fillets of 1 mm radius to the model. The model after creating the fillets is shown in Figure 17-44.

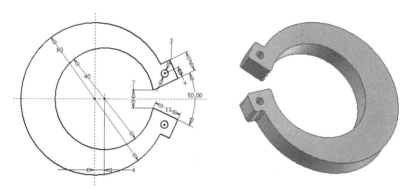

Figure 17-43 Dimensions for circlip   *Figure 17-44 Final model of circlip*

Applying iMates to the Circlip

1. Choose the **Create iMate** tool from the **Author** panel of the **Manage** tab; the **Create iMate** dialog box is displayed. Now, choose the **Insert** button from the **Type** area.

2. Choose the **>>** button from the lower right corner of the dialog box; the dialog box expands.

3. Enter **insert_2** in the **Name** edit box. Note that this is the name you entered in the **Match List** area of the **Create iMate** dialog box while setting the iMate of the shaft, refer to Figure 17-42.

4. Choose the **Matching** tab from the **Create iMate** dialog box and then choose the **Add name to list** button from the **Match List** area; an edit box is displayed in the list box.

5. Enter **insert_1** in the edit box displayed. Note that this is the name you had specified as the name of iMate of the shaft.

6. Choose the inner edge of the circlip.

7. Accept the default settings for the rest of the options. Next, choose the **Apply** button and then the **Cancel** button.

8. Save the model with the name *circlip.ipt* and then close the file.

Assembling the Circlip and the Shaft Using iMates

1. Start a new assembly file and choose the **Place** tool from the **Component** panel of the **Assemble** tab; the **Place Component** dialog box is displayed.

Place

2. Place the component *shaft.ipt* in the graphics window.

3. Again invoke the **Place Component** dialog box by choosing the **Place** tool from the **Assemble** tab.

4. Choose the **Automatically generate iMates on place** button from the **iMates** area of the **Place Component** dialog box.

5. Open the part file *circlip*; the circlip is automatically assembled to the shaft, as shown in Figure 17-45.

Figure 17-45 Final model after applying the iMates

6. Save the assembly with the name *iMate_assembly.iam* at the location given below:

   C:\Inventor_2011\c17\Tutorial2

Self-Evaluation Test

Answer the following questions and then compare them to those given at the end of this chapter:

1. In Autodesk Inventor, you cannot find the Center of Gravity of an assembly in the drawing environment. (T/F)

2. The features created by using 2D sketches are known as placed features. (T/F)

3. iMates are used to place parts in their proper positions automatically. (T/F)

4. The **Translation** tab is available in the **Create iMate** dialog box. (T/F)

5. The **Scale** tool is used to resize the selected sketched entities with respect to the specified _____.

6. The triad of the Center of Gravity can be used for measuring the _____.

7. You can specify the punching depth in the _____ area for creating a Sheet Metal Punch iFeature.

8. The file format of iFeature is _____.

9 You need to _____ the existing border before inserting a new type of border into a sheet.

10. When you open the required *.ide* file, the _____ indicator is activated automatically for inserting the iFeature.

Review Questions

Answer the following questions:

1. You cannot set the priority of the Mate reference in the **Create iMate** dialog box. (T/F)

2. Only one button is available in the **Selections** area of the **Create iMate** dialog box. (T/F)

3. A feature must include a Center Point for creating a Sheet Metal Punch iFeature. (T/F)

4. The **iProperties** dialog box can be used for creating reports, updating BOM, and updating title blocks. (T/F)

5. When you open an *.idw* file, the **Drawing Resources** folder is displayed in the **Browser Bar**. (T/F)

6. When the **Size** indicator is activated, _____ will be displayed on the right pane of the **Insert iFeature** dialog box.

7. Which of the following buttons from the **Place Component** dialog box is used to insert a component with matching iMates into an assembly?

    (a) **Create iMate**   (b) **Interactively place with iMates**
    (c) **Create iFeature**   (d) **Automatically generate iMates on place**

8. Which of the following tabs is used to calculate and display the physical and inertial properties of a part or an assembly?

    (a) **Physical**   (b) **Summary**
    (c) **Project**   (d) **Custom**

9. Which of the following environments is invoked when you choose the **Define New Title Block** option from the shortcut menu of the **Title Blocks** node?

    (a) Drawing   (b) Part
    (c) Sketching   (d) Assembly

10. Which of the following dialog boxes will be displayed if you choose the **Define New Zone Border** option from the shortcut menu that is displayed on right-clicking on the **Border** node?

    (a) **Border**   (b) **Default Drawing Border Parameters**
    (c) **Title Block**   (d) **Name**

Exercise

Exercise 1

Create a nut according to the dimensions shown in Figure 17-46. The threads of the nut to be created are ANSI Metric M Profile with a size of 14 and M14X2 designation. Next, apply the iMate constraints on the nut and bolt (For dimensions of the bolt, refer to Tutorial 2 of Chapter 8). Assemble both the nut and the bolt using the iMates. The final model is shown in Figure 17-47.   **(Expected time: 45 min)**

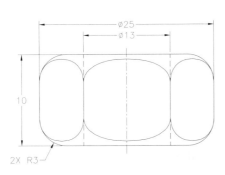

Figure 17-46 *Dimensions for creating the Nut*   ***Figure 17-47*** *Final assembly after applying the iMates*

Answers to Self-Evaluation Test
1. F, **2.** F, **3.** T, **4.** F, **5.** base point, **6.** distances, **7. Depth, 8.** *.ide, **9.** delete, **10. Position**

Index

Other Publications by CADCIM Technologies

The following is the list of some of the publications by CADCIM Technologies. Please visit www.cadcim.com for the complete listing.

Autodesk Inventor Textbooks
- Autodesk Inventor 2010 for Designers
- Autodesk Inventor 2009 for Designers
- Autodesk Inventor 2008 for Designers

Solid Edge Textbooks
- Solid Edge ST2 for Designers
- Solid Edge ST for Designers
- Solid Edge V20 for Designers

NX Textbooks
- NX 7 for Designers
- NX 6 for Designers
- NX 5 for Designers

Autodesk Alias Textbooks
- Learning Autodesk Alias Design 2010
- Autodesk AliasStudio 2009 for Designers

SolidWorks Textbooks
- SolidWorks 2010 for Designers
- SolidWorks 2009 for Designers

CATIA Textbooks
- CATIA V5R20 for Designers
- CATIA V5R19 for Designers
- CATIA V5R18 for Designers

EdgeCAM Textbooks
- EdgeCAM 11.0 for Manufacturers
- EdgeCAM 10.0 for Manufacturers

ANSYS Textbook
- ANSYS 11.0 for Designers

Pro/ENGINEER Textbooks
- Pro/ENGINEER Wildfire 5.0 for Designers
- Pro/ENGINEER Wildfire 4.0 for Designers
- Pro/ENGINEER Wildfire 3.0 for Designers

Autodesk Revit Textbooks
*   Autodesk Revit Architecture 2011 for Architects & Designers
*   Autodesk Revit Architecture 2010 for Architects & Designers
*   Autodesk Revit Architecture 2009 for Architects & Designers

AutoCAD Civil 3D Textbook
*   AutoCAD Civil 3D 2009 for Engineers

AutoCAD Map 3D Textbook
*   AutoCAD Map 3D 2011 for Geospatial Analysts

AutoCAD LT Textbooks
*   AutoCAD LT 2011 for Designers
*   AutoCAD LT 2010 for Designers
*   AutoCAD LT 2009 for Designers

Autodesk 3ds Max Design Textbooks
*   Autodesk 3ds Max Design 2011: A Tutorial Approach
*   Autodesk 3ds Max Design 2010: A Tutorial Approach
*   3ds Max Design 2009: A Tutorial Approach

Autodesk 3ds Max Textbooks
*   Autodesk 3ds Max 2011: A Comprehensive Guide
*   Autodesk 3ds Max 2010: A Comprehensive Guide
*   3ds Max 2008: A Comprehensive Guide

Autodesk Maya Textbooks
*   Autodesk Maya 2011: A Comprehensive Guide
*   Autodesk Maya 2010: A Comprehensive Guide
*   Character Animation: A Tutorial Approach

Computer Programming Textbooks
*   Learning Oracle11g
*   Learning ASP.NET AJAX
*   Learning Java Programming
*   Learning Visual Basic.NET 2008
*   Learning C++ Programming Concepts
*   Learning VB.NET Programming Concepts

Coming Soon: New Textbooks from CADCIM Technologies
*   ANSYS Workbench 12.0 for Designers
*   AutoCAD Civil 3D 2011 for Engineers
*   Autodesk Revit Structures for Structural Drafters and Detailers
*   SolidWorks 2011- A Tutorial Approach